NATURAL DISASTERS

THIRD CANADIAN EDITION

Patrick L. Abbott
San Diego State University

Claire Samson
Carleton University

McGraw-Hill Education | McGraw-Hill Ryerson

McGraw-Hill Ryerson

Natural Disasters
Third Canadian Edition

ISBN-13: 978-1-25-903079-6
ISBN-10: 1-25-903079-2

2 3 4 5 6 7 8 9 WEB 1 9 8 7 6 5

Printed and bound in Canada.

Director of Product Management: *Rhondda McNabb*
Senior Product Manager: *Kimberley Veevers*
Executive Marketing Manager: *Joy Armitage Taylor*
Product Developer: *Sarah Fulton*
Senior Product Team Associate: *Marina Seguin*
Supervising Editor: *Stephanie Gay*
Photo/Permissions Editor: *Indu Arora*
Copy Editor: *Julie Kretchman, First Folio Resource Group Inc.*
Proofreader: *Loretta Johnson, First Folio Resource Group Inc.*
Plant Production Coordinator: *Michelle Saddler*
Manufacturing Production Coordinator: *Lena Keating*
Cover and Interior Design: *Mark Cruxton*
Cover Image: *The Canadian Press/Aaron Vincent Elkaim*
Page Layout: *Laserwords*
Printer: *Webcom*

Library and Archives Canada Cataloguing in Publication

Abbott, Patrick L., author
Natural disasters / Patrick L. Abbott, San Diego State University, Claire Samson, Carleton University. —Third Canadian edition.

Includes index.
ISBN 978-1-25-903079-6 (pbk.)

1. Natural disasters—Textbooks. I. Samson, Claire, 1960-, author II. Title.
GB5014.A33 2015 904'.5 C2014-905570-6

About the Authors

Patrick L. Abbott

Patrick Abbott is a native San Diegan. Pat earned his MA and PhD degrees in geology at the University of Texas at Austin. He benefited greatly from the depth and breadth of the faculty in the Department of Geological Sciences at Austin; this was extended by their requirement to take five additional graduate courses outside the department. Developing interests in many topics helped lead to writing this textbook.

Pat's research has concentrated on the Mesozoic and Cenozoic sedimentary rocks of the southwestern United States and northwestern Mexico. Studies have focused on reading the history stored within the rocks—depositional environments, provenance, paleoclimate, palinspastic reconstructions, and high-energy processes.

Pat has long been involved in presenting earth knowledge to the public, primarily through local TV news. He has produced award winning videos for TV broadcast. In 2012, he appeared in every episode of the H2 (The History Channel 2) TV series *Serial Killer Earth*. During part of each year, Pat lectures on cruise ships that visit all continents; currently he is doing so as a Smithsonian Lecturer.

Claire Samson

Originally from Quebec City, Claire Samson is a professional engineer with an undergraduate degree in engineering physics from Laval University, a Masters of Science in geological sciences from McGill University, and a PhD in physics from the University of Toronto.

Claire has a wide range of experience, in both industry and academia. She has been a research associate at Cambridge University in England, and has worked for the Shell Oil group at three locations in the Netherlands. Upon relocating to Canada in 2000, she joined Neptec Design Group, an Ottawa high-tech company specializing in vision systems for space applications. In 2003, she was appointed to the Department of Earth Sciences at Carleton University and served as departmental Chair from 2010 to 2013. Claire now teaches introductory and advanced courses on Natural Disasters, and Exploration Geophysics.

Claire's research activities proceed on several fronts, including 3D imaging of earth materials, electromagnetic prospecting, and planetary geology. In both her research and field work, Claire is keen to introduce new technologies such as unmanned air vehicles and laser imaging, and to involve industry partners.

Claire is an enthusiastic world traveller. She has visited over 40 countries and speaks four languages.

Brief Contents

Contents

VICTORIA
3

4

5

6

7

8

9

10

11

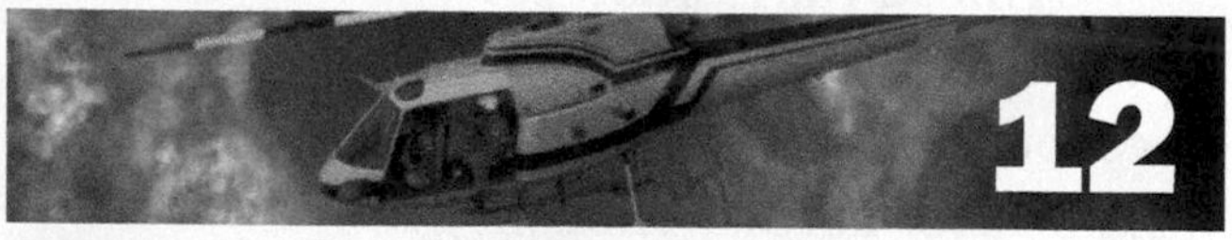

Fire 317

Mass Movements and Snow Avalanches 347

14

15

Preface

New to the Third Canadian Edition

The third edition of this book brings an updated and expanded Canadian focus on natural disasters in the context of a changing climate. The aim is to move beyond the headlines and develop a better understanding of the processes that lead to natural disasters. Concepts are illustrated by new case histories. Recent catastrophes, such as the 2013 floods in Southern Alberta and the Toronto ice storm bluntly exposed the fragility of our infrastructure to severe weather events. These types of events are predicted to become more prevalent in the future. The third edition contributes to an increased awareness of the risks associated with natural hazards and features society's response to the challenge.

Chapter-by-chapter content changes are as follows:

Chapter One: A Global and Canadian Outlook on Natural Disasters

- New Human Focus box: Paul Kovacs, Institute for Catastrophic Loss Reduction.
- Six new figures.
- New subsection: Role of Government.

Chapter Two: Earth's Internal Energy and Plate Tectonics

- Chapter 2 merges content from Chapters 2 and 3 of the second Canadian Edition.
- New Human Focus box: Pascal Audet, Researcher on Plate Tectonics.
- Three new figures.

Chapter Three: Earthquake Geology, Seismology, and Engineering

- New subsection on earthquakes in divergent zones, includes new figure of the seismicity of the East African Rift System.
- New table listing recent earthquakes with a large number of fatalities.
- Relocated material about the Haiti 2010 earthquake to this chapter.
- New Human Focus box: Gail Atkinson, Canada Research Chair in Earthquake Hazards and Ground Motions.
- Five new figures.

Chapter Four: When the Earth Shakes in Canada

- New Human Focus box: John Cassidy, Research Scientist, Natural Resources Canada.
- New Human Focus box: Marie de L'Incarnation and the 1663 Charlevoix earthquake.
- New subsection on 2012 Haida Gwaii earthquakes, including three new figures.
- New In Greater Depth box: Seismicity Induced by Human Activities.
- Sixteen new figures.

Chapter Five: Volcanic Eruptions and Landforms

- Added new perspective on Vesuvius that emphasizes volcanic hazards.
- New data on thermal energy flux of eruptions.
- Six new figures.

Chapter Six: Volcanic Case Histories: Killer Events

- New Human Focus box: John Stix, Volcanologist.
- Material on volcanoes affecting weather.
- New material on mitigation.
- New material on monitoring.
- Sixteen new figures.

Chapter Seven: Tsunamis

- New In Greater Depth box: Fukushima Daiichi Nuclear Incident.
- New Tsunami hazard map of Canada.
- Added text and four new figures about the 2011 Tohoku tsunami.
- Updated map showing the location of the DART tsunami warning instruments.
- Ten new figures.

Chapter Eight: The Ever Changing Climate

- Expanded and updated section: Climate Observations and Predictions.
- Seven new figures.

Chapter Nine: Severe Weather

- New Human Focus box: David Phillips, Senior Climatologist, Environment Canada.
- New subsection and figure on haboobs.
- New subsection and figure on lake-effect snow.
- New subsection on 2013 Toronto ice storm, includes two new figures.
- Nine new figures.

Chapter Ten: Hurricanes

- Reorganized content. Material on winds and storm surges is now a section.
- New subsection on Hurricane Sandy (merged with Hurricane Katrina).
- New section on hurricanes as energy conversion engines to better explain the physics of hurricanes.
- New subsection and figure on Typhoon Haiyan.
- Twelve new figures.

Chapter Eleven: Floods

- New text and figures on 2013 southern Alberta floods.
- New subsection and figure on 2013 Toronto flash flood.
- Seven new figures.

Chapter Twelve: Fire

- Enhanced section on climate change, including new figure.
- Seven new figures.

Chapter Thirteen: Mass Movements and Snow Avalanches

- Reorganized the material on snow avalanches. There are now subsections addressing causes and types of snow avalanches.
- New subsection on avalanche safety, including two new figures.
- New material on sinkholes (catastrophic subsidence).
- New Canadian map of landslide susceptibility.
- Ten new figures.

Chapter Fourteen: Hazards from Space

- Reorganized chapter: impact hazards are now discussed before geomagnetic hazards.
- New subsection on the 2013 Chelyabinsk midair explosion.
- New subsection on the recently discovered Tunnunik crater.
- New figure on comet ISON.
- New figure showing a shock wave.
- New table: Ten Closest Observed Comet Encounters in History.
- Seven new figures.

Themes and Approach

Natural Disasters, Third Canadian Edition, focuses on natural disasters: how the normal processes of the Earth concentrate their energies and deal heavy blows to humans and their structures. The following themes are interwoven throughout the book:

- Energy sources underlying disasters
- Climate change
- Plate tectonics
- Complexities of multiple variables operating simultaneously
- Practical mitigation strategies

The third Canadian edition aims to explain important principles about the Earth and then develop further understanding through numerous case histories.

The primary organization of the book is based on an energy theme.

Chapter 1 leads off with data describing worldwide and Canadian trends about natural disasters. Chapter 2 examines the energy sources underlying disasters: (1) Earth's internal energy from its formative impacts and continuing decay of radioactive elements, (2) energy from the Sun, (3) gravity, and (4) impacts with asteroids and comets. It introduces the theory of plate tectonics, which is the foundation required to develop an understanding of earthquakes and volcanoes.

Disasters fuelled by Earth's internal energy are addressed in Chapters 3 to 7 and are organized on a plate-tectonics theme. Chapter 3 covers the basic principles of earthquake geology, seismology, and engineering. Chapter 4 focuses on Canadian earthquakes: Why do they occur where they do? What significant seisms shook Canada in the past? Chapters 5 and 6 discuss volcanoes; their characteristic magmas are organized around the three Vs—viscosity, volatiles, and volume. Eruptive behaviours are related to plate-tectonic settings. Chapter 7 discusses tsunamis. Case histories are employed to enliven the text throughout.

Chapter 8 introduces the concepts of climate and weather and is followed by Chapters 9 through 12, which cover disasters fuelled by solar energy. Chapter 9 introduces the basic principles of meteorology and applies them to severe weather phenomena such as thunderstorms, hail, and tornadoes. Chapter 10 examines hurricanes. The emphasis on water continues in Chapter 11 on floods and how human activities increase flood damage. Chapter 12 on fire examines the liberation of ancient sunlight captured by photosynthesis and stored in organic material.

Disasters powered primarily by gravity are covered in Chapter 13 on mass movements and snow avalanches. Many types are discussed and illustrated, from falls to flows and slides to subsidence, from earth materials to snow.

Finally, Chapter 14 examines impact mechanisms in detail and includes plans to protect Earth from future threats. It also expands on the hazards related to our planet's proximity to the Sun by incorporating material on geomagnetic hazards.

There is a lot of material in this book, probably too much to cover in one semester. But the broad range of natural disasters topics allows each instructor to select those chapters that cover his or her interests and local hazards. The goal is to involve the students in a lifetime of understanding the Earth, atmosphere, oceans, and skies—to observe, think, explain, and discuss.

Why the Book Was Written

We are all engaged, amazed, shaken, and moved by the news of great natural disasters broadcast on the media. Could similar events take place in Canada? Have they occurred in the past in our country? Several universities and colleges throughout Canada offer courses on natural disasters, reaching large classes of undergraduate students. Students want to understand why natural disasters happen not only abroad but also closer to home. This book has been tailored to meet this dual perspective.

Students are equally interested in society's response to natural disasters. In our class at Carleton University in Ottawa, several people have experienced a great natural disaster, the 1998 St. Lawrence River Valley ice storm. Discussing the event brings back vivid memories. It raises questions about the decision-making processes that authorities are faced with during emergency situations, which is a topic addressed throughout the book.

Finally, our large class is a microcosm of society in which all fields of activity are represented, from architecture to zoology. This book therefore endeavours to broaden the topic of natural disasters beyond the natural sciences and economics, to include elements of visual arts, archeology, and anthropology.

Third Canadian Edition Features

New to this edition: Each chapter opens with Learning Outcomes that identify for students what they will know and be able to demonstrate by the end of the course. Each chapter opener also includes an outline that alerts students to the main themes of the chapter.

CHAPTER EIGHT

8

The Ever Changing Climate

EXTERNAL ENERGY

"All across the world, in every kind of environment and region known to man, increasingly dangerous weather patterns and devastating storms are abruptly putting an end to the long-running debate over whether or not climate change is real. Not only is it real, it's here, and its effects are giving rise to a frighteningly new global phenomenon: the man-made natural disaster."

—Senator Barack Obama, 3 April 2006

Outline

- A Global Energy Budget
- Global Warming
- Climate Observations and Predictions
- Summary

LO1 Distinguish between climate and weather.

LO2 Describe what happens to solar radiation that reaches Earth.

LO3 Explain the greenhouse effect.

LO4 Summarize the different processes of the hydrologic cycle.

LO5 Give examples of several observations of climate change.

During the summer, the Canadian Coast Guard icebreaker Amundsen is dedicated to scientific research in the Arctic, including the study of the impact of climate change on the northern environment.

Source: Lee Thomas/Alamy Images/GetStock.com

Over **100** new images and figures have been added to the Third Canadian Edition to engage and inform students.

Canadian and world maps help to identify key areas of topical coverage and discussion.

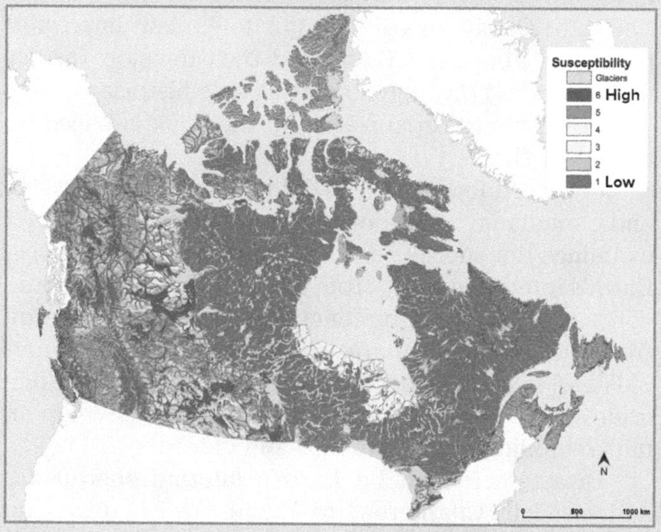

In Greater Depth boxes zoom in on a particular topic in more detail without interrupting the main flow of the text. Several boxes present information about what to do in the case of natural disasters.

IN GREATER DEPTH

What to Do Before, During, and After an Earthquake

Before

We have seen that earthquakes don't kill us: it is our own buildings and belongings that fall when the Earth shakes that harm us. What should you do to prepare for an earthquake? *First*, walk into each room of your home, assume strong shaking has begun, and carefully visualize what might fall (for example, ceiling fan, chandelier, mirror, china cabinet, gas water heater). Now reduce the risk. Nail them. Brace them. Tie them. Velcro™ them. Lower them. Remove them.

Second, walk outside, assume strong shaking, and visualize what might fall (for example, trees, power lines, brick chimneys). Now reduce the risk, where possible. Trim them. Chop them. Replace them.

Third, repeat the visits inside and outside your home. This time, locate safe spots where protection exists, for example, under a heavy table, beneath a strong desk, or under a bed. Remember these safe spots so you can use them quickly when shaking begins.

During

After examining your home, prepare yourself to stay composed during the shaking. Drop, cover, and hold on (Figure 4.28 and Figure 4.41a). Remember that the severe shaking probably will last only 5 to 60 seconds. So, be calm and protect yourself for one minute. In most places, if you are inside, you should stay inside; if you are outside, stay outside.

After

Expect aftershocks. If you feel aftershocks, stay where you are until they stop.

Do a safety check around your home. Check for fire hazards such as gas leaks and damaged electrical wiring (Figure 4.41b). Check for structural damage to your home. Approach chimneys with caution. Turn on a battery-powered radio for information and damage reports (Figure 4.41c).

(a) (b) (c)

Figure 4.41 Simple earthquake safety steps.

Source: Reproduced with the permission of Natural Resources Canada, 2011.

Human Focus boxes examine natural disasters from the unique perspectives of experts, researchers, witnesses, and survivors. There are eight new Human Focus boxes in the Third Canadian Edition.

Art reproductions, historical photographs, and panoramas show the wonders of the natural world and the drama of disasters through the eyes of artists and photographers.

Study aids are found at the end of each chapter.

- *Summaries* reiterate the main points of the chapter in crisp bullet-point format.
- *Terms to Remember* include all the boldfaced terms that are defined in the glossary at the end of the book.
- *Questions for Review* help students test their knowledge.
- *Questions for Further Thought encourage students to* examine issues in a broader perspective and stimulate debate.
- *Interesting Websites* are recommended Internet sites where readers can learn more about chapter topics.

Supplements

connect

McGraw-Hill Connect™ is a web-based assignment and assessment platform that gives students the means to better connect with their coursework, with their instructors, and with the important concepts that they will need to know for success now and in the future. With Connect, instructors can deliver assignments, quizzes and tests easily online. Students can practise important skills at their own pace and on their own schedule. Connect was developed for the third Canadian edition by Jovan Stefanovicz of the University of Toronto. It provides 24/7 online access to an eBook—an online edition of the text—to aid them in successfully completing their work, wherever and whenever they choose.

For the Instructor

Computerized Test Bank

Available for Macintosh or Windows users, the computerized test bank, revised by Jovan Stefanovic of the University of Toronto, uses EZ Test—a flexible and easy-to-use electronic testing program—allowing instructors to create tests from book-specific items. EZ Test accommodates a wide range of question types and allows instructors to add their own questions. Test items are also available in Word format (rich text format). For secure online testing, exams created in EZ Test can be exported to WebCT, Blackboard, and EZ Test Online. EZ Test comes with a Quick Start Guide and, once the program is installed, users have access to a User's Manual and Flash tutorials. Additional help is available online at www.mhhe.com/eztest.

Instructor's Manual

Prepared by Claire Samson, our Canadian author, the Instructor's Manual contains a chapter overview, learning outcomes, and additional critical thinking questions for each chapter.

PowerPoint Lecture Outlines

Assembled by William Mark Buhay of the University of Winnipeg, these full-colour slides include chapter outlines, outcomes and key figures, and cover the essential information in each chapter.

Image Gallery

The complete set of visuals from the text can be downloaded from the Image Gallery on Connect and easily embedded into instructors' PowerPoint slides.

Superior Learning Solutions and Support

The McGraw-Hill Ryerson team is ready to help you assess and integrate any of our products, technology, and services into your course for optimal teaching and learning performance. Whether it's helping your students improve their grades, or putting your entire course online, the McGraw-Hill Ryerson team is here to help you do it. Contact your Learning Solutions Consultant today to learn how to maximize all of McGraw-Hill Ryerson's resources.

For more information on the latest technology and Learning Solutions offered by McGraw-Hill Ryerson and its partners, please visit us online: www.mheducation.ca/he/solutions.

Acknowledgments

I am indebted to an extensive network of scientists and engineers from the Canadian earth science community, research collaborators, students, and friends who helped me update and enrich the Third Canadian edition. In particular, I would like to thank the following people for their outstanding contributions:

- Gail Atkinson, Pascal Audet, John Cassidy, Paul Kovacs, David Phillips, and John Stix for contributing their expertise and granting me interviews for the Human Focus boxes
- Greg Brooks of Natural Resources Canada for his insight on floods
- Anne Trépanier of Carleton University, who introduced me to the ideas of Marie de L'Incarnation
- Maurice Lamontagne for sharing his expertise on seismicity induced by human activities
- My colleague Brian Cousens who took me aboard his field trip to Iceland so that I could experience recent volcanism first hand
- My students at Carleton University for their enthusiasm!

The quality of the book was significantly improved by the insights provided by comments from the following reviewers:

Chris Ayles, Camosun College
Michael Badyk, Humber College
William Mark Buhay, University of Winnipeg
Brent Doberstein, University of Waterloo
Stan Dosso, University of Victoria
Taly Drezner, York University
John Gosse, Dalhousie University
Judith Patterson, Concordia University
Jovan Stefanovic, University of Toronto

In closing, I would like to sincerely thank the team at McGraw-Hill Ryerson for their mentoring and encouragement. Many thanks to my husband and four children for their patience as every family holiday we take together always includes numerous "geo-stops"! The adventure continues!

Claire Samson
mlcsamson@gmail.com

CHAPTER ONE

1

A Global and Canadian Outlook on Natural Disasters

People leaving Stanley Mission, northern Saskatchewan, in front of advancing forest fires on 22 May 2014.
Source: Hans Peterson.

"Mankind was destined to live on the edge of perpetual disaster. We are mankind because we survive."

—James A. Michener, 1978, Chesapeake

Outline

- Natural Disasters and Natural Hazards
- Worldwide Trends
- The Canadian Perspective
- Vulnerability and Risk
- How Do Canadians Prepare for Natural Disasters?
- Summary

LO1 Distinguish between natural disasters and natural hazards.

LO2 Explain the relationship between frequency and magnitude of natural disasters.

LO3 Describe natural disaster trends in Canada and the world.

LO4 Define risk and mitigation.

Behind every natural disaster is a human story affecting a village or our global village. The catastrophe might be the evacuation of a small First Nation community such as Stanley Mission in northern Saskatchewan in front of advancing forest fires (see photo on chapter opening page), or an event of international proportion such as the Tohoku earthquake and tsunami in Japan. The hazard and the scale might be different, but in each case the strength of the human spirit leads the path towards recovery. This book will explore several natural hazards posing a threat to humans from an earth science perspective, against the backdrop of an ever-changing climate. Focus is on the Canadian people and the Canadian landscape. Reaching beyond the emotions and sensationalism of the headlines, an understanding of the science behind the dynamic processes shaping planet Earth will guide our actions toward building a society more resilient to natural disasters.

LO1 Natural Disasters and Natural Hazards

Natural disasters are extreme natural events in which a large amount of **energy** is released in a short time with catastrophic consequences for life and infrastructure in the vicinity. The word "disaster" originates from Ancient Greek and combines the prefix "dis," meaning "without," and the word "astro," meaning "celestial body"; Greek astrologers believed in a connection between calamities and unfavourable positions of the planets in the sky.

There is no universal definition of "**natural disaster.**" A natural disaster generally involves significant casualties and disruption to society, large economic losses, and calls for exterior help. It gets attention from the media and government officials. The key aspect is its impact on society. The expression "natural disaster" is somewhat of a misnomer, giving the impression that these disasters are primarily the fault of nature. In fact, natural disasters are often experienced when society ignores hazardous conditions in the natural environment. In the words of David Phillips, "they have a human signature" (see Human Focus box: David Phillips, Senior Climatologist, Environment Canada, in Chapter 9).

Natural hazards become natural disasters when they intersect with vulnerable communities. Unstable snow and rock and high water levels are natural hazards with the potential to cause harm. Snow avalanches large enough to bury a person occur several times a day during the winter months in the Rockies. The great majority, however, happen in remote uninhabited areas and are not considered natural disasters. Snow avalanches are declared natural disasters only when they kill people or engulf infrastructure at the foot of the slopes. This is what happened to the small Inuit community of Kangiqsualujjuaq in northern Quebec on 31 December 1999 as several people had gathered in the school gym to celebrate the arrival of the new millennium. In a few seconds, tonnes of snow slid from a 150-m steep hill nearby and smashed into the building, burying people inside. This snow avalanche, a tragic natural disaster, left 9 people dead and 25 people critically injured. Evacuation of the injured was especially challenging due to the remoteness of the community, located 1500 km north of Montreal.

Sites with natural hazards need to be studied and understood. Their risk must be evaluated. Then we can try to prevent natural hazards from causing natural disasters. Remember: *Natural hazards are inevitable, but natural disasters are not.*

LO2 FREQUENCY, RETURN PERIOD, AND MAGNITUDE

Several metrics are used to describe hazard levels, including frequency, return period, and magnitude.

The **frequency** of an event is the number of occurrences in a given length of time. For example, on average, the Earth experiences one great earthquake per year. The following earthquakes, which struck near populated areas, made international news: Bam, Iran (2003); offshore Northern Sumatra, Indonesia (2004); Kashmir, Pakistan (2005); Sichuan, China (2008); and Tohoku, Japan (2010) (Table 3.7 in Chapter 3). Another way of expressing how often events occur is the **return period**, which is the length of time between similar events. The frequency and return period are the inverse of one another:

$$Frequency = \frac{1}{Period}$$

and

$$Period = \frac{1}{Frequency}$$

Let us illustrate this relation with an example. On average, four former tropical cyclones affect Atlantic Canada annually. The frequency of these storms is four times per year; the corresponding return period is therefore three months (12 months ÷ 4 cyclones).

The longer the return period, the smaller the chance of an event occurring in any given year. For example, since the conquest of the French in North America by Great Britain in 1763, historical documents reveal that major rockfalls (those causing fatalities and/or severely damaging buildings), occur approximately every 25 years along the Cap-aux-Diamants cliff in Old Quebec City. This translates into a 4% chance of rockfall in any one year (1/25 = 4%). A common misinterpretation is to use the return period to predict exactly when a similar event will happen in the future. A return period of 25 years does not mean that if a rockfall has just occurred, the next one won't happen for another 25 years. Frequency and return period are based on statistical probabilities; they are not and should not be used as forecasting measures.

The **magnitude** is related to the amount of energy fuelling a natural event. An expression of magnitude, for example, is the force of hurricane winds. The energy released during an earthquake, based on the amplitude of ground motion, is also frequently quoted in terms of magnitude.

Larger-magnitude disasters happen less often. For example, clouds and rain are common, but hurricanes are uncommon; streams overflow frequently, but large floods are infrequent.

Knowing the frequency, return period, and magnitude for a type of event in a given area provides us with useful information, but it does not answer all our questions. There are still the cost–benefit ratios of economics to consider. For example, given an area with a natural hazard that puts forth a dangerous pulse of energy with a return period of 600 years, how much money should be spent constructing a building that will be used for about 50 years before being torn down and replaced? Is it wise to spend additional money to guarantee that the building will withstand the rare destructive event?

LO3 Worldwide Trends

THE NUMBER OF GREAT NATURAL DISASTERS IS INCREASING WITH TIME

Great natural disasters—tsunamis, earthquakes, hurricanes, floods, and heat waves—commonly kill thousands of people, leave hundreds of thousands homeless, and devastate regional economies. These extremely traumatic events so overwhelm regions that international assistance is needed to rescue and care for people, clean up the destruction, and begin the process of reconstruction. The annual occurrence of great natural disasters ranges from zero (in 1952 and 2009) to 15 (in 1993), with an average of nearly five (Figure 1.1). The yearly trend is upward; the increase is partly due to Earth's human population more than doubling in size since 1960 (Figure 1.11).

Table 2.1, in Chapter 2, divides natural hazards in two subgroups. A first subgroup, the "geological hazards" includes phenomena such as **earthquakes**, **tsunamis**, and volcanic eruptions. A second subgroup, the "weather-related hazards," includes **storms**, **floods**, heat waves, **droughts**, and **wildfires**. Whereas the trend line of the geological disasters in Figure 1.1 is almost stable between 1950 and 2010, that of the weather-related disasters increases with time. These data point to a link between changing weather patterns, including those related to global warming, and the frequency of certain natural disasters.

Which great natural disasters are responsible for the most fatalities and which caused the most material destruction? Which part of the world is most affected? The year 2013 was a fairly typical year marked by storms and floods in several parts of the world, such as typhoon Haiyan in the Philippines (see Chapter 10) and the Southern Alberta deluge (see Chapter 11). The exception was a rare meteoritic impact in Russia (see Chapter 14) (Figure 1.2). Looking at the statistics

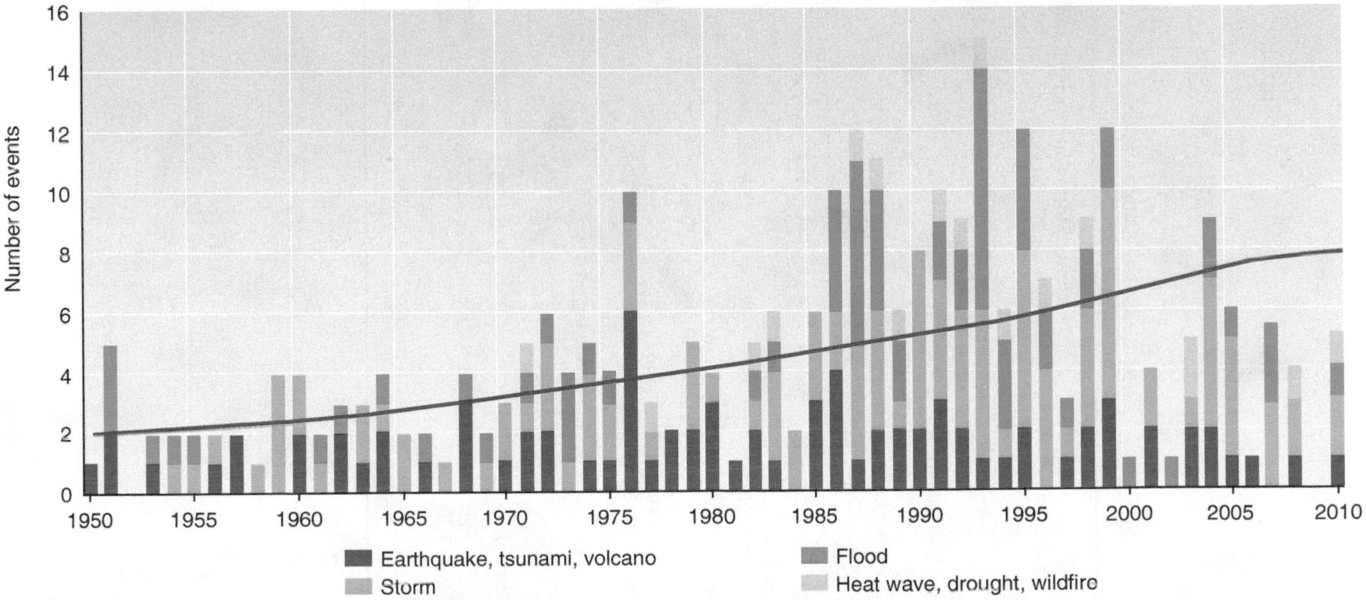

Figure 1.1
Great natural disasters, 1950–2010. Note the stable trend of the geological disasters (in red) and the increasing trend of the weather-related disasters (in green, blue, and yellow).
Source: © Munich Reinsurance Company.

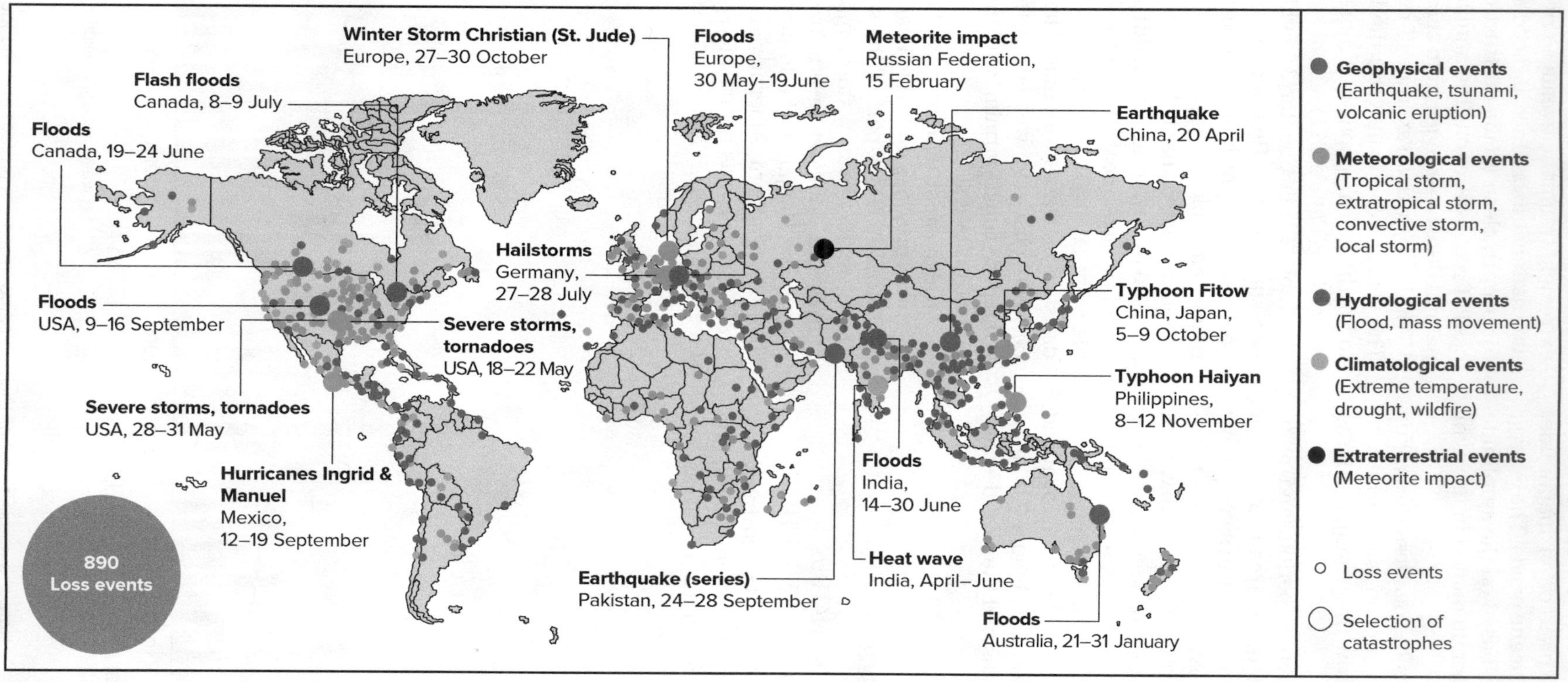

Figure 1.2
Geographical overview of the natural disasters of 2013.
Source: Munich Reinsurance Company.

for 2013 is instructive (Figure 1.3). The data show that storms and their consequences, floods, killed the most people and caused the most damage. Densely populated Asia dominated in terms of the number of disasters and fatalities. Where humans are concentrated, many more people are killed during each high-energy event.

The 40 deadliest disasters from 1970 to 2013 are shown in Table 1.1. Notice that 39 of the 40 disasters were due to natural causes. The most frequent mega-killers were earthquakes (24 of 40) and tropical cyclones (8 of 40). During these years, Asia was hit the hardest (28 of 40).

THE NUMBER OF NATURAL-DISASTER FATALITIES IS INCREASING WITH TIME

Figure 1.4 shows the increasing trend in the number of natural disaster fatalities in recent decades. The sawtooth shape of the curve is created by the great natural disasters, which kill many people in one event. The numbers presented actually understate the number of deaths because, in many cases, the statistics report only confirmed fatalities, not missing people.

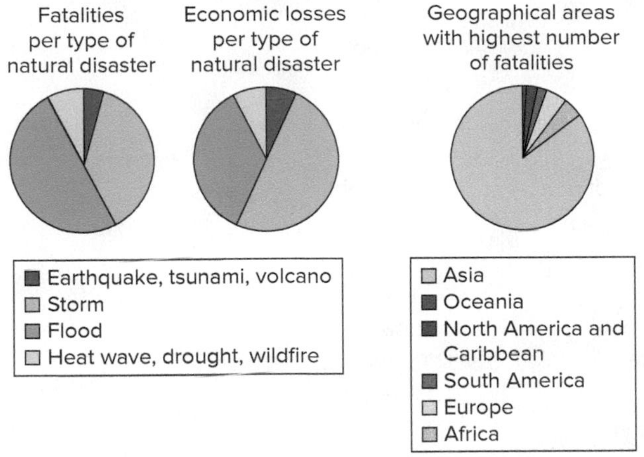

Figure 1.3
Natural disasters by type in 2013 based on a compilation of 890 major loss events.
Source: Munich Reinsurance Company.

THE NUMBER OF HUMAN-MADE DISASTERS HAS BEEN DECREASING IN RECENT YEARS

Human-made disasters encompass urban fires and explosions, aviation and maritime disasters, mining accidents, social unrest, and terrorism. After a sharp increase at the turn of the century, the number of human-made disasters has been decreasing overall since 2005 (Figure 1.5). An important factor in this decrease has been a greater awareness about safety—translating to increased investment in safety in the workplace and in transportation—even in the poorest countries. Since 2010, the numbers of human-made disasters and great natural disasters have been almost equal. Both types of disaster share common features. The same proactive approach to safety that helped curb the number of human-made disasters can lead to a reduction in the number of great natural disasters in the future. Making this happen will be a matter of social choice and prioritization.

ECONOMIC LOSSES FROM NATURAL DISASTERS ARE INCREASING WITH TIME

The deaths and injuries caused by natural disasters grab our attention and tug at our emotions, but natural disasters also lead to economic losses. The destruction and disabling of buildings, bridges, roads, and power-generation plants as well as transmission systems for

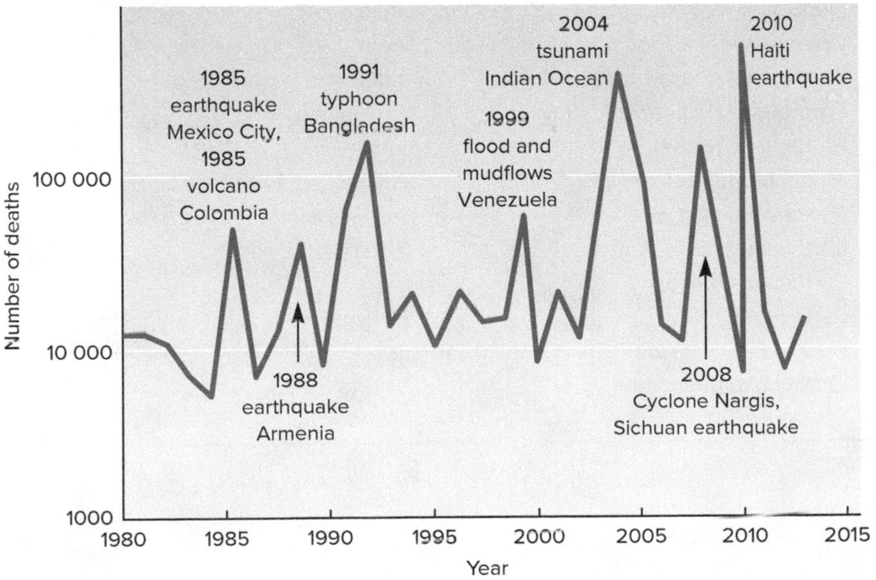

Figure 1.4
Deaths due to natural disasters, 1980–2013.
Source: © Swiss Re, sigma No 1/2011.

TABLE 1.1

The 40 Deadliest Disasters, 1970–2013 (The only event not due to natural causes is in italics)

Fatalities	Date/Start	Event	Country
300 000	14 Nov 1970	Cyclone	Bangladesh
255 000	28 Jul 1976	Earthquake (Tangshan)	China
245 000	26 Dec 2004	Earthquake and tsunami	Indonesia, Sri Lanka, India, Thailand
230 000	12 Jan 2010	Earthquake	Haiti
140 000	2 May 2008	Cyclone Nargis	Myanmar
140 000	30 Apr 1991	Cyclone Gorky	Bangladesh
88 000	8 Oct 2005	Earthquake	Pakistan
87 500	12 May 2008	Earthquake (Sichuan)	China
66 000	31 May 1970	Earthquake and landslide (Nevados Huascaran)	Peru
55 630	15 June 2010	Heat wave	Russia, Czech Republic
50 000	21 Jun 1990	Earthquake (Gilan)	Iran
35 000	Aug 2003	Heat wave	Europe
27 000	26 Dec 2003	Earthquake (Bam)	Iran
25 000	7 Dec 1988	Earthquake	Armenia
25 000	16 Sep 1978	Earthquake (Tabas)	Iran
23 000	13 Nov 1985	Volcanic eruption and mudflows (Nevado del Ruiz)	Colombia
22 000	4 Feb 1976	Earthquake	Guatemala
20 103	26 Jan 2001	Earthquake (Gujarat)	India
19 184	11 Mar 2011	Earthquake and tsunami	Japan
19 118	17 Aug 1999	Earthquake (Izmit)	Turkey
18 000	15 Dec 1999	Floods and mudslides	Venezuela
15 000	19 Sep 1985	Earthquake (Mexico City)	Mexico
15 000	*11 Aug 1979*	*Dam failure (Morvi)*	*India*
15 000	1 Sep 1978	Flood (Monsoon rains in north)	India
15 000	29 Oct 1999	Cyclone (Orissa)	India
11 000	22 Oct 1998	Hurricane Mitch	Honduras
11 000	25 May 1985	Cyclone	Bangladesh
10 800	31 Oct 1971	Flood	India
10 000	20 Nov 1977	Cyclone (Andhra Pradesh)	India
9 500	30 Sep 1993	Earthquake (Marashtra state)	India
8 000	16 Aug 1976	Earthquake (Mindanao)	Philippines
6 425	17 Jan 1995	Earthquake (Kobe)	Japan
6 304	5 Nov 1991	Typhoons Thelma and Uring	Philippines
5 778	26 May 2006	Earthquake (Yogyakarta)	Indonesia
5 422	30 Jun 1976	Earthquake (West Papua)	Indonesia
5 374	10 Apr 1972	Earthquake (Fars)	Iran
5 300	28 Dec 1974	Earthquake	Pakistan
5 112	15 Nov 2001	Floods and landslides	Brazil
5 000	23 Dec 1972	Earthquake (Managua)	Nicaragua
5 000	5 Mar 1987	Earthquake	Ecuador
2 160 550	Total deaths		

Source: © Swiss Reinsurance Company.

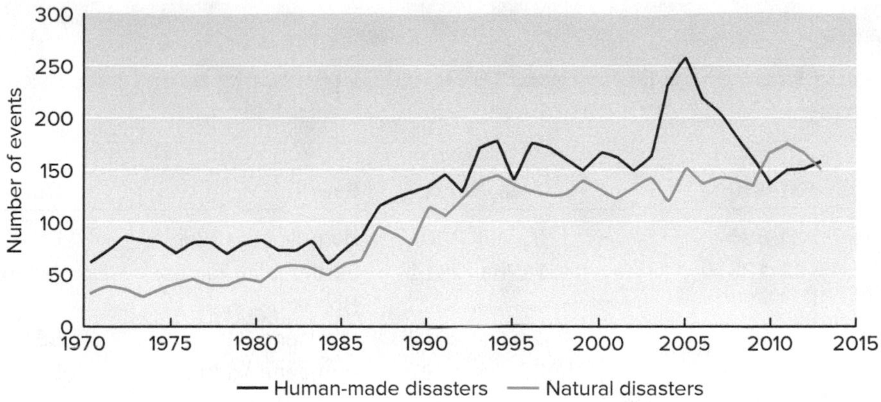

Figure 1.5
Number of human-made (black line) and great natural (blue line) disasters, 1970–2013.
Source: © Swiss Re, sigma No 1/2011.

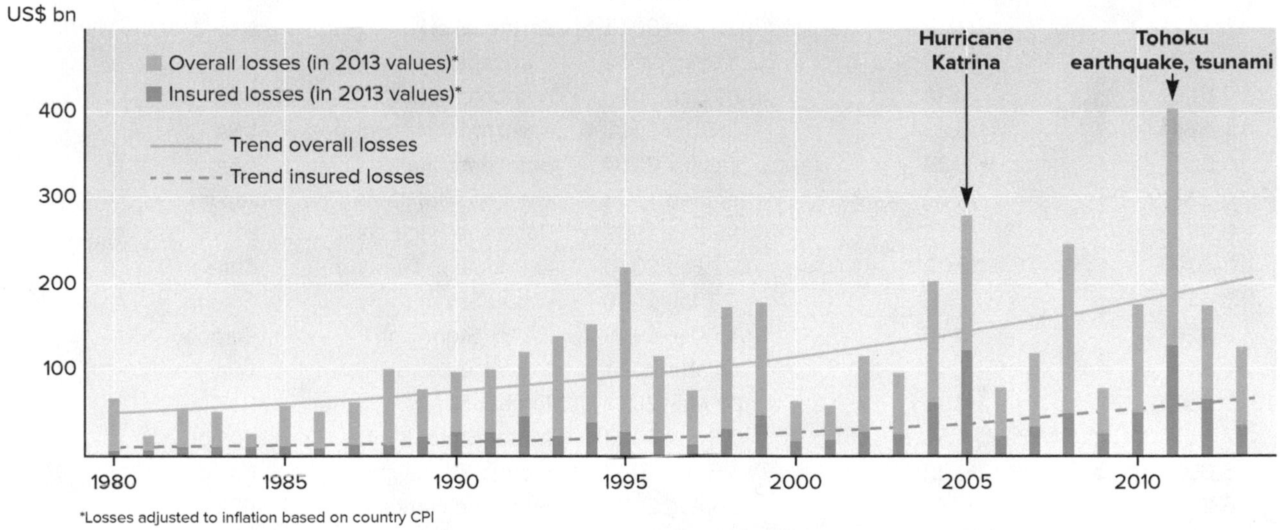

Figure 1.6
Losses from great natural disasters, 1950–2013.
Source: © Munich Reinsurance Company.

electricity, natural gas, and water—and all the other built works of our societies—add up to a huge cost. But the economic losses are greater than just damaged structures: industries and businesses are knocked out of operation, causing losses in productivity and wages for employees left without places to work.

The increasing trend in economic losses is evident when data are presented over long time intervals such as decades (Figure 1.6). Although hurricane Katrina in 2005 remains the most costly single event, the cumulative damage due to the Tohoku earthquake and tsunami (see Chapter 7) and several other events brought the cost of natural disasters to a historical maximum in 2011. The 40 costliest natural disasters between 1970 and 2013 from the insurance industry's perspective are listed in Table 1.2. Notice that 39 of the 40 most expensive disasters were due to natural processes. The list is dominated by storms (28 of 40), whereas earthquakes contributed only 6 events.

Compare Table 1.1 and Table 1.2. The locations of the costliest disasters for the insurance industry are different from the locations with the most fatalities. Hurricane Katrina does not even appear on the list of the deadliest disasters. Conversely, the deadliest disaster in recent decades, the 1970 cyclone in Bangladesh, is not included in Table 1.2. The highest insurance losses occurred in the United States (21 of 40), Europe (8 of 40), and Japan (5 of 40). Developed countries experience larger economic losses and fewer deaths. Their people are better insured, live in safer buildings, and have better warning and evacuation plans. In the developing world, the general population cannot

TABLE 1.2

The 40 Most Costly Insurance Disasters, 1970–2013 (the only event not due to natural causes is in italics)

Losses (millions of 2013 US$)	Fatalities	Date/Start	Event	Country
80 373	1 836	25 Aug 2005	Hurricane Katrina	USA
37 665	19 135	11 Mar 2011	Earthquake, Tsunami (Tohoku)	Japan
36 890	237	24 Oct 2012	Hurricane Sandy	USA
27 594	43	23 Aug 1992	Hurricane Andrew	USA
25 664	*2 982*	*11 Sep 2001*	*Terrorist Attack*	*USA*
22 857	61	17 Jan 1994	Earthquake (Northridge)	USA
22 751	136	6 Sep 2008	Hurricane Ike	USA, Caribbean
17 218	181	2 Sep 2004	Hurricane Ivan	USA
16 519	124	27 Jul 2011	Floods	Thailand
16 142	815	22 Feb 2011	Earthquake	New Zealand
15 570	35	19 Oct 2005	Hurricane Wilma	USA
12 510	34	20 Sep 2005	Hurricane Rita	USA
11 594	123	15 Jul 2012	Drought in the corn belt	USA
10 313	24	11 Aug 2004	Hurricane Charley	USA
10 031	51	27 Sep 1991	Typhoon Mireille	Japan
8 924	71	15 Sep 1989	Hurricane Hugo	USA
8 876	562	27 Feb 2010	Earthquake, Tsunami	Chile
8 648	95	25 Jan 1990	Winter Storm Daria	Europe
8 426	110	25 Dec 1999	Winter Storm Lothar	Europe
7 856	354	22 Apr 2011	Tornadoes	USA
7 587	155	20 May 2011	Tornadoes	USA
7 112	54	18 Jan 2007	Winter Storm Kyrill	Europe
6 602	22	15 Oct 2007	Storms, floods	Europe
6 593	38	26 Aug 2004	Hurricane Frances	USA
6 274	55	22 Aug 2011	Hurricane Irene	USA
5 909	64	25 Feb 1990	Winter Storm Vivian	Europe
5 869	26	22 Sep 1999	Typhoon Bart	Japan
5 548	–	4 Sep 2010	Earthquake	New Zealand
5 240	600	20 Sep 1998	Hurricane Georges	USA, Carribbean
4 925	41	5 Jun 2001	Tropical Storm Allison	USA
4 872	3 034	13 Sep 2004	Hurricane Jeanne	USA, Carribean
4 593	45	6 Sep 2004	Typhoon Songda	Japan, South Korea
4 216	45	2 May 2003	Tornadoes, Hailstorms	USA
4 134	25	27 May 2013	Floods	Central Europe
4 100	70	10 Sep 1999	Hurricane Floyd	USA, Bahamas, Columbia
3 979	59	1 Oct 1995	Hurricane Opal	USA
3 926	6 425	17 Jan 1995	Earthquake (Kobe)	Japan
3 838	–	27 Jul 2013	Hailstorms	Germany, France
3 487	45	27 Dec 2012	Winter Storm Martin	France
3 406	25	24 Jan 2009	Winter Storm Klaus	France, Spain
$508 631 Million	37 837 Total deaths			

Source: © Swiss Reinsurance Company.

HUMAN FOCUS

Paul Kovacs, Institute for Catastrophic Loss Reduction

I live in Ontario. However, when hurricane Andrew struck Florida in 1992, thousands of kilometres away, it changed my life.

I am an economist and started my career working for government developing economic policies. I transitioned to the private sector and represented the Canadian Manufacturers Association at a tumultuous time when the North American Free Trade Agreement was negotiated and the Harmonized Sales Tax was introduced. I later joined the Insurance Bureau of Canada. In the last 25 years, my career has revolved around the study of natural hazards from an insurance perspective.

Hurricane Andrew sent shock waves throughout the insurance industry. The enormous amount of damage and the ensuing hefty claims submitted by homeowners caused the largest number of insurance companies to go bankrupt since the 1906 San Francisco earthquake. The insurance industry was not ready for large catastrophes. Realizing that little research had been conducted on mitigation against natural hazards, in 1997 I created the Institute for Catastrophic Loss Reduction, hosted at Western University. Since then, the Institute has established more than 30 research chairs in various aspects of risk reduction from political science to seismology.

If the main challenge when the Institute was first created was addressing the consequences of large but infrequent events, a new risk has now emerged: adaptation to a changing climate. As part of the Institute's outreach activities, I present to various groups. I ask the audience: "Do you feel the climate has changed in the last 30 years? Do you anticipate that it will continue to change?" A majority of people say they do. We are seeing more and more short-lived intense events, such as the torrential rainfalls in Toronto in 2005 and 2013, that strike with little warning and cause extensive property damage. Flooding is especially problematic. In Canada, unlike in most industrialized nations, flood coverage is not included in a typical homeowner insurance policy. In 1970, in response to hurricane Hazel, the federal government created the disaster financial assistance arrangements (DFAA) to provide relief when insurance is not available; as such, DFAA are often used in the case of flood disasters. The 2013 floods in Southern Alberta might lead to a re-examination of this aid mechanism. It is likely that the government will chose to intervene less and open the door to private flood insurance. After all, Canadians trust the private sector to cover other risks, for example, the risk of driving motor vehicles.

The Institute for Catastrophic Loss Reduction and the insurance industry are strong advocates for increasing our knowledge of natural hazards with a particular focus on their impact on the economy. They lobby all levels of government for improvements to the National Building Code of Canada and the building of more resilient municipal infrastructure.

Figure 1.7
Paul Kovacs, Founder and Executive Director, Institute for Catastrophic Loss Reduction.
Source: Paul Kovacs, Institute for Catastrophic Loss Reduction.

afford a safety net, and governments are stretched for resources. In the event of a great natural disaster, poor countries have no alternative other than turning to the international community. The International Red Cross and Red Crescent Movement play a pivotal role in this respect, channelling practical and financial help to those affected. Individual donors, however, have a short attention span, and often funds dry up before the situation has even stabilized. Official country-to-country aid tends to suffer from administrative delays. In 2006, to alleviate these problems, the United Nations launched a $500 million fund—the Central Emergency Relief Fund—to jump-start relief operations.

The Canadian Perspective

THE NUMBER OF NATURAL DISASTERS IN CANADA IS INCREASING

In line with global trends, statistics show that the number of natural disasters per year in Canada has been increasing from 1900 to 2012 (Figure 1.8). As the number of geological disasters has remained stable, the overall increase reflects mainly a rise in the number of weather-related disasters. As with the global trend, the increase is closely related to population growth. From 1900 to 2011, the population of Canada has increased more than sixfold, from 5 to 31 million (Figure 1.9).

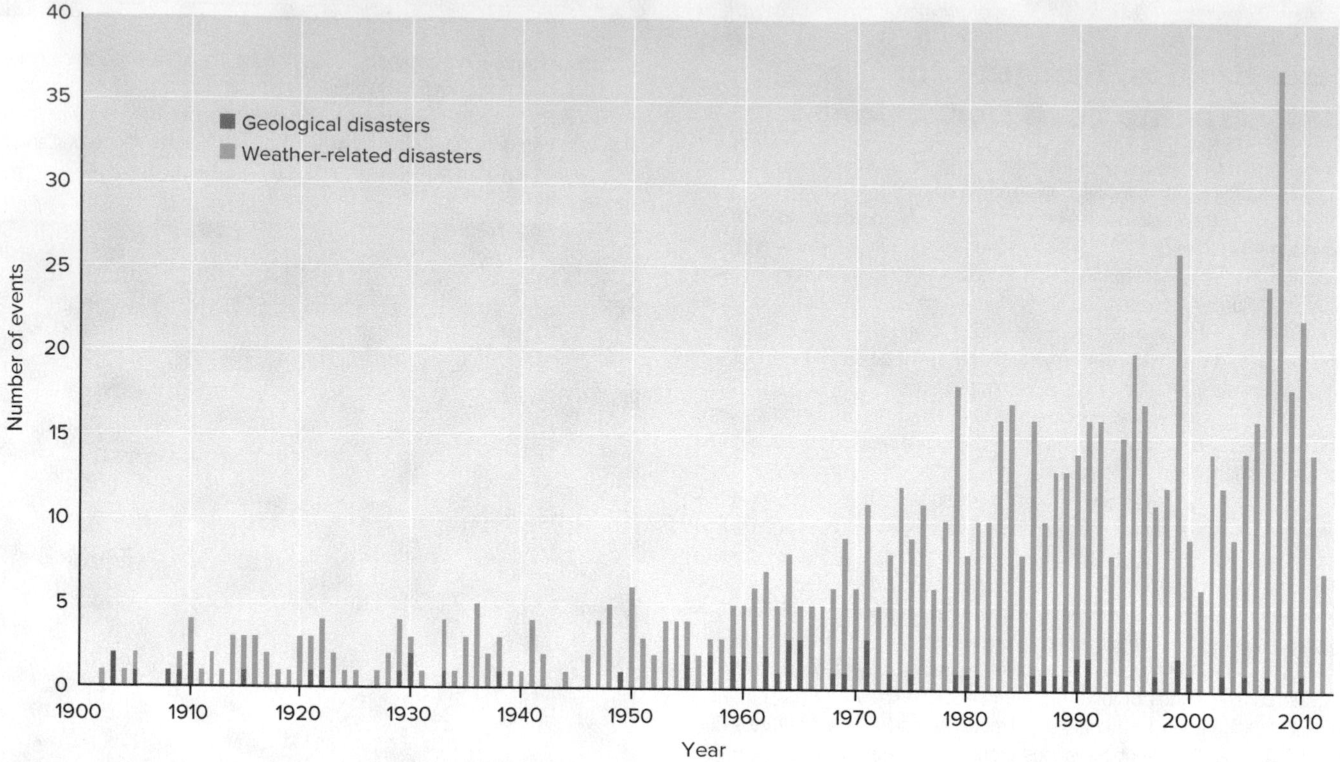

Figure 1.8

Canadian natural disasters, 1900–2012.

Source: Canadian Natural Disasters 1900–2012, Canadian Disaster Database, http://cdd.publicsafety.gc.ca Data from 2006, 2007, 2008. 2009, 2010, and 2012 are taken from the Canadian disasters database of Public Safety Canada. Reproduced with permission.

Events such as floods, which are part of the natural rhythm of rivers, commonly inundate farmers' fields. However, the same floods might start to be reported as "natural disasters" after subdivisions are built on the rivers' flood plains. The increase in the number of weather-related disasters also indicates that weather events have become more extreme in the last 50 years and that Canadian society has not adapted adequately.

The impact of the media should not be neglected in the analysis of the data presented in Figure 1.8. Canada's first television station, CBFT-TV, began broadcasting in Montreal in 1952. The steep increase in the overall number of natural disasters started at the same time. Is it a coincidence? Television was instrumental in broadening Canadians' awareness of major events both at home and in the "global village," a term coined by University of Toronto Professor Marshall McLuhan. This societal trend continues today with the rapid deployment of journalists and audio/video links everywhere in the world and the availability of instant information through the Internet and smart phones.

THE NUMBER OF NATURAL-DISASTER FATALITIES IN CANADA IS DECREASING

Table 1.3 lists the deadliest Canadian disasters from 1900 to 2013. Contrary to the global trend, a majority of disasters (26 of 40) are not due to natural causes. Several entries in the table reflect the dangers associated with travelling across the vast expanses of Canada several decades ago. Three major disasters are of biological origin: the 1918 influenza epidemic, the 1953 polio epidemic, and the recent 2009 H1N1 epidemic. The H1N1 epidemic showed that biological disasters are still a threat, even for a population with high standards of hygiene and accessible medical care. In an expert review commissioned by the City of Ottawa in 2004, for example, a flu pandemic was identified as the most serious threat to the National Capital Region, ahead of an earthquake and a nuclear accident. Although Ottawa is the centre of Canada's political life, the risk of a terrorist attack ranked only seventh in the list.

In spite of the increase in the number of natural disasters in Canada (Figure 1.8), related fatalities have been decreasing, as shown in Figure 1.10. The highest peak corresponds to the July 5–17, 1936 pan-Canadian heat wave, during which temperatures from the Ottawa River Valley to Southern Saskatchewan were in excess of 32°C for one and half weeks, causing the deaths of 1180 people. The 1916 peak is the great forest fire that destroyed 800 000 km^2 of boreal forest in the region of Cochrane in northern Ontario and officially claimed the lives of 73 people

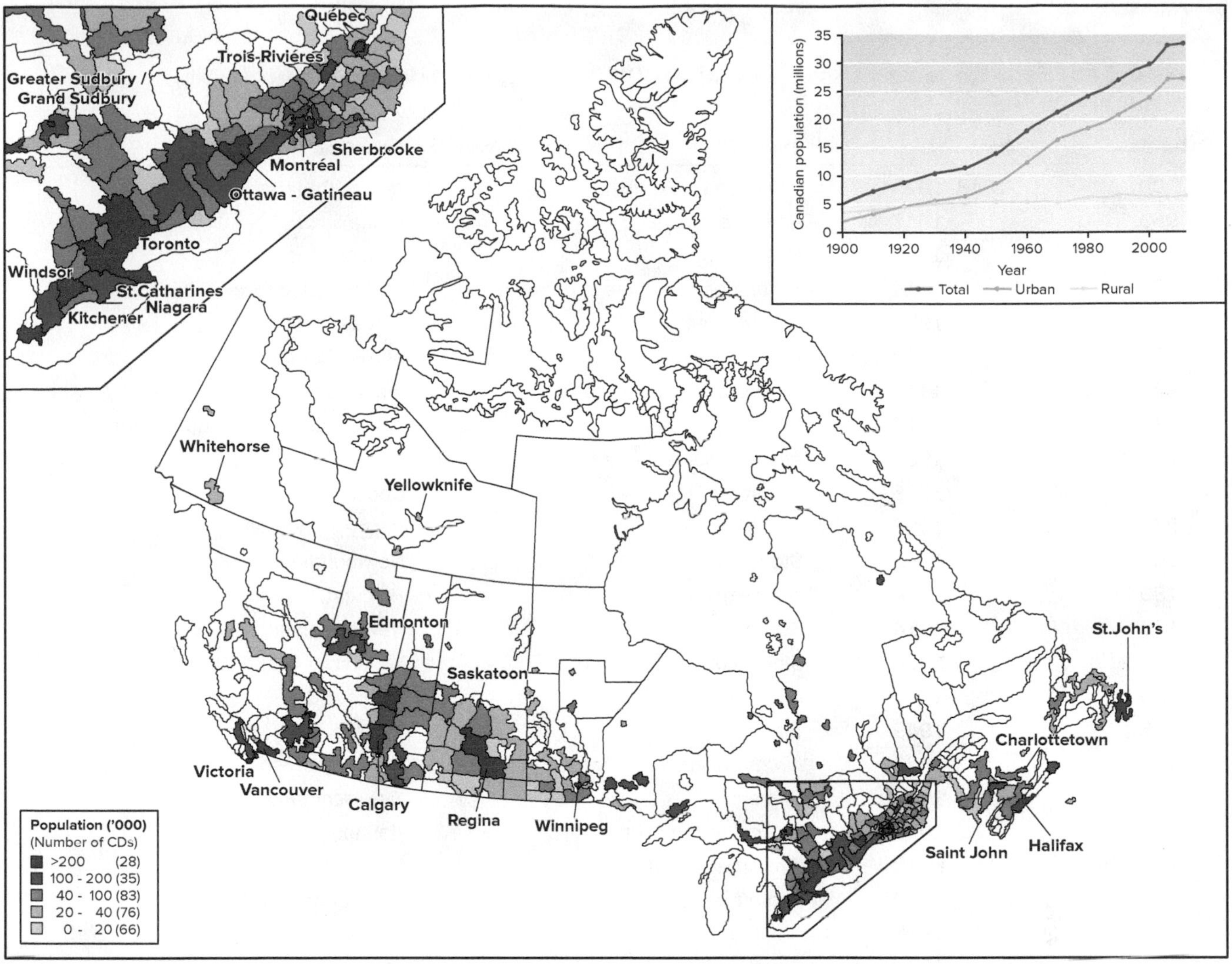

Figure 1.9

Population distribution map of Canada by census division (CD) (2011). Less than 1% of the population lives in the white areas. The insert shows the growth of the Canadian population between 1900 and 2011.

Source: Demography Division, Statistics Canada.

(the actual death toll probably reached hundreds). Most of the other peaks coincide with severe storms in 1913, 1914, 1942, and more recently in 1982, causing ships and an ocean-drilling rig, the *Ocean Ranger*, to sink.

What factors have helped Canadian society become more resilient to natural disasters? Undoubtedly, this success has been achieved by a multifaceted approach that includes improved engineering, long-term prevention, extensive disaster education, better warning systems, and rapid intervention.

IN CANADA, ECONOMIC LOSSES ARE MOSTLY DUE TO WEATHER-RELATED DISASTERS

Weather-related disasters dominate the list of the most costly Canadian disasters (Table 1.4). The increasing frequency at which weather-related disasters occur is of serious concern as climate-change scenarios predict that meteorological activity will intensify in the future (see Chapter 8).

In Canada, written historical records exist only since the arrival of Europeans in the sixteenth century, and the statistics presented in this section cover only the years 1900–2013. In terms of geological processes, a century represents only a quick snapshot. A word of caution: the impact of geological disasters such as earthquakes and volcanoes is under-represented in statistics not because the risk does not exist, but because danger has not materialized in historical times. Canada's costliest natural disasters (Table 1.4) do not make the international list (Table 1.2) because Canada has not experienced a great natural disaster in its history.

TABLE 1.3

The 40 Deadliest Canadian Disasters 1900–2013 (Events not due to natural causes are in italics)

Fatalities	Date	Event	Location
50 000	1918–1925	*Influenza epidemic*	Across Canada
1 963	1917	*Halifax explosion*	Halifax, NS
1 180	1936	Heat wave	Across Canada
1 024	1914	*Sinking of the* Empress of Ireland	St. Lawrence River, QC
481	1953	*Polio epidemic*	Across Canada
425	2009	*H1N1 epidemic*	Across Canada
343	1918	*Sinking of the* Princess Sophia	West Coast, BC
270	1913	Storm	Lakes Huron, Erie, and Ontario
256	1985	*Aircraft accident due to terrorist bomb*	Gander, NF
233	1916	Forest fire	Cochrane area, ON
229	1998	*Aircraft accident*	Peggy's Cove, NS
203	1942	Storm	Newfoundland
189	1914	*Mine explosion*	Hillcrest, AB
173	1914	Storm	Newfoundland
126	1906	*Sinking of the* Valencia	Vancouver Island, BC
125	1902	*Mine explosion*	Fernie, BC
118	1949	*City fire*	Toronto, ON
118	1963	*Aircraft accident*	Sainte-Thérèse-de-Blainville, QC
117	1982	Blizzard	Newfoundland
115	1928	*Sinking of the* Acorn	Halifax, NS
109	1970	*Aircraft accident*	Pearson Airport, ON
101	1963	*Aircraft accident*	West Coast, BC
100	1908	*City fire*	Fernie, BC
99	1942	*City fire*	St. John's NF
88	1918	*Mine explosion*	Pictou County, NS
81	1954	Hurricane Hazel	Southern Ontario
79	1957	*Aircraft accident*	Quebec City QC
77	1914	Blizzard	Labrador, NF
76	1927	*City fire*	Montréal, QC
76	1941	Blizzard	Prairie provinces
75	1907	*Bridge collapse*	Quebec City, QC
75	1957	*Radioactive release*	St. Lawrence, NF
75	1958	*Mine collapse*	Springhill, NS
73	1911	Forest fire	Cochrane, ON
70	1903	Mass movement	Frank, AB
69	1940	Storm	Great Lakes, Lake Ontario
65	1917	*Mine explosion*	New Waterford, NS
64	1901	*Mine explosion*	Grand Forks, BC
63	1910	*Derailment*	Spanish River, ON
62	1910	Snow avalanche	Rogers Pass, BC

Source: 40 Deadliest Canadian Disasters 1900–2013, Canadian Disaster Database http://cdd.publicsafety.gc.ca, Public Safety Canada. Reproduced with permission.

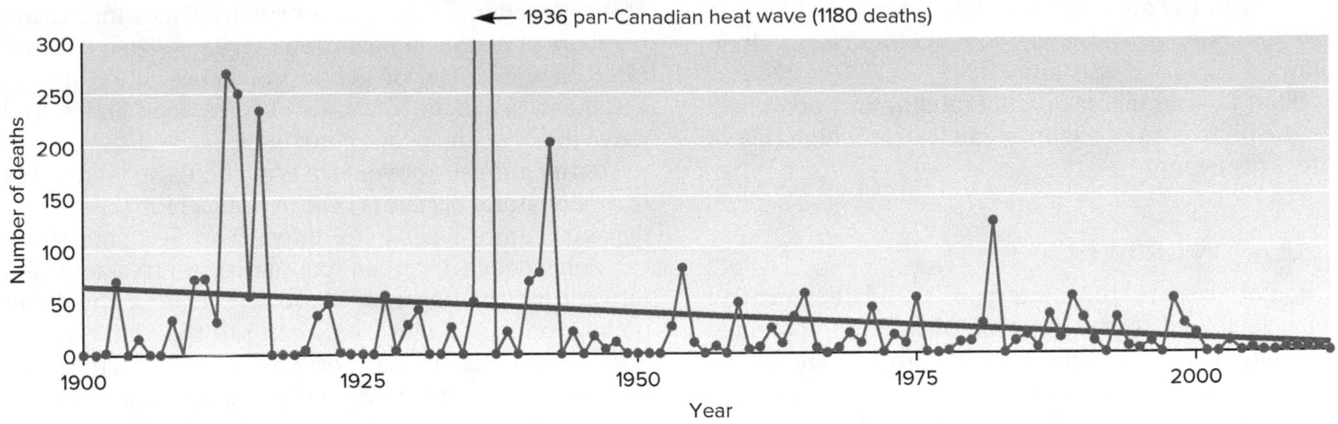

Figure 1.10

Deaths due to natural disasters in Canada (1900–2012). The trend is decreasing.

Source: Deaths due to natural disasters in Canada, 1980 - 2012 Canadian Disaster Database, http://cdd.publicsafety.gc.ca, Public Safety Canada. Reproduced with permission.

TABLE 1.4

Costs of Natural Disasters to the Canadian Insurance Industry in Excess of $200 Million

Total Insured Cost Not Adjusted for Inflation (million CDN$)	Fatalities	Date	Event	Location
1700	4	2013	Flood	Southern Alberta
1295	28	1998	St. Lawrence River Valley Ice Storm	Ontario to New Brunswick
940	0	2013	Storm and flood	Toronto, ON
700	0	2011	Forest fires	Slave Lake, AB
590	0	2005	Storm and flood	Toronto, ON
500	0	2010	Wind and thunderstorm	Southern Alberta, Saskatchewan
400	0	2010	Hail storm	Calgary, AB
386	0	1999	Hail storm	Calgary, AB
355	2	2009	Wind storm	Alberta, AB
343	0	1991	Hail storm	Calgary, AB
300	0	2005	Flood	Calgary, AB
250	Unknown	2003	Forest fires	Alberta and British Columbia
225	0	2011	Wind and rainstorm	Alberta
225	11	2013	Ice Storm	Toronto, ON
218	10	1996	Flood	Saguenay, QC
215	27	1987	Tornado	Edmonton, AB
215	0	1993	Flood	Winnipeg, MB
207	10	1996	Flood	Saguenay, QC

Source: Reproduced with the permission of the Institute for Catastrophic Loss Reduction.

LO4 Vulnerability and Risk

In the context of natural disasters, **vulnerability** is the likelihood that a community will suffer either fatalities or physical damage when exposed to hazards in the environment. **Risk** can be defined as the product of vulnerability and hazard:

$$Risk = Vulnerability \times Hazard$$

From the equation above, we can see that the same hazard poses a more significant threat to vulnerable communities. A large earthquake (severe hazard) could cause significant damage to the highly populated downtown core of Vancouver (high vulnerability); therefore risk is high. A similar earthquake (severe hazard) occurring in the sparsely populated Arctic is likely to cause less damage to human communities (low vulnerability); therefore risk is low.

What factors increase vulnerability and, combined with the proximity of hazards, can lead to a high risk of natural disasters?

POPULATION GROWTH

On a global scale, the pattern of population growth is closely linked to the increase of life and economic loss related to natural disasters. Figure 1.11 shows the growth of the human population worldwide. In 2011, the global population reached 7 billion and it is heading toward 8 billion by 2023. Notice the continuing decline in the number of years it has taken for a net gain of each additional 1 billion people on the Earth. The global population has been growing exponentially at about 1.2% per year for a doubling time of approximately 58 years. Even after subtracting all the human lives lost each year to natural disasters, accidents, diseases, wars, and epidemics such as AIDS, the human population has recently grown by about 80 million per year. This is equivalent to a net addition of 2.5 people per second.

More recently, the growth has changed to a linear increase of population with time. This is expected as the **carrying capacity** of the Earth is approached. Some experts anticipate global population to level off at 9 or 10 billion. Population growth places increasing numbers of people in hazardous settings. They live and farm on the slopes of active volcanoes, build homes and industries in the lowlands of river flood plains, and move to hurricane-prone coastlines.

As mentioned above, Asia is particularly vulnerable to great natural disasters because of its high population density (Figure 1.12). In addition, there is a geographical coincidence between populated centres and significant natural hazards. Large segments of the Asian population live in close proximity to the active volcanoes of the Pacific Ring of Fire, and to earthquake-prone areas. Therefore, Asia is particularly at risk from great natural disasters because of its high population density (high vulnerability) and its high frequency of catastrophic geological events (severe hazards).

The distribution of the Canadian population leads to contrasting circumstances (Figure 1.9). Since the 1930s, the Canadian population has been largely concentrated in cities. The large metropolitan areas of Toronto, Montreal, and Vancouver, where almost one-third of Canadians live, are vulnerable because of their high population density. On the other hand, centres of fewer than 1000 people—from Abbey, Saskatchewan to Zeballos, British Columbia—are vulnerable because they are scattered on an immense territory and, in the event of an emergency, help might take a long time to reach them.

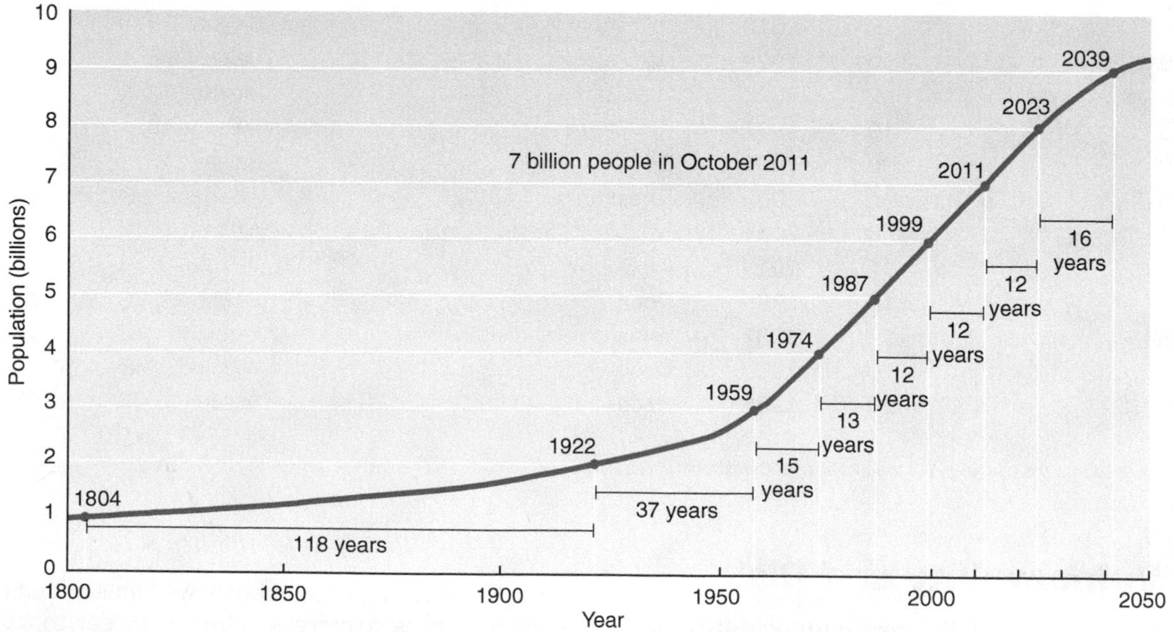

Figure 1.11
Growth of the global population of humans. Notice how the time to add each additional billion people has decreased to date but is projected to start increasing in the future.
Source: © United States Census Bureau.

ROLE OF GOVERNMENT

As the global population of humans increases, the number of deaths by natural disasters is expected to rise, but the relationship has complexities. Analyses by Gregory van der Vink and students at Princeton University show that between 1964 and 1968, about 1 person in 10 000 was killed by a natural disaster. Between 2000 and 2004, even though the population of humans doubled, the death rate by natural disaster dropped to about 1 person in 100 000.

Van der Vink and students compared deaths by natural disaster to the levels of democracy and economic development within 133 nations with populations greater than 1 million that experienced five or more natural disasters between 1964 and 2004. Democracy is assessed by the World Bank's Democracy Index, and economic development by gross domestic product (GDP). The Princeton researchers state that more than 80% of deaths by natural disaster between 1964 and 2004 took place in 15 nations, including China, Bangladesh, and Indonesia. For these 15 countries, 87% are below the median democracy index and 73% are below the median GDP. The correlation between high GDP and low death totals shows exceptions in Iran and Venezuela, two oil-rich nations with significant GDP but low democracy indices. These exceptions suggest a greater importance for democracy than GDP: the stronger the democracy index, the lower the death totals from natural disasters. In a thought-provoking paragraph in their conclusion, van der Vink and students state: "Deaths from natural disasters can no longer be dismissed as random acts of nature. They are a direct and inevitable consequence of high-risk land use and the failures of government to adapt or respond to such known risks."

OVERRELIANCE ON TECHNOLOGY

Although scientific advances have resulted in a better understanding of natural hazards, contributing to enhanced safety, the overreliance of our modern societies on technology has created new vulnerabilities. Modern city life depends on complex and interrelated technological networks, including power transmission lines, telephone and Internet cables, water mains, and pipelines. Other networks, less tangible but equally important, include advanced systems for communications and data transmission that ensure the smooth flow of goods and services. In contrast with these multiple links, however, urban life has also proven to be very lonely for some of the most fragile members of society.

In the event of a natural disaster, the failure of a network can cascade in a dangerous domino effect. Imagine the immediate aftermath of a medium-size earthquake in a crowded city centre. Buildings are structurally intact but power lines are damaged and some gas lines have ruptured. In the ensuing power blackout, out-of-commission traffic lights cause congestion, impeding the movement of emergency response vehicles dispatched to stop gas leaks. During heat waves, prolonged power blackouts often occur because there is not enough electricity to supply the demand for air conditioning. Think of the hopelessness of a senior citizen with reduced mobility who, without functioning elevators, becomes literally trapped in his overheated apartment in a high-rise apartment building. These are simple examples. In many cases, systems are so complex that it is difficult even to predict the cascading effects of the failure of a single system. Any factor disrupting the intricate flows of energy and matter necessary to our modern lifestyles could potentially lead to a collapse of society. Unfortunately, we are far more dependent on these flows than we were, say, a century ago.

POVERTY AND AFFLUENCE

Poor countries are already struggling to meet the basic needs of their citizens. They do not have enough resources to invest in long-term solutions that would decrease their vulnerability, such as safer buildings and early-warning systems. In the short term, they do not have the response infrastructure, such as ambulances, pumps, and fire trucks, to deal with critical situations effectively.

A magnitude 6.6 earthquake struck San Simeon, California on 22 December 2003. Four days later, an earthquake of exactly the same magnitude shook Bam, Iran, located in a similar geological environment. The San Simeon earthquake disturbed the lunchtime rush hour and caused two fatalities. The Bam earthquake was a tragedy of international proportion with 41 000 fatalities. Why were the consequences of the two events so different? Californians have invested massively to ensure their infrastructure is earthquake resistant, using the most recent advances in engineering seismology. In contrast, in remote areas of Iran, people live in traditional houses made of sun-dried, mud-brick walls topped by heavy roofs, according to designs unchanged in millennia. Many of these buildings, including the Bam Citadel, the largest adobe structure in the world, completely disintegrated during the earthquake.

Compare death and destruction along the path of hurricane Jeanne in September 2004. Jeanne formed over the Caribbean Sea and first reached hurricane status near the eastern tip of the Dominican Republic. It declined slightly in intensity and travelled offshore north of Haiti. It regained strength over the Bahamas, veered east, and made landfall in Florida as a category

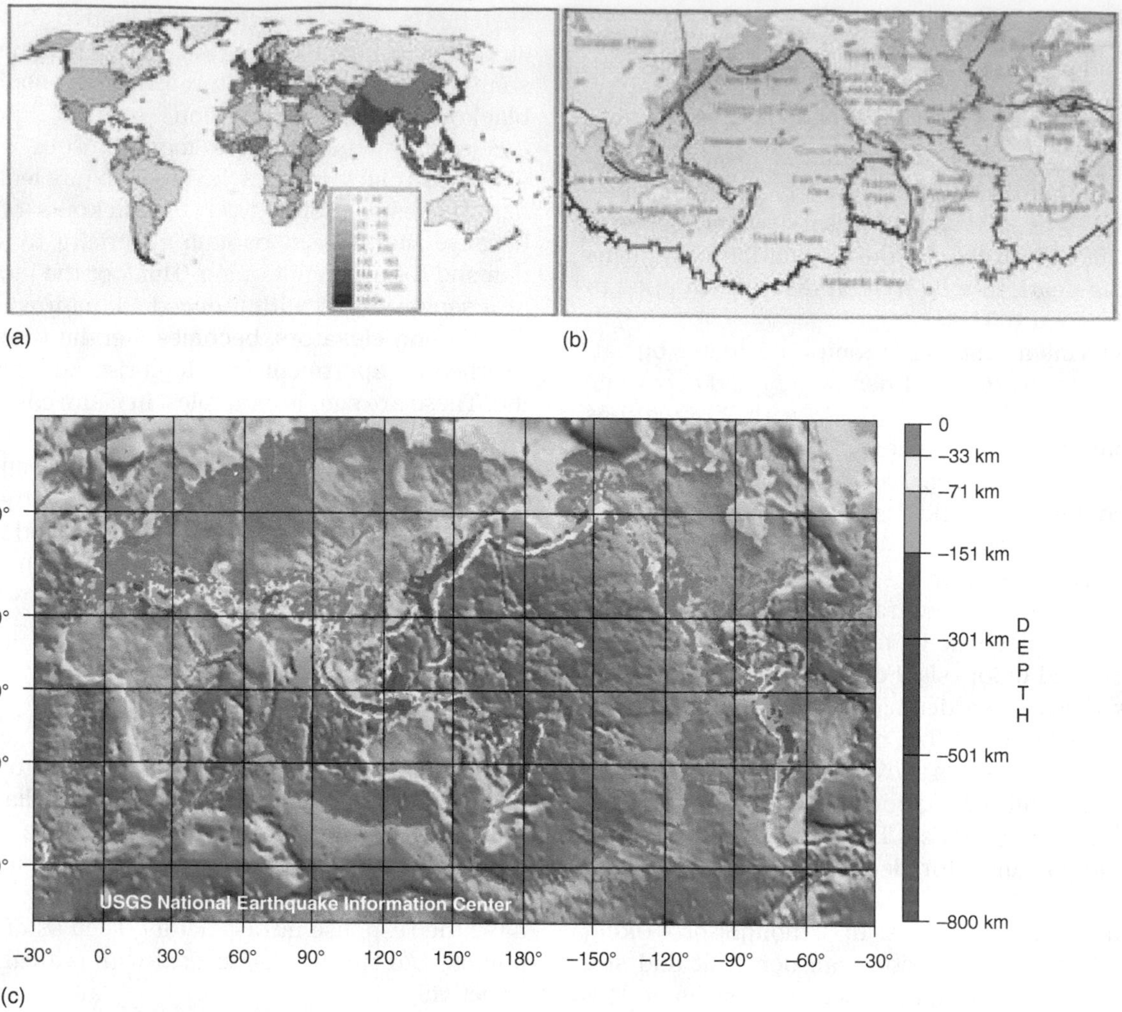

Figure 1.12

(a) World population density per square kilometre. (b) Red dots mark active volcanoes. (c) Earthquake epicentres, 1975–1995. Colour coding of epicentres indicates depths of hypocentres.

Source: (a) David Vignoni, 6 December 2005 http://commons.wikimedia.org/wiki/Image:World_population_density_map.PNG. (b) United States Geological Survey. (c) After USGS National Earthquake Information Center.

3 hurricane. Haiti is the poorest country in the western hemisphere. Although Jeanne did not strike the country directly, heavy rains caused floods and mudslides, leaving more than 3000 people dead. The disaster struck the poorest of the poor. In contrast, the death toll in Florida was five people and the insurance bill was more than US$4 billion.

Nevertheless, there are vulnerabilities associated with affluent lifestyles. The number of fatalities due to snow avalanches in Canada, for example, has steadily been rising. Between 1970 and 1999, there was an average of 10 fatalities per year. Since 2000, however, the average is 13 fatalities per year, the year 2003 being especially tragic with 29 deaths. This increase is largely attributable to a significant rise in the numbers of recreationists heading off into the backcountry, assisted by improvements in equipment that make it easier for skiers, boarders, and snowmobilers to venture into avalanche terrain. Education might be the key to reversing that trend (see Human Focus box: Jim Bay, Avalanche Consultant, in Chapter 13).

SOCIAL BEHAVIOUR

Authorities around the world, from local groups to central governments, are working to reduce the vulnerability of their communities by raising the awareness of the general public. They provide practical advice in the form of leaflets, evacuation drills, and short courses about what to do in case of danger. Short and crisp messages, such as the international tsunami warning sign (Figure 7.31 in Chapter 7) posted in coastal areas around the Pacific and Indian oceans, are often the most effective.

Unfortunately, in some cases public education efforts are met by fatalism or apathy. The return periods of several natural disasters such as volcanic eruptions often span several generations. People forget the tragedies of the past and repeat the same mistakes. Mount Vesuvius (see Chapter 5) erupted violently in 79 **CE** (common era), causing the destruction of the Roman cities of Pompeii and Herculaneum. Volcanism was intermittent until 1631 when a more sustained phase of activity started, lasting until 1944. During this 300-year period, historical records report 24 eruptions. Dating of ash and other eruptive products reveals that Mount Vesuvius experiences an eruption similar to that of 79 CE every 2000 years. Today, even with this well-documented eruptive history, the city of Naples, home to one million people, lies at the foot of the majestic volcano.

Another counterproductive attitude is the overreliance on "society" to fix problems in the event of a natural disaster. This mindset leads individuals to neglect simple but important precautions such as designing a home evacuation plan and keeping a home emergency kit (see In Greater Depth box: Home Emergency Kit and Plan).

How Do Canadians Prepare for Natural Disasters?

The Canadian federal institution responsible for emergency management is Public Safety Canada (PSC). PSC is an "all-hazards" organization coordinating the handling of events as diverse as natural disasters, technological failures, threats to public health, and terrorism. In practice, the organization focuses on managing emergencies, and decides after the fact whether to label a particular event a "disaster."

PSC's approach is based on the four pillars of emergency management: response, recovery, preparedness, and mitigation (Figure 1.13). **Response** refers to the actions taken immediately after an emergency has occurred. It includes interventions by police, medical teams, and firefighters. Effective response is swift and coordinated. Its objective is to get the situation under control as quickly as possible. **Recovery** takes much longer and aims at getting the situation "back to normal"; that is, to its pre-disaster state. Depending on the extent of physical and psychological trauma, it might take several decades for a community to rebuild.

Preparedness and mitigation are long-term actions based on the lessons learned during past disasters and aimed at reducing the impact of future events. **Preparedness** includes taking proactive steps to plan for disasters and putting in place the resources needed to cope with them. Stockpiling goods and conducting regular building evacuation drills are examples of preparedness. In Southern British Columbia, where seismic risk is highest in Canada, children practise earthquake drills in school. Earthquake noise is played over the public address system and children are taught to duck under their desks quickly and to hold firmly to their desks' legs. When the "earthquake" is over, children congregate in the schoolyard where teachers ensure that everyone is accounted for. **Mitigation** involves activities to reduce risk. For example, in the aftermath of hurricane Hazel (see Chapter 10), the City of Toronto "sterilized" the floodplains of several rivers and small creeks in the Don and Humber drainage basins. To mitigate further flood risk, no further urban development is allowed in these floodplains. Instead, these areas are dedicated to recreational use. **Adaptation** is a new term that has emerged with the debate on climate change. Whereas mitigation activities strive to eliminate hazards, adaptation calls for making gradual adjustments towards minimizing harm.

Emergency management in Canada follows a "bottom-up" strategy in a hierarchical jurisdictional environment. The responsibility for health and safety rests mainly in the individual. Moving up one level, municipal responders handle 95% of emergencies, mainly following up on calls to the 911 phone line. The underlying assumption is that municipalities are aware of the hazards facing their communities and are closer to the citizens. When a natural disaster strikes, however, municipal resources can become overwhelmed. Provincial authorities are then called upon for assistance. As a final resort, following a provincial request, the federal government assumes leadership. PSC

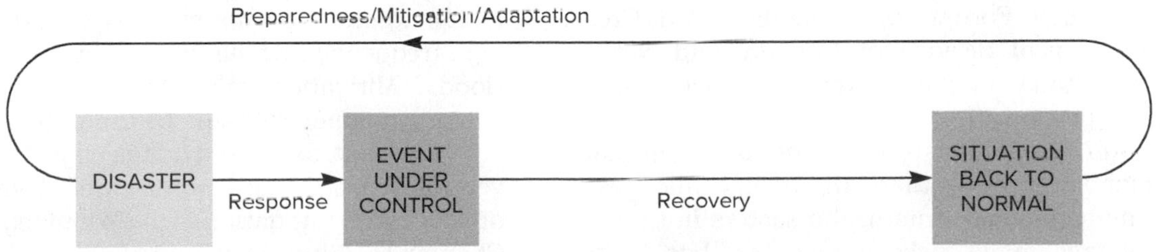

Figure 1.13
Emergency management concepts. The length of the arrows indicates duration: response covers a short period of time, whereas recovery takes much longer. Preparedness, mitigation, and adaptation are feedback loops representing long-term actions.

IN GREATER DEPTH

Home Emergency Kit and Plan

In the case of a major disaster, regardless of its nature, Public Safety Canada (PSC) recommends that you and your family plan to be autonomous for 72 hours, while emergency responders attend to those in urgent need. Be ready by preparing a home emergency kit (Figure 1.14) and a plan. In winter, pay special attention to staying warm.

Figure 1.14
Be proactive about your safety in case of a natural disaster by preparing a home emergency kit.
Source: Natural Resources Canada.

Basic items you will need to survive for 72 hours:

- ☐ **Water**—at least two litres of water per person per day (include small bottles that can be carried easily in case of an evacuation order)
- ☐ **Food** that won't spoil, such as canned food, energy bars, and dried foods (remember to replace the food and water once a year)
- ☐ **Manual can opener**
- ☐ **Flashlight and batteries**
- ☐ **Candles and matches or lighter** (remember to place candles in sturdy containers and to put them out before going to sleep)
- ☐ **Battery-powered or wind-up radio** (and extra batteries)
- ☐ **First aid kit**
- ☐ Special items such as **prescription medications, infant formula,** and **equipment for people with disabilities**
- ☐ **Extra keys** for your car and house
- ☐ Some **cash** in smaller bills, such as $10 bills (travellers cheques are also useful) and change for payphones
- ☐ A copy of your emergency plan including **contact information**

To create your emergency plan, you will need to think about:

- where the exits are from your home and neighbourhood
- a meeting place to reunite with family or roommates
- a designated person to pick up your children should you be unavailable
- close-by and out-of-town contact persons
- health information
- a place for your pet to stay
- the risks in your region
- the location of your fire extinguisher, water valve, electrical box, gas valve, and floor drain.

PSC has created an online tool to help you make an emergency plan. Visit www.getprepared.gc.ca.

Source: Basic Emergency Kit at www.getprepared.gc.ca/cnt/kts/bsc-kt-eng.aspx and Make an Emergency Plan at www.getprepared.gc.ca/cnt/plns/mk-pln-eng.aspx Reproduced with the permission of the Minister of Public Works and Government Services 2014.

coordinates the response, most often solely at a strategic level. It liaises with organizations such as the Canadian Armed Forces, the Canadian Red Cross, the Meteorological Service of Canada, and Natural Resources Canada for the delivery of concrete assistance on the ground.

Although the administrative structure is in place and the mandate is clear, there are many challenges to effective management of natural disasters in Canada. Canadians face many risks but society has limited resources. How should risks be prioritized? The recovery period after a natural disaster is a good time to reflect and plan for the future. The temptation, however, is too often to prepare for the last disaster, not the next one. Should mitigation efforts privilege low-frequency/high-magnitude events such as volcanic eruptions or high-frequency/low-magnitude events such as local floods? Mitigation, with its long-term benefits, is in general tougher to "sell" to the public than response activities, but, as the old adage says, "an ounce of prevention is worth a pound of cure." A shining example of successful mitigation is the Winnipeg floodway (see Chapter 11). Since its completion in 1968, the floodway has saved Winnipeg from flooding more than 20 times, most recently in 2013, by safely channelling excess water away from the downtown area.

SUMMARY

- Several hazardous conditions in the natural environment—unstable slopes or severe weather, for example—can cause harm to society. Several aspects contribute to increase the vulnerability of communities, including a high population density and a number of socio-economic factors.
- Natural disasters occur when natural processes suddenly release a large amount of energy, causing disruption to society. At any one site, in general, the greater the magnitude of a disaster, the less frequently it occurs.
- Worldwide, the number of geological disasters has remained stable in the last century whereas the number of weather-related disasters keeps increasing.
- Great natural disasters are associated with a large number of fatalities and widespread destruction. Their frequency is increasing, a phenomenon partly linked to population growth. The two deadliest types of event are earthquakes and tropical cyclones.
- In the last century in Canada, major transport accidents, large-scale technological failures, and biological disasters have outnumbered natural disasters. An integrated approach to emergency management, including response, recovery, mitigation, and preparedness, has contributed to reduce the number of natural-disaster fatalities.
- The long-term trend is for economic losses associated with natural disasters to continue to increase. Worldwide, between 1970 and 2013, six of the ten most costly natural disasters to the insurance industry have been tropical cyclones. Between 1900 and 2013, 16 of 18 of the most costly natural disasters to the Canadian insurance industry were weather-related.
- Canadian citizens are encouraged to be proactive about natural disasters by preparing a home emergency kit and plan.

Terms to Remember

adaptation
carrying capacity
CE
droughts
earthquakes
energy
floods
frequency
great natural disaster
magnitude
mitigation
natural disaster
natural hazard
preparedness
recovery
response
return period
risk
storms
tsunamis
vulnerability
wildfires

Questions for Review

1. What is the difference between a natural disaster and a natural hazard?
2. What is the relationship between the magnitude of a given disaster and its frequency of occurrence?
3. Since 1950, did the frequency of geological disasters and the frequency of weather-related disasters change over time?
4. What natural disasters killed the most people worldwide since 1970? Where in the world are deaths from natural disasters the highest? Where in the world are insurance losses from natural disasters the highest?
5. What natural disasters killed the most Canadians since 1900? What natural disasters were the most costly to Canadian insurers?
6. What factors increase the vulnerability of communities to natural disasters, worldwide and in Canada?
7. What are the particular challenges faced by poor countries affected by natural disasters?
8. In Canada, what guiding principles are applied to managing emergencies due to natural disasters?
9. What are the four pillars of emergency management? In which order do they occur in the chain of events following a natural disaster?

Questions for Further Thought

1. Would we call a large earthquake or major volcanic eruption a natural disaster if no humans were killed or buildings destroyed?
2. Should all building designs be made disaster-proof, thus reducing the large number of fatalities?
3. How are mass media influencing the perception that the number of natural disasters is increasing with time?
4. What are the strengths and weaknesses of the "bottom-up" (from the individual to the central government) and "top-down" (from the central government to the individual) models of emergency management?

5. In natural disaster management, what percentage of resources should be allocated to response and recovery versus mitigation and preparedness?
6. What can Canadians do to reduce the vulnerability of their communities to natural disasters?
7. Is the United Nations Central Emergency Relief Fund an effective mechanism to help poor countries affected by natural disasters?

Interesting Websites

- Stop Disasters! A disaster simulation game from the United Nations International Strategy for Disaster Reduction
  http://www.stopdisastersgame.org/en/
- Natural Hazards, The Atlas of Canada, Natural Resources Canada
  http://atlas.nrcan.gc.ca/site/english/maps/geology.html#naturalhazards
- All Hazards Monitor, National Oceanic and Atmospheric Administration, United States
  http://www.noaawatch.gov/index.php
- Forces of Nature, *National Geographic*
  http://www.nationalgeographic.com/forcesofnature/interactive/index.html
- Canadian Disaster Database, Public Safety Canada
  http://www.publicsafety.gc.ca/prg/em/cdd/index-eng.aspx
- Get Prepared, Public Safety Canada
  http://www.getprepared.gc.ca/index-eng.aspx
- Canada's Platform for Disaster Risk Reduction
  http://www.publicsafety.gc.ca/cnt/mrgnc-mngmnt/dsstr-prvntn-mtgtn/pltfrm-dsstr-rsk-rdctn/index-eng.aspx
- Institute for Catastrophic Loss Reduction
  http://www.iclr.org/
- Prepare for Severe Weather, Insurance Bureau of Canada
  http://www.ibc.ca/en/Natural_Disasters/index.asp

CHAPTER TWO

2

Earth's Internal Energy and Plate Tectonics

Cross-section through the lithosphere showing the steeply dipping Juan de Fuca plate (left) being subducted beneath the North American plate (right). This tomographic image has been computed using signals from global earthquakes using an approach similar to medical imaging with X-rays. The lengths of the horizontal and vertical scale bars are 30 km and 20 km, respectively.

Source: Stephane Rondenay, University of Bergen.

Many geologists have maintained that movements of the Earth's crust are concentrated in mobile belts, which may take the form of mountains, mid-ocean ridges or major faults . . . This article suggests that these features are not isolated, that few come to dead ends, but that they are connected into a continuous network of mobile belts about the Earth which divide the surface into several large rigid plates.

—John Tuzo Wilson, Nature, 1965

Outline

- Energy Sources of Natural Hazards
- Origin of the Sun and Planets
- The Earth's Early History
- The Layered Earth
- Plate Tectonics: Recycling the Earth's Outer Layers
- Evidence of Plate Tectonics
- Plate-Tectonic Setting of Earthquakes and Volcanoes
- Summary

LO1 List the sources of energy fueling natural hazards.

LO2 Describe the Earth's internal structure.

LO3 Explain the behaviour of materials under stress.

LO4 Explain how plate tectonics operates.

LO5 Evaluate the evidence for plate tectonics.

LO6 Explain the relationship between plate tectonics and the location of earthquakes and volcanoes.

LO1 Energy Sources of Natural Hazards

Disasters occur where and when the Earth's natural processes concentrate energy and then release it, killing and causing destruction. As the world's population increases, more and more people find themselves living close to the Earth's most dangerous places. As historian Will Durant (1885–1981) remarked: "Civilization exists by geologic consent, subject to change without notice."

The natural hazards that have the potential to kill and maim unwary humans can be classified on the basis of the four sources of energy that fuel the Earth's dynamic processes: (1) the Earth's internal energy; (2) solar energy, (3) gravity, and (4) impacts with extraterrestrial bodies (Table 2.1). The use of tabs on the chapter openers will highlight the sources of energy associated with the different natural disasters.

Energy in the Earth's interior comes mainly from the ongoing decay of **radioactive elements**, with smaller contributions from impacts and gravitational compaction, acquired earlier in the Earth's history. Radioactive atoms are unstable and must eject subatomic particles to attain stability. This decay mechanism, **nuclear fission**, is accompanied by a release of energy. At the beginning of the Earth, there were abundant, short-lived radioactive **isotopes**, such as aluminium-26, that are now effectively extinct, as well as long-lived radioactive isotopes, many of which have now expended much of their energy (Table 2.2). The young Earth had a much larger complement of radioactive isotopes and a much greater **heat** production from them than it does now (Figure 2.1). The immense amount of heat generated, however, did not readily escape because heat conducts very slowly through rock. Some of this early heat is still flowing to the surface today and provides enough energy for tectonic plates to move, **volcanoes** to erupt, and earthquakes to shake.

About a quarter of the Sun's energy that reaches the Earth evaporates and lifts water into the atmosphere to begin the **hydrologic cycle** (Figure 8.5). At the same time, the constant pull of gravity helps bring atmospheric moisture down as snow and rain. On short timescales, unequal heating of the oceans and **atmosphere** at the Earth's poles versus the equator creates density differences in water and air that are acted on by gravity to create weather, including storms and drought. On a long timescale, the Sun and gravity power the agents of **erosion—glaciers**, streams, underground waters, winds, ocean waves, and currents—that wear away the **continents** and dump their broken pieces and dissolved remains into the seas. Solar energy is also stored in plant tissue to be released later as fire.

Gravity is an attraction between objects. It is a **force** that humans are unable to modify; it cannot be increased, decreased, reversed, or reflected. The law of gravity states that two bodies attract each other with a force directly proportional to the product of their masses and inversely proportional to the square of the distance between them:

$$gravity = \frac{G \times mass\ 1 \times mass\ 2}{distance \times distance}$$

where G is a universal constant. At equal distances, the greater the mass of a body, the greater its gravitational force. The relatively great mass of the Earth has powerful effects on smaller masses such as ice and rock, causing snow avalanches and landslides.

An energy source for disasters arrives when visitors from outer space—**asteroids** and **comets**—impact the Earth. Impacts were abundant and important early in the Earth's history. In recent times, collisions with large bodies have become less frequent. The Earth travels over 950 million kilometres around the Sun each year—an orbital speed in excess of 108 000 km/h. The kinetic energy of this orbital motion is about 2.7×10^{33} joules (Figure 2.2). When this tremendous amount of energy is involved in a head-on collision with a large asteroid moving 65 000 km/h or a comet travelling 150 000 km/h, the effects on life are catastrophic and worldwide.

TABLE 2.1

Energy and Natural Hazards

Source of Energy	Natural Hazard
Earth's internal energy	Earthquake Tsunami Volcanic eruption
Solar energy	Meteorological storm Flood Drought Wildfire Magnetic storm
Gravity	Mass movement Snow avalanche
Impact energy	Impact with space objects

Geological hazards

Weather-related hazards

TABLE 2.2

Some Radioactive Isotopes in Nature

Parent	Decay Product	Half-Life (billion years)
Carbon-14	Nitrogen-14	0.000 005 73 (5730 years)
Aluminum-26	Magnesium-26	0.000 72 (720 000 years)
Uranium-235	Lead-207	0.71
Potassium-40	Argon-40	1.3
Uranium-238	Lead-206	4.5
Thorium-232	Lead-208	14
Rubidium-87	Strontium-87	47
Samarium-147	Neodymium-147	106

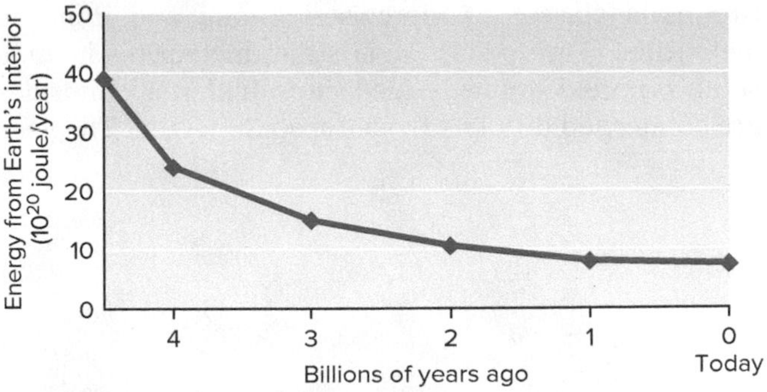

Figure 2.1
The rate of heat production from decay of radioactive atoms has declined throughout the history of the Earth. The flow of energy from Earth's interior is on a slow decline curve heading toward zero.

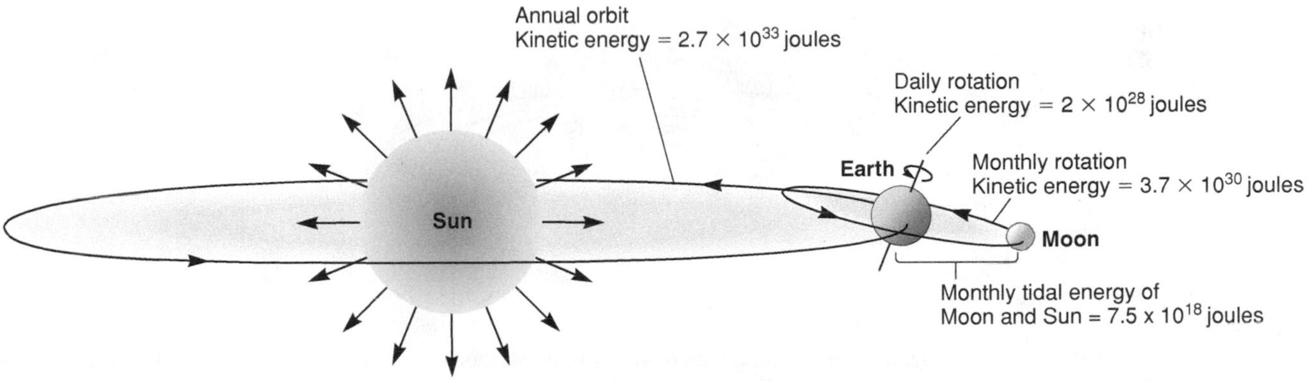

Figure 2.2
The rotations and orbits of the Earth-Moon-Sun system involve tremendous amounts of energy.

Origin of the Sun and Planets

Impacts are not rare and insignificant events in the history of our Solar System; they were probably responsible for its formation. The Solar System was born from a rotating spherical cloud of gas, ice, dust, and other solid debris—the solar nebula (Figure 2.3a). Gravity acting on matter within the cloud attracted particles, bringing them closer together. Small particles stuck together and grew in size, resulting in greater gravitational attraction to nearby particles and thus more collisions. As matter drew inward and the size of the cloud decreased, its speed of rotation increased and it began flattening into a disk. The greatest accumulation of matter occurred in the centre of the disk, building toward today's Sun (Figure 2.3b). The two main constituents of the Sun are the lightweight **elements** hydrogen (H) and helium (He). As its central mass grew larger, the Sun's internal temperature increased to about 1 000 000°C and the process of **nuclear fusion** began. In nuclear fusion, the smaller hydrogen atoms combine (fuse) to form helium with some mass converted to energy. We Earthlings feel this energy as **solar radiation** (sunshine). The remaining rings of matter in the revolving Solar System formed into large bodies as particles continued colliding and coalescing to create the planets (Figure 2.3c).

The inner planets (Mercury, Venus, the Earth, Mars) formed so close to the Sun that solar radiation drove away most of their volatile gases and easily evaporated liquids, leaving behind rocky planets. The next four planets outward (Jupiter, Saturn, Uranus, Neptune) are giant icy bodies of hydrogen, helium, and other frozen material.

Jupiter, with its enormous mass, created in its vicinity a zone of gravitational perturbations too unstable for the formation of large bodies. Chunks of rock remained as discrete entities instead of amalgamating. They still orbit around the Sun in the asteroid belt located between Mars and Jupiter, and are the main source of **meteorites** found on the Earth. There are two main classes of meteorites: stony and iron-rich meteorites (Figure 2.4). Most stony meteorites include small rounded grains, called **chondrules**. Chondrules are condensed droplets from the solar nebula. They are approximately 4.57 billion years old and represent the oldest and most primitive material in the Solar System. Iron meteorites are more evolved, having experienced processes that segregated metals from other elements.

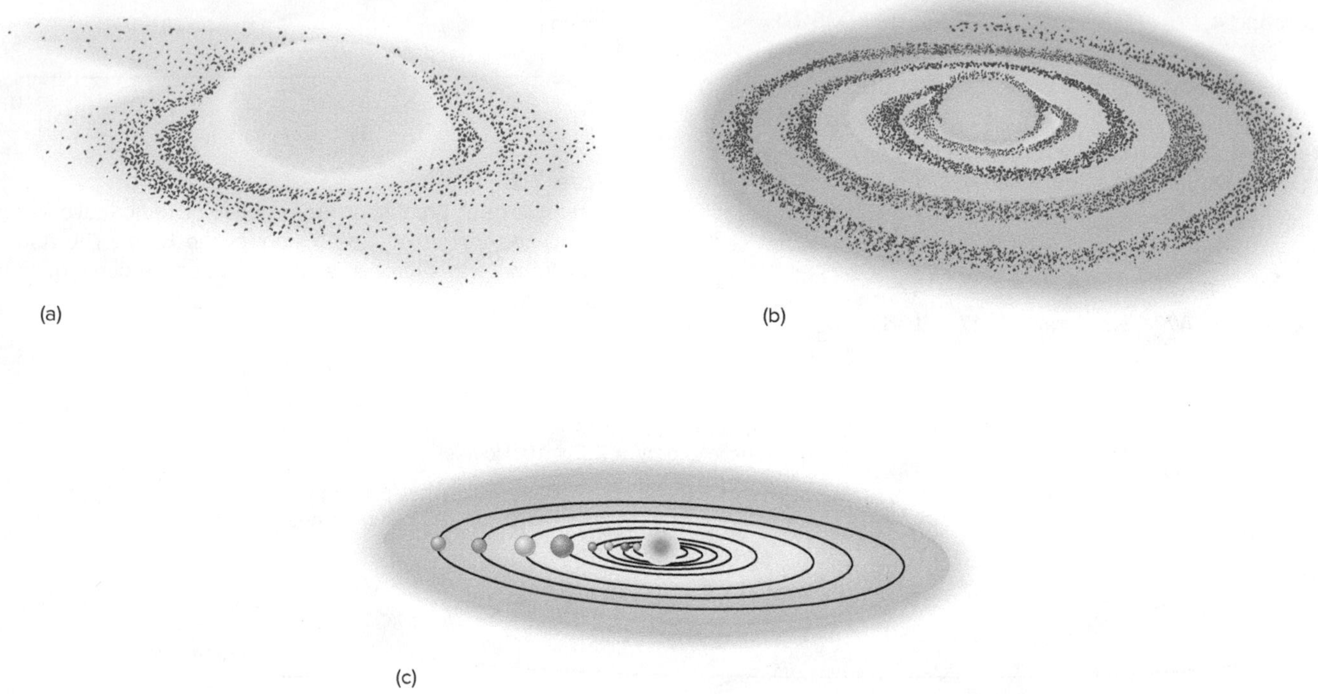

Figure 2.3
Origin of the Solar System. (a) Initially, a huge, rotating spherical cloud of ice, gas, and other debris formed. (b) Spinning mass contracted into a flattened disk with most mass in the centre. (c) Ignited Sun is surrounded by planets, which grew as particles collided and stuck together. The Earth is the third planet from the Sun.

Figure 2.4
Canadian meteorites. (a) Tagish Lake is a stony meteorite found in 2000 in northern British Columbia. It features abundant chondrules, seen as rounded grains within its rust-coloured matrix. (b) Annaheim is an iron-rich meteorite found in 1916 some 100 km east of Saskatoon by a farmer who was mowing hay. Note the well-developed "thumbprints" generated as the meteorite passed through the Earth's atmosphere.

Source: (a) Reproduced with permission of the Royal Ontario Museum © ROM (ROM2006_7156_30). (b) Reproduced with the permission of Natural Resources Canada 2014, courtesy of the Geological Survey of Canada (Photo 2008-186 by Richard Herd).

The Earth's Early History

The time it took to build the Earth as we know it is possibly as short as 30 million years Some 4.57 billion years ago, the Earth in its infancy grew from random collisions of debris that formed a more or less homogeneous mixture of materials: bits and pieces of metal-rich particles (similar to iron-rich meteorites), rocks (similar to stony meteorites), and ices (of water, carbon dioxide, and other compounds). But the Earth did not remain homogeneous. The very processes of planet formation (Figure 2.5) created tremendous quantities of heat, which fundamentally changed the young planet. The heat that transformed the early the Earth came from impact energy, decay of radioactive isotopes, and gravitational energy.

As the internal temperature of the Earth rose beyond 1000°C, it passed the melting points of iron at various depths below its surface. Iron forms about one-third of the Earth's mass, and although it is much denser than ordinary rock, it melts at a much lower temperature. The buildup of heat caused a large quantity of iron to melt. The high-density liquid iron was pulled by gravity toward the Earth's centre. As these gigantic volumes of liquid iron moved inward to form the Earth's **core,** they released a tremendous amount of gravitational energy that converted to heat and probably raised the Earth's internal temperature by another 2000°C. The release of this massive amount of heat would have produced widespread melting, which in turn may have enabled low-density materials to rise and form (1) a primitive **crust** of low-density rock at the surface of the Earth; (2) large oceans; and (3) a dense atmosphere. The formation of the iron-rich core was a unique event in the history of the Earth. The planet was changed from a somewhat homogeneous ball into a density-stratified mass with the denser material in the centre and progressively less-dense materials outward to the atmosphere. It seems that oceans and small continents existed by 4.4 billion years ago. The oldest rocks found to date on Earth are 4.03 billion years old and originate from northern Canada (Figure 2.6). Life was probably present as photosynthetic bacteria 3.5 billion years ago, and large continents existed at least 2.5 billion years ago when the process of plate tectonics was initiated.

The recognition of the Earth's great age came late in human history; it started with James Hutton in the 1780s. Hutton carefully observed the Scottish landscape around him and thought deeply about it. For example, he saw rock walls built by the Romans that had stood for 15 centuries with only slight change. If 1500 years was not long enough to break down a wall, then, Hutton wondered, how much time had been required to break down hard rock into the abundant pebbles and sand grains he saw in nearby rivers? And how much more time had been necessary to lift the pebbly and sandy sedimentary rocks to form hills? All the active processes that Hutton observed worked slowly, so he concluded that great lengths of time must be required and that the Earth was very old. Small, everyday changes on the Earth add up to major results over long periods of time.

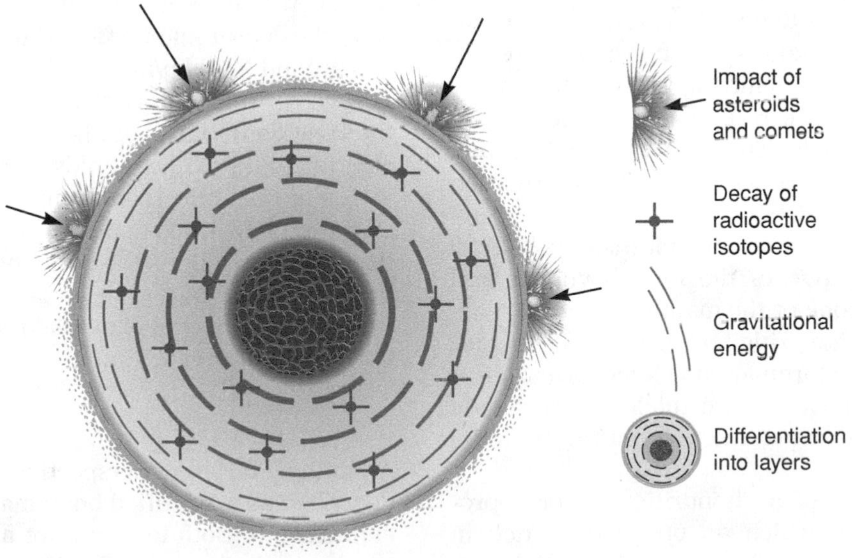

Figure 2.5
Heat-generating processes during the formative years of the Earth include impact energy, decay of radioactive isotopes, and gravitational energy. Increasing heat caused the Earth to differentiate into layers.

(a)

(b)

Figure 2.6
(a) The Acasta gneiss, found 350 km northeast of Yellowknife in the Northwest Territories, is dated at 4.03 billion years old by measuring the decay of uranium into lead. (b) Short-lived isotopes contained in rocks from Nuvvuagittuq in northern Quebec suggest that they may be 300 million years older than the Acasta gneiss. Although this age is still not confirmed, they may be the oldest rocks on the Earth.

Source: (a) Reproduced with the permission of Natural Resources Canada 2014, courtesy of the Geological Survey of Canada (Photo 2007-178 by Marc St-Onge). (b) © Jonathan O'Neil, McGill University.

LO2

The Layered Earth

The Earth today is differentiated into layers that can be described either as (1) layers of different densities due to varying chemical and mineral compositions or (2) layers of different strengths (Figure 2.10).

DENSITY LAYERS

At the Earth's centre is a dense, iron-rich core measuring about 7000 km in diameter. The inner core is a solid mass 2450 km in diameter with temperatures up to 4300°C. The outer core is mostly liquid, and convection currents within it are responsible for generating the Earth's magnetic field. The core is roughly analogous in composition to a melted mass of iron-rich meteorites.

Surrounding the core is a rocky **mantle** nearly 2900 km thick, comprising 83% of the Earth's volume and 67% of its mass. The rock of the mantle can be approximated by melting a chondritic meteorite in the laboratory and removing most iron-loving elements and some volatiles. The uppermost 700 km thickness of mantle is depleted in light elements and thus differs from the zone below.

Continued melting of a chondritic meteorite produces a separation in which an upper froth rich in low-density elements rises above a residue of denser elements. The low-density material is similar to continental crust that, through melting and separation, has risen above the uppermost mantle. All the years of heat flow from the Earth's core toward its surface have "sweated out" many low-density elements to form the continental crust. Today, the continents comprise only 0.1% of the Earth's volume.

As we can see, the Earth can be described as a series of floating layers where less-dense materials rest upon layers of successively denser materials. The core, with densities up to 16 000 kg/m^3, supports the mantle, with densities ranging from 5700 to 3300 kg/m^3. Atop the denser mantle float the continents, with densities around 2700 kg/m^3, which in turn support the salty oceans, with densities of about 1030 kg/m^3, and then the least-dense layer of all—the atmosphere. The concept of floating layers holds true on smaller scales as well. For example, the oceans contain layered masses of water of differing densities. Very cold, dense Antarctic water flows along the ocean bottoms and is overlaid by cold Arctic water, which is overlaid by extra-salty water, which in turn is overlaid by warmer, less-dense seawater (Figure 8.8).

STRENGTH LAYERS

Adopting a different perspective, the Earth can also be described as a stratified body made of layers of different strength. Both temperature and pressure decrease continuously from the Earth's core to its surface, yet their effects on materials are different (see In Greater Depth box: Material Deformation).

IN GREATER DEPTH

LO3

Material Deformation

When materials are subjected to sufficient external forces or **stress**, they will deform or undergo **strain**. Stress can be applied perpendicular to the surface of a body, causing it to stretch under **tension** or to contract under **compression**. On the other hand, **shear stress**, which is applied parallel to the surface, tends to deform a body along internal planes slipping past one another (Figure 2.7).

Materials respond to stress in different ways (Figure 2.8). Stress may produce **elastic**, or recoverable, deformation, such as when you pull on a spring. The spring deforms while you pull it, but when you let go, it recovers and returns to its original shape. If greater stress is applied, **ductile**, or permanent, deformation may occur.

However, these definitions do not allow for the effect of time. How do materials behave under stress over different time scales? If stress is applied rapidly to a material, it might fracture abruptly or break into pieces in **brittle** deformation. If stress is applied for a longer time or at higher temperatures, some solids yield to pressure by deforming and flowing, that is, by behaving like fluids. This type of behaviour is called "**plastic**" in the sense used by William James in his 1890 *Principles of Psychology.* He defined "plastic" as "possession of a structure weak enough to yield to an influence, but strong enough not to yield all at once."

A familiar example of a material exhibiting a variety of behaviours is glacier ice. The ice's behaviour depends on the amount of pressure confining it. Near the surface, there is little pressure on the rigid ice and it abruptly fractures when stressed (Figure 2.9a). When a glacier is hit with a rock hammer, solid chunks of brittle ice are broken off. On the other hand, deep within the glacier, where the weight of overlying ice creates a lot of pressure, the ice deforms and flows. Atoms are changing positions within the ice and most move downhill to positions of lower stress. At no instant in time does the glacier fit our everyday concept of a liquid, yet over time, the glacier is flowing downhill as a highly **viscous** fluid (Figure 2.9b).

The response of earth material to pressure and temperature is a complex balance of different effects. When a material such as rock is subjected to the same large amounts of stress on all sides, it compresses. When

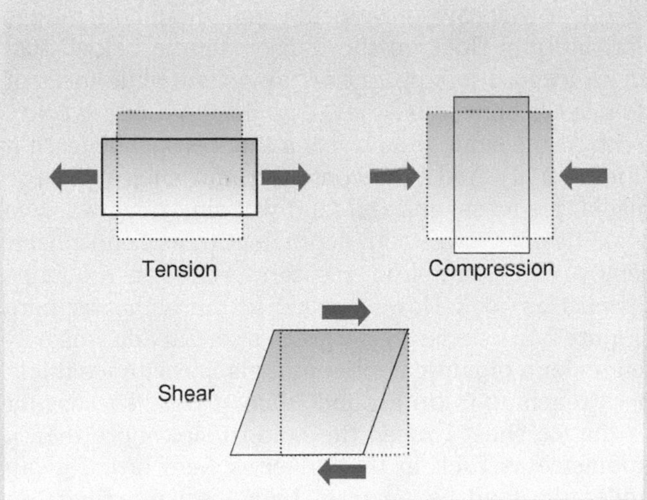

Figure 2.7
A square of material deforms into an elongated rectangle under tension or compression. It becomes a parallelogram when shear stress is applied.

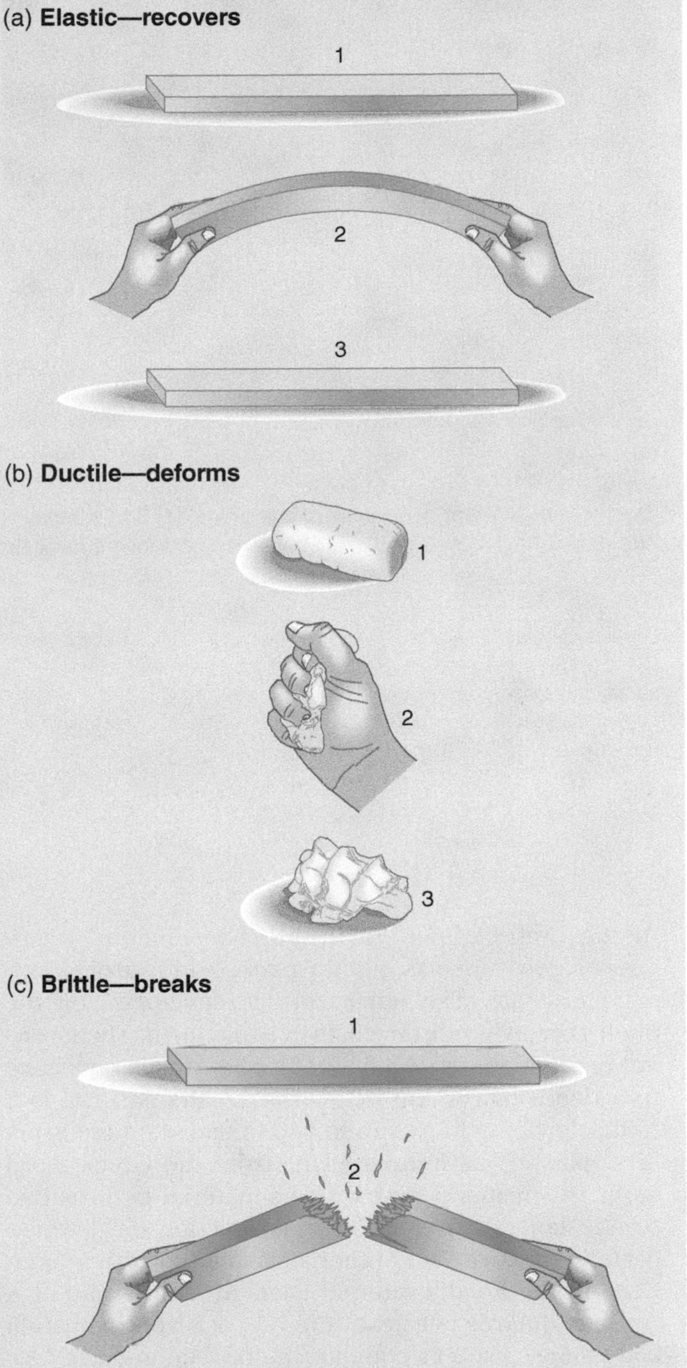

Figure 2.8
Behaviour of materials. (a) Elastic: bend thin board; let it go and board recovers its original shape. (b) Ductile: squeeze a wad of bubblegum or Silly Putty®; let it go and it stays in the deformed shape. (c) Brittle: bend thin board sharply and it breaks.

continued

(a) (b)

Figure 2.9
Examples of different behaviours of glacier ice. (a) Brittle behaviour on a short time scale: iceberg calving off Hubbard glacier, Disenchantment Bay, Alaska. (b) Plastic behaviour on a long time scale: the Elephant Foot glacier from East Greenland flowing toward the sea.
Sources: (a) © Royce Bair; (b) Dr. Fiona Darbyshire, GEOTOP-UQAM McGill, Université du Québec à Montréal.

stresses coming from different directions vary, then strain can occur. When the differences in stress are low, then strain is elastic and reversible. As stress differences increase, permanent strain eventually occurs. Increasing temperature causes rock to expand in volume and become less dense and more capable of flowing. Increasing pressure causes rock to decrease in volume and become denser and more rigid. Most rocks are brittle at the low temperatures and low pressures found at the Earth's surface. They fracture and create faults. Most rocks become ductile at the high temperatures and high pressures found at greater depths. They deform plastically, producing undulations called folds.

At the centre of the Earth is the inner core, where intense pressure has tightly packed iron atoms into solid crystals. The inner core is enveloped by the outer core, where iron exists in liquid form. The **mesosphere**, which extends from the core-mantle boundary to a depth of 360 km below the Earth's surface, is a "stiff plastic" solid. Surrounding the mesosphere is the "soft plastic" **asthenosphere** (from the Greek word *asthenes,* meaning "weak"). The material in these two plastic layers flows in large convection cells where certain areas rise and other sink due to spatial variations in the Earth's internal heat. At a flow rate of a few centimetres per year, it takes rock approximately 250 million years to complete a convection cycle (see In Greater Depth box: Heat Transfer). Finally, the outer layer of the Earth is the rigid **lithosphere** (from the Greek word *lithos,* meaning "rock") whose thickness ranges from a few kilometres under the oceans to about 100 km under the continents (Figure 2.11). From the perspective of geological disasters, the most important boundary between the different strength layers is the boundary between the lithosphere and asthenosphere.

Isostasy

The concept of **isostasy** applies a buoyancy principle to the low-density continents and mountain ranges that literally float on the denser mantle below. Just as an iceberg juts up out of the ocean while most of its mass is beneath sea level, so does a floating continent. At the same time it has a thick "root" beneath it (Figure 2.11). Add a load onto the land, such as a large glacial ice mass, and the land will sink downward as rock flows outward at depth in the asthenosphere; remove the load, and the land rises or rebounds upward as rock flows inward in the asthenosphere (Figure 2.12). Some 18 000 years ago, Canada was buried under a gigantic continental glacier with ice thickness reaching 5 km around Hudson Bay. The weight of the ice sheet caused the land to sink more than a kilometre as rock in the asthenosphere oozed away under the load as an ultra high viscosity fluid. By 10 000 years ago, the ice sheet had melted and retreated. Responding elastically, the long-depressed landmass, now freed from its heavy load, is currently rebounding upward at a velocity of a few millimetres per year (Figures 2.13 and 2.14).

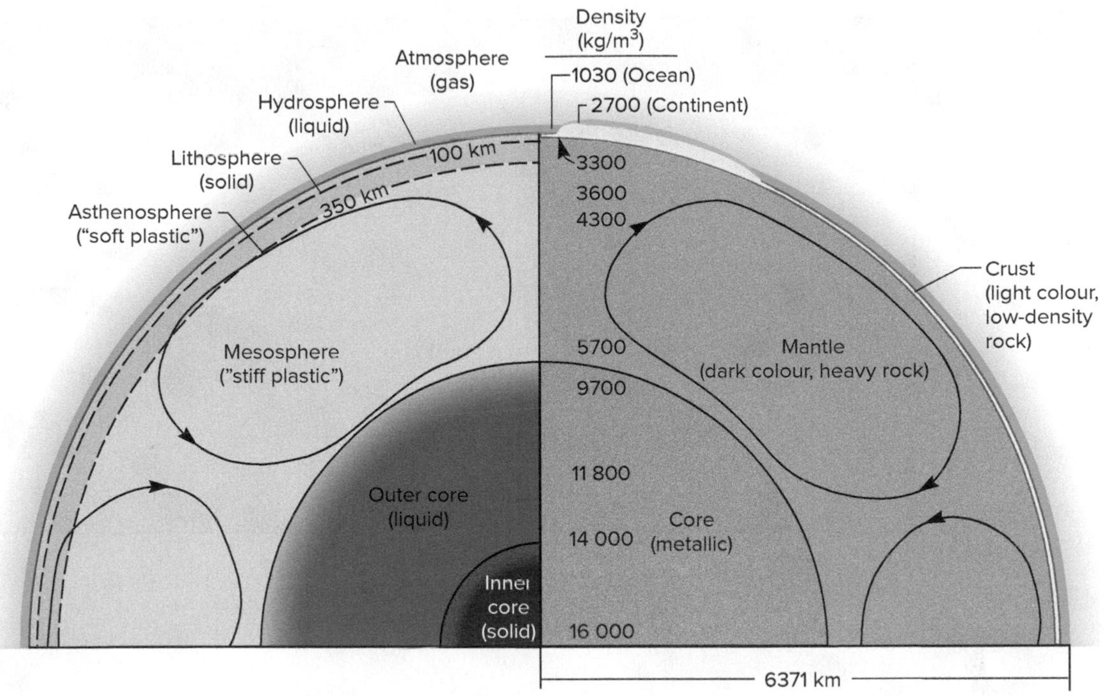

Figure 2.10

Layering within the Earth. Both pressure and temperature decrease from the centre of the Earth to the surface. Left: layers with different physical properties and strength. Right: density stratification. Low-density materials float atop higher-density materials. Arrows indicate large convection cells, similar to those shown in Figure 2.15.

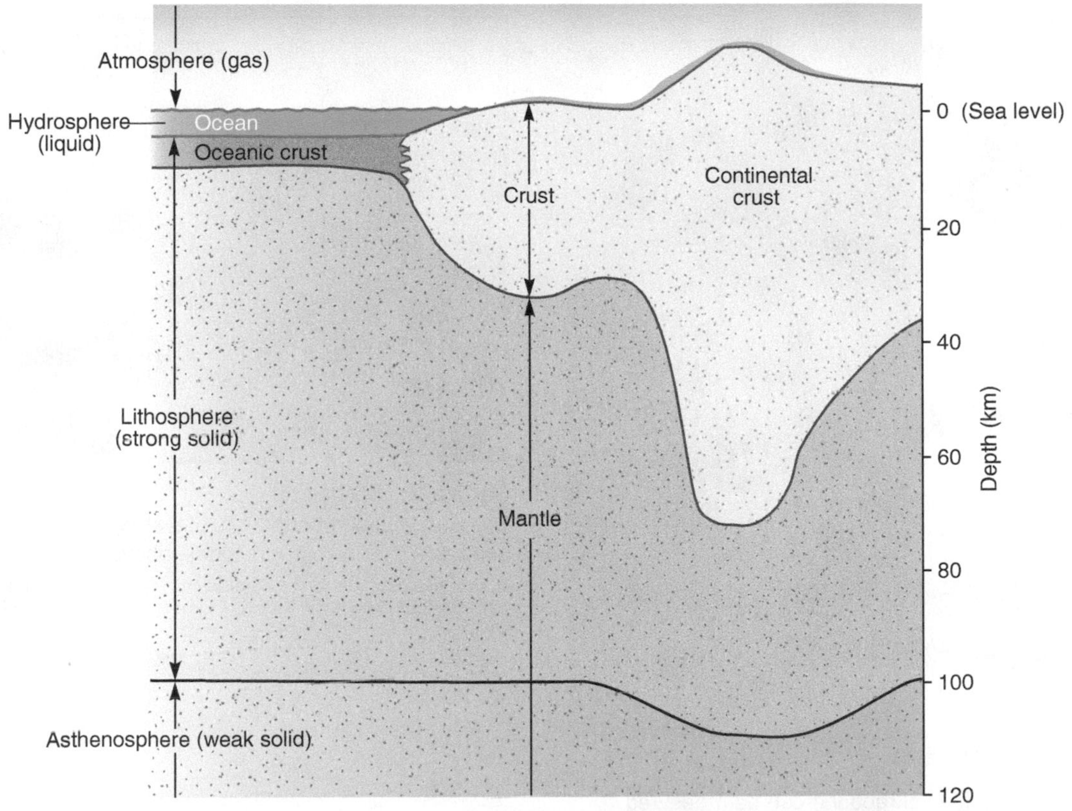

Figure 2.11

Upper layers of the Earth may be recognized (1) compositionally, as lower-density crust separated from the underlying higher-density mantle, or (2) on the basis of strength, as strong, solid lithosphere riding atop weak, solid asthenosphere. Notice that the lithosphere includes both the crust and the uppermost mantle.

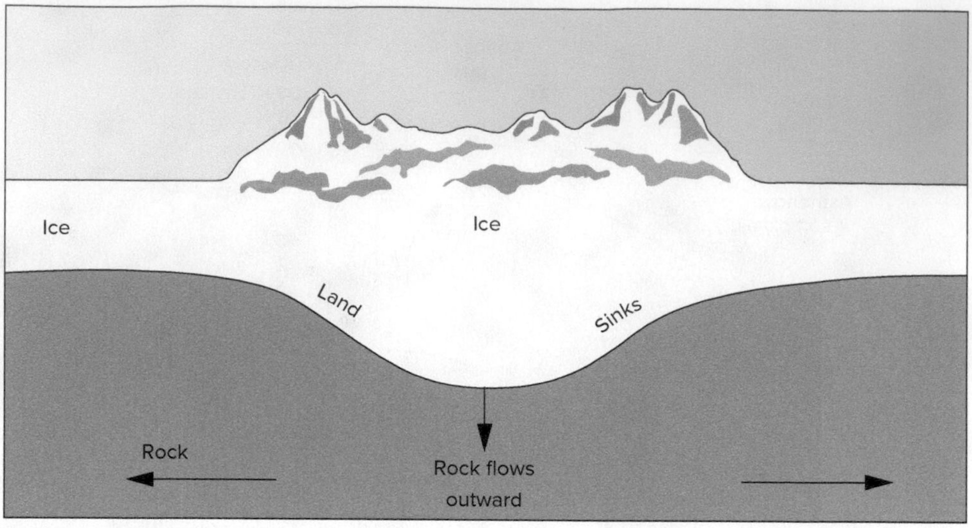

Figure 2.12
Land sinks as the weight of ice causes rock at depth to flow outward.

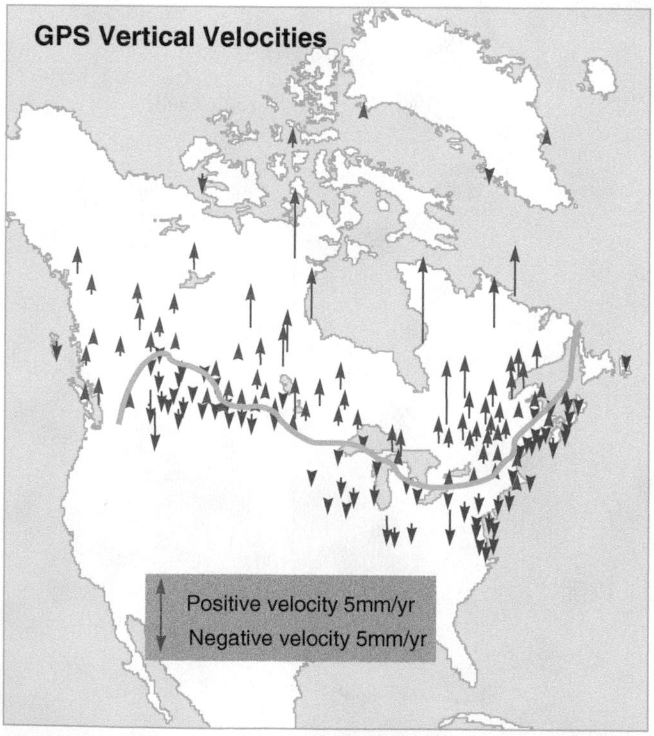

Figure 2.13
The velocity of the post-glacial rebound can be measured using the global positioning system (GPS). The Hudson Bay area where the ice load was heaviest during the last glaciation is rising the most quicky.
Source: NOAA.

Figure 2.14
The post-glacial rebound has elevated beaches in the Boothia peninsula, Northwest Territories, above present-day sea level.
Source: Reproduced with the permission of Natural Resources Canada 2014, courtesy of the Geological Survey of Canada (Photo A89S0039 by Robert Rainbird).

IN GREATER DEPTH

Heat Transfer

Above absolute zero (−273° C), molecules are constantly vibrating. We perceive this random motion as heat. Heat can be transmitted through solids and fluids by conduction, through fluids by convection, and through a vacuum by radiation.

Consider a pot of boiling water over an electrical spiral heating element (Figure 2.15). The three heat transfer mechanisms—**conduction**, **convection**, and **radiation**—are redistributing heat in the room. Heat is transmitted from the element to the pot and water, and directly from the element to the ambient air by conduction through collisions between neighbouring molecules. Heat transfer occurs between the water vapour and the air by convection and conduction when the two fluids mix. The element emits invisible infrared radiation that warms the air.

On a planetary scale, the same processes are active. Heat from the interior of the Earth flows to the surface by conduction through the different layers of the Earth. In the mesophere and asthenosphere, heat is redistributed by the flow of plastic solids. Hot, less-dense material rises while cold, denser material sinks, creating large organized circulation patterns called convection cells. Solar radiation travels through space to warm the Earth's surface.

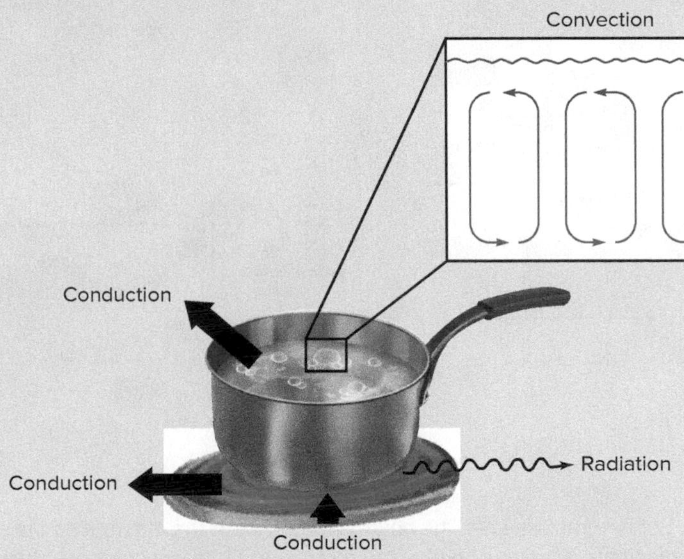

Figure 2.15
The three heat mechanisms at work. Boxed area: Convection cells form in the water. Warm, low-density water rises (red). Cool, high-density water sinks (blue). Water is heated at the bottom of the pot. It cools by losing heat at the surface.

LO4 Plate Tectonics: Recycling the Earth's Outer Layers

The surface of the Earth is in a delicate vertical balance. In addition to vertical isostatic uplift, major adjustments and movements also occur horizontally. These horizontal movements between the lithosphere and asthenosphere bring us into the realm of plate tectonics.

The lithosphere of the Earth is broken into pieces called **plates** (Figure 2.16). Comparing Figures 1.12, and 2.16 and 2.17 shows that earthquakes and volcanic eruptions do not occur at random locations but are mostly distributed along the edges of the plates, where lithospheric stresses are mainly concentrated. Life on the edge is precarious!

The study of the movements and interactions of the plates is known as **plate tectonics**. The Greek word *tekton* comes from architecture and means "to build"; it has been adopted by geologists to describe the deformation and movement within the Earth's outer layers, and the building of **topography**. A topographic and bathymetric map of the world reveals several prominent features created by tectonic forces—on continents, for example, the Himalayas and the Tibetan Plateau, and the cordillera of the West Coast of the Americas; and on the ocean floor, for example mid-oceanic **ridges**, deep trenches, and chains of volcanic islands and seamounts (Figure 2.18 and Figure 2.19). To grasp the concepts of plate tectonics, however, we must adopt a new perspective when looking at a world map. We must move our focus away from the continental coastlines and concentrate on plate boundaries.

The **tectonic cycle** can be simplified as follows (Figure 2.20). First, melted asthenosphere flows upward as magma and cools to form new lithosphere on the ocean floor (**seafloor spreading**). Second, the new lithosphere slowly moves laterally away from the zones of oceanic crust formation. It glides on top of the underlying asthenosphere, carrying the low-density continents as on a conveyor belt. Third, when the leading edge of a moving plate of oceanic lithosphere collides with another plate, the denser plate turns downward and is pulled by gravity back into the asthenosphere (**subduction**), while the less-dense, more

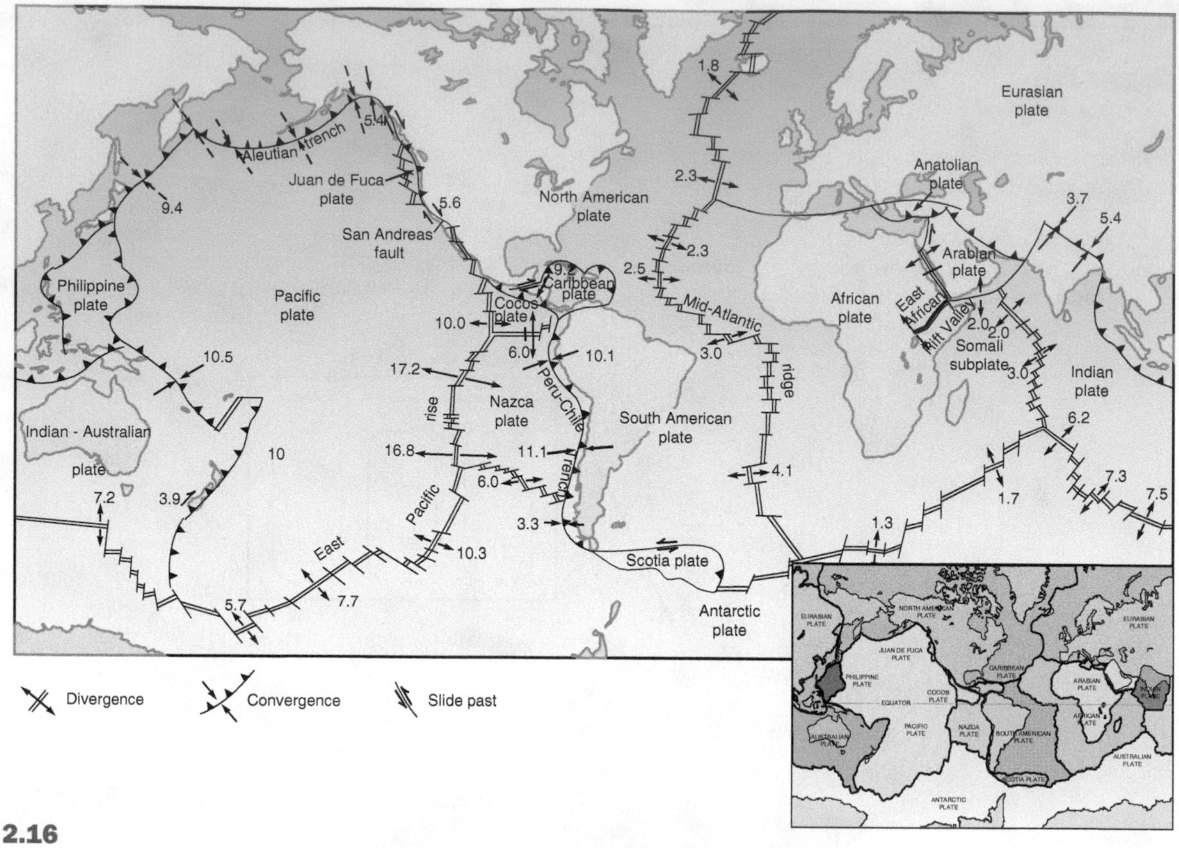

Figure 2.16

A tectonic view of the world. In the context of natural disasters, the boundaries between the different plates are more important than the familiar continental coastlines. Arrows indicate the direction of plate movement. Plate velocities are shown in centimetres per year.

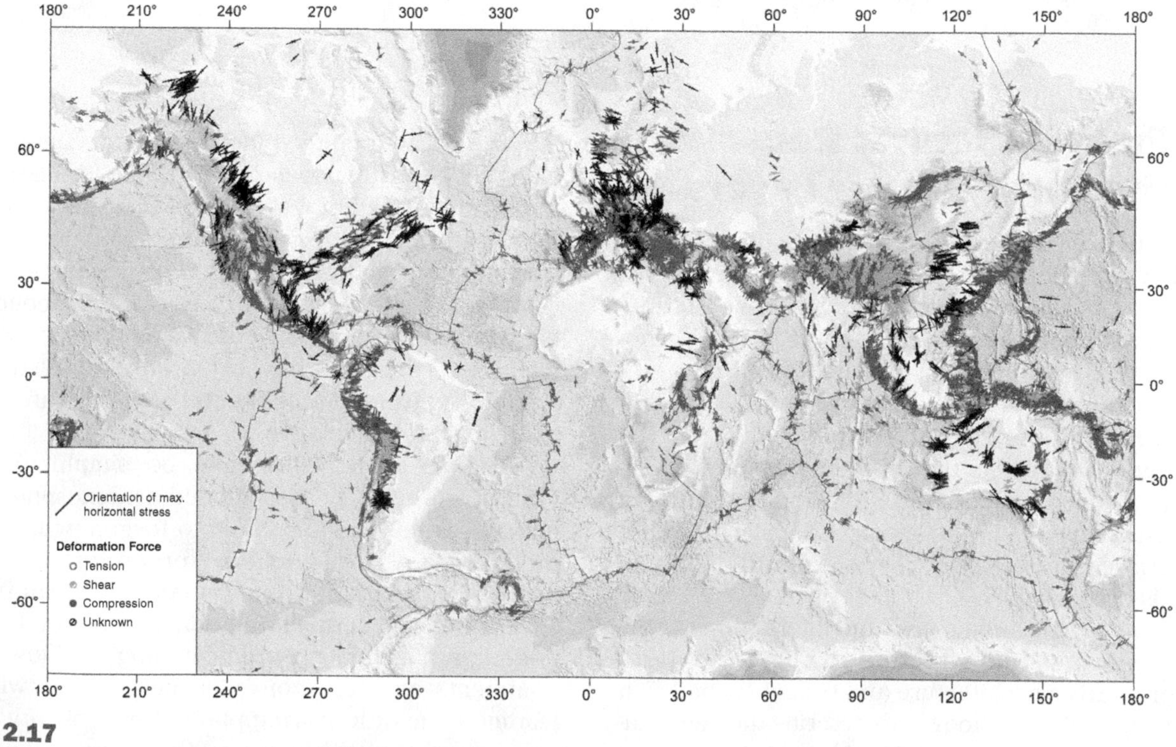

Figure 2.17

World stress map.

Source: Heidbach, O., Tingay, M., Barth, A., Reinecker, J., Kurfeß, D. und Müller, B. (2010). Global crustal stress pattern based on the World Stress Map database release 2008. *Tectonophysics* 462, doi:10.1016/j.tecto.2009.07.023, (online available at: www.world-stress-map.org).

Figure 2.18

Topographic and bathymetric map of the world. Red and dark blue correspond to the most elevated and depressed regions, respectively.

Source: NOAA http://whale.wheelock.edu/whalenet-stuff/MAPSindex.

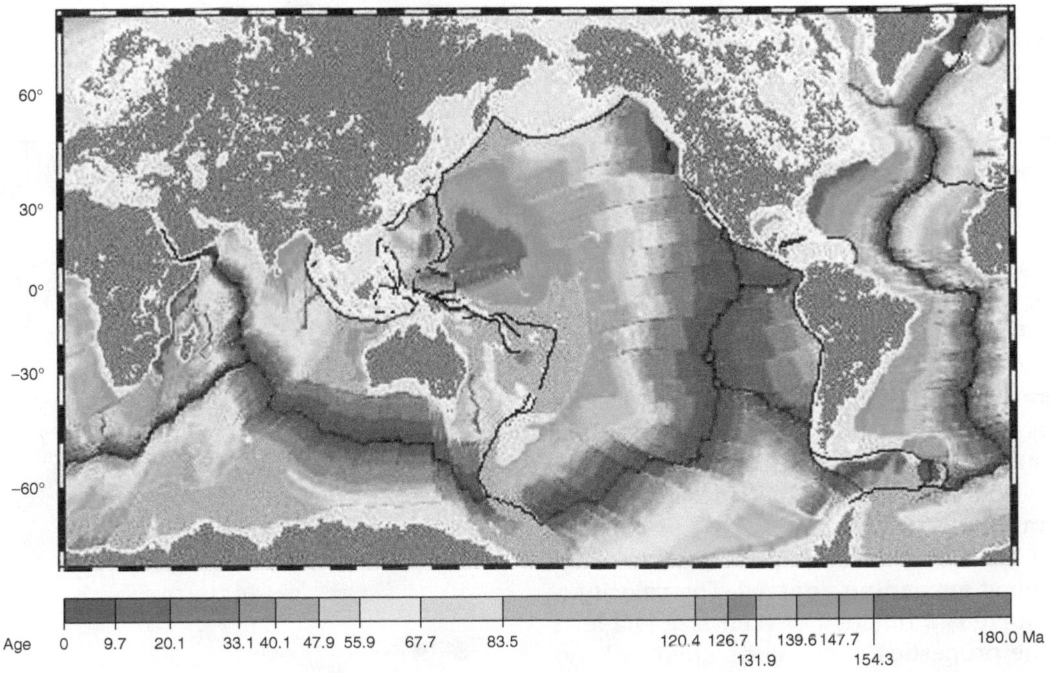

Figure 2.19

Age of the ocean basins.

Source: Mueller, R.D., Roest, W.R., Royer, J-Y., Gahagan, L.M., and Sclater, J.G., 1997. Digital isochrons of the World's ocean floor. *Journal of Geophysical Research* Volume 102, No. B2, p. 3211–3214. 10 February 1997. Plate 1(a) on page 3212. Copyright 1997 by the American Geophysical Union.

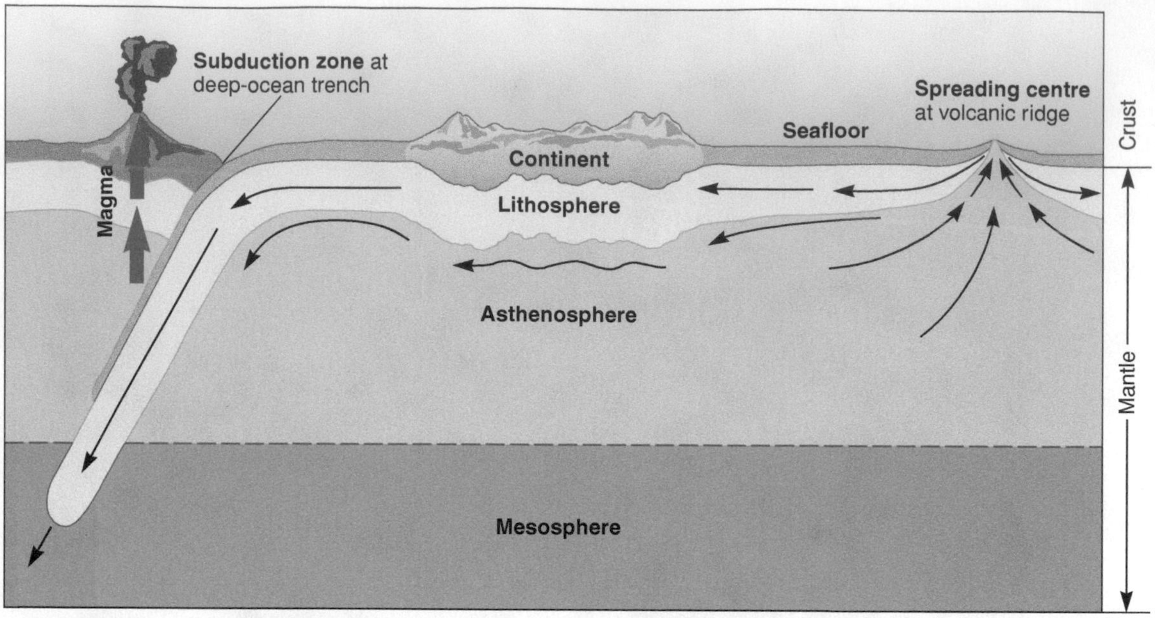

Figure 2.20

Schematic cross-section of the tectonic cycle. First, magma rises from the asthenosphere to the surface at the oceanic volcanic ridges where it solidifies and adds to the plate edges. Second, as the rock cools, the plate moves away laterally. Third, the plate continues to cool, grows thicker at its base, becomes denser, collides with a less-dense plate, and subducts. It is ultimately reassimilated in the asthenosphere.

Source: Adapted from A. Cox and R. B. Hart, *Plate Tectonics: How It Works.*

buoyant plate overrides it. Last, the plate pulled into the asthenosphere is reabsorbed. The time needed to complete this cycle is commonly in excess of 250 million years.

Another way that plate tectonics can be visualized is by using a hard-boiled egg as a metaphor for the Earth. Consider the brittle shell of the hard-boiled egg as the lithosphere, the slippery inner lining of the shell as the asthenosphere, the egg white (albumen) as the rest of the mantle, and the yolk as the core. This hand-held model of brittle pieces being moved atop a softer layer below is a small-scale analogue to the interactions between the Earth's lithosphere and asthenosphere.

The outer few hundred kilometres of the Earth are constantly being recycled according to the tectonic cycle, with convection being the main driving mechanism of plate movement (see In Greater Depth box: Heat Transfer). Convection cells near the top of the asthenosphere couple with the underside of the lithosphere and drag the plates (Figure 2.21). This phenomenon is called "slab pull" and complements the "ridge push" occurring at **spreading centres**. The velocity at which plates move is a function of their size and location, and of the properties of the underlying asthenosphere. The Nazca plate, which is subducting under the west coast of South America, is currently the fastest moving plate, causing vigorous seismic and volcanic activity in Peru and Chile.

Figure 2.22 shows how the Earth's outer layers are operating today in plate-tectonic action and introduces the four tectonic environments: (1) **divergent zones**, (2) **convergent zones**, (3) transform plate boundaries, and (4) **hot spots**.

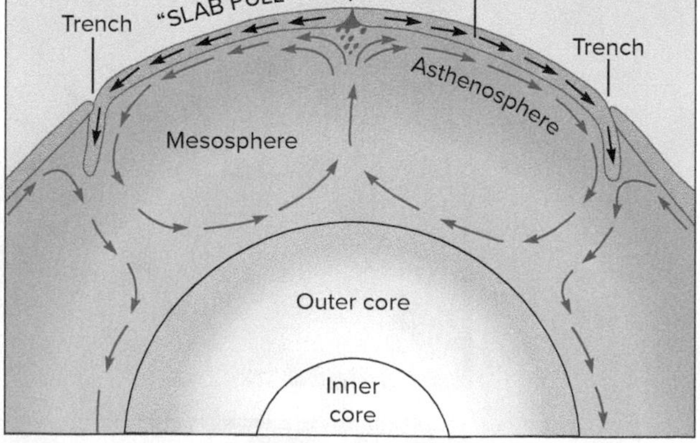

Figure 2.21

Convection cells drive the movement of tectonic plates. Note how the red arrows near the top of the asthenosphere are in the same direction as the black arrows in the lithosphere.

Source: Modified from the United States Geological Survey. http://pubs.usgs.gov/gip/dynamic/unanswered.html

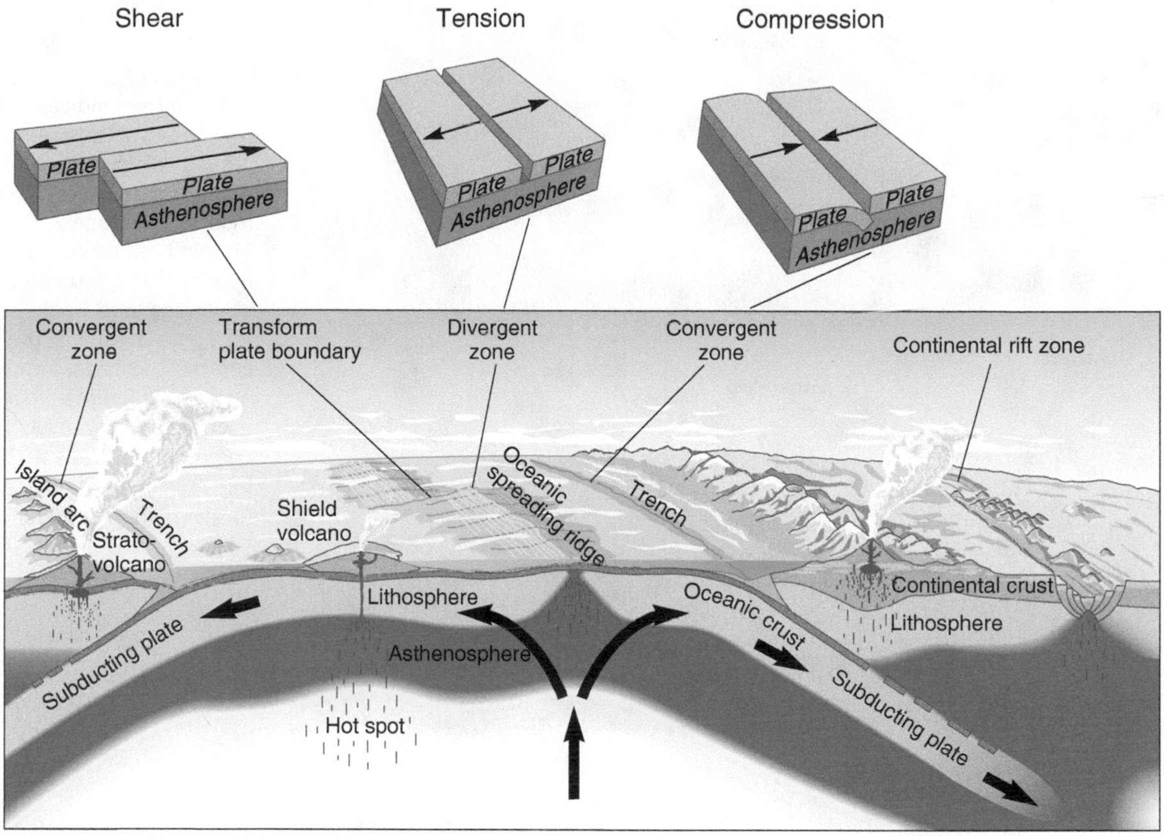

Figure 2.22

Three-dimensional view of different tectonic environments. Convection cells are indicated by black arrows.

Source: Kious and Tilling, *United States Geological Survey.*

1. Divergent zones

Plates are pulled apart under tension at divergent zones causing a reduction in pressure on superheated asthenosphere rock, which liquefies and rises (Figure 2.23a). The buildup of magma and heat causes expansion and topographic elevation of the overlying lithosphere into a dome (Figure 2.23b). Gravity may then pull the dome downward, thus creating down-dropped **rift** valleys. As the faulting progresses, magma rises up through the cracks to build volcanoes (Figure 2.23c). As rifting and volcanism continue, seafloor spreading processes take over, the down-dropped linear rift valley becomes filled by the ocean, and a new sea is born (Figure 2.23d).

In certain locations, the elevated dome rock fractures into a pattern radiating out from a **triple junction**, a point where three plate edges touch (Figure 2.24a). For example, three linear pull-apart basins meet at the south end of the Red Sea at the Afar Triangle triple junction (Figure 2.24b). This triple junction is geologically young, having begun about 25 million years ago. To date, spreading in the Red Sea and Gulf of Aden has been enough to split off the African plate, create an Arabian plate, and allow seawater to flood between them. But the East African rift system has not yet been pulled far enough apart for the sea to fill it. Will spreading continue far enough to split a Somali plate from Africa? It is simply too early to tell. Sometimes the rifting process comes to a halt before separating a continent. These **failed rifts** create zones of weakness in the crust.

2. Convergent zones

Plates deform under compression at convergent zones. The three basic classes of collisions are (1) oceanic plate versus oceanic plate, (2) oceanic plate versus continent, and (3) continent versus continent.

If oceanic plates are involved, subduction will occur (Figure 2.25). The younger, warmer, less-dense plate will override the older, colder, denser plate, which will then bend downward and be pulled back into the mantle. At Gros Morne National Park in Newfoundland, some 500 million years ago, a large piece of oceanic lithosphere was scraped off the downgoing plate as it was subducting. The material stayed trapped in the subduction zone and can be found today above sea level at the Tablelands (Figure 2.26). The Tablelands offer geologists exceptional access to the complete thickness of the oceanic lithosphere from the upper mantle to the Earth's surface.

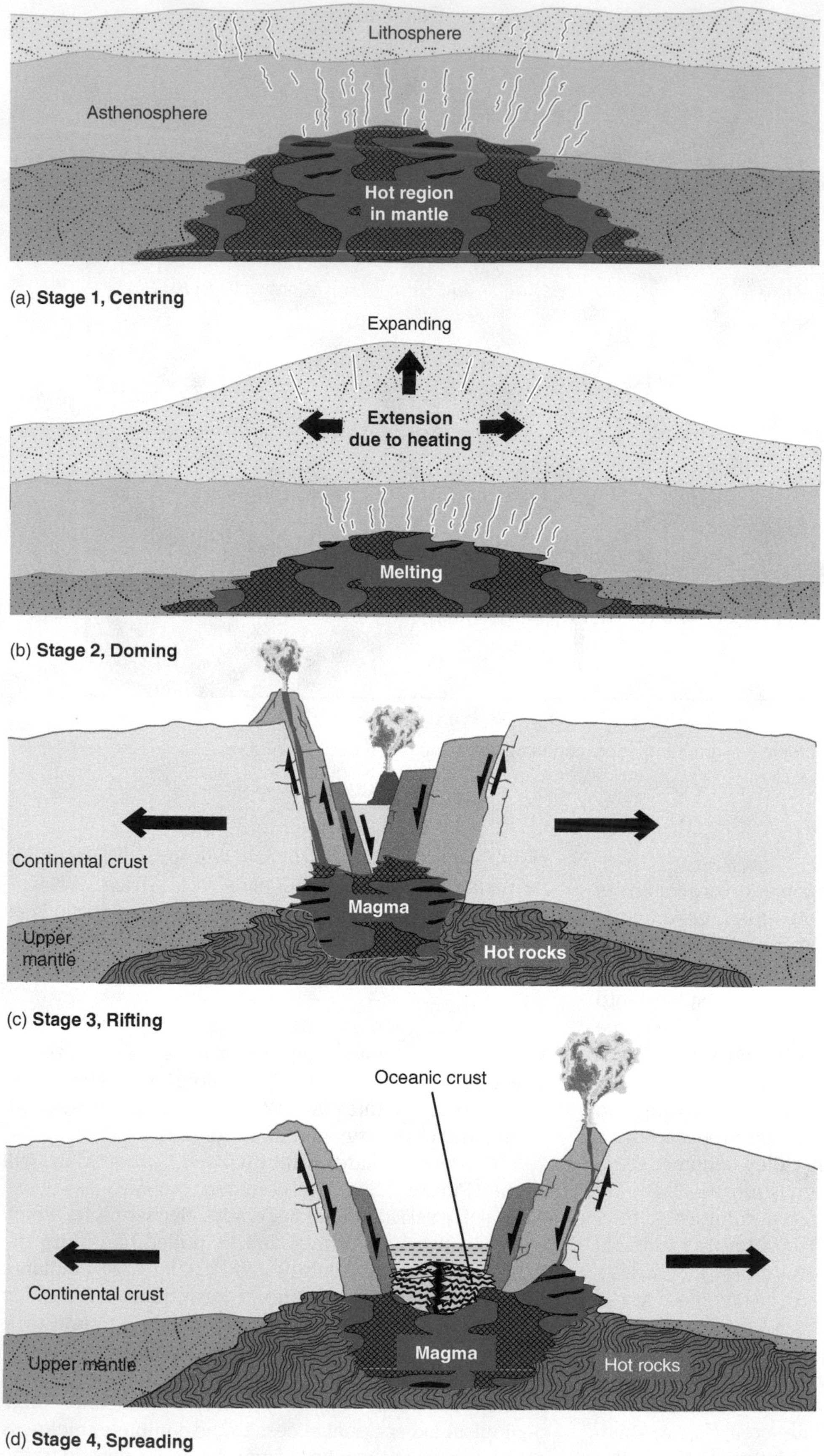

Figure 2.23
A model of the stages in the formation of an ocean basin (black arrows indicate tension.) (a) Stage 1, Centring: Moving lithosphere centres over an anomalously hot region of the mantle. (b) Stage 2, Doming: Mantle heat causes surface doming through uplifting, stretching, and fracturing. (c) Stage 3, Rifting: The dome's central area sags, forming a valley. Fractures provide escape for magma; volcanism is common. (d) Stage 4, Spreading: Pulling apart has advanced, forming a new seafloor.

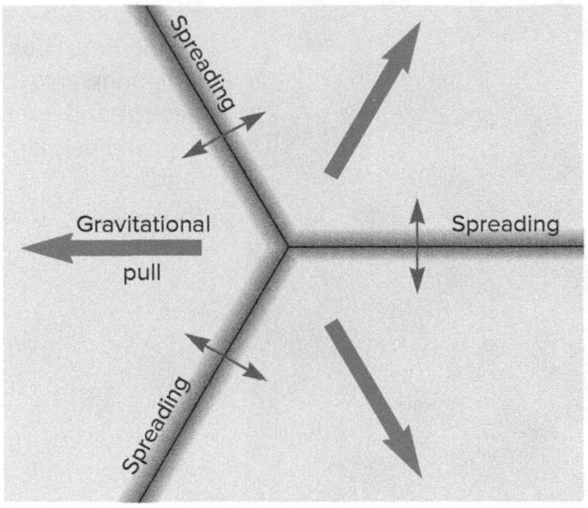

(a)

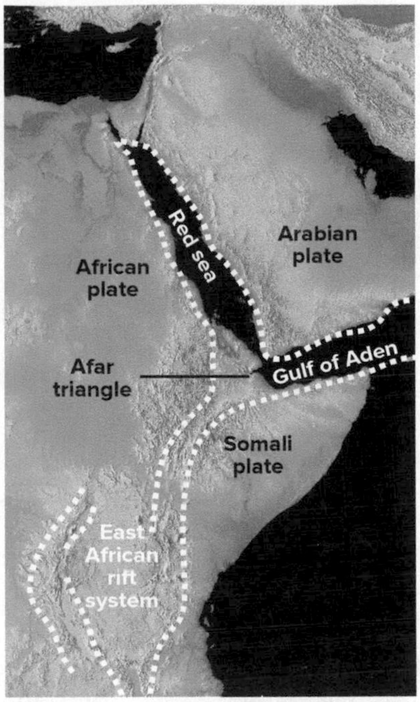

(b)

Figure 2.24
Triple junction. (a) Schematic example. (b) Northeast Africa is being torn apart by three spreading centres: the Red Sea, the Gulf of Aden, and the East African rift system. The spreading centres meet at a triple junction in the Afar Triangle.

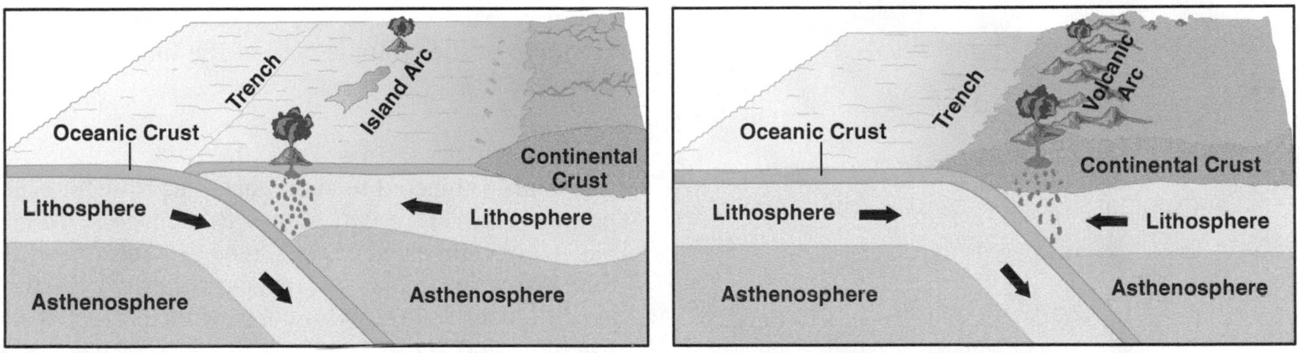

Figure 2.25
(a) Oceanic–oceanic convergence results in the formation of a deep offshore trench and volcanoes on the seafloor. Over time, the erupted lava and volcanic debris pile up until submarine volcanoes rise above sea level to form an island arc. (b) Oceanic–continental convergence creates a coastal trench and a chain of continental volcanoes.

If two continents are involved, they will not subduct because their huge volume of low-density, high-buoyancy rock simply cannot sink to great depth. Oceanic plates are destroyed by subduction and reassimilation within the mantle, whereas continents float about on the asthenosphere in perpetuity.

The grandest continental pushing match in the modern world is the ongoing ramming of Asia by India. When Gondwanaland began its breakup (Figure 2.41a), India started to move northward toward Asia. The 5000 km of seafloor (oceanic plate) that lay in front of India's northward path had all subducted beneath Asia by about 40 million years ago. Then, with no seafloor left to separate them, India punched into the exposed underbelly of Asia (Figure 2.27). Since the initial contact, the assault has remained continuous. India has moved 2000 km farther north, causing complex accommodations within the two plates as they shove into, under, and through each other accompanied by folding, overriding, and stacking of the two continents into the huge mass of the Himalayas and the Tibetan Plateau. Before this collision, the crusts of India and Asia were each about 35 km thick. Now, the combined crust has been thickened to 70 km to create the

Figure 2.26
Bonne Bay, Gros Morne National Park, Newfoundland. The barren hills in the background are the Tablelands, an exposed sequence of ancient oceanic lithosphere.
Source: © Jean H. Bédard.

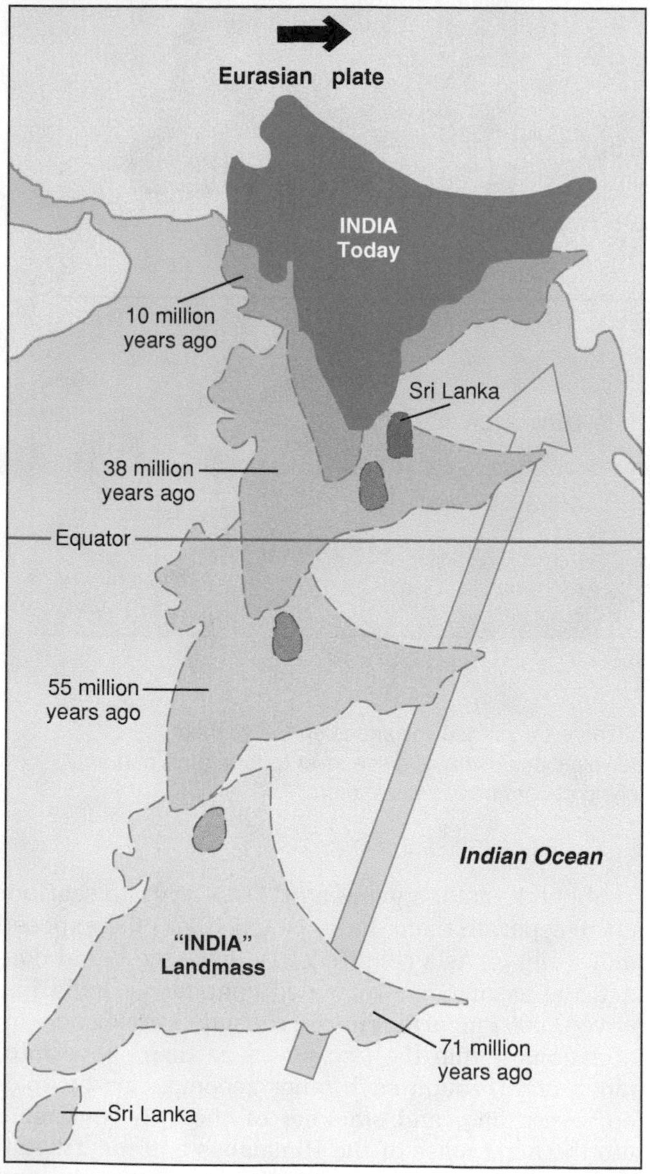

Figure 2.27
Map showing the movement of India (green arrow) during the last 71 million years. India continues to shove into Asia at a velocity of 5 cm per year.

highest-standing continental area on the Earth. In an area the size of France, the average elevation exceeds 5000 m. Each year, India continues to move about 5 cm into Asia along a 2000 km front. The affected area includes India, Pakistan, Afghanistan, the Tibetan Plateau, much of eastern Russia, Mongolia, and most of China. A relatively simple experiment to illustrate this effect uses a horizontal jack to push into a pile of modelling clay, deforming it under the force of compression (Figure 2.28). The experimental deformation is similar to the tectonic map of the India–Asia region (Figure 2.29).

3. Transform plate boundaries

Plates are subjected to shear stress at transform plate boundaries. Figure 2.31 shows this process. Tectonic plates are rigid slabs of rock, tens of kilometres thick, that are wrapped around a near-spherical Earth. To accommodate the Earth's curvature, the plates must fracture, and these fractures are **transform faults**, first recognized by John Tuzo Wilson in 1965 (see Human Focus box: John Tuzo Wilson (1908–1993): The Father of Plate Tectonics). In the region between two spreading centres, the relative motions of the two plates are in opposite directions. However, to both the right and the left of the spreading centres, the two slabs are moving in the same direction. In the first case, the plates are separated by a transform fault (for example, the San Andreas fault, shown in Figure 3.27, which marks the boundary between the North American and the Pacific plates); in the second case, by a fracture zone.

4. Hot spots

Hot spots are unrelated to plate movements. Hot spots are isolated regions of high temperature originating deep in the mesosphere. Hot spots produce excess heat, causing hotter rock with lower density; these **plumes** of buoyant hot rock rise through the mesophere, begin to melt near the top of the overlying asthenosphere, and

Figure 2.28
Simulated collision of India into Asia. A wedge is slowly jacked into layered modelling clay confined on its left side but free to move to the right. From top to bottom of figure, notice the major faults that form as the masses are compelled to move to the right. Compare this pattern to the tectonic map of India and Asia in Figure 2.29.

Source: © P. Tapponier, et al. (1982). *Geology*, 10, 611–16.

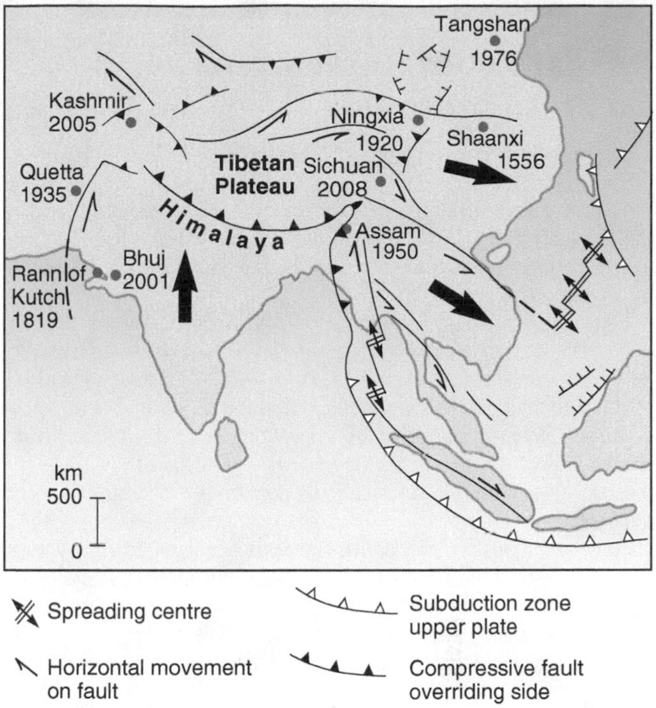

Figure 2.29
Tectonic map showing India pushing into Asia, forcing Indochina to escape to the southeast and driving a large block of China to the east. The ongoing collision causes devastating earthquakes, each killing tens or hundreds of thousands of people. Major earthquakes include three in India, two in the state of Gujarat: in 1819 at Rann of Kutch and in 2011 near Bhuj, and one in the state of Assam in 1950; four in China: in 1556 in Shannxi, in 1920 in Ningxia, in 1976 at Tangshan, and in 2008 in Sichuan; and two in Pakistan, in 1935 in Quetta, and in 2005 in Kashmir.

pass up through the lithosphere as magma (Figure 2.32). Reaching the surface, they build volcanoes on the seafloor, such as in Hawaii, or on continents, such as in Yellowstone National Park in the northwestern United States.

In summary, the combination of convection in the asthenosphere and gravity pulling on spreading centres and on down-going plates at subduction zones keeps the lithospheric plates moving. Thus, an ongoing tectonic cycle operates where each moving part stimulates and maintains motions of the others in a large-scale, long-term recycling operation. Plate tectonics provides us with new perspectives about the Earth that are quite different from those encountered in our life experiences. Because the Earth is so much older and so much larger than a human being, we must set aside our personal time and size scales. If we change our time perspective to millions or billions of years, and our size perspective to continents and plates, then, and only then, can we begin to understand the Earth. Plate velocities are measured using the global positioning system (GPS) (Figure 2.16) and are comparable to those of fingernail growth. An active plate may move 1 cm in a year—only 75 cm in a human lifetime. But when we consider the Earth over its own time span of 4.5 billion years, there is plenty of time for small events to add up to big results.

So far, plate tectonics has been recognized only on the Earth. Mars is a one-plate planet where several hot spots have been identified although none currently feed active volcanoes. Because the Martian lithosphere is static, lava outpours at the same location over tens of millions of years, creating gigantic volcanoes. Venus seems to have experienced a dramatic resurfacing event 750 million years ago and its surface has not significantly evolved since then, other than bearing the scars from numerous impacts with space bodies.

HUMAN FOCUS

Pascal Audet, Researcher on Plate Tectonics

I study large-scale tectonic processes, and recently joined the Department of Earth Sciences at the University of Ottawa. I was fortunate to do my Ph.D. at the University of British Columbia and start my research career at the University of California, Berkeley, both located in active tectonic zones along the western edge of the North American plate. Tectonic plates were in movement "in my backyard!"

My research focuses on the process of subduction in the Cascadia Subduction Zone, offshore British Columbia, in particular, on the role of fluids in the earthquake cycle. I use seismic waves from distant earthquakes to compute tomographic images of the subsurface, similar to what is done in medical imaging (see photo of chapter opener). These faraway earthquakes are not a natural hazard in this case but a source of signal! From the velocity at which the seismic waves propagate, I reconstruct in detail the structure of the subduction zone, and identify areas where trapped fluids under high pressure may act as lubricants and facilitate slip. I want to better understand the transition zone between brittle areas, where rock is susceptible to breaking and generating a large earthquake, and the deeper ductile areas where deformation is continuous. This will further our understanding of the hypocentre location and size of future earthquakes affecting southern British Columbia.

In earth sciences, it is important to test hypotheses and methodologies in different parts of the world. My research has taken me to the west coast of Costa Rica where the Cocos plate is subducting beneath the Caribbean plate. In this region, the downgoing oceanic plate has a complicated internal structure and is moving fast. Energy is released regularly in major earthquakes of magnitude 7 or 8, whereas the Cascadia Subduction Zone is quieter and thought to be building up stress towards a great earthquake of magnitude 9. Fluids are likely playing a key role in these different behaviours.

Recently, I have installed seismic recording stations in central Yukon (Figure 2.30). This area is one of the most seismically active regions of Canada but is poorly understood, in part because of its remote location and sparse instrument coverage. With the new seismic array complementing stations from the Canadian National Seismograph Network (Figure 4.6), data will become available to better assess earthquake risk, in a region where critical infrastructure, such as pipelines, may be built in future years. I am also planning to use the data to study a distinctive oceanic terrain, the Yakutat block, which is relatively light and has resisted subduction. The Yakutat block is colliding against the continent, causing the continued uplift of mountain ranges in southern Yukon including Mount Logan, Canada's highest peak.

Plate tectonics is a vibrant field of fundamental and applied research and Canada provides a wonderful natural laboratory.

Figure 2.30
Pascal Audet at work installing a seismic station in central Yukon. The station is powered by solar panels and telemeters data to Ottawa via a large satellite dish.
Source: Rick Moore, Nanometrics.

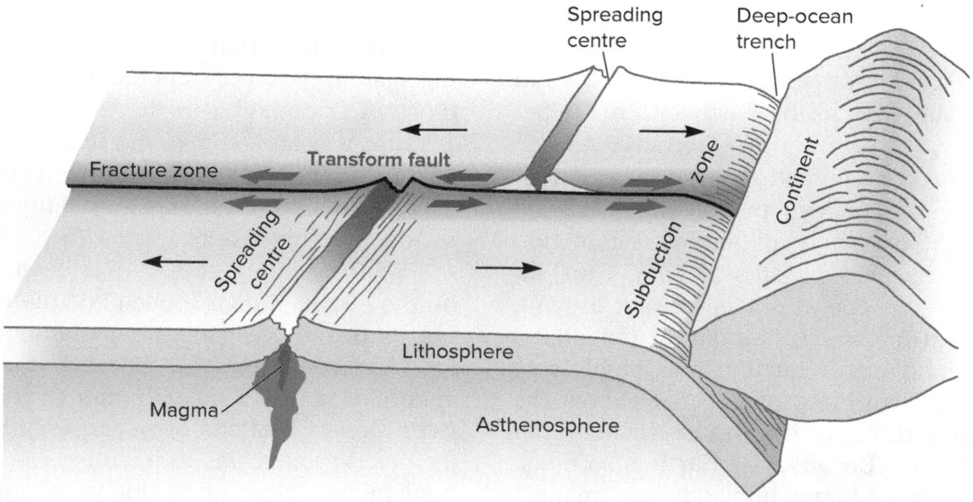

Figure 2.31
Plate-tectonics model of transform faults. Notice that the transform fault connects the two separated spreading centres (large blue arrows); the seafloor moves in opposite directions here. Beyond the spreading centres, the two plates move in the same direction and are separated by a fracture zone (large red arrows); there is no transform fault here.

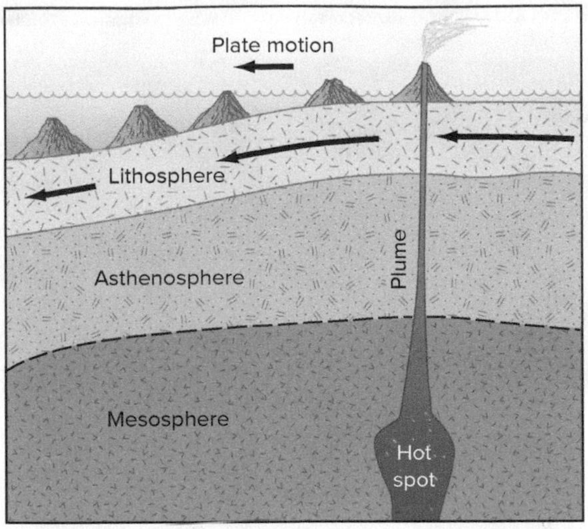

(a) Cross-section

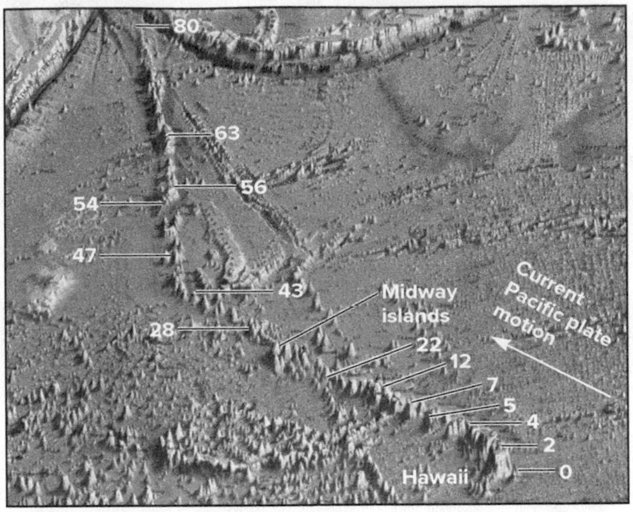

(b) Map

Figure 2.32
A hot spot and its path. (a) Cross-section shows a hot spot in the mesosphere, from which hot mantle rock rises up through the asthenosphere and lithosphere as a plume of magma supplying a volcano. Because the lithospheric plate keeps moving, new volcanoes are formed. (b) Map shows the Hawaiian Islands–Emperor Seamount chain of hotspot-fed volcanoes with their radiometric ages in millions of years. The linear pattern of volcano ages testifies to movement of the Pacific plate through time. Note how the Pacific plate changed direction between 47 and 43 million years ago.

LO5

Evidence of Plate Tectonics

MAGNETIZATION PATTERNS ON THE SEAFLOORS

John Tuzo Wilson, a professor of geophysics at the University of Toronto, was instrumental in formulating several of the key concepts of plate tectonics in the mid-1960s (see Human Focus: John Tuzo Wilson (1908–1993): The Father of Plate Tectonics). It is rare in science to find widespread agreement on a broadly encompassing theory such as plate tectonics. But when data from the Earth's **magnetic field** locked inside seafloor rock were widely understood, skeptics around the world became convinced that seafloor spreading occurs and that the concept of plate tectonics is valid.

As the lava erupted from a volcano cools below the **Curie point** (approximately 550°C) at the surface of the Earth, atoms in its iron-bearing minerals become magnetized in the direction of the Earth's magnetic field (see In Greater Depth box: The Earth's Magnetic Field in Chapter 14). The atoms behave like compass needles, pointing toward the north **magnetic pole** when the magnetic field has a normal polarity or toward the south magnetic pole when the magnetic field has a reverse polarity. Many volcanic rocks also contain minerals with radioactive elements that allow determination of their age. When the magnetic polarity and age of each rock layer are plotted together in a vertical column, a timescale of magnetic polarities can be built (Figure 2.34).

Since the late 1940s, research vessels criss-crossing the oceans have towed magnetometers to measure the magnetization of the seafloor. As the number of voyages grew and more data were obtained, a striking pattern began to emerge (Figure 2.35). The floor of the oceans is striped by parallel bands of magnetized rock that show alternating polarities. The pattern is symmetrical and parallel with mid-ocean ridges. That is, each striped piece of seafloor has its twin on the other side of the oceanic ridge. Magma is injected into the ocean ridges where it is imprinted by the Earth's magnetic field as it cools to form new rock. Then the seafloor is physically pulled away from the oceanic ridges as if they were parts of two large conveyor belts going in opposite directions (Figure 2.36). How stunning it is that the widths of magnetized seafloor strips (Figure 2.35) have the same ratios as the lengths of time between successive reversals of the Earth's magnetic field (Figure 2.34). This means that distance in kilometres is proportional to time in millions of years.

AGES FROM THE OCEAN BASINS

Another stunning fact discovered during the exploration of the oceans is the youthful age of the ocean basins. The oldest rocks on the ocean floors are about 200 million years of age; this is less than 5% of the age of the Earth. Why? Because the ocean basins are young features that are continuously being formed and destroyed. Along the oceanic ridges, volcanism is

HUMAN FOCUS

John Tuzo Wilson (1908–1993): The Father of Plate Tectonics

John Tuzo Wilson (Figure 2.33) was born in Ottawa in 1908, the first child of Henrietta Tuzo and John Armistead Wilson. His mother was an accomplished mountaineer and his father an engineer. This heritage was reflected by Tuzo Wilson's choice of studies: he graduated from the University of Toronto in 1930 with a double major in geology and physics, and earned a second undergraduate degree from the University of Cambridge in England, taking a collection of lectures in the same topics. After a brief period of employment at the Geological Survey of Canada, Tuzo Wilson went on to do a PhD at Princeton where he met Harry Hesse and Maurice Ewing, leading scientists studying geological processes in ocean basins. Like many young men of his generation, Tuzo Wilson's career was interrupted by World War II, during which he served overseas as an engineer in the Canadian Army. After the war, Tuzo Wilson returned to Canada to become a professor of geophysics at the University of Toronto.

Initially opposed to continental drift, Tuzo Wilson developed his vision of a dynamic Earth through several years of study of the different geological domains that have amalgamated to form the Canadian Precambrian Shield. The word "vision" is particularly fitting here since Tuzo Wilson's problem-solving approach was largely visual and stemmed from field observations and the detailed examination of maps. He is reported to have reflected on the formation of the Hawaiian islands using the bucolic image of someone lying on his back in a stream and blowing bubbles to the surface through a straw.

Between 1963 and 1966, Tuzo Wilson presented his views on hot spots and transform faults in three papers that would cause a revolution in the earth sciences. His first paper, entitled "A Possible Origin of the Hawaiian Islands," was first rejected by the leading American geophysical journal before being published in the *Canadian Journal of Physics,* not exactly a widely read journal in earth science circles! Nevertheless, Tuzo Wilson went on to make an outstanding contribution in providing an integrated framework for understanding geology at a planetary scale.

Tuzo Wilson was not only a towering figure in the earth science community, but also a gifted communicator. After retiring from the University of Toronto, he became director-general of the Ontario Science Centre, a pioneering interactive science museum, and shared his passion for science with a large public.

Two seamounts, located 200 km west of Vancouver Island, have been named in Tuzo Wilson's honour, a very appropriate gesture to acknowledge the contribution of the scientist who provided insight into their formation. The tectonic cycle is also often referred to as the Wilson cycle.

Figure 2.33
Prof. Tuzo Wilson in the Andes (Chile) in 1960. A few years later, Tuzo Wilson would put forward ideas initiating a new understanding of the process of mountain building.
Source: Photo courtesy of Susan Wilson.

active, and new seafloor is forming. Moving away from the ridges, the seafloor rocks become progressively older (Figure 2.19).

OCEANIC HOT SPOTS

Hot spots have active volcanoes above them on the Earth's surface. The volcanoes rest on moving plates that carry them away from their hot-spot source. This process forms lines of extinct volcanoes on the ocean floor, from youngest to oldest, pointing in the direction of plate motion (Figure 2.32). In other words, the ages of the former volcanoes increase with their distance from the hot spot.

BATHYMETRY

Bathymetry provides additional supporting evidence for plate tectonics (Figure 2.18). The greatest mountain ranges on the Earth, the oceanic ridges, lie on the seafloor and extend more than 65 000 km. These long and continuous volcanic ridges form at spreading centres where plates pull apart and magma rises to fill the gaps. Above the oceanic ridges, the water depth is relatively shallow. However, moving progressively away from the ridges, the water depth increases systematically with seafloor age (Figure 2.36). This is due to the cooling and contraction of the oceanic crust with a resultant increase in density. Also, there is some down-warping

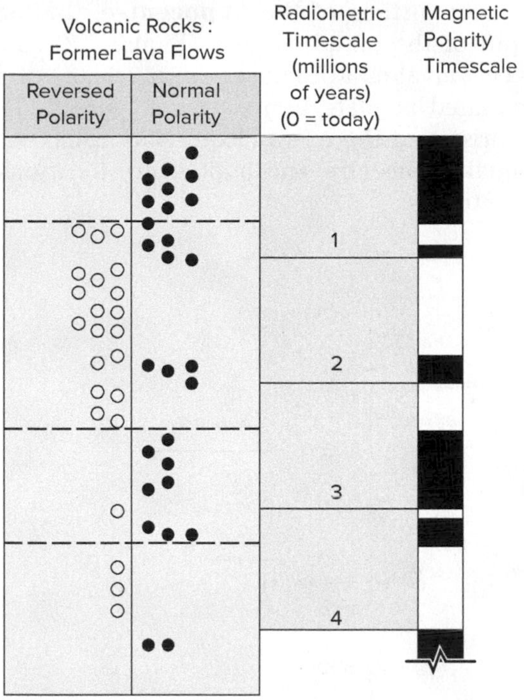

Figure 2.34
A portion of the magnetic polarity timescale. Magnetic polarity measurements in volcanic rocks combined with radiometric ages determined from the same rocks allow the building of a timescale based on magnetic polarity reversals. Notice the unique and nonrepetitive pattern of the polarity reversals.
Source: © John Wiley & Sons, Inc.

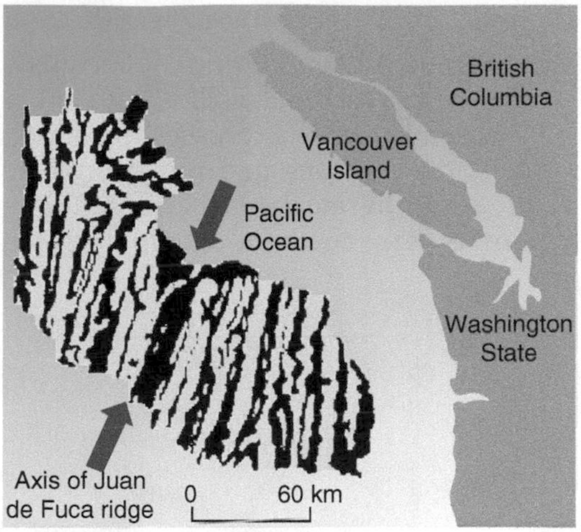

Figure 2.35
Map of the magnetically striped Pacific Ocean floor off Vancouver Island. Black areas are magnetized pointing to a north pole (normal polarity) and yellow areas to a south pole (reverse polarity). Notice the mirror-image patterns on each side of the Juan de Fuca ridge (see location map in Figure 4.15).

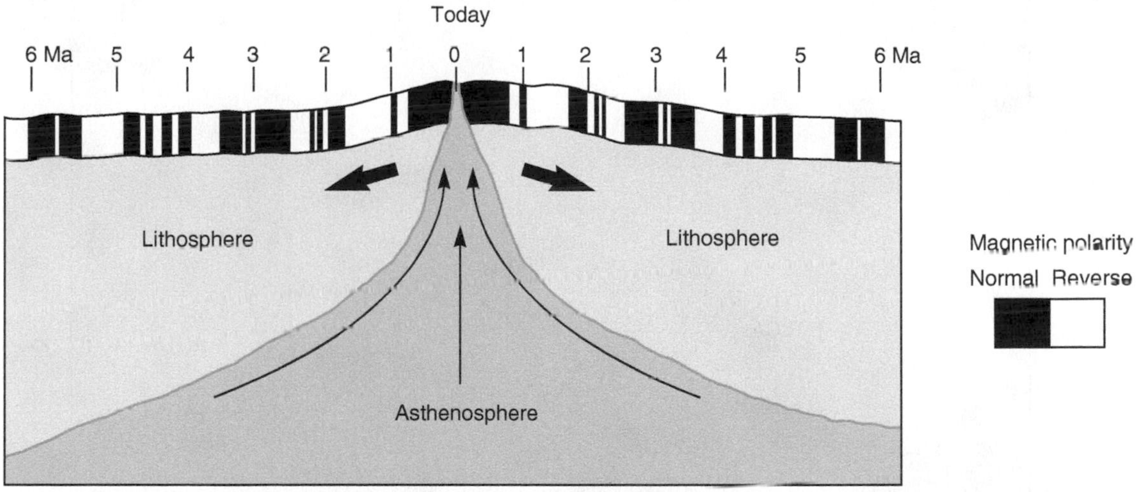

Figure 2.36
Cross-section of magnetically striped seafloor. Numbers above the seafloor are radiometric ages in millions of years. The mirror-image pattern documents movements away from the oceanic ridge.

due to the weight of **sediments** deposited on the seafloor. The older the seafloor, the more time it has had to accumulate a thick cover of silt, clay, and fossils.

The ocean floor has an average depth of 3.7 km, but depths greater than 11 km exist in elongate, narrow **trenches**. These long, deep trenches have been known since the *Challenger* oceanographic expedition in the 1870s, but they were not understood until the 1960s, when it was recognized that they coincide with subducting plates turning downward to re-enter the asthenosphere.

EARTHQUAKE EPICENTRES AND HYPOCENTRES

The lithosphere is broken into rigid plates that move away from, slide past, and collide into other rigid plates. These global-scale processes generate **faults** where the Earth ruptures and the two sides move past each other in earthquake-generating events. The **epicentre** of an earthquake is the projection on the Earth's surface of the **hypocentre**, the location at depth of the initial rupture (Figure 3.2). Because most earthquakes are caused by a release of stress accumulated at plate boundaries (Figure 2.17), it is no surprise that there is a close relationship between earthquake epicentre and hypocentre locations, and plate tectonics.

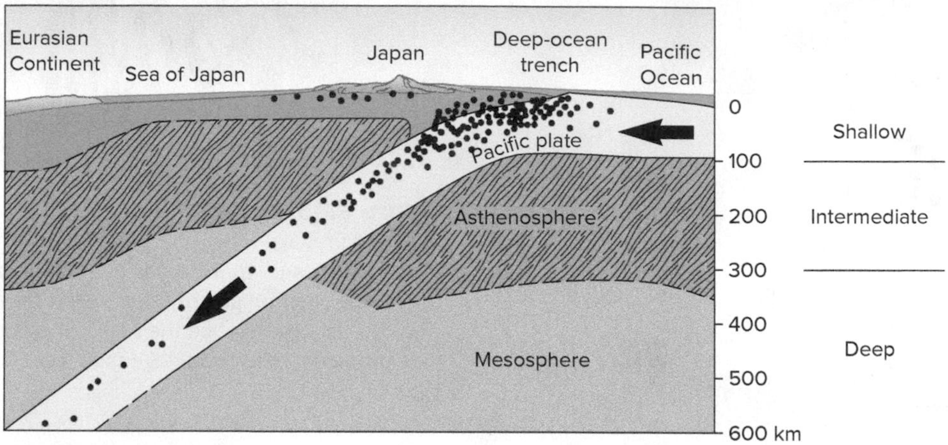

Figure 2.37
Cross-section showing earthquake hypocentre locations at depth; notice the inclined plane defined by the earthquake hypocentres. The earthquake locations outline the subducting plate beneath Japan. At shallow depths, earthquakes are generated in brittle rocks in both subducting (yellow) and overriding (orange) plates. At greater depths, only the interior of the subducting Pacific plate is cold enough to maintain the rigidity necessary to produce earthquakes.

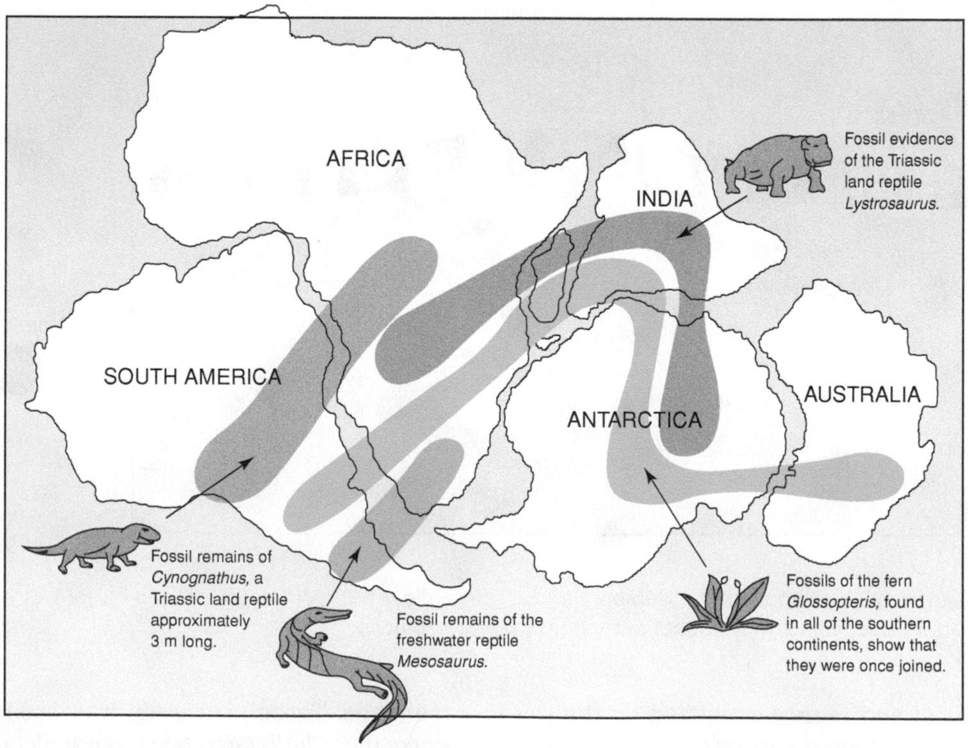

Figure 2.38
The distribution of several fossils is continuous when continents are restored to the position they occupied when these life forms existed.

Source: United States Geological Survey.

Earthquake epicentres outline tectonic plates. The map of earthquake epicentres (Figure 1.12c) can be viewed as a connect-the-dots puzzle. Each epicentre represents a place where one major section of rock has moved past another section. If you take your pen and connect the epicentres, you will define the edges of the tectonic plates, the separately moving pieces of lithosphere (compare Figures 1.12c and 2.16). Earthquake hypocentres follow subducting plates. Hypocentres are classified as shallow (depth less than 100 km), intermediate (depth ranging from 100 to 300 km), or deep (depth ranging from 300 to 800 km). Intermediate and deep hypocentres are found along inclined planes adjacent to ocean trenches (Figure 1.12c and Figure 2.37). These hypocentres define the subducting plates being pulled forcefully back into the asthenosphere.

CONTINUITY OF GEOLOGICAL FEATURES

The continuity of mountain ranges and fossils across oceans (Figure 2.38) suggests that all the continents were once united in a supercontinent (Figure 2.40).

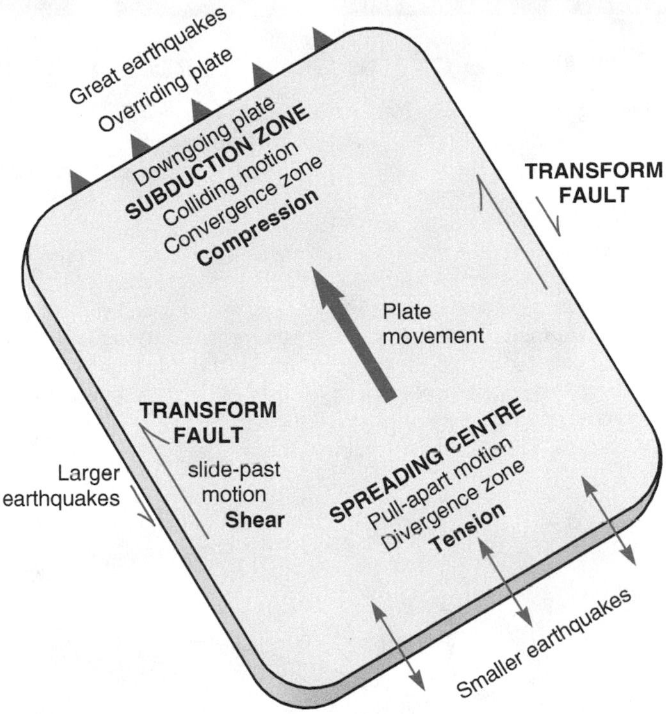

Figure 2.39
Map view of an idealized plate and earthquake hazards along its edges.

LO6 Plate-Tectonic Setting of Earthquakes and Volcanoes

Figure 2.39 shows an idealized tectonic plate and assesses the varying earthquake hazards that are concentrated at plate edges. Our main emphasis here is to understand plate-edge effects as a means of forecasting where earthquakes are likely to occur and what their frequencies and sizes may be. Qualitative relationships between tectonic environments and earthquake characteristics are summarized in Table 2.3.

The divergent, pull-apart motion at spreading centres causes rock in tension to fail. Rock ruptures relatively easily when subjected to tension. Furthermore, the expanded volumes of warm rock in the oceanic ridge systems have a higher heat content and a resultant decrease in rigidity. This heat-weakened rock does not build up and store the huge stresses necessary to create large earthquakes. Thus, earthquakes at spreading centres are typically too small to destroy buildings and kill people.

At subduction zones and in continent–continent collisions, rock deforms mainly under compression. The convergent motions pulling an oceanic plate back into the asthenosphere at a subduction zone or pushing continents together involve incredible amounts of energy. This results in the Earth's greatest earthquakes (17 of 17 in Table 2.4), often associated with the largest number of fatalities (5 of 6 in Table 3.7).

TABLE 2.3

Tectonic Environments and Earthquake Characteristics

		Earthquake Characteristics		
Tectonic Environment	**Deformation Force**	**Frequency**	**Maximum Size**	**Maximum Hypocentre Depth**
Divergent zone	Tension	Frequent	Strong	Shallow
Convergent zone	Compression	Infrequent	Great	Deep
Transform fault	Shear	Infrequent	Major	Shallow
Hot spot	Tension Compression	Frequent	Strong	Shallow

IN GREATER DEPTH

The Dance of the Continents

Undoing the seafloor spreading of the last 220 million years restores the continents of today into the supercontinent **Pangaea** (*pan* meaning "all" and *gaea* meaning "Earth"), which once covered 40% of the Earth. Although the present continents had yet to form, Figure 2.40 shows their relative positions within Pangaea before its breakup. The remaining 60% of the Earth's surface was a massive ocean called Panthalassa (meaning "all oceans").

Figure 2.41a shows the breakup of Pangaea at 180 million years before present. An equatorial spreading centre separated the northern supercontinent **Laurasia** from the southern supercontinent **Gondwanaland.** Much of the sediment deposited in the Tethys Sea at that time has since been uplifted to form mountain ranges from the Himalayas to the Alps. Another spreading centre began opening the Indian Ocean and separating Africa–South America from Antarctica–Australia.

At 135 million years ago, seafloor spreading had begun opening the North Atlantic Ocean, India was moving toward Asia, and the South Atlantic Ocean was a narrow sea similar to the Red Sea today (Figure 2.41b).

By 65 million years ago, seafloor spreading had opened the South Atlantic Ocean and connected it with the North Atlantic, and Africa came into contact with Europe, cutting off the western end of the Tethys Sea to begin the Mediterranean Sea (Figure 2.41c). Although the modern world had become recognizable, note that North America and Eurasia were still connected and that Australia had not yet left Antarctica.

Nearly half of the present ocean floor was created during the last 65 million years (Figure 2.19). India rammed into Asia, continued opening of the North Atlantic split Eurasia from North America, and Australia moved a long way from Antarctica (Figure 2.41d).

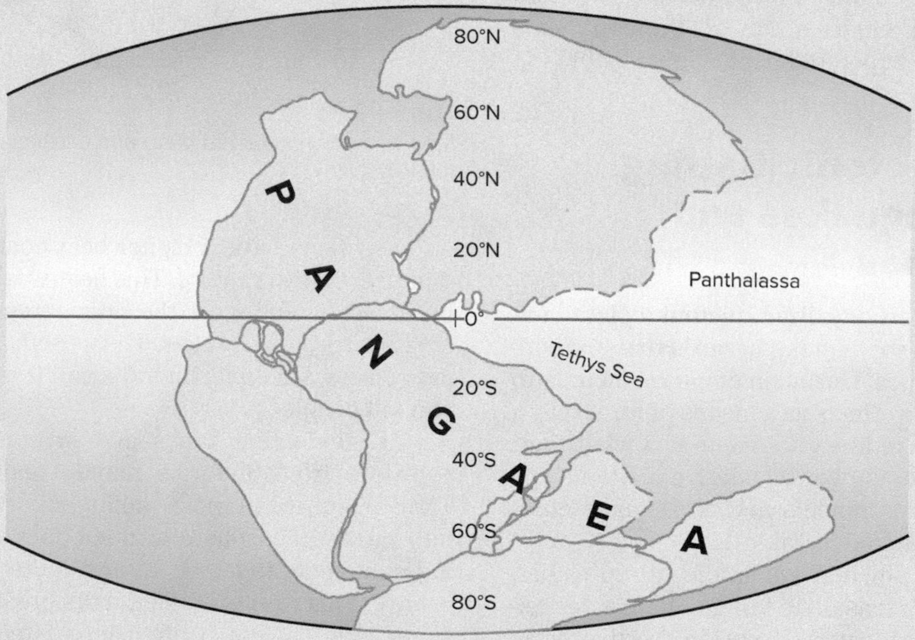

Figure 2.40

The supercontinent of Pangaea, 220 million years before present. The modern continents are drawn to be recognizable in this restoration. The superocean of the time (Panthalassa) exists today in shrunken form as the Pacific Ocean.

Source: © 1970 American Geophysical Union.

continued

At transform faults, the plates slide past each other in dominantly horizontal movements and are subjected to shear stress. This process creates large earthquakes as irregularities along the edges of the plate boundaries retard movement. It takes a lot of stored energy to overcome the rough surfaces, non-slippery rock, and bends in faults. When these impediments are finally overcome, a large amount of seismic energy is released. Magma movements beneath active volcanoes generate the small and shallow earthquakes that are typical of hot spots.

Figure 2.42 revisits the idealized tectonic plate, this time focusing on volcanic hazards. Over 80% of the

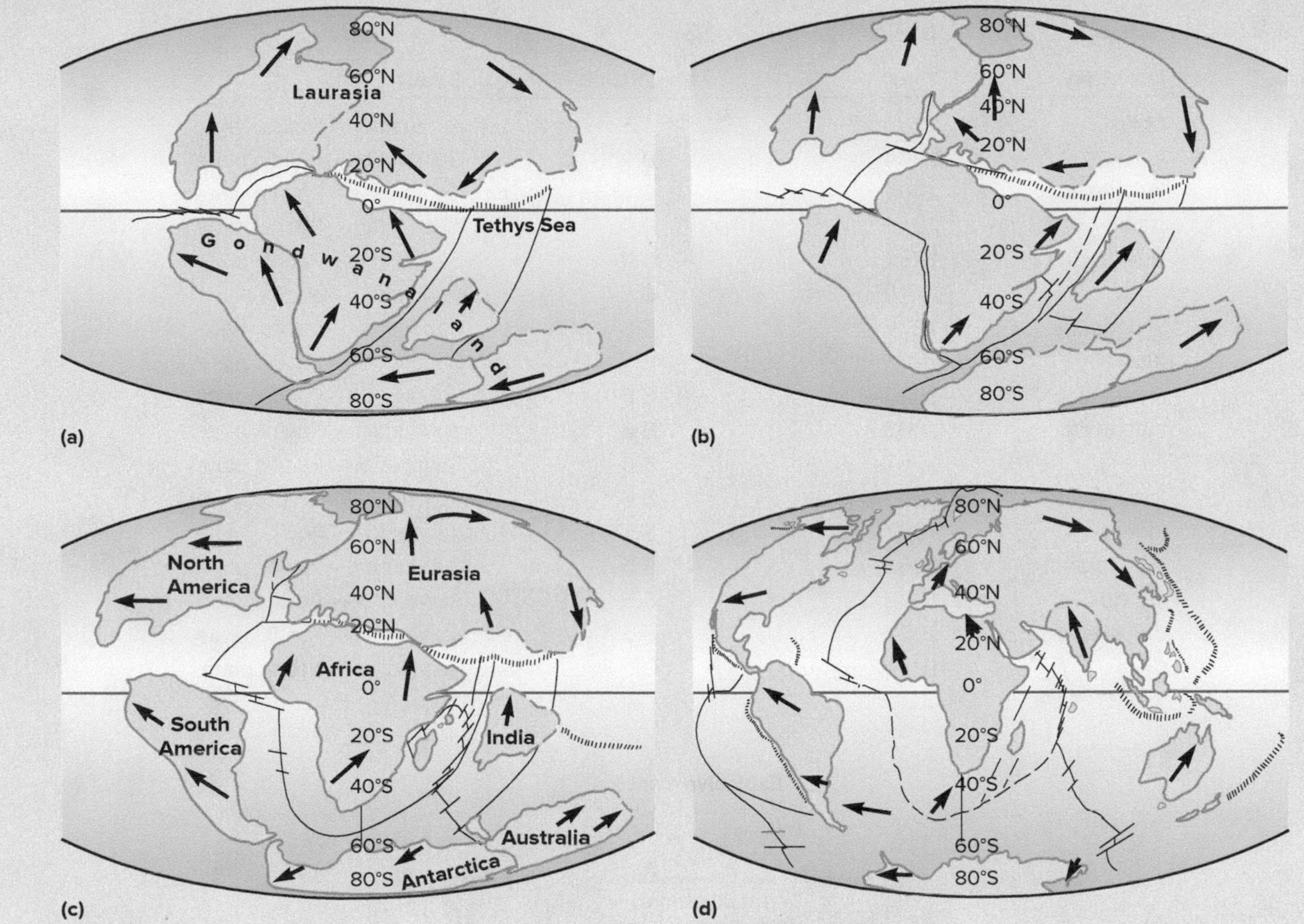

Figure 2.41
Changing positions of the continents. (a) 180 million years ago. (b) 135 million years ago. (c) 65 million years ago. (d) Today.

Earth's magma extruded through volcanism is found at the oceanic spreading centres. Solid, but hot and ductile, mantle rock rises upward into regions of lower pressure, where rock can melt and flow easily as lava on the surface in peaceful eruptions. The worldwide rifting process releases enough magma to create 20 km^3 of new oceanic crust each year. Virtually all this volcanic activity takes place below sea level and is harmless to humans.

Subduction zones cause tall and beautiful volcanic mountains, but the volume of magma released at subduction zones is small compared to that released at spreading centres. Subduction zones account for the eruption of approximately 10% of all magma. When oceanic lithosphere collides with another plate, the denser plate bends downward and re-enters the asthenosphere in the process of subduction. If the subducting oceanic plate is pulled beneath another oceanic plate, an **island arc** of volcanoes forms, such as Japan and the Aleutian Islands of Alaska (Figure 2.25a). If the subducting oceanic plate is pulled beneath a continent-carrying plate, a line of active volcanoes builds on the continent edge, such as the Cascade Range of British Columbia and the northwestern United States (Figure 2.25b).

Most other volcanism occurs above hot spots, accounting for the remaining 10% of all extruded magma (Figure 2.32).

Transform faults and continent–continent collision zones have little or no associated volcanism. Thinking three-dimensionally, this is understandable. At a transform fault, the two plates simply slide past each other horizontally and at all times keep quite an effective "lid" on the hot asthenosphere some 100 km below. At continent–continent collision zones, the continental rock stacks into extra-thick masses that deeply bury the hot mantle rock, making it difficult for magma to rise to the surface.

TABLE 2.4

The Earth's Greatest Earthquakes, 1900–2013

Rank	Location	Year	Magnitude	Cause
1.	Chile	1960	9.5	Subduction—Nazca plate
2.	Alaska	1964	9.2	Subduction—Pacific plate
3.	Indonesia	2004	9.1	Subduction—Pacific plate
4.	Japan	2011	9.0	Subduction—Pacific plate
5.	Kamchatka	1952	9.0	Subduction—Pacific plate
6.	Chile	2010	8.8	Subduction—Nazca plate
7.	Ecuador	1906	8.8	Subduction—Nazca plate
8.	Alaska	1965	8.7	Subduction—Pacific plate
9.	Indonesia	2012	8.6	Subduction—Pacific plate
10.	Indonesia	2005	8.6	Subduction—Pacific plate
11.	Alaska	1957	8.6	Subduction—Pacific plate
12.	Assam	1950	8.6	Collision—India into Asia
13.	Indonesia	2007	8.5	Subduction—Pacific plate
14.	Kuril Islands	1963	8.5	Subduction—Pacific plate
15.	Banda Sea	1938	8.5	Subduction—Pacific/Indian plate
16.	Kamchatka	1923	8.5	Subduction—Pacific plate
17.	Chile	1922	8.5	Subduction—Nazca plate

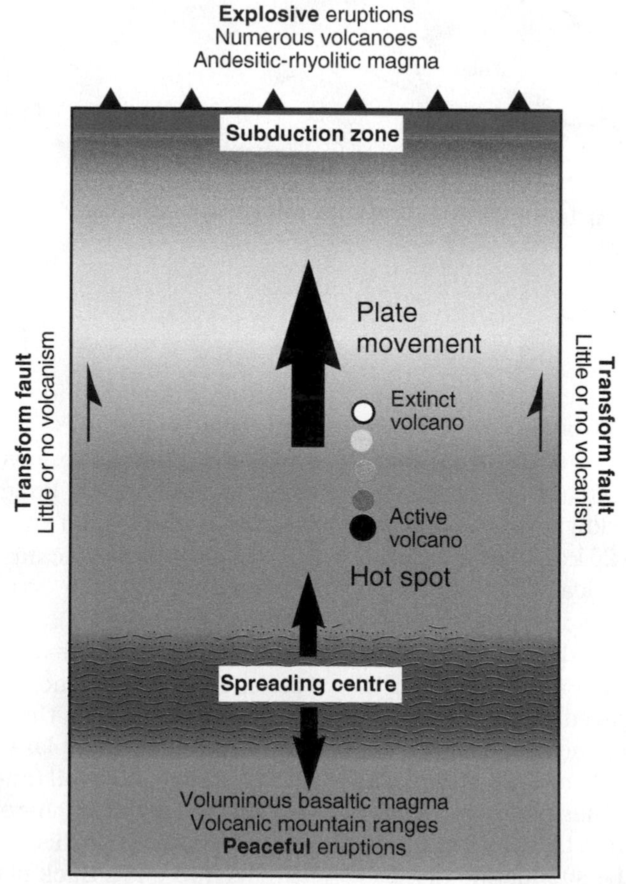

Figure 2.42
Map view of an idealized plate and volcanic hazards along its edges.

SUMMARY

- The Solar System formed over a relatively short period of time; therefore, meteorites and planets all have approximately the same age. The Earth is about 4.57 billion years old.
- Massive amounts of internal heat within the early Earth caused widespread melting. Gravity has pulled the Earth into layers of differing density, ranging from a heavy metallic core outward through layers of decreasing density through the mantle to the continents, then the ocean, and finally, the atmosphere. The Earth can also be described as a stratified body with layers of differing strength. The solid inner core is surrounded by the liquid outer core. Large convection cells slowly circulate material in the plastic mesosphere and asthenosphere. The Earth's outer layers are the rigid lithosphere, the hydrosphere, and the atmosphere.
- The main source of the Earth's internal energy is heat generated by the ongoing decay of radioactive elements. Smaller contributions come from relic impact energy and gravitational attraction. Because several radioactive isotopes have reached stability, the flow of internal energy is slowly decreasing with time. Nevertheless, the Earth's internal energy still drives major processes responsible for earthquakes and volcanoes.
- The Earth's outer layer, the lithosphere, is broken into a dozen large tectonic plates, and several smaller ones. Plates are approximately 100 km thick. Larger plates are several thousands of kilometres across.
- The boundary between the rigid lithosphere and the underlying plastic asthenosphere provides a sliding surface for plates to move. Convection in the asthenosphere and gravity are the driving mechanisms of plate movement.
- The tectonic cycle describes the recycling of the Earth's outer layers over a time period of approximately 250 million years. Different processes take place in the four different tectonic environments: (1) divergent zones, (2) convergent zones, (3) transform plate boundaries, and (4) hot spots. New lithosphere is created by seafloor spreading when plates are pulled apart at divergent zones. Old lithosphere is reabsorbed into the asthenosphere by subduction where two plates of differing densities collide. Transform faults accommodate the alongside movements of plates without creation or destruction of lithosphere. Hot spots originate deep in the Earth and are the source of isolated plumes of partially molten rock rising through the asthenosphere and lithosphere.
- Ocean studies have contributed solid evidence tectonic plate movement. Magnetization patterns on the seafloor delineate the newly formed lithosphere in space and time. Bathymetric surveys have mapped deep subduction trenches and relatively shallow volcanic ridges.
- Oceans and continents are fundamentally different. Ocean floors are relatively young features on the surface of the Earth, being constantly recycled by seafloor spreading and subduction. Continents comprise older lower-density rock that rides on top of the denser rock of the moving plates.
- Most earthquakes are caused by fault movements and occur preferentially along the edges of tectonic plates. Magma movement in the shallow subsurface at spreading centres and hot spots tends to induce swarms of small earthquakes. The dominantly horizontal movements at transform faults produce large earthquakes. The compressional movements at subduction zones and continent–continent collisions generate the largest earthquakes.
- Most volcanic eruptions occur underwater at spreading centres where an enormous volume of lava solidifies to form new seafloor.

Terms to Remember

asteroids
asthenosphere
atmosphere
bathymetry
brittle
chondrules
comets
compression
conduction
continents
convection

Questions for Review

1. What energy source is mainly responsible for earthquakes? Snow avalanches? Floods? Impacts with space bodies?
2. What energy sources caused the interior of the early Earth to heat up?
3. What can we learn from the study of stony meteorites? From the study of iron-rich meteorites?
4. Where are the oldest known Earth rocks found? How old are they?
5. How did the Earth's continents, ocean, and atmosphere form?
6. How did the Earth become segregated into layers of differing density?
7. What are the differences between brittle, ductile, and elastic behaviour?
8. What causes vertical movements of the Earth's surface?
9. What several lines of evidence indicate that the continents move about the Earth?

convergent zones
core
crust
Curie point
divergent zones
ductile
elastic
elements
epicentre
erosion
failed rifts
faults
force
glaciers
Gondwanaland
gravity
heat
hot spots
hydrologic cycle
hypocentre
island arc
isostasy
isotopes
Laurasia
lithosphere
magnetic field
magnetic pole
mantle
mesosphere
meteorites
nuclear fission
nuclear fusion
Pangaea
plastic
plates
plate tectonics
plumes
radiation
radioactive elements
ridges
rift
seafloor spreading
sediments
shear stress
solar radiation
spreading centres
strain
stress
subduction
tectonic cycle
tension
topography
transform faults
trenches
triple junction
viscous
volcanoes

10. What evidence indicates that seafloors spread?
11. What are the ages of (a) the oldest rocks on the continents, and (b) the oldest rocks making up the ocean floor?
12. Draw and label a cross-section that explains the tectonic cycle.
13. Sketch a sequence of cross-sections that shows how a continent is separated to accommodate an ocean basin.
14. Describe a deep-ocean trench. How does one form?
15. Why do deep earthquakes tend to occur within inclined bands?
16. Why are the Himalayas the world's highest mountain range?
17. Why are earthquakes at subduction zones many times more powerful than spreading-centre earthquakes?
18. How do hot spots help determine the directions of plate motions?

Questions for Further Thought

1. Approximately what percentage of geological time does your lifetime represent? Why is it challenging to understand Earth processes from a human perspective?
2. Why is it difficult to unravel the early history of the Earth?
3. The Earth is commonly called "terra firma," literally meaning "firm ground." Does this make good geological sense?
4. If the heat flow from the Earth's interior ceased, what would happen to the landmasses? After the internal heat flow had stopped for 100 million years, how would the Earth appear to a future visitor from space?
5. Why did the realization that the Earth's surface is broken into large plates come about only a few decades ago?
6. How can plate velocity be measured?
7. Is East Africa likely to pull away from the rest of Africa to form a Somali plate?
8. If a space body with active Earth-style plate tectonics is found, what would this discovery reveal about the internal structure of this body?

Interesting Websites

- This Dynamic Earth, United States Geological Survey
  http://pubs.usgs.gov/gip/dynamic/dynamic.html
- Plate tectonics animations, Educational Multimedia Visualization Center, University of California, Santa Barbara (select Downloads.)
  http://emvc.geol.ucsb.edu
- Interactive visualization of plate tectonics
  http://www.gplates.org
- Predicted future continental shapes, NASA Science
  http://science.nasa.gov/science-news/science-at-nasa/2000/ast06oct_1

CHAPTER THREE

3

Earthquake Geology, Seismology, and Engineering

Concrete buttresses reinforce a school building in Victoria, British Columbia. All schools in the province are being retrofitted with earthquake-resistant features.

Photo: © Claire Samson.

A bad earthquake at once destroys our oldest associations: the earth, the very emblem of solidity, has moved beneath our feet like a thin crust over a fluid; one second of time has created in the mind a strange idea of insecurity, which hours of reflection would not have produced.

—Charles Darwin, 1835, notes for *The Voyage of the Beagle*

Outline

LO1 Describe how energy is released during an earthquake.

LO2 List the characteristics of seismic waves.

LO3 Locate the epicentre and estimate the magnitude of an earthquake from seismogram measurements.

LO4 Use the Mercalli intensity scale to describe what people and infrastructure experience during an earthquake.

LO5 Explain the different factors affecting intensity and earthquake damage.

LO6 Give examples of earthquakes in different tectonic environments.

LO7 Describe mitigation strategies against earthquakes.

Figure 3.1
Offset of tilled farmland in Southern California by a movement of the Imperial fault in 1979. View is to the east; the west side of the fault (closest to you) has moved northward (to your left).
Photo: © Pat Abbott.

The earth beneath our feet moves, releasing energy that shifts the ground and sometimes topples cities. Some earthquakes are so immense that their energy is equivalent to thousands of atomic bombs exploded simultaneously. The power of earthquakes to destroy human works, to kill vast numbers of people, and to alter the very shape of the land has left an indelible mark on many civilizations. Earthquake unpredictability instills an uneasy respect and fear in humankind that, through the millennia, has helped shape thoughts about life and our place in it.

LO1 What Is an Earthquake?

The word "earthquake" is effectively a self-defining term—the Earth quakes, the Earth shakes, and we feel the vibrations. Earthquakes may be created by volcanic activity, meteorite impacts, undersea mass movements, underground nuclear explosions, and more; but most commonly they are caused by sudden Earth movements along faults. A fault is a **fracture**, a crack in the Earth across which the two sides move relative to each other (Figure 3.1). Stresses build up in rock until they are so great that the rock fractures and shifts along a fault. The radiating shock waves sent off as the rock ruptures and moves are what we experience as an earthquake.

A fault rupture is not a one-time movement that produces "the earthquake." In fact, we never have just one earthquake. The stresses that build up in the rock in an area are released by a series of movements along the fault, or several faults, that continue for weeks, months, or years. Each fault movement generates an earthquake; the biggest one is called the **mainshock**, the smaller ones before it are known as **foreshocks**, and the smaller ones after it are called **aftershocks**. There are no differences between these earthquakes other than size; they are all part of the same series of stress releases along the fault. The probability of large aftershocks is especially high in the days and weeks following the mainshock. Sometimes a big earthquake is followed by an even bigger earthquake. In this case, the first earthquake is reclassified as a foreshock.

Faults are not simple planar surfaces that glide readily when subjected to stress. Instead, faults are complex zones of breakage where rough and interlocking rock is held together over an irregular surface that extends many kilometres below the ground. Stress must build up over many years before enough energy is stored to allow a rupture on a fault. Ruptures almost always occur along pre-existing faults. The initial break occurs at a weak point on the fault and then propagates rapidly along the fault surface. The point where the fault first ruptures is known as the hypocentre. The point on the Earth's surface directly above the hypocentre is called the epicentre (Figure 3.2). The portion of the fault surface where rock moves is called the rupture area, and the amount by which rock on one side of the fault moves with respect to the other side is the slip. (Can you estimate the slip in Figure 3.1? Check your answer in the Questions for Review at the end of the chapter). Only in some cases does the rupture area extend to the Earth's surface and the fault leave an imprint on the ground (Figure 3.1 and Figure 3.27). The rupture area is limited to depths where rock is brittle. Below this region, rock is subjected to high temperatures and becomes ductile. It no longer fails suddenly.

The nineteenth-century recognition that fault movements cause earthquakes was a fundamental advance. With this relationship in mind, geologists go into the field to map active faults, which helps identify earthquake-hazard belts.

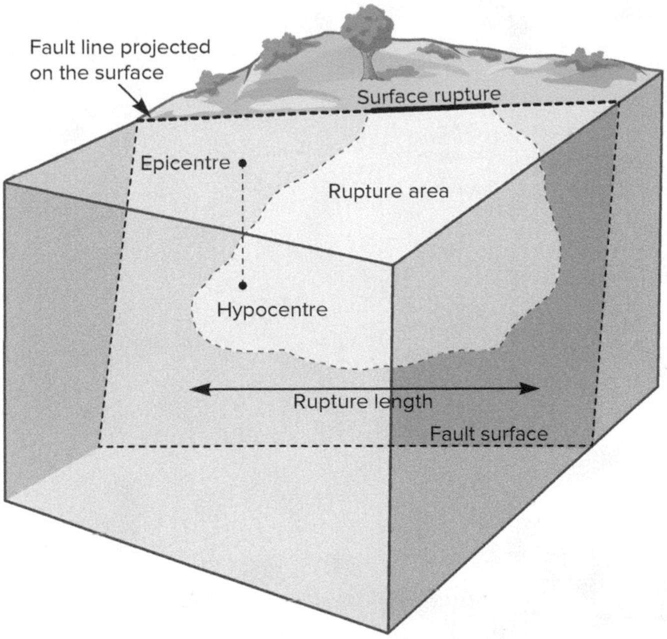

Figure 3.2
Block diagram of a fault surface. The hypocentre is the point on the fault surface at depth where the rupture began; the epicentre is the point on the Earth's surface directly above the hypocentre. Notice that because the fault surface is inclined, the epicentre does not plot on the trace of the fault at the surface.

Figure 3.3
Replica of Chang Heng's seismoscope, a large bronze urn decorated with eight dragon and frog pairs. Inside the enclosure, a vertical metal rod stands in a precarious equilibrium (inverted pendulum). The slightest earth movement triggers it to fall and hit a lever that, in turn, causes one of the dragons to drop a ball into the mouth of the frog below, indicating the direction of horizontal earth motion.
Photo: © Claire Samson.

Recording Earth Motions

The study of earthquakes is known as **seismology** (after **seism**, meaning "earthquake"). The earliest earthquake-indicating device known was invented in China in 132 CE by Chang Heng (Figure 3.3). The modern era of instrumentation began about 1880 and continues to evolve but the basic requirement of earthquake-monitoring technology remains to record the 3-D movement of earthquake waves together with their exact **arrival time** and durations. This is achieved by having instruments detect Earth motions (**seismometers**); record them as north–south horizontal movements, east–west horizontal movements, and vertical movements; and assign them a time stamp.

To accurately record the passage of seismic waves, a seismometer needs to have a part that remains as stationary as possible while the Earth beneath it vibrates. The classic way to accomplish this is by building a pendulum seismometer with a heavy mass suspended on a frame (Figure 3.4). The support frame rests on the Earth and moves as the Earth does, but the mass suspended by a wire must have its **inertia** overcome before it moves. The differences between motions of the frame and the hanging mass are recorded as a wiggle trace by a pen on a drum of paper.

A modern seismograph station (Figure 3.5) is equipped with three seismometers, each recording one component of the Earth motion (north–south horizontal, east–west horizontal, and vertical). Most permanent stations are located in vaults to isolate the instruments from traffic vibrations. Seismometers are placed on concrete slabs in direct contact with bedrock for good coupling. Other stations are designed for temporary deployment, often in remote locations. They are powered by solar panels and telemeter data via a satellite link (Figure 2.30).

Analysis of the seismic records (**seismograms**) allows seismologists to identify the different kinds of seismic waves generated by the fault movement, to estimate the amount of energy released (magnitude), and to locate the epicenter or hypocentre.

LO2 Seismic Waves

A GENERAL DESCRIPTION OF WAVES

Throw a rock into a pond, play a musical instrument, or experience a fault movement, and the water, the air, or

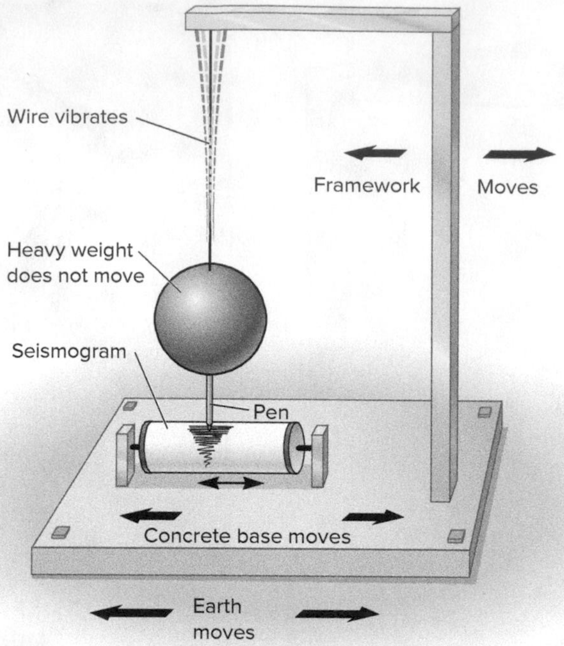

Figure 3.4
Pendulum seismograph: The Earth moves, the seismograph framework moves, and the hanging wire vibrates, but the suspended heavy mass and pen beneath it remain relatively steady. Ideally, the pen holds still while the Earth moves beneath the pen to produce an inked line.

the Earth will transmit waves of energy that travel away from the initial disturbance. Waves can be described in terms of distance and time (Figure 3.6). Describing waves in terms of distance is useful, for example, when mapping the ocean surface and measuring the distance between successive waves. This distance is referred to as the **wavelength** and is expressed in metres. Describing waves in terms of time is useful, for example, when measuring the amount of time between successive ocean waves reaching the beach. This length of time is referred to as the **period** and is expressed in seconds. The number of waves reaching a point during one second is called the frequency. Frequency is expressed in **hertz** (Hz) where 1 Hz equals one cycle per second. As mentioned in Chapter 1, period and frequency are inversely related. For example, if five waves pass a given point in 1 second, then the frequency is 5 Hz and the period is 0.2 second.

The **amplitude** of a wave is its displacement above or below the undisturbed position. Waves lose energy as they propagate away from the initial disturbance. Their amplitude decreases with distance, a phenomenon called attenuation (Figure 3.7). High-frequency waves attenuate over shorter distances than low-frequency waves as can be seen by comparing the waveforms of

Figure 3.5
Modern seismograph station with three orthogonally aligned seismometers deployed on a large concrete slab in direct contact with bedrock. The seismometer on the right, with all protective covers removed, shows the suspended mass on a boom. The unit on the left has its protective cover in place while the centre unit is fitted with its heat shield. During normal operations, the seismometers are covered by bell jars that are evacuated, further reducing the effects of temperature and protecting against air currents (insert).
Photos: © Claire Samson.

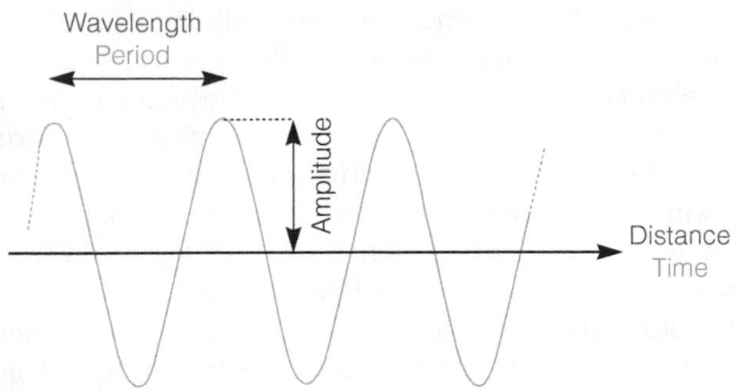

Figure 3.6
Wave motion. The horizontal arrow represents the undisturbed position, that is, the position of the medium when no wave is present. The orange line represents the position of the medium as a wave travels through it. The amplitude is the displacement from the undisturbed position. The section of the wave that rises above or lies below the undisturbed position is called a crest or a trough, respectively. When wave motion is plotted versus time, the length of time between successive crests/troughs corresponds to one period. When wave motion is plotted versus distance, successive crests/troughs are separated by one wavelength.
Source: © Claire Samson.

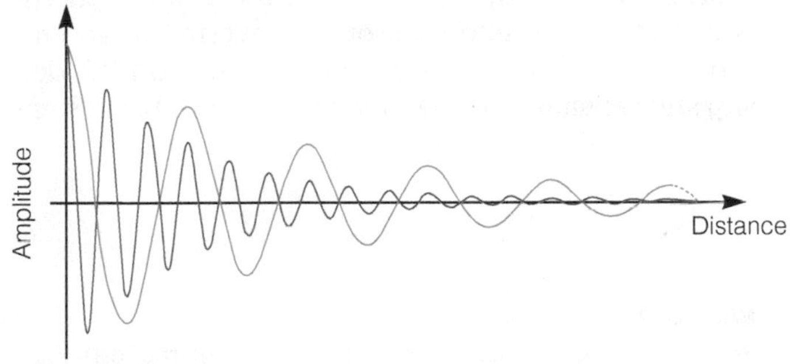

Figure 3.7
Attenuation. The amplitude of seismic waves decreases with increasing distance from the epicentre. This effect is more pronounced for high-frequency waves (in blue) than for low-frequency waves (in green).
Source: © Claire Samson.

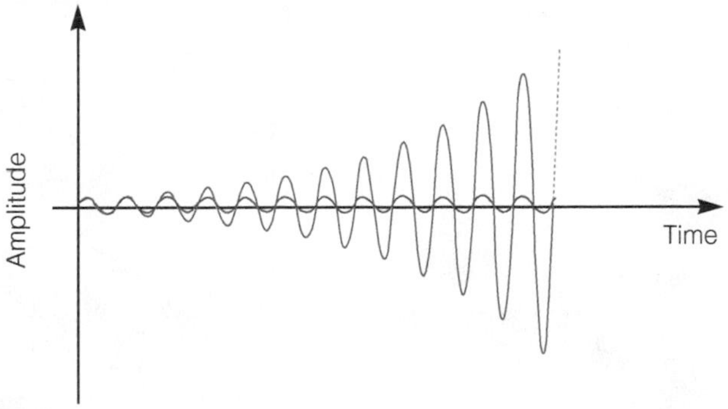

Figure 3.9
Resonance. When a mechanical system is disturbed by a forcing function (in blue) of frequency equal to its natural frequency, it starts to oscillate at progressively higher amplitudes (in red).
Source: © Claire Samson.

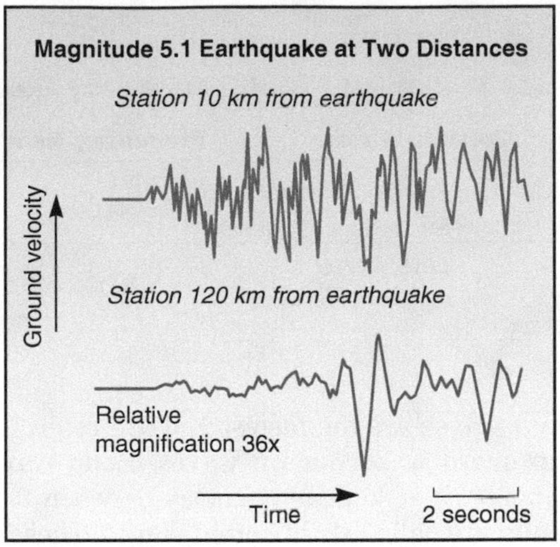

Figure 3.8
Comparison of seismograms from the same earthquake recorded at two different stations. The waveforms on the seismogram from the closest station (top) are rich in high frequencies, whereas the waveforms on the seismogram from the station farther away (bottom) are dominated by lower frequencies.
Source: A. Michael, S. Ross, and D. Schaff, "The Music of Earthquakes; Waveforms of Sound and Seismology" in *American Scientist* (2002).

the same earthquake recorded at different distances from the epicentre (Figure 3.8).

The velocity of propagation of a wave in a medium is an intrinsic characteristic of that material. If the material properties change, so will the velocity. Waves will adapt by accelerating, decelerating, or changing direction.

Each mechanical system, for example, an ocean wave or a guitar string, is characterized by a particular **natural frequency**, which is the frequency at which the system vibrates when disturbed. When external forces are imposed on a system at exactly its natural frequency, their energy reinforces internal vibrations. Vibrations grow larger and larger—a wave phenomenon called **resonance** (Figure 3.9). As we will see later in this chapter, earthquake waves can induce resonances in earth materials and buildings with dramatic consequences.

BODY WAVES

When the Earth shakes, it releases energy in **seismic waves** that pass through the whole body of the planet (**body waves**) and others that move near the surface only (**surface waves**) (Table 3.1).

TABLE 3.1

Seismic Waves and Their Frequency Range

Seismic Waves		Frequency Range [Hz]
Body waves	Primary (P) waves Secondary (S) waves	0.02 – 30
Surface waves	Love waves Rayleigh waves	0.002 – 0.1

Body waves are the fastest and are referred to as either primary or secondary waves. Body waves are most abundant at high frequencies between 0.02 and 30 Hz, and are called short-period waves. These waves attenuate over short distances and are therefore most energetic close to the hypocentre/epicentre.

Primary Waves

The **primary (P) wave** (also known as the compressional wave) is the fastest and thus is the first to reach a seismograph station. P waves move in a push–pull fashion of alternating pulses of compression (push) and extension (pull) (Figure 3.10a). They travel through any material, be it solid, liquid, or gas. Their velocity depends on the density and compressibility of the materials through which they pass. The greater the resistance to compression, the greater the velocity of the seismic waves passing through packed atomic structures. Representative velocities for P waves are about 5.0 km/s in igneous rocks (e.g., granite) and 3.0 km/s in sedimentary rocks (e.g., sandstone). P waves in water slow to 1.5 km/s. Because P waves and sound waves are both compressional waves, they can travel through air. P waves may emerge from the ground, and if you are near the epicentre, you may be able to hear those P waves pulsing at around 15 Hz as low, thunderous noises.

Secondary Waves

The **secondary (S) wave** (also known as the shear wave) is the second wave to reach a seismograph station. S waves are transverse waves that propagate by shearing particles in their path at right angles to the direction of propagation in the vertical or horizontal plane (Figure 3.10b). S waves travel only through solids. On reaching liquid or gas, the S wave energy is reflected back into rock or is converted to another form. The velocity of an S wave depends on the density and resistance to shearing of materials. Liquids and

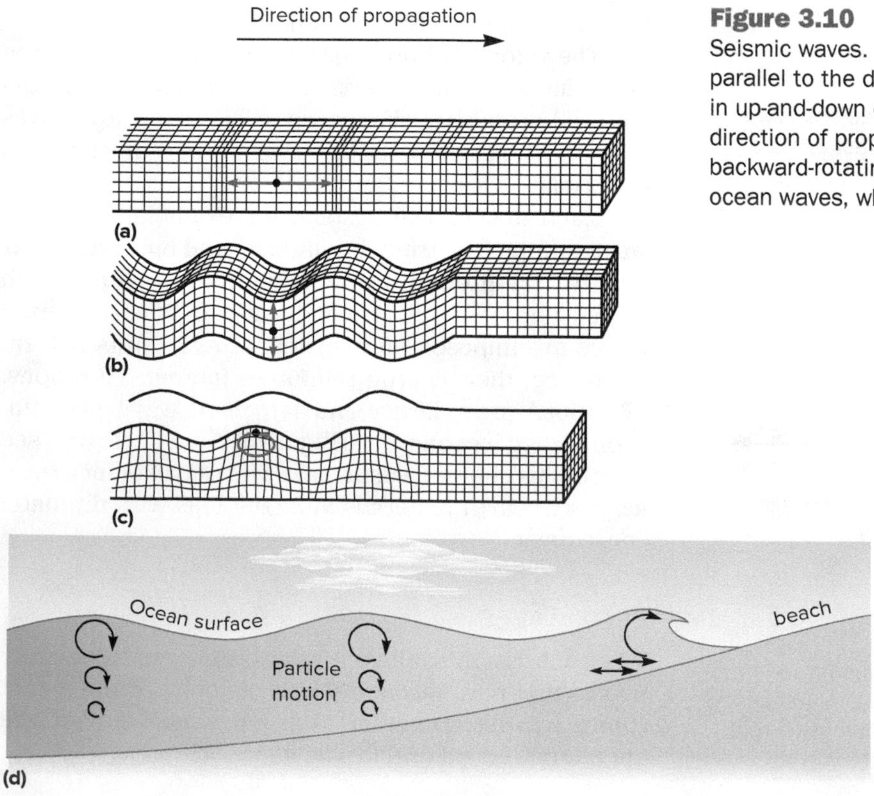

Figure 3.10
Seismic waves. (a) P waves move in a push–pull motion parallel to the direction of propagation. (b) S waves move in up-and-down or side-to-side motions perpendicular to the direction of propagation. (c) Rayleigh waves advance in a backward-rotating motion, as opposed to (d) water droplets in ocean waves, which move in forward-rotating circles.

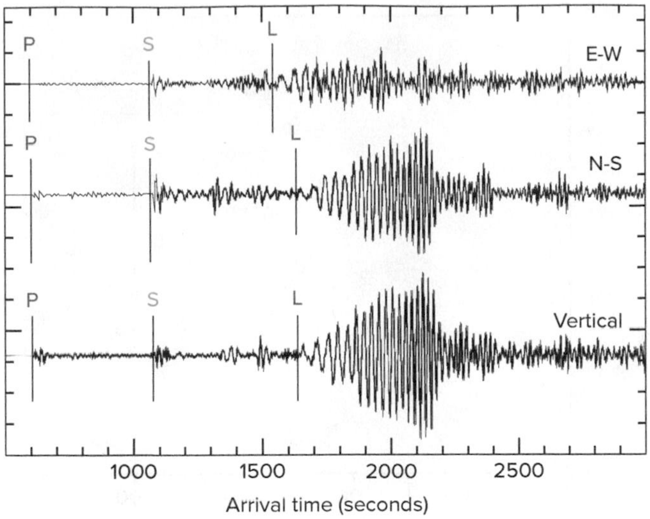

Figure 3.11

The El Salvador earthquake of 13 January 2001 (M_s of 7.8) recorded at Taloyoak, Nunavut. Letters P, S, and L indicate the arrival times of P, S, and surface waves, respectively. The difference in arrival times between P and S waves is approximately 500 seconds.

Source: Reproduced with the permission of Natural Resources Canada 2014, courtesy of Earthquakes Canada.

gases do not have shear strength and thus cannot transmit S waves. Representative velocities for S waves in igneous and sedimentary rocks are about 3.0 km/s and 1.7 km/s, respectively. With their up-and-down and side-to-side motions, S waves can inflict severe damage to buildings.

SURFACE WAVES

Seismic waves that travel near the Earth's surface are of two main types—Love and Rayleigh waves. Both Love and Rayleigh waves are referred to as L waves (long waves) because they take longer periods of time to complete one cycle of motion and are the slowest moving. The frequencies of surface waves are typically between 0.002 and 0.1 Hz. Because of their low attenuation, surface waves carry significant amounts of energy long distances away from the epicentre.

Love waves generally travel faster than Rayleigh waves. Their side-to-side motion is similar to S waves propagating in a horizontal plane roughly parallel to the Earth's surface. Like S waves, they do not move through water or air. Love waves are particularly hazardous because buildings are often not designed to withstand horizontal stress.

Rayleigh waves advance in a backward-rotating elliptical motion (Figure 3.10c) similar to paths of water molecules in waves of water, except that droplets move in forward-rotating orbits (Figure 3.10d). The shaking produced by Rayleigh waves causes both vertical and horizontal movement. The rolling waves pass through both ground and water. The often-heard report that an earthquake feels like one is rocking in a boat at sea well describes the passage of Rayleigh waves.

Figure 3.11 is a three-component seismogram of a large earthquake recorded several thousand kilometres from the epicentre. The P waves are recorded first, followed by S waves, and finally by the surface waves. Note that the amplitudes of the higher-frequency P and S waves are smaller that those of the surface waves because of stronger attenuation. With its large amplitude and long duration, the surface wavetrain can be particularly destructive.

LO3 Locating the Epicentre of an Earthquake

P waves travel about 1.7 times faster than S waves. The method for determining the location of the epicentre of an earthquake exploits the corollary that follows: the farther away from the earthquake's origin, the greater the difference in arrival times between P and S waves (Figure 3.12). Seismograms from three seismograph stations must be available to determine an earthquake's origin (Figure 3.13). The method will be described step by step using as an example the regional earthquake (magnitude 3.2) that occurred on 1 May 1992 and was recorded by the Mont-Orford (MOQ), Manicouagan (MNQ), and James Bay (JAQ) stations in Quebec.

The first step is to determine the arrival times of the P and S waves on the seismograms and to calculate the differences between them. In Figure 3.13, this arrival time difference is 38 seconds for station MOQ, 50 seconds for station MNQ, and 115 seconds for station JAQ. The second step is to read the corresponding distances on the plot of arrival time versus epicentral distance (Figure 3.12b). This yields epicentral distances of 300 km, 375 km, and 800 km for stations MOQ, MNQ and JAQ, respectively. The epicentre will be on the circumference of three circles, each with its centre point coinciding with one station location and its radius equal to the corresponding epicentral distance. The third and final step is to plot these circles on a map (Figure 3.14). The three circles all intersect at exactly one point—the epicentre of the earthquake, in this case La Malbaie, in Charlevoix, Quebec. Although located thousands of kilometres away from plate boundaries, the Charlevoix region has been the scene of several destructive earthquakes since the establishment of New France in the seventeenth century. We will explore this topic in more detail in the next chapter.

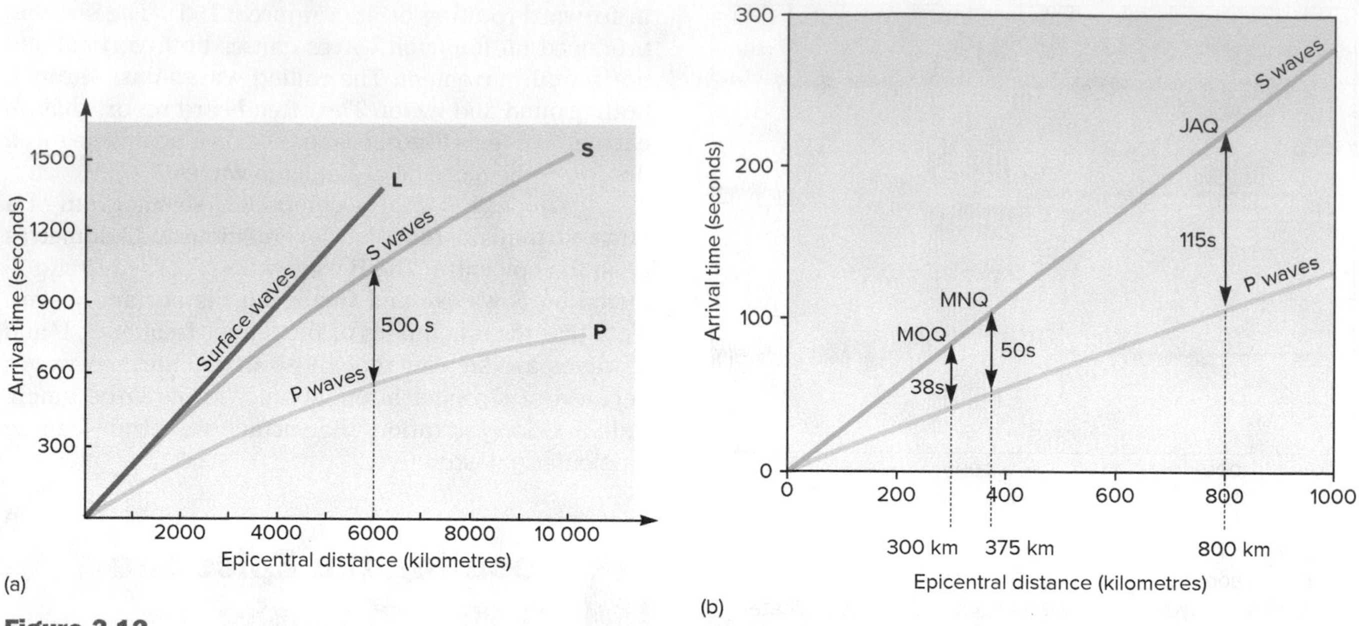

Figure 3.12
(a) Plot of arrival time versus epicentral distance for seismic waves. The difference in arrival times between P and S waves of approximately 500 seconds in Figure 3.11 corresponds to an epicentral distance of 6000 km. (b) Zoomed view showing the arrival time differences between P and S waves, and epicentral distances for the three seismograms of Figure 3.13.
Source: © Claire Samson.

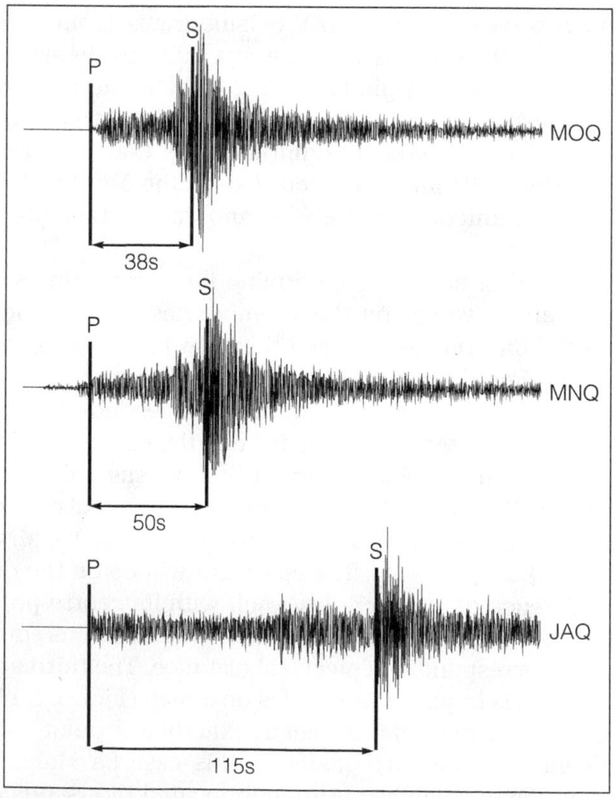

Figure 3.13
Seismograms of the regional 1 May 1992 earthquake (magnitude 3.2) recorded by stations MOQ, MNQ, and JAQ in Quebec.
Source: Reproduced with the permission of Natural Resources Canada 2014, courtesy of Earthquakes Canada.

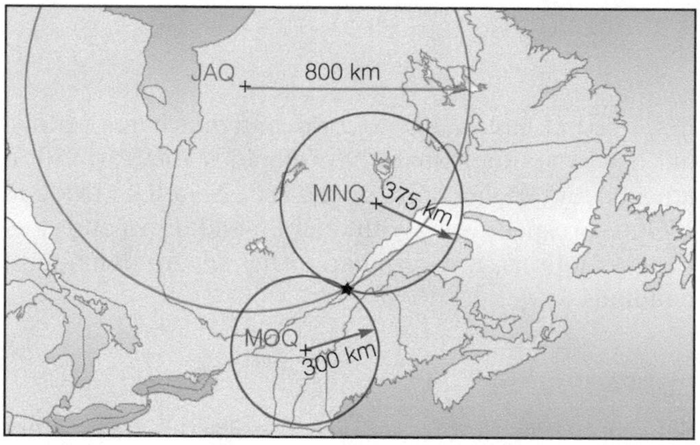

Figure 3.14
Location of the epicentre of the 1 May 1992 earthquake by triangulation. The three circles intersect uniquely at La Malbaie, Quebec.
Source: © Claire Samson.

Magnitude—The Energy Released During an Earthquake

Magnitude is an estimate of the energy released during an earthquake. It is commonly measured from the amplitude of seismic waves on a seismogram.

RICHTER SCALE

Several systems are available to assess the magnitudes of earthquakes. The best-known system is the Richter scale. In 1935, Charles Richter of the California

Institute of Technology devised a quantitative scheme to describe the magnitude of Californian earthquakes, that is, of events with shallow hypocentres that are located less than 500 km from seismograph stations. Richter based his scale on the idea that the bigger the earthquake, the greater the shaking of the Earth and thus the greater the amplitude of the seismic waves. To standardize this relationship, he defined magnitude as the logarithm to the base ten of the maximum seismic wave amplitude (in millimetres) recorded at a distance of 100 km from the epicentre. Since not all seismograph stations sit 100 km from the epicentre, corrections are made for distance.

The Richter magnitude for an earthquake can be computed quickly, and this is one of the reasons for its great popularity with the deadline-conscious print and electronic media. Upon learning of an earthquake, usually by phone calls from reporters, anyone with access to a seismogram can rapidly measure (1) the amplitude of the seismic waves and (2) the difference in arrival times between P and S waves. Figure 3.15 has reduced Richter's equation to a nomograph, which allows easy determination of magnitude. Take a couple of minutes to determine the magnitude of the earthquake whose seismogram is printed above the nomograph.

For every tenfold increase in the amplitude of the recorded seismic wave, the Richter magnitude increases one number, for example, from 4 to 5. The energy released by earthquakes increases even more rapidly than the tenfold increase in amplitude of the seismic waves. For example, if the amplitude of the seismic

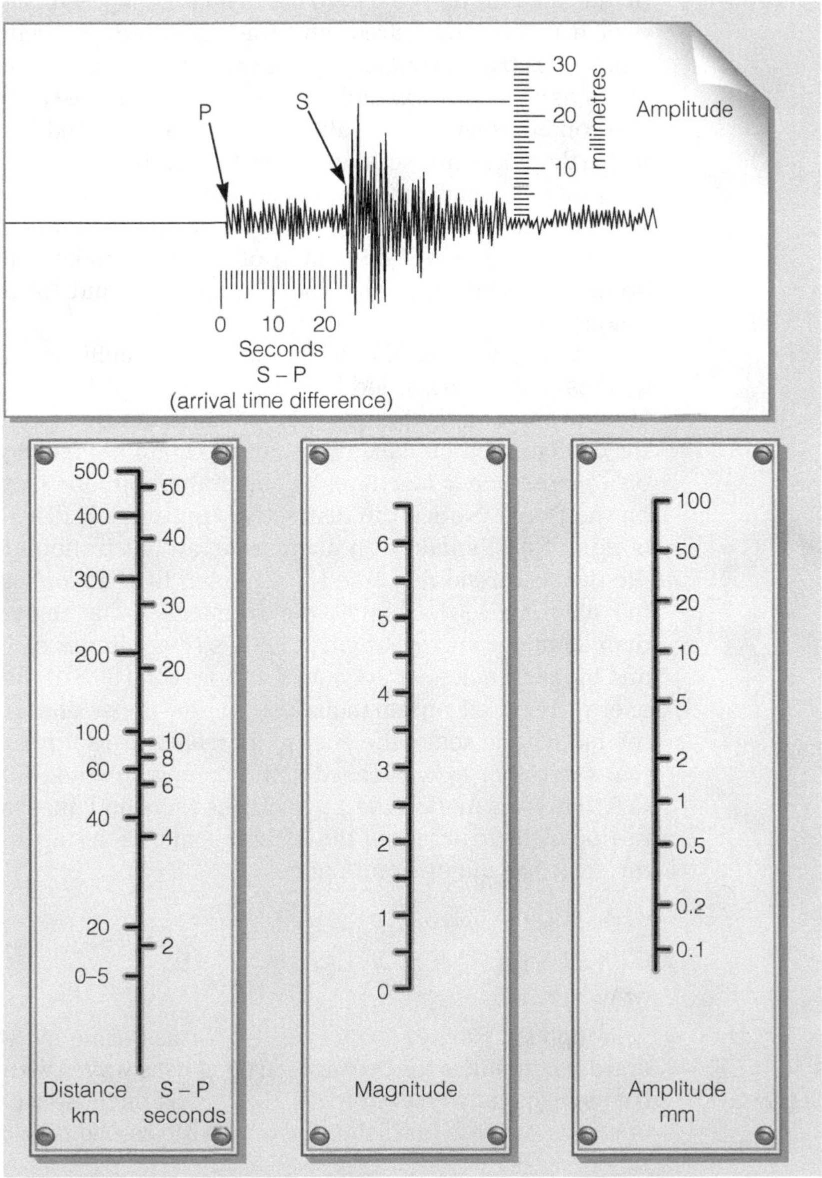

Figure 3.15
Nomograph of the Richter scale allowing earthquake magnitudes to be estimated graphically. On the seismogram, read the difference in arrival times between P and S waves in seconds and plot the value on the left column of the nomograph. Next, read the maximum amplitude of the S wave and plot this value on the right column. Draw a line between the two marked values, and it will pass through the earthquake magnitude on the centre column. Check your answer in the Questions for Review at the end of the chapter.

TABLE 3.2

Magnitude and Released Energy

Richter Magnitude	Energy Increase	Energy Compared to Magnitude 4
4		1
5	= 48 magnitude 4 earthquakes	48 ×
6	= 43 magnitude 5 earthquakes	2 050 ×
7	= 39 magnitude 6 earthquakes	80 500 ×
8	= 35 magnitude 7 earthquakes	2 800 000 ×

TABLE 3.3

Magnitude and Duration of Shaking

Richter Magnitude	Duration of Strong Ground Shaking (seconds)
4–4.9	0–5
5–5.9	2–15
6–6.9	10–30
7–7.9	20–50
8–8.9	30–90

TABLE 3.4

Earthquakes in the World Each Year

Magnitude	Number of Earthquakes Per Year	Description
8.5 and up	0.3	Great
8–8.4	1	
7.5–7.9	3	Major
7–7.4	15	
6.6–6.9	56	Strong (destructive)
6–6.5	210	
5–5.9	800	Moderate (damaging)
4–4.9	6 200	Light
3–3.9	49 000	Minor
2–2.9	350 000	Very minor
0–1.9	3 000 000	

waves increased 10 000 times (10 × 10 × 10 × 10), the Richter magnitude would move up from a 4 to an 8. However, the energy released would increase by a factor of 2 800 000 (Table 3.2).

What does this increase mean in everyday terms? If you feel a magnitude 4 earthquake while sitting at your dinner table, and then a magnitude 8 comes along while you are still at the table, would you really be shaken 2 800 000 times as hard? No. The greater energy of the magnitude 8 earthquake would be spread out over a much larger area, and the magnitude 8 event would dissipate its energy over a time interval about 20 times as long (for example, 60 seconds as opposed to 3 seconds, as shown in Table 3.3). The actual shaking in earthquakes above magnitude 6 does not increase very much (approximately three times as much shaking for each step up in magnitude). A larger magnitude means that the intense shaking of an earthquake will be experienced by people in a larger area, and for a longer time.

Each year, the Earth is shaken by millions of quakes that are recorded by seismometers (Table 3.4). Most are below magnitude 2.5, which is the threshold for detection by humans (you can replicate the feeling of a magnitude 2 "earthquake" by stamping your foot on the floor). Notice the distinctive "pyramidal" distribution of earthquakes by magnitude, an illustration of the general trend described in Chapter 1—the smaller the magnitude, the higher the frequency. The fewer than 20 major and great earthquakes (magnitudes of 7 and higher) each year account for more than 90% of the energy released by earthquakes. At the upper end of the magnitude scale, the energy increases are so great that more energy is released going from magnitude 8.9 to 9 than from magnitude 1 to 8. These facts underscore the logarithmic nature of the Richter scale; each step up the scale has major significance.

OTHER MEASURES OF EARTHQUAKE MAGNITUDE

Although the Richter scale is useful for assessing moderate earthquakes that occur nearby, it uses waves with frequencies between 0.5 to 10 Hz. Waves of these frequencies saturate for distant or very large earthquakes;

TABLE 3.5

Magnitude and Rupture Length

Magnitude	Rupture Length (km)
4	0.1
5	1
6	10
7	100

they do not become more intense as an earthquake becomes larger. For example, the Richter scale assesses both the 1906 San Francisco earthquake and the 1964 Alaska earthquake as being of magnitude 8.3. However, using other scales, the San Francisco earthquake is a magnitude 7.8 and the Alaska seism is a 9.2. The Alaska earthquake was at least 100 times larger in terms of energy.

The Richter scale is now restricted to measuring only local earthquakes with moderate magnitudes (noted as M_L [magnitude—local]). Because earthquakes generate both body waves that travel through the Earth and surface waves that follow the Earth's uppermost layers, two other magnitude scales have long been used: m_b and M_s. The body wave (m_b) scale uses amplitudes of P waves with frequencies between 0.1 and 10 Hz, whereas the surface wave scale (M_s) uses Rayleigh waves with frequencies in the order of 0.05 Hz. Early on, all magnitude scales were considered to be equivalent, but now we know that earthquakes generate different proportions of energy at different frequencies. For example, larger earthquakes with their larger rupture areas (Figure 3.2) radiate more of their energy as lower-frequency seismic waves. Thus, for major and great earthquakes, body wave magnitudes (m_b) will significantly underestimate the actual size of the earthquake. Even a composite of these three methods of determining earthquake magnitude (M_L, m_b, and M_s) does not necessarily yield the true size of an earthquake.

Moment Magnitude Scale

Rupture length (Figure 3.2) greatly influences earthquake magnitude (Table 3.5). In an effort to more accurately determine earthquake size, seismologists have developed alternative measures based on parameters describing fault rupture. The seismic moment (M_0) relies on the amount of movement along the fault that generated the earthquake; that is, M_0 equals the shear strength of the rock times the rupture area of the fault times the average displacement (slip) on the fault. Moment is a more reliable measure of earthquake size; it measures the amount of energy released by the movement along the whole rupture surface. Seismic moment has been incorporated into a new earthquake magnitude scale by Hiroo Kanamori, the moment magnitude scale (M_w), where

$$M_w = 2/3 \log_{10} (M_0) - 6$$

The moment magnitude scale is used for big earthquakes. It is more accurate than other methods because it is tied directly to physical parameters such as rupture area, slip, and energy release.

The three largest moment magnitudes calculated to date are the 1960 Chile earthquake (M_s of 8.5; M_w of 9.5), the 1964 Alaska earthquake (M_s of 8.3; M_w of 9.2), and the 2004 Sumatra event (M_s of 8.8; M_w of 9.1). These gigantic earthquakes occurred at subduction zones and triggered deadly tsunamis. A variety of energetic events are placed on a scale for comparison in Figure 3.16.

LO4 Intensity—What We Feel During an Earthquake

During the tens of seconds that a large earthquake lasts, we feel ourselves rocked up and down and shaken from side to side. It is an emotional experience, and the drama of our accounts varies according to our locations during the shaking and our personalities. But for personal narratives to be meaningful to future generations, common threads or reference points are needed to bind the accounts together. In the late 1800s, descriptive schemes appeared that were based on the intensity of effects experienced by people and buildings. The most widely used scale came from the Italian professor Giuseppi Mercalli in 1902; it was modified by Charles Richter in 1956. The scale has 12 divisions of increasing intensity labelled with Roman numerals (Table 3.6). Mercalli intensities are crucial for assessing magnitudes of historical events before there were instrumented records, thus allowing us to assess the return period between major earthquakes.

Earthquake magnitude scales are used to assess the energy released during an earthquake; earthquake intensity scales assess the effects on people and buildings. As elegantly phrased by Simon Winchester: "Intensity requires an audience; magnitude requires only the divining powers of machines."

LO5 FACTORS AFFECTING INTENSITY

An earthquake has only one magnitude. The same earthquake, however, has different effects in different areas and is therefore assigned a range of

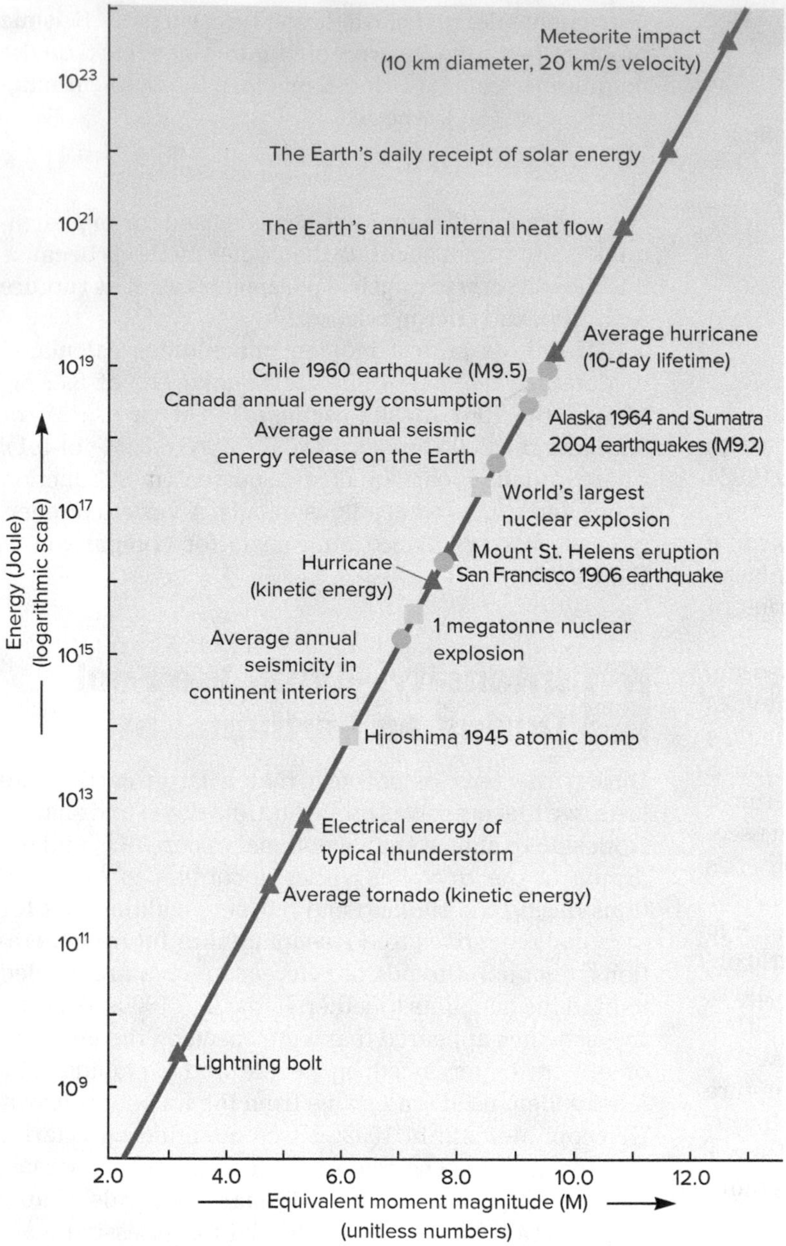

Figure 3.16
Equivalent moment magnitude of a variety of seismic events (green dots), human-made events (yellow squares), and other phenomena (red triangles).

Source: Modified from A. C. Johnston, US Geological Survey.

intensities. The geographical distribution of intensities is often presented on **isoseismal maps** where contours are drawn outlining areas of equal intensity (Figure 3.17). The largest contour delineates the **felt area**, the surface over which the earthquake was felt by people.

For a given earthquake, the Mercalli intensity at a given location depends on several factors: (1) earthquake magnitude, (2) epicentre location, (3) distance from the epicentre, (4) hypocentre depth, (5) duration of shaking, (6) local soil conditions, and (7) building style. These factors need to be considered in assessing the earthquake threat to any region and even to specific buildings.

Earthquake Magnitude

The relationship between magnitude and intensity is obvious—the more energy released during an earthquake, the higher the odds for death and damage.

Epicentre Location

Similarly, the relationship between epicentre location and intensity is straightforward—densely populated areas are especially vulnerable to fatalities and damage.

Distance from Epicentre

The relationship between distance and damage also seems obvious—the closer to the hypocenter or epicentre,

TABLE 3.6

Modified Mercalli Scale of Earthquake Intensity

I Not felt except by a very few people under especially favourable circumstances.

II Felt by only a few people at rest, especially those on upper floors of buildings or those with a very sensitive nature. Delicately suspended objects may swing.

III Felt quite noticeably indoors, especially on upper floors, but many people do not recognize it as an earthquake. Vibrations are like those from the passing of light trucks. Standing automobiles may rock slightly. Duration of shaking may be estimated.

IV Felt indoors during the day by many people, outdoors by few. Light sleepers may be awakened. Vibrations are like those from the passing of heavy trucks or as if a heavy object struck the building. Standing automobiles rock; windows, dishes, and doors rattle; glassware and crockery clink and clash. In the upper range of IV, wooden walls and frames creak.

V Felt indoors by nearly everyone, outdoors by many or most. Many are awakened. Many are frightened; some run outdoors. Some dishes, glassware, and windows break. Minor cracks form in plaster. Small objects may move, liquids spill and small bells ring. Tall objects sway.

VI Felt by all; many frightened and run outdoors. Excitement is general. Dishes, glassware, and windows break in considerable quantities. Knick-knacks, books, and pictures fall. Furniture moves or overturns. Weak plaster walls and some brick walls crack. Damage is slight.

VII Frightens all; difficult to stand. Noticed by drivers of automobiles. Large bells ring. Damage is negligible in buildings of good design and construction; slight to moderate in well-built ordinary buildings; and considerable in badly designed or poorly built buildings, adobe houses, and old walls. Numerous windows and some chimneys break. Small landslides and caving of sand and gravel banks occur. Waves form on ponds; water becomes turbid.

VIII Fright is general and alarm approaches panic. Disturbs drivers of automobiles. Heavy furniture overturns. Damage is slight in specially designed structure, but considerable in ordinary substantial buildings, including partial collapses. Frame houses move off foundations if not bolted down. Most walls, chimneys, towers, and monuments fall. Spring flow and well-water levels change. Cracks appear in wet ground and on slopes.

IX General panic. Damage is considerable in masonry structures, even those built to withstand earthquakes. Well-built frame houses are thrown out of plumb. Ground cracks conspicuously. Underground pipes break. In soft-sediment areas, sand and mud are ejected from ground in fountains and leave craters.

X Most masonry structures are destroyed. Some well-built wooden structures and bridges fail. Ground cracks badly with serious damage to dams and embankments. Large landslides occur on riverbanks and steep slopes. Railroad tracks bend slightly.

XI Few, if any, masonry structures remain standing. Great damage occurs to dams and embankments, commonly over great distances. Supporting piers of large bridges fail. Broad fissures form in the ground, earth slumps and slips in soft, wet ground. Underground pipelines are completely out of service. Railroad tracks bend greatly.

XII Damage is nearly total. Ground surfaces seen to move in waves. Lines of sight and level distort. Objects are thrown up in air.

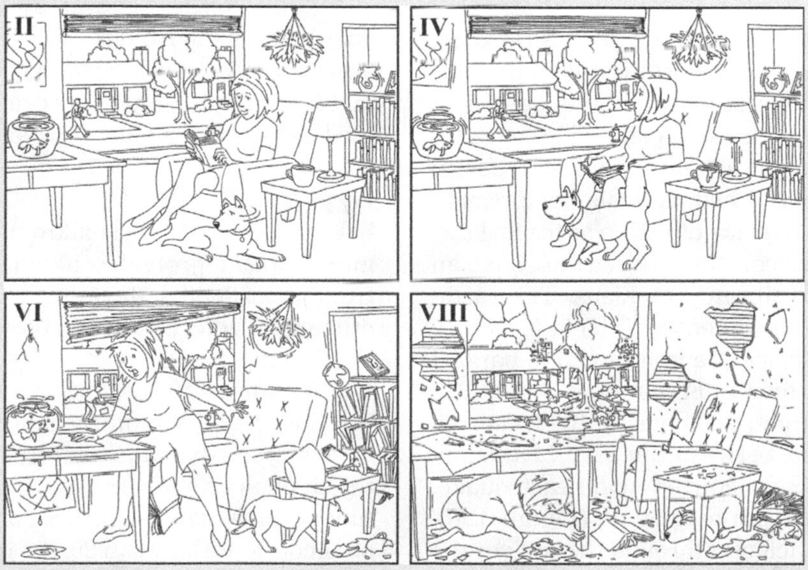

IN GREATER DEPTH

Liquefaction

Liquefaction is a phenomenon of saturated soils in which the behaviour of poorly consolidated sediments transforms from that of a solid to that of a liquid.

Soils are a loose assemblage of solid particles with the space between them filled by air and water in various proportions. In saturated soils, all the space between particles is occupied by water (Figure 3.17a). When saturated soils are disturbed—by strong earthquake shaking or rapid loading with excess weight, for example—the particles attempt to move closer to one another but are prevented from doing so by the water trapped between them. Water pressure builds up, which weakens the bonds between particles. Pressure may become so high that many of the soil particles lose contact with each other and begin to float freely in the water (Figure 3.17b). Under such circumstances, soils lose strength and stiffness, and therefore the ability to support loads. An extreme example occurred during the 1964 Niigata, Japan, earthquake. A group of apartment buildings founded on saturated soil sank and tilted severely. Remarkably, they suffered little structural damage (Figure 3.18). Liquefied sediments in the subsurface can also trigger spectacular mass movements in which rafts of earth materials move downslope like floating pieces of ice on a river (Figure 13.23).

Susceptibility to liquefaction depends on soil characteristics and the depth of the water table. This information is often summarized on a regional liquefaction hazard map like that of Victoria, British Columbia (Figure 3.19).

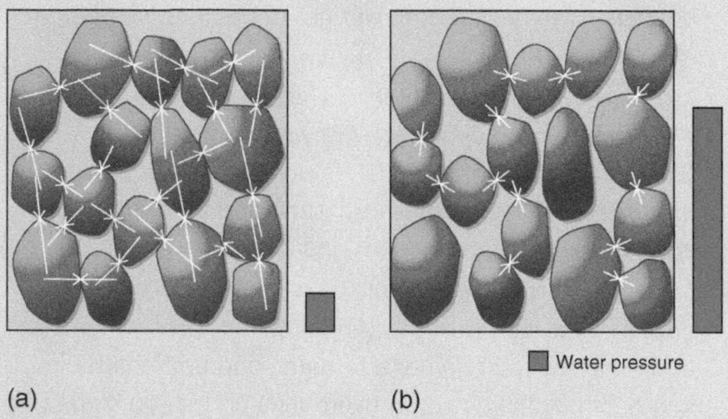

Figure 3.17
(a) Saturated soil. The length of the arrows represents the size of the binding forces between individual solid particles. The forces are large when water pressure is low. (b) Liquefied soil. Binding forces are weaker due to the increased water pressure.

Source: J. Johansson, Department of Civil Engineering, University of Washington, 2000.

Figure 3.18
Soil liquefied under the foundations of several apartment buildings in Niigata, Japan, during the 16 June 1964 earthquake (magnitude 7.5).

Source: Courtesy of the National Service for Earthquake Engineering EERC, University of California, Berkeley.

the greater the damage. But this is not always the case, as regional geology plays an important role in the spatial distribution of intensities. Consider the isoseismal map of the 1925 Charlevoix earthquake (Figure 3.20). Contours of equal intensity are not concentric circles centred on the epicentre. They are ellipses oriented northeast-southwest in the same direction as the St. Lawrence River Valley and the contact between the Canadian Precambrian Shield and the Appalachians. The earthquake was felt with greater intensity (VII) in Montreal, 400 km away from the epicentre in a direction parallel to the geological trend, than in Fredericton (V–VI), 325 km away in a direction perpendicular to the trend. An interesting comparison is between the 1925 Charlevoix earthquake and the 1918 Vancouver Island earthquake, both seisms of roughly equal magnitude (Figure 3.20). Seismic waves travel efficiently through the rock of the continental interior of eastern North America and carry energy far away from the epicentre. On the other hand, seismic waves travelling through the pervasive fractures and faults of the Canadian cordillera are rapidly attenuated, resulting in a much smaller felt area.

Hypocentre Depth

Seismic waves from shallow hypocentres will induce more violent ground shaking than those originating from great depths, the latter having been significantly attenuated before reaching the Earth's surface.

Duration of Shaking

The duration of shaking is underappreciated as a significant factor in damages suffered and lives lost. Consider the shaking times in Table 3.3. For example, if a magnitude 7 earthquake shakes a community vigorously for 50 seconds, rather than 20, the increase in damages and lives lost can be enormous.

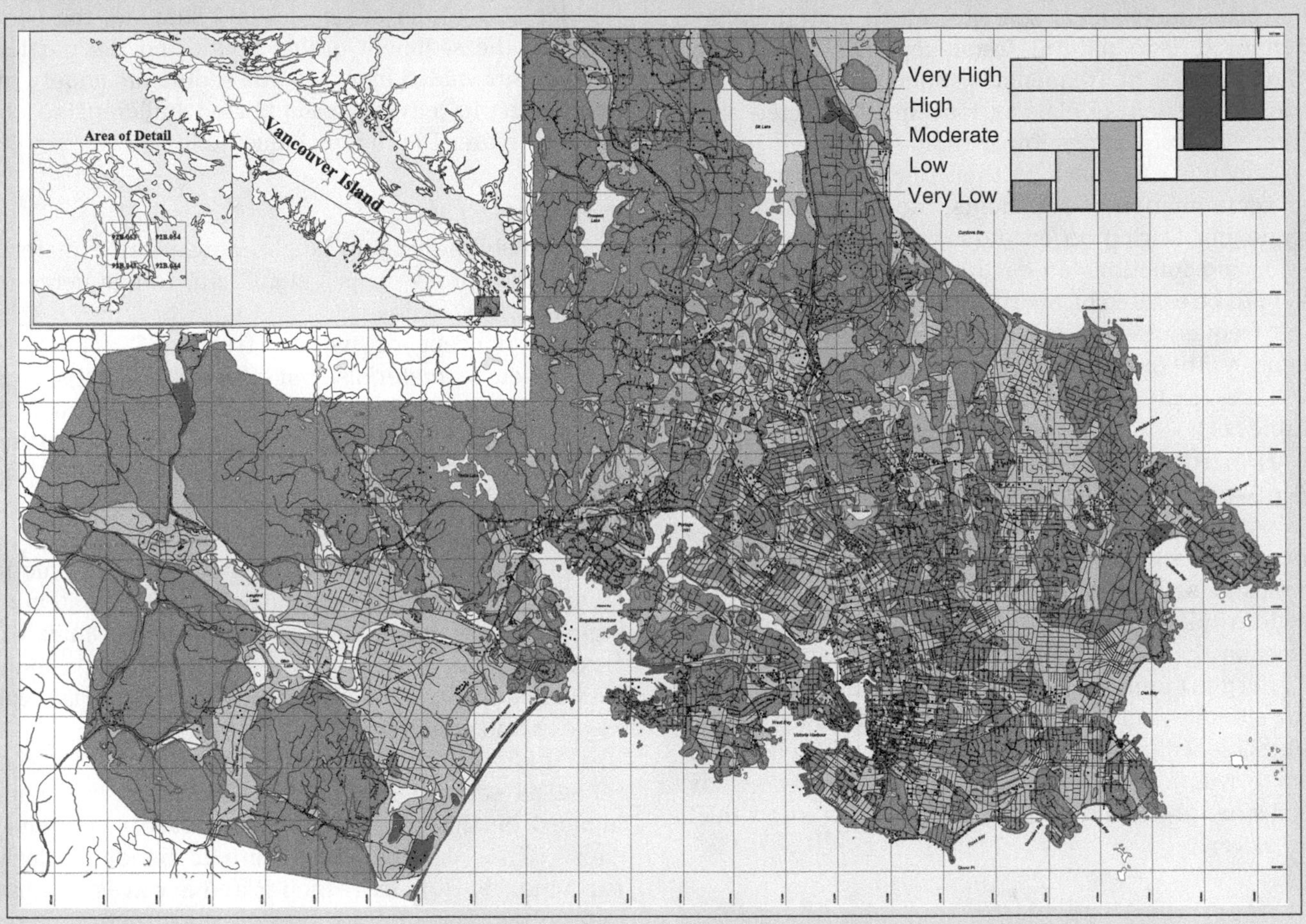

Figure 3.19

Liquefaction hazard map of Victoria, British Columbia. Liquefaction potential is greatest in geologically young beach sand and peat, and in artificial fills.

Source: Copyright © Province of British Columbia. All rights reserved. Reprinted with permission of the Province of British Columbia. www.ipp.gov.bc.ca.

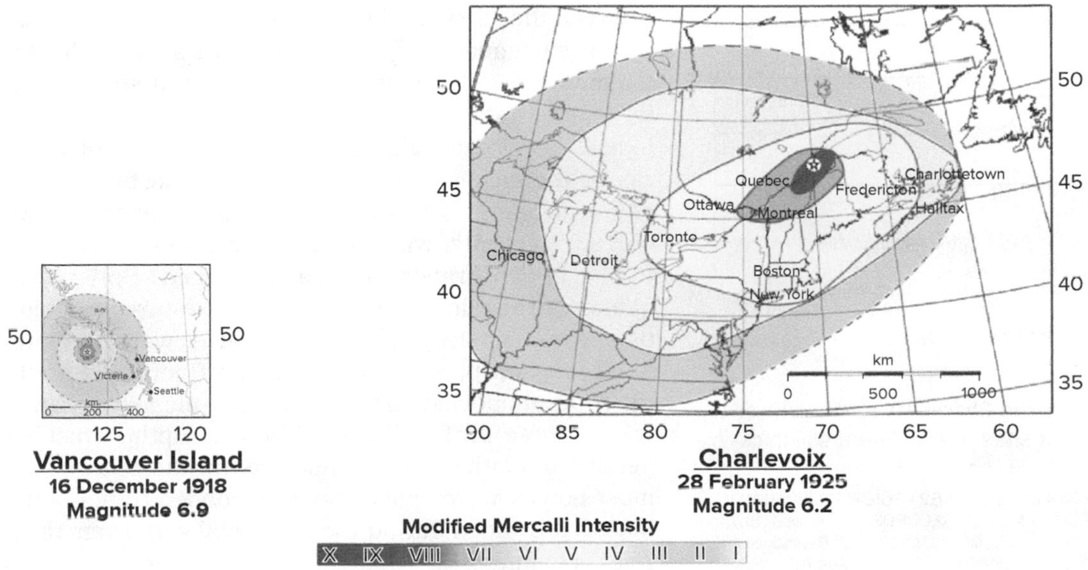

Figure 3.20

Isoseismal maps of the 1918 Vancouver Island and 1925 Charlevoix earthquakes plotted at the same scale.

Source: The M7 Vancouver Island Earthquake of December 6, 1918 http://www.earthquakescanada.nrcan.gc.ca/historic-historique/events/19181206-eng.php. "Reproduced with the permission of Natural Resources Canada, 2014." Intensity of the 1925 Charlevoix-Kamouraska Earthquake http://www.earthquakescanada.nrcan.gc.ca/historic-historique/events/19250301-intsi-eng.php "Reproduced with the permission of Natural Resources Canada, 2014."

Local Soil Conditions

Like other mechanical systems, earth materials have a characteristic natural frequency. Hard rock typically vibrates at frequencies higher than 1 Hz. Soft sediments, such as clay or loosely compacted sand, vibrate at frequencies lower than 1 Hz. Their natural frequency is controlled by their thickness: the greater the accumulation of sediments, the lower the natural frequency. During an earthquake, seismic waves act as forcing functions on earth materials. Hard rock is likely to be excited by energetic P and S waves because their frequencies overlap. Soft or water-saturated sediments, with their lower natural frequency, will tend to have their shaking amplified by surface waves (Table 3.1).

How strong is the amplification effect? The velocity of a seismic wave depends on the type of rock the wave is travelling through. Seismic waves move faster through hard rock and slower through softer rock and sediment. When seismic waves pass from harder rock into softer rock, they slow and thus must increase their amplitude to carry the same amount of energy. Figure 3.21 shows ground acceleration at four sites in Ottawa, Ontario, during the 2005 Charlevoix, Quebec, earthquake (magnitude 4.7) whose epicentre was located 525 km away. Note how seismic waves are preferentially amplified at sites with a thick soil cover.

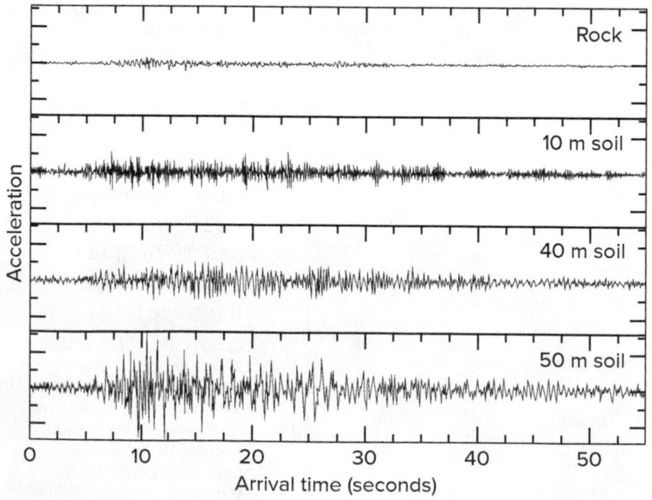

Figure 3.21

Ground acceleration caused by the Charlevoix earthquake of 6 March 2005 recorded at four sites with different soil thickness in Ottawa, Ontario.

Source: Modified from fig. 4, page 384 of Paper 1162 - SOIL AMPLIFICATION IN OTTAWA FROM URBAN STRONG GROUND MOTION RECORDS by J. Adams ftp://seismo.nrcan.gc.ca/pub/hazardpubs/9CCEE_Adams_p1162.pdf Reproduced with the permission of Natural Resources Canada, 2014 (John Adams).

The case of water-saturated sediments is especially problematic. Under strong ground shaking, the bonds between the sediment grains break and the particles become suspended in water. The sediments liquefy and lose strength, leaving unsupported buildings to sink (see In Greater Depth box: Liquefaction).

Building Style

Building style—notably height, construction material, and architecture—plays a significant role in perceived earthquake intensity.

The concept of natural frequency applies not only to earth materials, but also to buildings. Typically, buildings sway with a frequency of about 10 Hz divided by the number of storeys. A one-storey bungalow shakes back and forth quickly at about 10 Hz. A 30-storey high-rise building sways much more slowly at a frequency of about 0.3 Hz. The natural frequencies of buildings are also affected by their construction materials. A building of a given height and architectural style will have a lower frequency if it was built with flexible materials such as wood or steel, and a higher frequency if it was constructed of stiff materials such as brick and concrete.

Buildings have natural frequencies in the same range as seismic waves (Table 3.1). The resonance induced by this overlap of frequencies is a common cause of the catastrophic failure of buildings during earthquakes. High-frequency P and S waves will have their vibrations amplified by rigid construction materials and short buildings. Low-frequency surface waves will have their movements increased in tall buildings with low frequencies of vibration. If these tall buildings also lie on soft, water-saturated sand or mud, then disaster may strike.

In his book *Perils of a Restless Planet,* author Ernest Zebrowski draws an interesting comparison between the 1906 San Francisco and the 1908 Messina, Sicily, earthquakes. Both seisms had similar Richter magnitudes (8.3 versus 7.5) and affected societies at the same stage of scientific knowledge and technological development. Although Messina did not experience the ensuing fires, the death toll in the Sicilian city reached 83 000 people, corresponding to a mere 45% survival rate, whereas the survival rate was close to 99% in San Francisco. What happened? Both earthquakes struck in the early morning hours, catching people in their sleep. In Messina, houses were predominantly masonry, with massive stone floors and brick-tile roofs supported by timber set into niches in granite walls. These stiff buildings failed abruptly, crushing people to death. In San Francisco, on the other hand, most homes were small, flexible wooden-frame buildings that swayed during the earthquake and remained relatively intact.

LO6 Earthquakes at Divergent Zones

The seismicity map of Africa illustrates the characteristics of earthquakes in convergent zones well. The map is exclusively populated with epicentres of earthquakes of magnitude 6 or less, occurring at shallow depth (<33 km). Compare Figure 2.24b and Figure 3.22 and see how epicentres follow the thin and stretched lithosphere along the different branches of the East African Rift System.

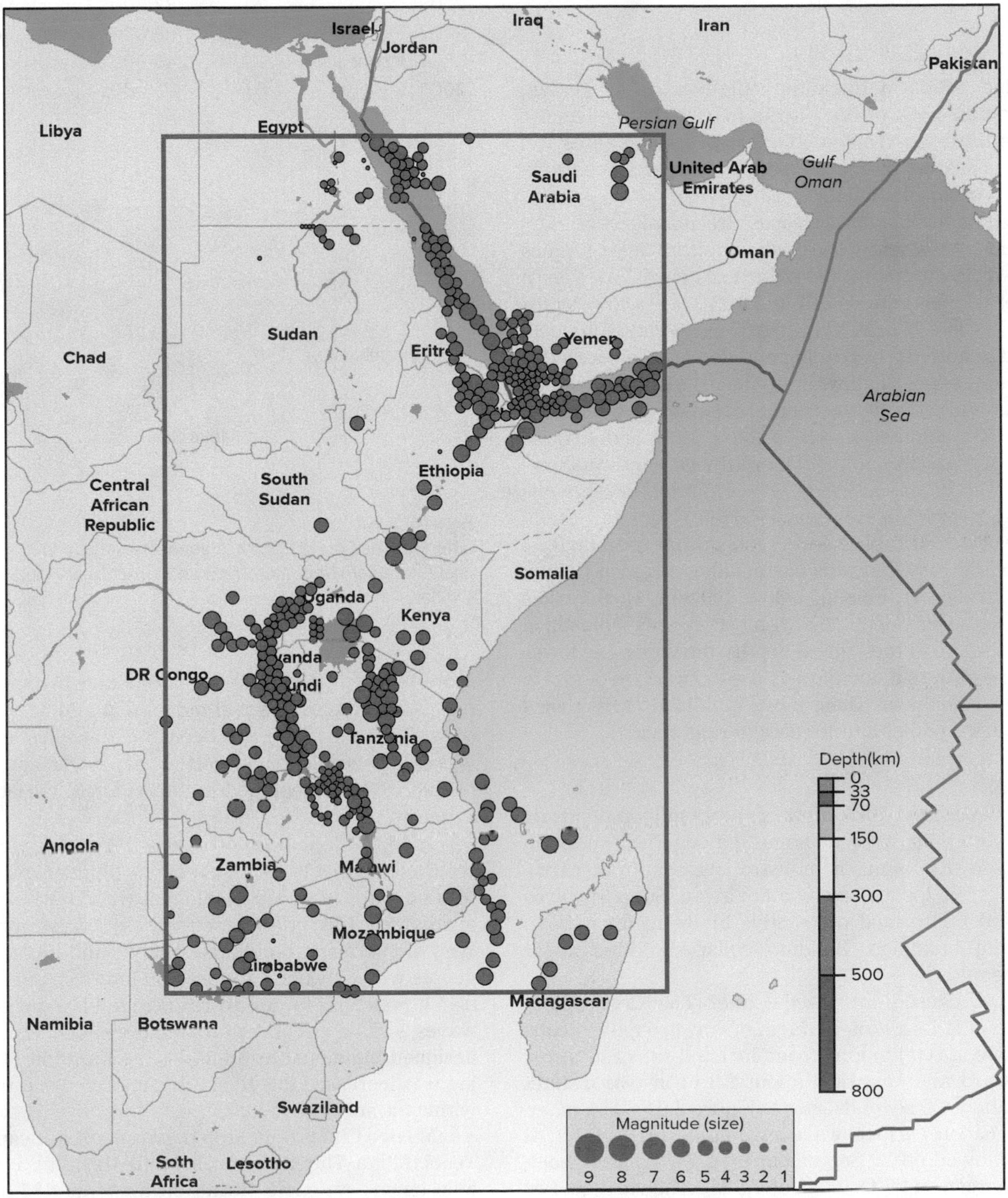

Figure 3.22

Seismicity associated with the East African Rift System (2008–2013).

Source: screen capture from viewer made by IRIS (Incorporated Research Institutions for Seismology) www.iris.edu

Earthquakes at Convergent Zones

The greatest earthquakes in the world occur where plates collide. Earthquakes in these areas are associated with a distressing number of fatalities (Table 2.4 and Table 3.7).

EARTHQUAKES IN SUBDUCTION ZONES

Imagine pulling a thick rigid plate into the weaker, deformable rock of the Earth's mantle that resists the plate's intrusion. This subduction process creates tremendous stores of energy, which are released periodically as great earthquakes.

Although subduction zones are mainly characterized by convergence, earthquakes from these regions result from different types of stresses in shallow versus deeper realms (Figures 2.37 and 3.23). At shallow depths (typically less than 30 km), crustal earthquakes are generated in both the overriding and downgoing plates due to compression. Shallow earthquakes also occur along the megathrust fault, the contact between the overriding and downgoing plates, where shear stress is dominant. These earthquakes, termed **"megathrust earthquakes,"** release enormous amounts of energy and cause widespread destruction. Sixteen of Earth's 17 greatest earthquakes listed in Table 2.4 were megathrust earthquakes; so was the 1700 Cascadia earthquake in British Columbia (Chapter 4). Finally, below 100 km, earthquakes occur in the subducting plate only as rock fail, mostly in compression. At these great depths, the upper and lower surfaces of the subducting slab are too warm to generate large earthquakes. Thus, these intra-slab earthquakes occur in the cooler interior area of rigid rock.

Mexico City, 1985

On 19 September 1985, most of the 18 million residents of Mexico City were at home, having their morning meals. At 7:17 a.m., a monstrous megathrust earthquake broke loose some 350 km away. Seismic waves travelled far to deal destructive blows to many 6- to 16-storey buildings. Building collapses killed about 9000 people.

What caused this earthquake? The Cocos plate made one of its all-too-frequent downward movements. This time, a 200 km long front, inclined 188 east, thrust downward and eastward about 2.3 m in two distinct jerks about 26 seconds apart (Figure 3.24). The mainshock had a surface wave magnitude (M_S) of 8.1. It was followed on 21 September by a 7.5 M_S aftershock and another on 25 October of 7.3 M_S. The earthquakes were not a surprise to seismologists. A pragmatic way of forecasting the locations of future earthquakes uses the **seismic-gap method**. If segments of one fault have moved recently, then it seems reasonable to expect that the unmoved portions will move next and thus fill the gaps. Before these seisms occurred, the epicenter area was called the Michoacan seismic gap, and many instruments had been deployed in the region to measure the expected big event.

TABLE 3.7

Mega-Killer Earthquakes, 2003–2013

Year	Location	Magnitude	Deaths	Cause
2011	Japan	9.0	19 135	Subduction
2010	Haiti	7.0	230 000	Transform fault
2008	China	7.9	87 500	Continent collision
2005	Pakistan	7.6	88 000	Continent collision
2004	Indonesia	9.1	245 000	Subduction
2003	Iran	6.6	27 000	Continent collision

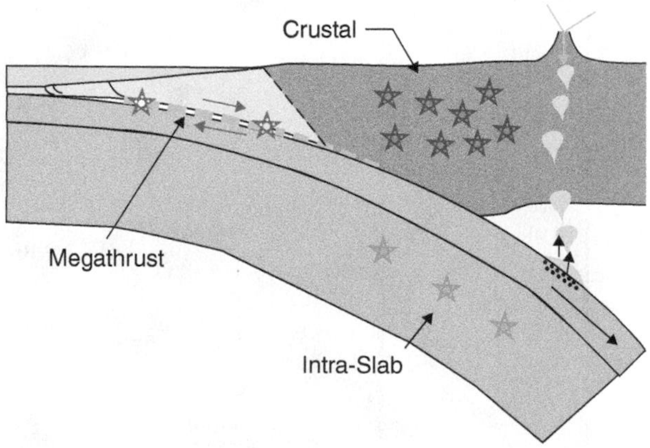

Figure 3.23
Different types of earthquakes generated at subduction zones (modified after Hyndman). The megathrust fault is indicated by a yellow dashed line.

Many of the coastal towns near the epicentre received relatively small amounts of damage. Yet in Mexico City, over 5700 buildings were severely damaged, with 15% of them collapsing catastrophically. Why did so many buildings collapse and kill so many people when Mexico City lies 350 km from the epicentre? It was largely due to resonance between seismic waves, soft lake-sediment foundations, and improperly designed buildings. In addition, the duration of shaking was increased due to seismic energy being trapped within the soft sediments.

Mexico City is built atop the former Aztec capital of Tenochtitlan. The Aztecs built where they saw a favourable omen—an eagle sitting on a cactus and holding a writhing snake in its mouth. The site was Lake Texcoco, a broad lake surrounded by hard volcanic rock. With population increasing, portions of Lake Texcoco

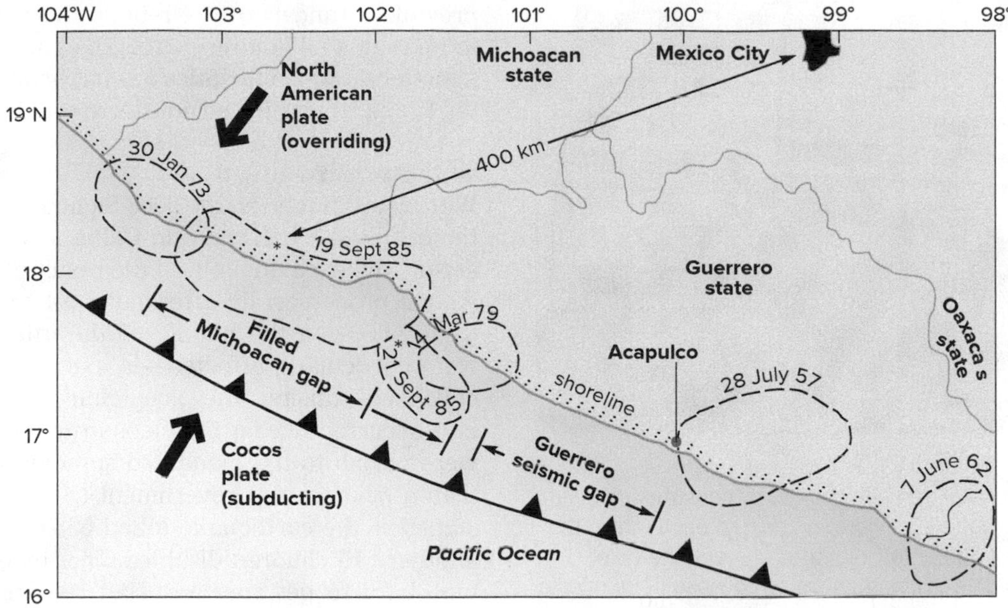

Figure 3.24
Map of coastal Mexico showing dates of earthquakes and felt areas (dashed lines) during Cocos plate subduction events. The Michoacan seismic gap was filled by the 1985 seisms. The Guerrero seismic gap is overdue for a major movement. Although seismic-gap analysis is logical, it yields only expectations, not guarantees. One segment of a fault can move two or more times before an adjoining segment moves once.

have been drained, and large buildings have been constructed on the weak lake-floor clays.

Building damages were the greatest and the number of deaths the highest where three factors combined and created resonance (Figure 3.9): (1) the earthquakes sent a tremendous amount of energy in seismic waves in the 1 to 2 Hz frequency band; (2) areas underlain by thick, soft clays vibrating at 1 to 2 Hz frequencies amplified the seismic waves; and (3) buildings of 6 to 16 storeys vibrated in the 1 to 2 Hz frequency band. Where all three factors were in place, disaster struck. Design flaws in the failed buildings also contributed to the disaster (Figure 3.25), including structurally weak first storeys with large openings for windows and parking spaces, poorly joined building wings, odd-shaped buildings prone to twist on their foundations, and buildings of different heights and vibration frequencies that sat close together and bumped into each other during the earthquake (Figure 3.25c and Figure 3.26).

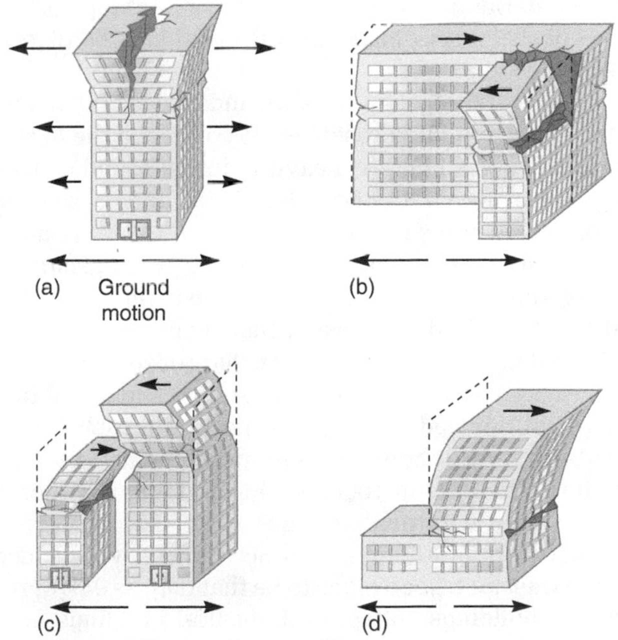

Figure 3.25
Some building-response problems during the Mexico City earthquake. (a) The amplitude of shaking increases higher up the building. (b) A building with a long axis perpendicular to ground motion suffers more shaking. (c) Buildings with different heights sway at different frequencies and bang into each other. (d) A building with different heights is more likely to break apart.

EARTHQUAKES IN CONTINENT-CONTINENT COLLISIONS

The ongoing collision of India with Asia jars a gigantic area with great earthquakes (Figure 2.29).

Tangshan, China, 1976

The deadliest earthquake in recent times occurred directly beneath the city of Tangshan. A fault ruptured

Figure 3.26
Mexico City earthquake damage caused by constructing buildings with different periods of vibration next to each other. The four-storey building on the left repeatedly struck the taller Hotel de Carlo (middle building), causing collapse of its middle floors (Figure 3.25c). The taller building on the right also was damaged by hammering from the Hotel de Carlo.
Photo: © NOAA.

at a depth of 11 km in a local response to the regional stress created by the collision of India with Asia. The earthquake was much larger than local officials expected. Building codes were lenient—fatally so. This poor decision was instrumental in the deaths of over 240 000 people.

In 1976, Tangshan was an industrial and mining city with two million residents. It contained the largest coal mines in China, so heavy industry found a home there also. Its coal, steel, electricity, and diesel- and locomotive-engine industries combined to create about 1% of China's gross national product. For Tangshan residents, the night of 27 July was unusually warm with rain and wind. Most unusual that night were the fireballs and lightning of all colours that rolled through the sky. At 3:42 a.m. on 28 July, the ground began the rumbling that reduced the city to almost total rubble. Most residents were at home in densely packed houses made of mud bricks held together by poor-quality mortar and covered with mud-and-lime roofs that had grown heavier through the years as new layers were added. Home was not a good place to be that day, as 93% of residential buildings collapsed. Industrial buildings fared somewhat better; still, 78% of them collapsed. Overall, older buildings performed better than newer ones. Some of the luckier individuals were nightshift coal miners hard at work thousands of metres below the surface during the earthquake. Although 13 of these 15 000 miners died, as a group, they fared far better than their day-shift comrades. Collapsing homes killed 6500 of 85 000 off-duty miners. Through it all, the human spirit prevailed. Tangshan was rebuilt and is again home to more than a million residents. They now live and work in better designed facilities as, in response to this disaster, China has instituted a modern building code.

Sichuan Province, China, 2008

With 69 000 fatalities, the 2008 Sichuan earthquake was the deadliest earthquake in China since the Tangshan seism. The earthquake was the result of the same geological processes; its aftermaths all too familiar. The earth shook in the middle of the afternoon. Schools were particularly affected—in excess of 7000 of them collapsed—raising the suspicion that irregularities had occurred during their construction and that they were not up to the mandated standards. It took more than a year for the government to release the morbid statistics: the earthquake killed 5335 students and left another 546 children disabled. Distressed parents lobbied hard to get answers. Had lessons been learned from Tangshan?

Earthquakes along Transform Faults

The transform faults forming the sides of some tectonic plates have dominantly horizontal movements that cause major earthquakes. Examples are numerous and include the San Andreas fault in California, the Enriquillo-Plantain Garden fault in Haiti, and the Queen Charlotte fault in British Columbia (Chapter 4).

THE WORLD'S MOST FAMOUS FAULT: THE SAN ANDREAS FAULT

The famous San Andreas fault runs literally through the backyards of millions of Californians (Figure 3.27). The 1200 km long fault is part of a complex system of subparallel faults (Figure 3.28) and exhibits different behaviours at different points along its length. In 1906, the northernmost section of the fault broke loose just offshore near the city of San Francisco, rupturing northward and southward simultaneously over a distance of 430 km. When movement stopped, the western side of the fault (located on the Pacific plate) had shifted northward a maximum of 6 m horizontally with respect to the eastern side (located on the North American plate). Today, the San Francisco section of the San Andreas fault has a deficit of earthquakes; apparently it is a **locked zone**. Virtually all the stress from plate tectonics is stored as elastic strain for many decades. When the fault finally can take no more it ruptures in a big event. The section to the south of San Francisco has frequent small to moderate-size earthquakes. It is a **creeping zone** where numerous earthquakes accommodate

Figure 3.27
The San Andreas fault slashes across the Carrizo Plain in southern California.
Photo: © Pat Abbott.

the plate-tectonic forces before they build to high levels. The creeping movements of the fault are shown by the small, ongoing offset of sidewalks, fences, buildings, and other features—millimetres per year.

San Francisco, 1906

Early in the 20th century, San Francisco was home to about 400 000 people who enjoyed a cosmopolitan city that had grown during the economic boom times of the late nineteenth century. During the evening of 17 April 1906, many thrilled to the special appearance of Enrico Caruso, the world's greatest tenor, singing with the Metropolitan Opera Company in Bizet's *Carmen.* But several hours later, at 5:12 a.m., the initial shock waves of a mammoth magnitude 8.3 earthquake arrived to begin the destruction of the city. One early riser told of seeing the earthquake approach as the street before him literally rose and fell like a series of ocean swells moving toward shore.

During a noisy minute, the violently pitching earth emitted dull booming sounds joined by the crash of human-made structures.

As repeated aftershocks startled and frightened the survivors, another great danger began to grow. Smoke arose from many sites as fires fed on the wood-filled rubble. Unfortunately, the same earthquake waves that wracked the buildings also broke most of the water lines, thus hindering attempts to stop the growing fires. From the business district and near the waterfront, fires began their relentless intrusion into the rest of the city. The fires did about ten times as much damage as the earthquake itself, destroying buildings covering 490 city blocks. More than half the population lost their homes. Problems continued in the months that followed as epidemics of filth-borne diseases sickened Californians; more than 150 cases of bubonic plague were reported. When all the fatalities from earthquake-related injuries and disease are included, the death total from the earthquake may have been as high as 5000.

In his book *A Crack in the Edge of the World: The Great American Earthquake of 1906*, published in 2005 in anticipation of the centennial of the event, Simon Winchester emphasizes the fact the politicians and the press were quick to label the disaster a "fire-related event." Their perception was that the American public would have a fatalistic attitude toward an earthquake, and would hesitate to rebuild the city on the same hazardous location. Fire safety, on the other hand, was perceived as an issue that could be addressed by proper planning and modern technology. Surely, with careful mitigation, such a disaster would not repeat itself. Another legacy of the 1906 earthquake is the haste with which San Franciscans rebuilt their urban infrastructure (Figure 3.29). This problem haunts the city inhabitants today because much of the early rebuilding was done badly and is likely to fail in the next big earthquake.

THE ENRIQUILLO-PLANTAIN GARDEN FAULT

The Caribbean tectonic plate is a small one moving eastward below the huge North American plate (Figure 2.16). The northern boundary of the Caribbean plate is split between two parallel, east-west trending faults that pass through Haiti. The 2010 seism in Haiti was caused by movement along the southern of these faults, the Enriquillo-Plantain Garden fault.

Port-au-Prince, Haiti, 2010

At 4:53 p.m. on 12 January 2010, the earth moved in the Republic of Haiti, and its capital city, Port-au-Prince, collapsed, killing an estimated 100 000 to 159 000 people, seriously injuring another 300 000, and displacing 1.1 million more people. The adjective "natural" often

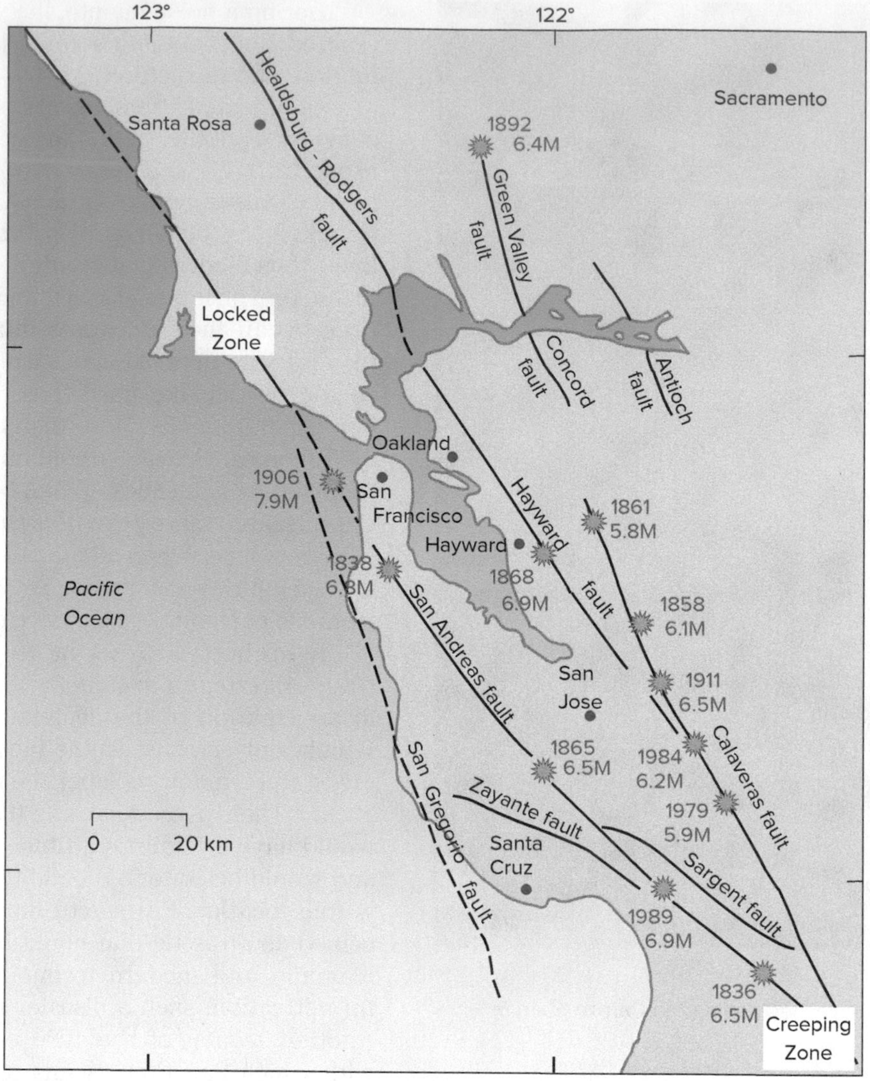

Figure 3.28
Locations and approximate sizes of significant earthquakes in the San Francisco Bay Area.
Source: © United States Geological Survey.

Figure 3.29
Heritage building from San Francisco, California. Note the uneven bricks. They were recycled from the rubble and incorporated into the walls of this building erected shortly after the 1906 earthquake.
Photo: © Claire Samson.

fails to convey the different facets of a catastrophic event. That is certainly true in this case. This catastrophe was truly a human—all too human—tragedy. With a relatively "modest" magnitude of 7.0, the earthquake did not make the list of the world's greatest earthquakes (Table 2.4). It does, however, figure on the list of recent earthquakes associated with the largest number of fatalities (Table 3.7). The death toll from this earthquake is more than double that from any previous magnitude 7 earthquake anywhere in the world.

Although earthquakes are part of Haiti's history, the country did not have a single seismograph station to monitor earthquake hazard until the seism of 2010. In 1751, most of the buildings in Port-au-Prince were destroyed in an earthquake. In 1770, another earthquake demolished most of the reconstructed city. In response to this double destruction, the French authorities required that buildings be constructed with wood, and they banned construction relying on concrete. Haiti gained independence from France in 1804. During its two centuries of independence, the Haitian population grew to 9.35 million people, most of whom suffer poverty, have low rates of literacy, and live in poorly constructed, concrete buildings. The lessons of their past about building construction were forgotten.

The deaths in the 2010 earthquake were due to badly constructed buildings, all of which were doomed before the ground started to shake. Building construction was not supervised, allowing bad materials to be used and bad construction practices to be employed. Bad materials include brittle steel, not enough cement, and too much dirty or salty sand in the concrete mixture. Bad construction practices include stopping vertical rods of reinforcement steel at horizontal floors just where they needed to be connected to ensure strength. But the major cause of death was widespread use of a concrete-blocks-as-filler style of floor slab construction. Weak, cheap concrete blocks containing large open spaces were placed in the mold before more expensive concrete was poured around them. These blocks just hang in place, supported only by the concrete around them. There are three major problems with these floor slabs: (1) they are weak, (2) they are heavy, and (3) they are supported by flimsy concrete columns that undergo shear failure when shaken. When one floor collapses, its added weight causes the underlying floor to collapse, and so on (Figure 3.30).

Canadians have shared a link with Haiti since the 1960s when many Haitians took refuge in Canada from the brutal Duvalier father-and-son dictatorships. Nobody personifies this special relationship with more grace than Canada's former Governor General, Michaëlle Jean. She visited Haiti only a few days after the event and declared, "I want the Haitian people to know: You are not alone." The Canadian population rallied behind her, raising $220 million in the first few weeks after the earthquake, an amount matched by the federal government. Ms. Jean continues her work tirelessly as UNESCO special envoy for Haiti. The task is daunting: everything needs to be done, corruption and mismanagement are endemic. In 2013, the Canadian government decided not to approve any new aid initiative until tangible progress is made.

Earthquakes at Hot Spots

When one thinks about natural hazards in Hawaii, it is volcanism that comes to mind. But the movement of magma at hot spots can cause earthquakes, including large ones. In fact, several active volcanoes around the world, including Kilauea, are under surveillance to detect signs of increased earthquake activity leading to an eruption. When magma is on the move at shallow depths, it can generate a nearly continuous swarm of relatively small near-surface earthquakes (Figure 3.31).

Magma movements also cause the formation of larger-scale topographic features and larger earthquakes. The land surface is commonly uplifted due to the injection of magma below the ground surface. But the land surface is also commonly down-dropped due to withdrawal of magma. The effects of subsurface magma movement, both compressive during injection and extensional during removal, combine with gravitational pull to cause large movements along faults.

On 29 November 1975, one of the seaward-inclined faults beneath Kilauea moved suddenly in a 7.2 magnitude seism. It happened at 4:48 a.m., when a large mass slipped for 14 seconds with a movement of about 6 m seaward and 3.5 metres downward. The movement of this mass into the sea caused a tsunami up to 12 m high. Campers sleeping on the beach were rudely awakened by shaking ground; those who didn't immediately hustle to higher ground were subjected to crashing waves. Two people drowned. This fault movement had an effect on subsurface magma analogous to shaking a carbonated drink in a bottle—gases escaping from magma unleashed an 18-hour eruption featuring magma fountains up to 50 m high.

LO7 Building in Earthquake Country

What causes deaths during earthquakes? Not the shaking of the Earth but our buildings, bridges, and other structures that collapse and fall on us. *Earthquakes don't kill, buildings do.* What can be done to mitigate the risk?

(a)

(b)

Figure 3.30
The Presidential Palace in Port-au-Prince (a) before and (b) after the 12 January 2010 earthquake. Note how the second floor has collapsed unto the first floor.

Source: (a) Cpl. Matthew McGregor/Department of National Defence/Associated Press; (b) Jorge Cruz, Associated Press.

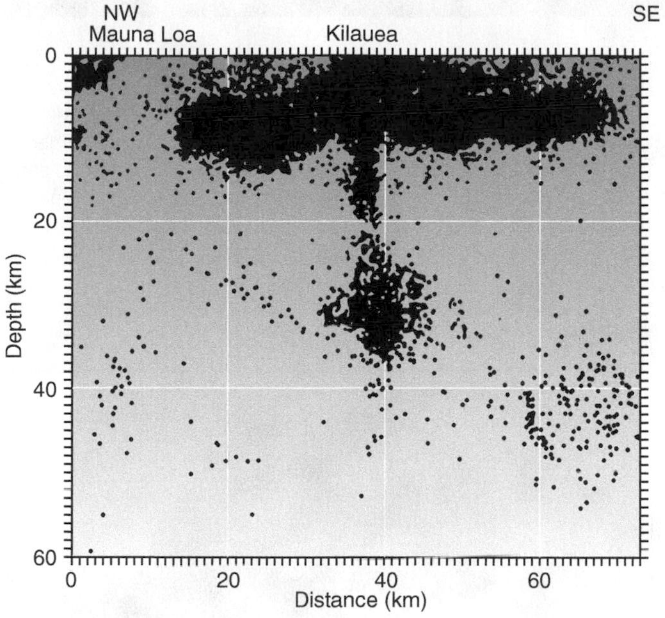

Figure 3.31
Cross-section showing hypocentres beneath Kilauea volcano, Hawaii, 1970–1983.

Source: © Geological Society of America, *Decade of North American Geology*, Vol N.

Figure 3.32
Inadequately braced house failed due to horizontal acceleration during the 1971 San Fernando, California, earthquake.

Photo: © Al Boost.

DESIGN CHALLENGES

Ground Motion

Ground motion during an earthquake is horizontal, vertical, and diagonal—all at the same time. Most buildings are designed to handle the large vertical forces caused by the weight of the building itself and its contents. They are designed with such large factors of safety that the additional vertical forces imparted by earthquakes are typically not a problem. Usually, the biggest concern in designing buildings to withstand large earthquakes is the sideways push from the horizontal components of movement (Figure 3.32).

Acceleration

Designs for buildings in earthquake areas must account for **acceleration** (Table 3.8). As seismic waves move the ground and the buildings up and down, and back and forth, the rate of change of velocity is known as acceleration. As an analogy, when you are in a car is moving at a velocity of 40 km/h in a given direction on a smooth road, you feel no force on your body. But if you stomp on the car's accelerator and rapidly speed up to 100 km/h, you feel a force pushing you back against the car's seat. Similarly, if you hit the brakes and decelerate rapidly, you feel yourself being thrown forward. This same type of acceleration is imparted to buildings when the ground beneath them moves during an earthquake. Because force is acceleration times mass, a building weighing

TABLE 3.8

Comparison of Magnitude, Intensity, and Acceleration

Magnitude	Mercalli Intensity		Acceleration (g)
2 and less	I-II	Usually not felt by people	less than 0.002
3	III	Felt indoors by some people	0.002–0.004
4	IV–V	Felt by most people	0.005–0.019
5	VI–VII	Felt by all; building damage	0.02–0.09
6	VII–VIII	People scared; moderate damage	0.10 0.19
7	IX–X	Major damage	0.20–0.99
8 and up	XI–XII	Damage nearly total	greater than 1.0

HUMAN FOCUS

Gail Atkinson, Canada Research Chair in Earthquake Hazards and Ground Motions

My research career has been dedicated to predicting the ground motions that will occur due to earthquakes. I do not try to predict when and where earthquakes will occur. Perhaps I should first explain why not. There has been a long-standing public and scientific interest in earthquake prediction. At first sight, earthquake prediction seems to be a commendable goal. Looking further into it, however, you might discover that the idea offers only a partial solution. To be effective, the prediction would have to be very accurate. How big will the earthquake be? Exactly where will it strike? Not only would the exact date need to be forecast, but warnings would have to be issued a few days in advance to give people enough time to evacuate, much like is done when a hurricane is advancing toward a populated coast. A large-scale evacuation is costly and not without risks. What if the seismologists get it wrong? Who will listen the next time there is a warning? And do we really think that a destroyed city is an acceptable outcome, even if it has been evacuated first? I believe that the best approach to mitigating earthquake risk is to understand the expected ground motions, and design facilities to withstand them, whenever they occur. This philosophy has motivated my research goals and activities.

I work with engineers and seismologists to develop the seismic hazard map (Figure 4.3) and the seismic provisions of the National Building Code of Canada (see In Greater Depth box: Seismic Provisions of the National Building Code of Canada, in Chapter 4). My research is multidisciplinary, involving an understanding of the seismological, engineering and policy implications of hazard. One challenge of my work is to convey risk information—expressed as the ground acceleration that has a certain chance of being exceeded over a long period of time such as 50 or 100 years—in a form that can be directly used by structural engineers and understood by policy makers. On another front, I work with earth scientists, as detailed knowledge of the soil conditions surrounding buildings has a major effect on ground motion. Clear, factual communication between team members having different backgrounds and perspectives is critical.

I often provide expert advice on the earthquake hazards to critical infrastructure, including nuclear power stations, schools, and hospitals. I have seen much progress in the approaches to analysis and design of new buildings and infrastructure over my career. Retrofitting existing buildings remains a major challenge, however. A lot of aging infrastructure in Canada's urban centres, such as bridges and overpasses, requires attention even when the ground is not shaking! But it is difficult to motivate people to spend scarce resources on earthquake retrofits, especially when the earthquake deficiencies of structures may not be readily apparent to most people. Here is a thought-provoking question: should existing buildings have a green-yellow-red earthquake safety designation on display for public view? Similar systems exist for restaurant hygiene and elevator inspections. It might be a powerful incentive for building owners to invest in earthquake safety.

Efforts to increase earthquake safety are linked to the amount of risk society is prepared to accept. Scientists have a very social role to play in conveying factual information to the public. I have been honoured to serve as president of the Seismological Society of America and the Canadian Geophysical Union. Independent professional associations such as these and the forums they provide are important contributors to the debate.

C. Samson would like to congratulate G. Atkinson for her election to the Royal Society of Canada in September 2014.

Figure 3.33
Gail Atkinson, Professor at University of Western Ontario.
Source: Photo courtesy of Gail Atkinson.

thousands of tonnes experiences large inertial forces, which may cause collapse.

The acceleration due to gravity on Earth is 9.8 m/s^2, which is referred to as 1.0 g and is used as a comparative unit of measure. Weak buildings begin to suffer damage at horizontal accelerations of about 0.1 g. At accelerations between 0.1 to 0.2 g, people have trouble keeping their footing, similar to being in the aisle of a fast-moving train or on a small boat in high seas. As an example, buildings in the Vancouver, British Columbia, area are typically designed to tolerate a 0.4 g acceleration. A building able to withstand a sideward

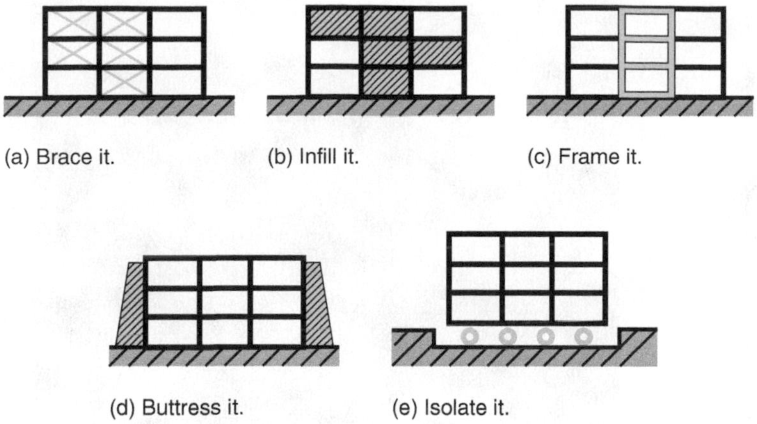

Figure 3.34
How to strengthen buildings. (a) Add braces. (b) Infill walls. (c) Add frames to exterior or interior. (d) Add buttresses. (e) Isolate building from the ground.
Source: © AIA/ACSA Council on Architectural Research.

pushing force equal to 40% of its own weight is considered earthquake resistant.

Stress

Different building materials respond differently to the stresses imposed on them during an earthquake. Wood is flexible and lightweight, and tends to deform elastically (Figure 2.10a). As stated earlier, these properties saved lives in the 1906 San Francisco earthquake. Steel has ductility and great strength when subjected to tension, but steel columns fail under excess compression (Figure 2.10b). Conversely, masonry and concrete resist compressional stresses well but suffer brittle failure all too easily under tension (Figure 2.10c).

ARCHITECTURAL SOLUTIONS

One of the problems in designing buildings for earthquake country is the need to eliminate the occurrence of resonance. This can be done in five ways: (1) Change the height of the building, (2) move most of the weight to the lower floors, (3) change the shape of the building, (4) change the type of building materials used, and (5) change the degree of attachment of the building to its foundation. For example, if the earth foundation is hard rock that efficiently transmits high-frequency vibrations, then build a flexible, taller building. Alternatively, if the earth foundation is a thick mass of soft sediment likely to couple with low-frequency shaking, then build a stiffer, shorter building.

The process of reinforcing existing buildings to increase their resistance to seismic shaking is known as **retrofitting**. Looking at some newly designed structures and building retrofits allows us to see how seismic strength is given to a building (Figure 3.34). The building components that must handle ground motion are basic. In the horizontal plane are floors and roofs. In the vertical plane are walls and frames. The ability to withstand Earth movements is enhanced by building bracing, shear walls, and other elements that tie the walls, foundation, and roof together so they do not separate and fail (Figure 3.35).

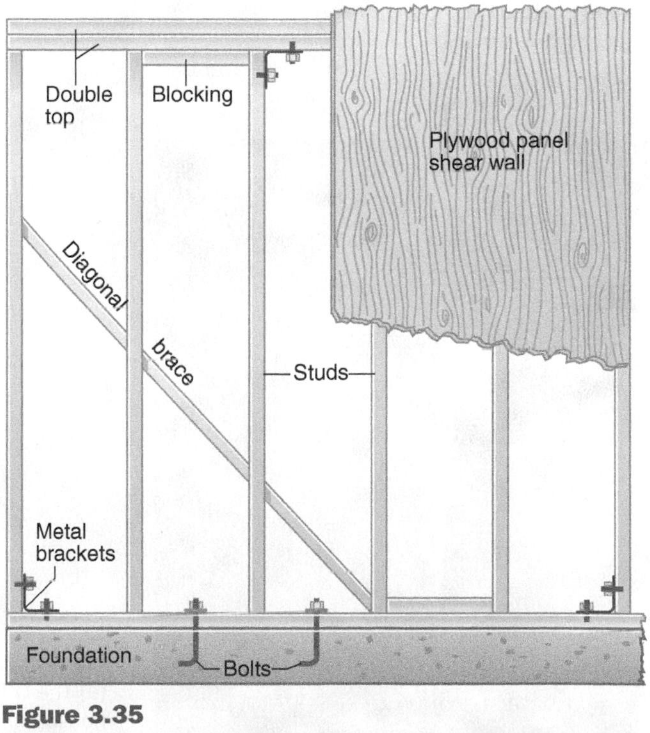

Figure 3.35
Modern one- and two-storey wood-frame houses typically perform well during seismic shaking as wood is able to handle large accelerations. How can a house be built to resist seismic waves? Bolt it. Bracket it. Brace it. Block it. Panel it with shear walls.

Figure 3.36
The CTC building in Santiago has a brace frame incorporated in its design, which is meant to represent a cellular phone from the 1990s. It withstood the magnitude 8.8 Maule earthquake in 2010, felt with an intensity of VIII in the Chilean capital, without damage.
Source: © Claire Samson.

Figure 3.37
This building from the campus of the University of Victoria has been retrofitted with metal braces to provide additional support to the ground floor.
Source: © Claire Samson.

(a)

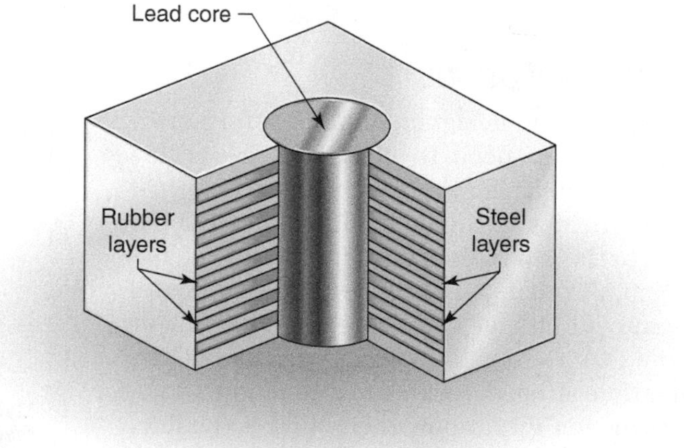

(b)

Figure 3.38
(a) The Office of Disaster Preparedness in San Diego County, California is housed in a two-storey, 650 m^2 building sitting on top of 20 lead-impregnated rubber supports (base isolators) that each weigh 1 tonne. (b) An example of a base isolator. This cut-away view into a 1 m–wide by 1 m–tall sandwich shows alternating layers of rubber (each 15 mm thick) and steel (each 3 mm thick) with a central core of lead. During an earthquake, the rubber and steel flex and the lead absorbs energy.
Source: © Pat Abbott.

Figure 3.39
The Qube building in Vancouver, British Columbia hangs from a central vertical support, free of the ground. Strong earthquake vibrations would cause it to oscillate rather than to dangerously deform.
Source: © Aaron Snider.

Bracing is an effective way to impart seismic resistance to a structure, especially against sideways movements of the ground (Figures 3.36 and 3.37). The bracing should be made of ductile materials that have the ability to deform without rupturing.

Shear walls (Figure 3.35) are partitions designed to relieve floors and roofs from horizontal forces. During an earthquake, shear walls resist side-to-side motion and transmit forces back to the ground. Shear walls must be strong themselves, as well as securely connected to each other and to the horizontal elements. Multi-storey parking garages are commonly built with insufficient shear walls. Builders do not want the added expense of more walls, which eliminate parking spaces and block the view of traffic inside the parking structure. These buildings are common casualties during earthquakes.

Buttresses (see photo on chapter opening page) and wall reinforcement also add strength to key elements of a structure.

Some modern designs employ **base isolation** where devices are placed on the ground or within the structure to absorb part of the earthquake energy. Base isolation uses wheels, ball bearings, shock absorbers, rubber supports (Figure 3.38) and other creative elements (Figure 3.39) to isolate a building from the worst of the shaking. The goal is to make the building react to shaking much like your body adjusts to accelerations and decelerations when you are standing in a moving train or bus.

SUMMARY

- Earthquakes are shaking ground caused most often by sudden movements along fractures in the Earth called faults.
- Earthquakes disperse their energy in seismic waves that radiate away from the hypocentre or point of fault rupture. The point on the surface above the hypocentre is the epicentre. Some seismic waves pass through the body of the Earth—the P waves (primary waves with a push–pull motion) and S waves (secondary waves with a shearing motion). Other seismic waves are long wavetrains travelling along the surface of the Earth (Love and Rayleigh waves).
- P waves travel about 1.7 times faster than S waves, and are the first to be recorded at a seismograph station. The difference in arrival times between P and S waves is greater farther from the hypocentre. The epicentre of an earthquake can be located by triangulating epicentral distances.
- Earthquake energy is assessed by its magnitude. Different estimates of magnitude are derived from different methods based on local shaking (Richter scale), body waves (m_b), surface waves (M_s), or seismic moment (M_w). The Earth has more than a million earthquakes each year, but more than 90% of the energy is released by the 12 to 18 largest events.

- Earthquake effects on structures and people are assessed via the Mercalli Intensity Scale. The factors affecting the Mercalli Scale are earthquake magnitude, epicentre location, distance from the epicentre, hypocentre depth, duration of shaking, local soil conditions, and building style.
- Seismic waves have different frequencies. Body waves commonly have a frequency between 0.02 and 30 Hz; surface waves have a lower frequency range, between 0.002 and 0.1 Hz. Where the frequencies of seismic waves match the natural frequencies of soils and buildings, resonance can occur and destruction may be great.
- Most deaths from earthquakes are due to building failures.
- Buildings in earthquake areas should be designed to withstand large accelerations. Building components that must stand up to seismic shaking are horizontal (floors, roofs) and vertical (walls, frames). Since horizontal and vertical components move at different frequencies, the horizontal and vertical components must be securely tied together using bolts, brackets, and braces.

Terms to Remember

acceleration
aftershocks
amplitude
arrival time
base isolation
body waves
creeping zone
felt area
foreshocks
fracture
hertz (Hz)
inertia
isoseismal maps
liquefaction
locked zone
mainshock
megathrust earthquakes
natural frequency
period
primary (P) wave
resonance
retrofitting
secondary (S) wave
seism
seismic-gap method
seismic waves
seismograms
seismology
seismometers
surface waves
wavelength

Questions for Review

Ans. In Figure 3.1, assuming that each crest and each trough are 1 m wide, the slip is 0.5 m.
Ans. In Figure 3.15, the earthquake magnitude is approximately 5.

1. How are foreshocks distinguished from aftershocks?
2. Does the Earth always open during an earthquake?
3. Why aren't there earthquake hypocentres at depths greater than approximately 700 km?
4. Evaluate the earthquake hazards in locked versus creeping segments of a fault.
5. How can arrival times of P and S waves be used to determine distance to the epicentre?
6. What are the differences between earthquake magnitude and earthquake intensity?
7. How do the various magnitude scales differ?
8. How is surface shaking affected as the depth to a hypocentre increases?
9. What is the seismic-gap method of forecasting earthquakes?
10. Will a tall building be affected more by high- or low-frequency seismic waves? Why?

Questions for Further Thought

1. Should we set off controlled explosions to relieve stress in rock and prevent a large earthquake in an area? What are the pros and cons?
2. How would you lay out the seismograph stations of a network to most accurately locate earthquake epicentres?
3. What is the quake potential of the Moon (moonquakes)? Does the Moon have similar numbers and magnitudes of quakes as the Earth? Why?
4. If you are in an airplane over the epicentre of a great earthquake, what will you experience?
5. Does a small earthquake mean that a larger earthquake is coming?
6. Is there a maximum magnitude for an earthquake?
7. What do scientists do after an earthquake?

Interesting Websites

- Earthquake Hazards Program, United States Geological Survey
  http://earthquake.usgs.gov/
- Seismic data, Incorporated Research Institutions for Seismology
  http://www.iris.edu
- Soil liquefaction, University of Washington
  http://www.ce.washington.edu/~liquefaction/html/main.html
- Virtual Earthquake, an interactive exercise to locate the epicentre and estimate the magnitude of earthquakes, Geology Labs Online
  http://nemo.sciencecourseware.org/VirtualEarthquake

CHAPTER FOUR

4 When the Earth Shakes in Canada . . .

In this article, we summarize Canada's "good", "bad" and "ugly" earthquakes. We define "good" earthquakes as those that either: have been widely felt, and therefore have made people more aware of (and perhaps better prepared for) future earthquakes; or those that are large enough to be "scientifically-useful"—they teach us about the potential impact of future earthquakes in Canada. "Bad" earthquakes are those that have caused significant damage (including landslides, structural damage, and other effects) in Canada, and "ugly" are some of the world's largest earthquakes (larger than magnitude 8).

—John Cassidy and co-authors, Geoscience Canada, 2010

Outline

- Seismic Risk and Mitigation in Canada
- Earthquakes of Canada's Pacific Coast
- Intraplate Earthquakes of Eastern Canada
- A Lot Still to Be Learned . . .
- Summary

LO1 Explain how seismic risk is assessed and mitigated in Canada.

LO2 Describe the tectonic setting of western Canadian earthquakes.

LO3 Explain how the geological record can be used to study prehistoric earthquakes.

LO4 State the different hypotheses for the origin of eastern Canadian earthquakes.

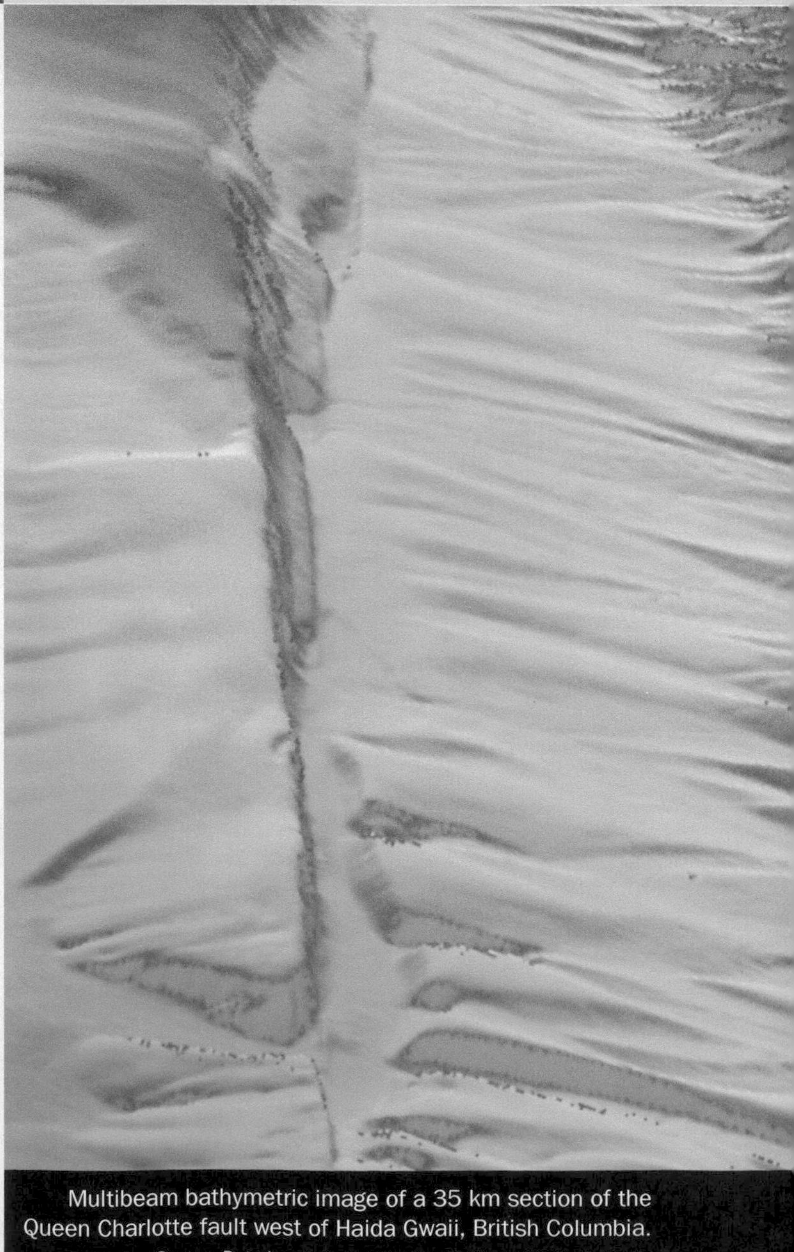

Multibeam bathymetric image of a 35 km section of the Queen Charlotte fault west of Haida Gwaii, British Columbia.

Source: Data image from J. Vaughn Barrie and Peter T. Harris (Barrie et al., 2013), multibeam data collected by the Canadian Hydrographic Service, Pacific.

Has Canada suffered a great earthquake in historical times? The mythology of the Aboriginal people of British Columbia and the states of Washington and Oregon is rich with references to earthquakes. Several groups carve earthquake masks representing ancestors who trigger tremors when they feel nature has been abused by humankind (Figure 4.1).

Oral traditions describe a major seism, followed by a tsunami, shortly before contact with the Europeans. The disappearance of the Pachena Bay people living on the West Coast of Vancouver Island, a band of more than 100 people, is attributed to this event. The account below has been transmitted from generation to generation by hereditary chiefs, and was gathered in the 1960s by ethnologists of the Canadian Museum of History. Concordant information from various sources—anthropological research, geological evidence, and historical records—points to the 1700 Cascadia megathrust earthquake whose associated tsunami reached the coast of Japan.

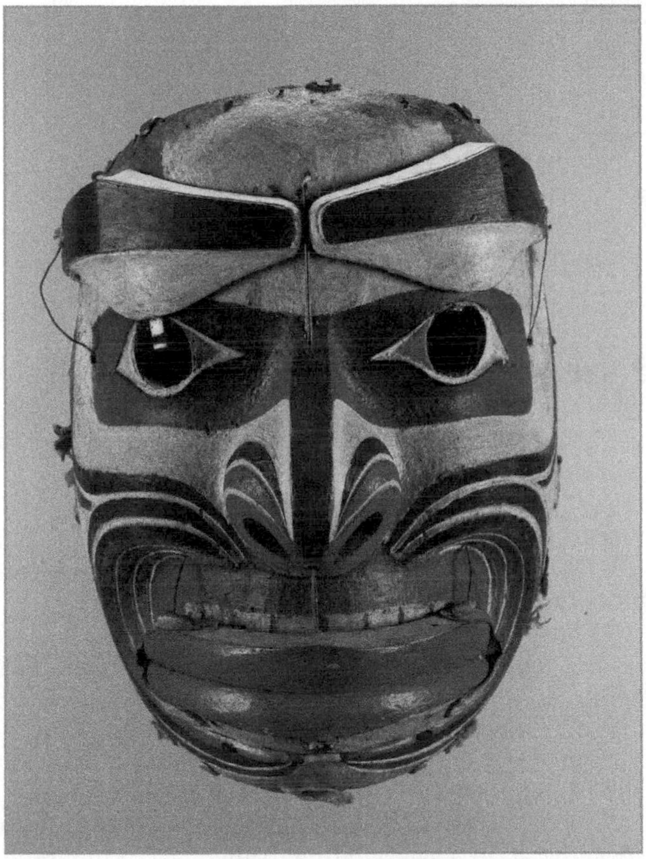

Figure 4.1
Earthquake mask from the Kwakiutl First Nation of northern Vancouver Island, Queen Charlotte Strait and Johnstone Strait, British Columbia.

Source: Used with permission of the Museum of Anthropology at the University of British Columbia.

> This was brought about by the Pachena Bay Chief, brought as dowry for this elder daughter to my grandfather's ancestor before the big earthquake, before the big flood. By that my grandfather's land reached Tsosayi:>at along with all chiefly rights, songs, topa:tis. Many are now today descended from that. Only my grandfather survived who now has many descendants. It is them now who are descendants from the first Pachena Bay people. It is said no one ever knew what happened. I think a big wave smashed into the beach. The Pachena Bay people were lost. Their food was whale meat. That is why they were living there. Nothing was known about what happened and what became of them. But they on their part who lived at Ma:lts'a:s, "House-Up-Against-Hill," the wave did not reach because they were on high ground. Right against a cliff were the houses on high ground at M'a:lsit, "Coldwater Pool." Because of that they came out alive. They did not drift out to sea along with the others.

Canada experiences approximately 3000 earthquakes per year. Only a few dozen of these, however, are strong enough to be felt. To plan adequately for the larger ones, we need to understand the hazard: where in Canada are earthquakes likely to strike, and what are their expected characteristics?

LO1 Seismic Risk and Mitigation in Canada

EARTHQUAKES IN CANADA: WHERE AND HOW SEVERE?

Earthquake research in Canada does not focus on the elusive "When will a major earthquake strike?" but on "Where are earthquakes likely to happen?" and "How strong will the associated ground shaking be?" As discussed in Chapter 1, a general definition of risk is the product of vulnerability and hazard. Let us tailor this definition to seismic risk. With regard to earthquakes, vulnerability is especially high in major urban centres where a large population, numerous high-rise buildings, and critical infrastructure (for example, major bridges and highways, power plants, hospitals, and schools) coexist. Seismic hazard is a more complex parameter to assess. This is due in part to the fact that historical records in Canada do not go back far in time, which makes estimating the return periods of rare, large events very challenging. The earliest records from Eastern Canada are accounts of the 1663 Charlevoix earthquake (see Human Focus box: Marie de L'Incarnation and the 1663 Charlevoix Earthquake). In Western Canada, records are limited to a mere 200 years. In 1793, Captain George Vancouver mentioned in his journal a severe earthquake felt near Nookta on the west coast of Vancouver Island.

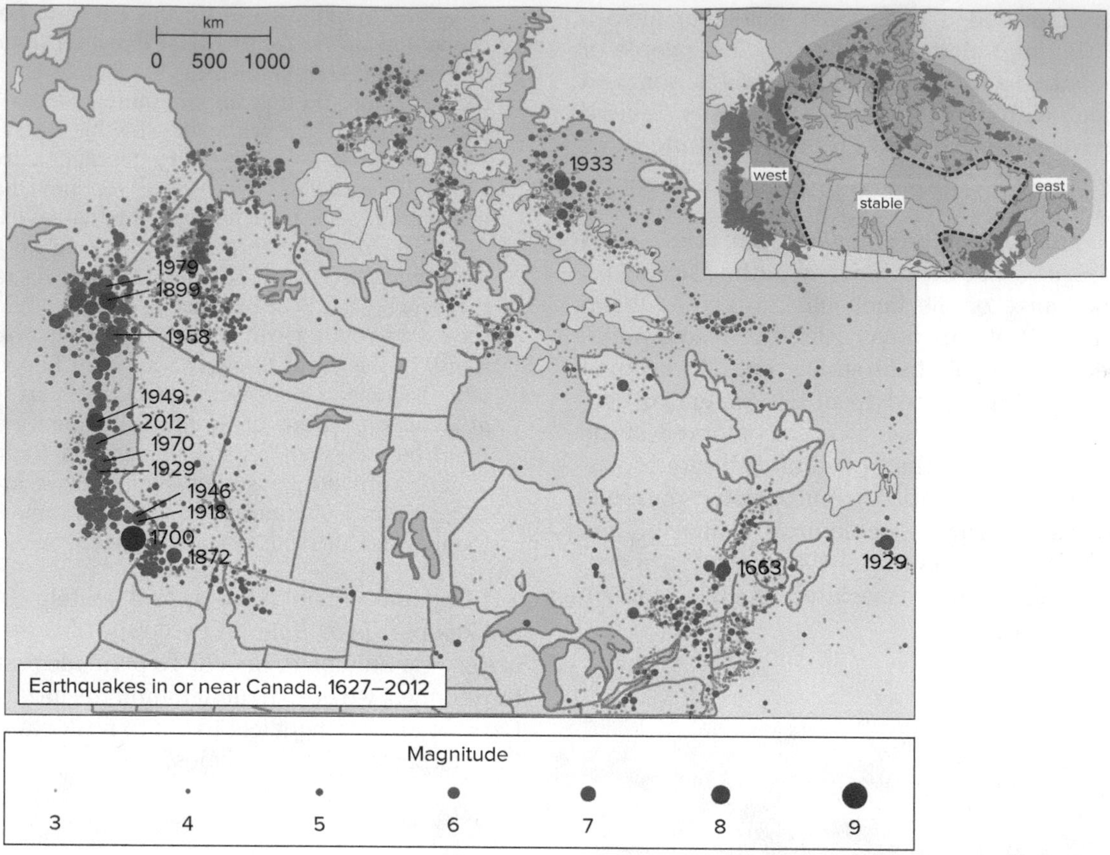

Figure 4.2

Seismicity map of Canada (1627–2012). Insert: Canada has a stable continental interior flanked by seismically active regions to the west, north, and east.

Source: Earthquakes in or near Canada, 1627–2012, http://www.earthquakescanada.nrcan.gc.ca/historic-historique/caneqmap-eng.php. Reproduced with the permission of Natural Resources Canada 2014, courtesy of Earthquakes Canada

Plotting the epicentres of all earthquakes of magnitude 3 or larger in Canadian history on a map allows a pattern to emerge. Broad regions can be defined: a central stable region and seismically active regions on the periphery (Figure 4.2). The western region includes a large band of epicentres along the coast of British Columbia, coinciding with the Cascadia subduction zone and the Queen Charlotte transform fault, and a cluster of events along the Richardson Mountains at the border between Yukon and the Northwest Territories. The eastern region covers the St. Lawrence River Valley and the Grand Banks plateau of the Atlantic continental shelf. It follows geological trends and extends to the north to include most of the Arctic Islands. Table 4.1 lists the fourteen largest earthquakes in or near Canada since 1627. The list is dominated by the events along the tectonically active west coast of British Columbia, yet it includes events from five provinces and territories. This overview of historical **seismicity** tells us where large earthquakes are more frequent. To complete our seismic hazard assessment we need to understand where large earthquakes could have a destructive impact. A map of seismic hazard in Canada can be compiled by integrating information about seismic wave propagation and geological trends. The map, shown in Figure 4.3, is based on predicted peak ground acceleration, since this parameter is closely related to the behaviour of buildings subjected to shaking. Figures 4.2 and 4.3 generally concur. Sensitive zones, however, are better defined in Figure 4.3.

The product of vulnerability and seismic hazard results in the seismic risk map shown in Figure 4.4. Vulnerability is a difficult parameter to assess in practice; therefore, population was used as the multiplier representing vulnerability in the calculation. Look at the large circles, representing a higher level of risk. They simply correspond to the largest population centres in Canada (from west to east, Victoria, Vancouver, Edmonton, Calgary, Windsor, London, the Greater Toronto Area, Ottawa, Montreal, Quebec City, Fredericton, Halifax, and St. John's). The dominant factor affecting seismic risk is the concentration of people and infrastructure in cities. Urban seismic risk is broken down in more detail in Figure 4.5. With close to two million inhabitants, the

TABLE 4.1

Earthquakes Near or in Canada of Magnitude 7 or Greater (1627–2013)

Magnitude	Date	Seismograph Records	Location	Impact: Mass Movements	Impact: Tsunami	Impact: Damage to Buildings
9.0	26 Jan 1700	NO	British Columbia—Cascadia subduction zone	YES	YES	YES
8.1	22 Aug 1949	YES	British Columbia—offshore Haida Gwaii (formerly Queen Charlotte Islands)	NO	YES	YES
8.0	4 Sep 1899	NO	Yukon — Alaska border	YES	YES	YES
7.9	10 Jul 1958	YES	British Columbia — Alaska border	YES	YES	YES
7.7	28 Oct 2012	YES	British Columbia — offshore Haida Gwaii	YES	YES	NO
7.4	24 Jun 1970	YES	British Columbia—south of Haida Gwaii	NO	NO	NO
7.4	15 Dec 1872	NO	Washington — Bristish Columbia border	NO	YES	YES
7.3	20 Nov 1933	YES	Northwest Territories—Baffin Bay	NO	NO	NO
7.3	23 Jun 1946	YES	British Columbia—Vancouver Island	YES	NO	YES
7.2	28 Feb 1979	YES	Southern Yukon — Alaska border	Unknown	NO	NO
7.2	18 Nov 1929	YES	Atlantic Ocean, south of Newfoundland (Grand Banks)	YES	YES	YES
7.0	26 May 1929	YES	British Columbia—south of Haida Gwaii	YES	YES	YES
7.0	5 Feb 1663	NO	Quebec—Charlevoix	YES	NO	YES
7.0	6 Dec 1918	YES	British Columbia—Vancouver Island	NO	NO	YES

Source: Reproduced with the permission of Natural Resources Canada 2014, courtesy of Earthquakes Canada.

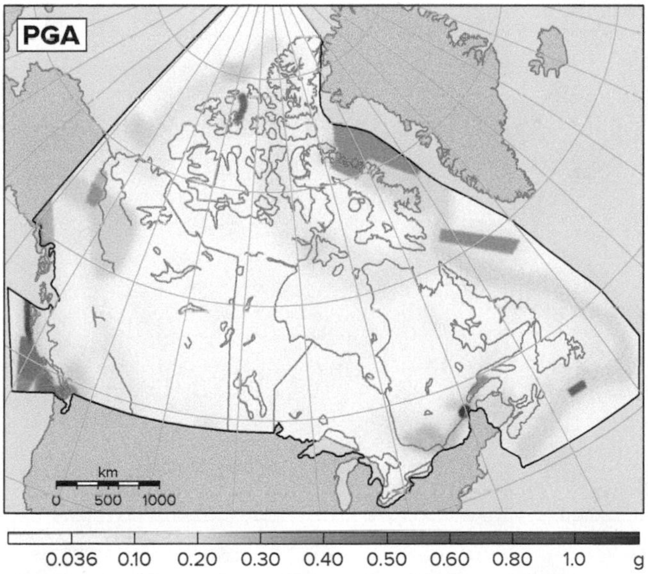

Figure 4.3
Seismic hazard map of Canada showing peak ground acceleration (PGA) that has a 2% chance of being exceeded in 50 years, for firm ground conditions (NHERP class C in Table 4.2). Peak acceleration is contoured in fractions of g (gravitational acceleration).

Source: 2010 NBCC seismic hazard map - PGA, aps-eng.php. Reproduced with the permission of Natural Resources Canada 2014, courtesy of Earthquakes Canada

highest level of seismic risk of all Canadian cities has been attributed to Vancouver. Victoria, which is located in the same tectonic environment, is fourth in the ranking because of its modest population of a third of a million (similar hazard, less vulnerability).

THE CANADIAN NATIONAL SEISMOGRAPH NETWORK

The Canadian National Seismograph Network (CNSN) is the cornerstone of earthquake monitoring in Canada. The CNSN is a pan-Canadian infrastructure including more than 100 seismograph stations and 60 **accelerographs** managed by Natural Resources Canada, a department of the federal government. In addition, the CNSN stations are supplemented by stations from local networks, and by stations deployed on a temporary basis. Compare Figure 4.2 and Figure 4.6 and note how the instruments are strategically deployed in seismically active areas.

Looking at the earthquake catalogue for Canada, one might get the impression that the number of earthquakes is increasing over time; there were very few earthquakes recorded in the 1600s whereas the CNSN can now locate 3000 earthquakes annually. Nevertheless, there is no reason to believe that we are

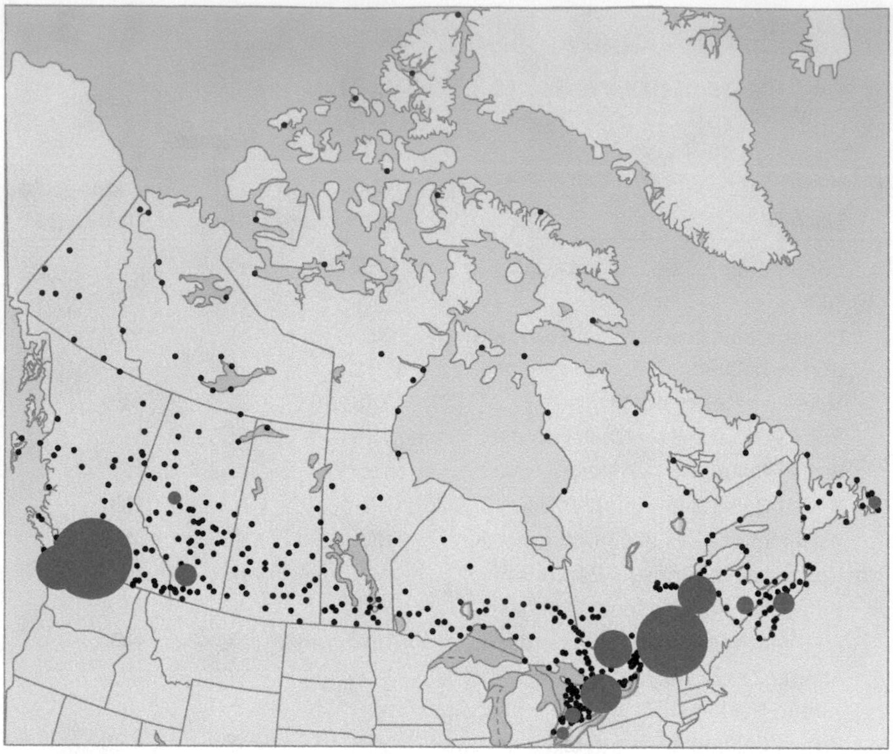

Figure 4.4
Map of seismic risk in Canada. Red circles indicate the areas of largest risk.

Source: Reproduced with the permission of Natural Resources Canada 2014, courtesy of Earthquakes Canada.

experiencing an increase in earthquake activity; what has increased is our capacity to report and to detect earthquakes. In the last 20 years or so, we have definitely had an increase in the number of earthquakes located each year simply because of the tremendous increase in the number of seismograph stations that allow the detection of tiny earthquakes that went unnoticed in the past.

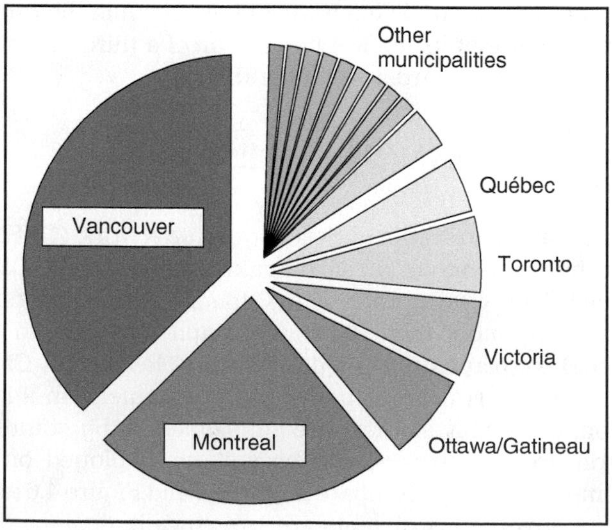

Figure 4.5
Urban seismic risk in Canada.

Source: *The Case for an Advanced National Earthquake Monitoring System for Canada's Cities at Risk*, John Adams, Garry Rogers, Stephen Halchuk, David McCormack, John Cassidy. 7th US Conference on Earthquake Engineering (Boston, USA, July 21–25, 2002), 10 pages. Page 10, Figure 3. Relative distribution urban seismic risk in Canada. http://earthquakescanada.nrcan.gc.ca/hazard-alea/2002/7USNCEE2002_Adams_etal.pdf. Reproduced with the permission of Natural Resources Canada 2014, courtesy of Earthquakes Canada.

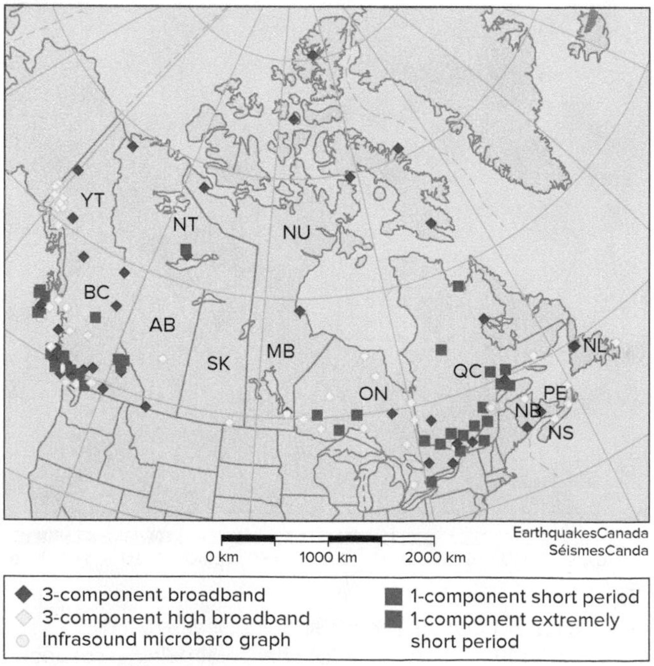

Figure 4.6
Canadian National Seismograph Network.

Source: Canadian National Seismograph Network Station Book map, http://www.earthquakescanada.nrcan.gc.ca/stndon/CNSN-RNSC/stnbook-cahierstn/index-eng.php?tpl_sorting=map. Reproduced with the permission of Natural Resources Canada 2014, courtesy of Earthquakes Canada

Data acquired by the CNSN contribute to the safety of Canadians in several ways. Seismic events above a certain threshold automatically trigger two tools for rapid response: the Automated Natural Hazard Alert Service (ANHAS) and shakemaps. In the longer term, seismicity maps are constantly being updated with new data from the CNSN, leading to an increased understanding of seismic hazard.

The Automated Natural Hazard Alert Service

ANHAS provides information about significant earthquakes anywhere in Canada, usually within 10 minutes of the event. The service is offered under contract to the Canadian railroad industry (five companies totalling more than 50 000 km of track), and hydroelectricity and nuclear energy generators. Clients receive notification of the earthquake characteristics (time, epicentre location, Richter magnitude) via several media links including e-mail, fax, and social media (@CANADAquakes). Following an alert, trains might be ordered to proceed at restricted speed or even stop along certain track segments until a slope stability inspection has been completed. Utility companies carry out inspections of their infrastructure located within a certain radius from the epicentre.

Shakemaps

Shakemaps (Figure 4.7) are representations of the ground shaking produced by an earthquake. They might be presented as maps of Mercalli intensity, similar to isoseismal maps (compare Figure 4.7 with Figures 3.17 and 4.12), however, the source of the information displayed is different. The data plotted on shakemaps are intensities calculated from data recorded by a network of seismographs during an earthquake. The gaps between seismograph stations are filled by predicted intensities. Isoseismal maps, on the other hand, are the product of human input. They are compiled from eyewitness accounts.

Shakemaps are automatically computed and posted within minutes following a moderate or large

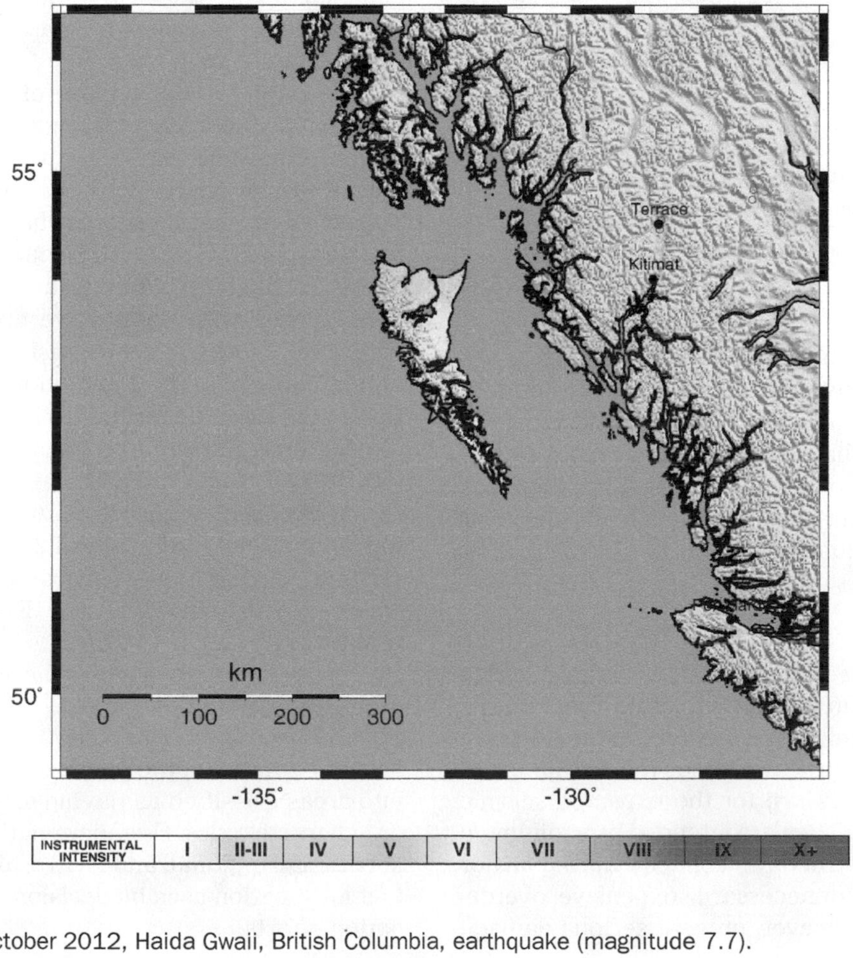

Figure 4.7
Shakemap of the 28 October 2012, Haida Gwaii, British Columbia, earthquake (magnitude 7.7).
Source: United States Geological Survey.

Site Class	Foundation Material	Shear Wave Velocity V_s in Top 30 m (m/s)
A	Hard rock	$V_s > 1500$
B	Rock	$760 < V_s \leq 1500$
C	Very dense soil and soft rock	$360 < V_s \leq 760$
D	Stiff soil	$180 < V_s \leq 360$
E	Soft soil	$V_s < 180$
F	Soil vulnerable to liquefaction	—

Source: NEHRP site classification source: http://www.nehrp.gov/index.htm.

Figure 4.8
Chimney damage in Port Alberni, British Columbia, caused by the 1946 Vancouver Island earthquake (magnitude 7.3).
Source: Reproduced with the permission of Natural Resources Canada 2014, courtesy of Earthquakes Canada
http://www.earthquakescanada.nrcan.gc.ca/historic-historique/events/images/19460623_1946chim.jpg

earthquake, which is their main advantage. They are a critical tool to improve the situational awareness of first responders who need to decide quickly where to provide assistance. Shakemaps are also used to run "what if?" scenarios in planning exercises. Earthquakes with different characteristics are "designed" and their consequences are evaluated.

SEISMIC ZONATION

The National Building Code of Canada is a concrete example of a long-term mitigation effort against seismic risk. The seismic guidelines included in the Code are used to design and construct buildings that are as earthquake-resistant as necessary for the expected seismic hazard of their setting. They are intended as a minimum standard to prevent structural collapse during major earthquakes, without unnecessary, expensive overdesign. They may not, however, prevent serious damage to individual structures. New buildings must adhere to the Code and thus represent less hazard than old buildings. Vintage unreinforced masonry buildings are the most likely to crumble during an earthquake. Tall brick chimneys are particularly fragile (Figure 4.8). The Code also outlines principles to be applied when retrofitting existing buildings.

Although the hypocentre of an earthquake might be located hundreds of kilometres away, the propagation of seismic waves in the last 30 m of the long path from the source to a particular site has a major impact on ground motion at that site. If there is overlap between the natural frequencies of the seismic waves, local soil conditions, and buildings, resonance might occur with destructive consequences. This is why the Code includes provisions for different foundation materials. The foundation materials are classified in the Code according to a scheme developed by the National Earthquake Hazard Reduction Program (NEHRP) in the United States. The NEHRP classification is based on the velocity of shear waves in the top 30 m of material (Table 4.2). Amplification effects are more severe at sites characterized by a low shear wave velocity. Class E and F sites are especially problematic.

Several Canadian cities have embarked on programs to map foundation materials within their boundaries (Figure 4.9). This activity is one component of **seismic zonation**, the process of subdividing a region into areas classified as having similar earthquake hazard characteristics. Seismic zonation can be completed at national, regional, and local scales. It conveys important information used by decision makers to direct mitigation efforts.

IN GREATER DEPTH

Seismic Provisions of the National Building Code of Canada

Seismic provisions—featured modestly in the appendix of the first edition of the National Building Code of Canada in 1941 before moving to the main text in 1953—have become increasingly sophisticated over the years. They include estimates of seismic hazard across the country, and a methodology for integrating this information in the design of buildings. The objective is to ensure a uniform level of protection for all structures. The provisions are periodically updated to reflect a better understanding of Canadian seismicity, advances in earthquake engineering research, and lessons learned from earthquake damage around the world. The 2010 edition of the Code includes new requirements for the use of braced wall panels, fastening, and framing in high-risk areas. The methodology used in the calculation of ground acceleration values has also been improved.

Seismic hazard estimates are directly related to the forces that a structure will be subjected to during an earthquake. The estimates are based on the expected ground motion for earthquakes of different magnitudes and epicentral distances. They have been computed for a broad range of frequencies (from 0.1 to 10 Hz), to account for the shaking induced by the different seismic waves. The estimates also include factors reflecting the different foundation materials of the NEHRP classification.

Since buildings are particularly vulnerable to shear stress, the most important factor that civil engineers must estimate in the design stage is the lateral earthquake force. In addition to seismic hazard at the building site, the lateral earthquake force equation includes the natural frequency of the proposed building, the number of storeys, and the flexibility of the structure, important parameters that were examined in Chapter 3. Everything else being equal, direct observations of earthquake damage have shown that buildings regular in shape perform better than irregular buildings, possibly because stresses are more evenly distributed through their structure. For this reason, more stringent seismic provisions apply to buildings with irregular shapes.

The current design standard for buildings is to be able to withstand an earthquake with a return period of 2500 years. A factor further tailors the design requirements depending on the importance of the buildings to society. Normal buildings are assigned a factor of 1.0, schools and storage facilities containing toxic substances a 1.3, and buildings needed for post-disaster recovery such as hospitals, water and sewage treatment facilities, and fire and police stations, a 1.5.

Canada is a world leader in earthquake engineering. This expertise has been captured in the seismic provisions of the National Building Code of Canada and is applied to the design of new, safe buildings. The most pressing demand is now to develop cost-effective strategies for retrofitting existing buildings.

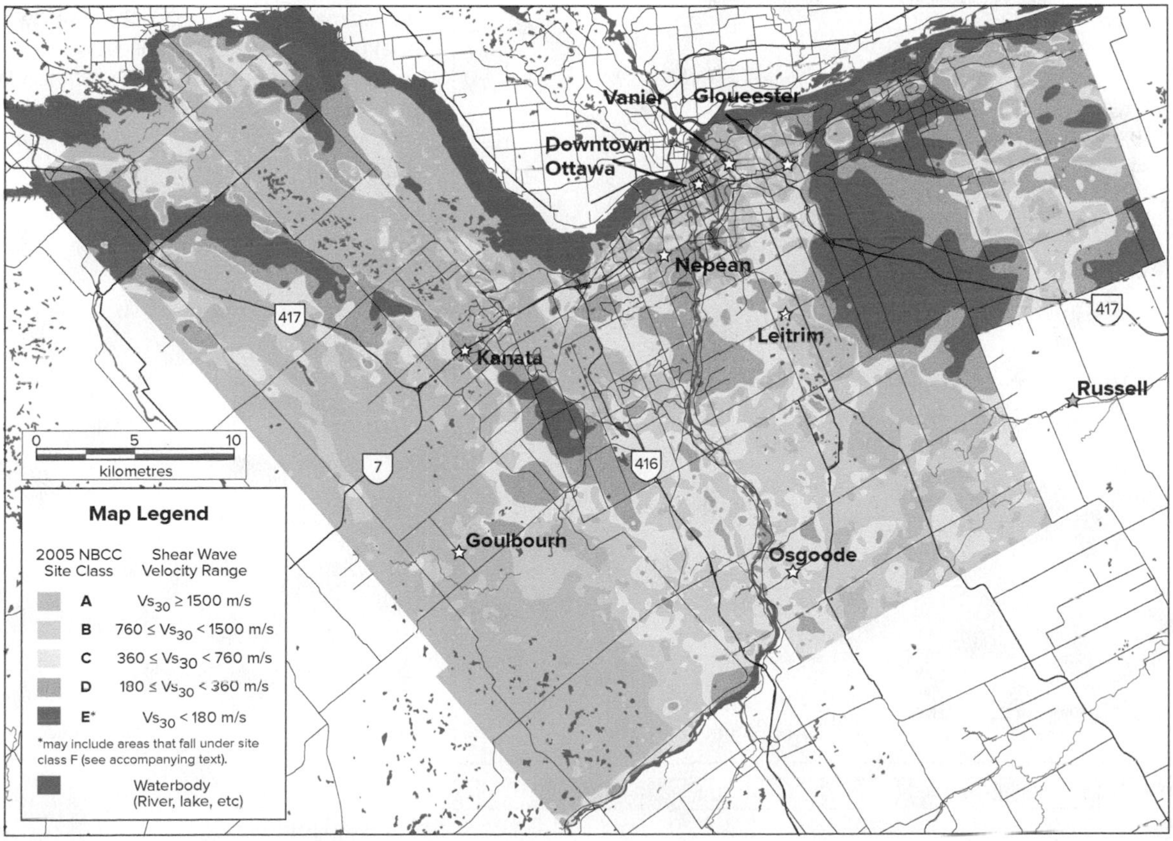

Figure 4.9

Seismic zonation map of Ottawa. Note how the NEHRP classes vary over very short distances.

Source: Natural Resources Canada.

IN GREATER DEPTH

Did You Feel It?

For more than a century, seismologists have sought input from the Canadian public following an earthquake. Data-gathering mechanisms have changed, but the effort continues.

The Dominion Observatory was established in 1905 in Ottawa on the model of the Royal Observatory at Greenwich, England, with the dual mandate of making precise longitude measurements and studying planet Earth (Figure 4.10). When an earthquake was strongly felt, the seismologists of the Dominion Observatory determined the intensity of shaking on Canadian territory. They collected information by sending questionnaires to local postmasters, a clerical process spanning months (Figure 4.12). The process also enabled them to locate epicentres when the coverage of the network of seismograph stations was sparse.

The tradition is maintaned today as the Observatory and adjacent buildings host a state-of-the-art seismograph station and serve as a telemetry hub as part of the Canadian National Seismograph Network. Seismologists from Natural Resources Canada now seek input from the Canadian population via a questionnaire called "Did You Feel It?" posted on their Website (http://earthquakescanada.nrcan.gc.ca/dyfi/index_eng.php). Sample questions include "Did the earthquake wake you up?," "Did objects fall off shelves?," and "Did you notice the swinging/swaying of doors or hanging objects?" Replies are processed automatically and georeferenced using postal codes. Gradually, a computer-generated isoseismal map begins taking shape (Figure 4.11).

Figure 4.10
Dominion Observatory, Ottawa, Ontario.
Photo: © Claire Samson.

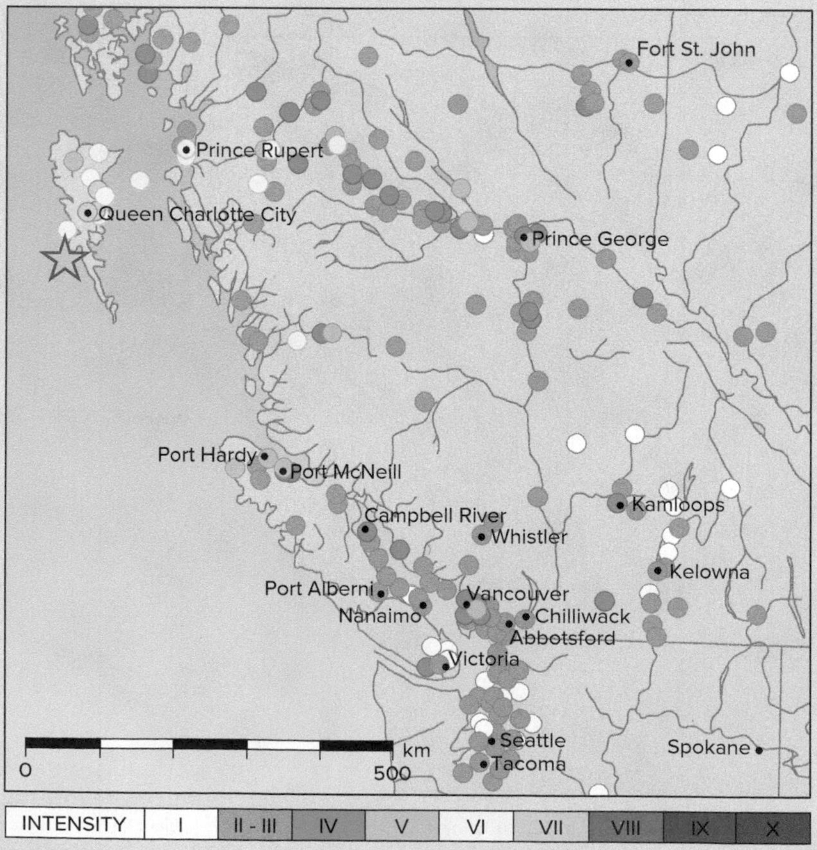

Figure 4.11
Isoseismal map of the 2012 Haida Gwaii earthquake, generated from replies to the "Did you feel it?" questionnaire posted on the Web. The red star indicates the earthquake epicentre. The earthquake was felt as far as Alberta and Washington State.
Source: Map of intensities garnered from felt reports submitted to the Earthquakes Canada web site (www.earthquakescanada.ca).

continued

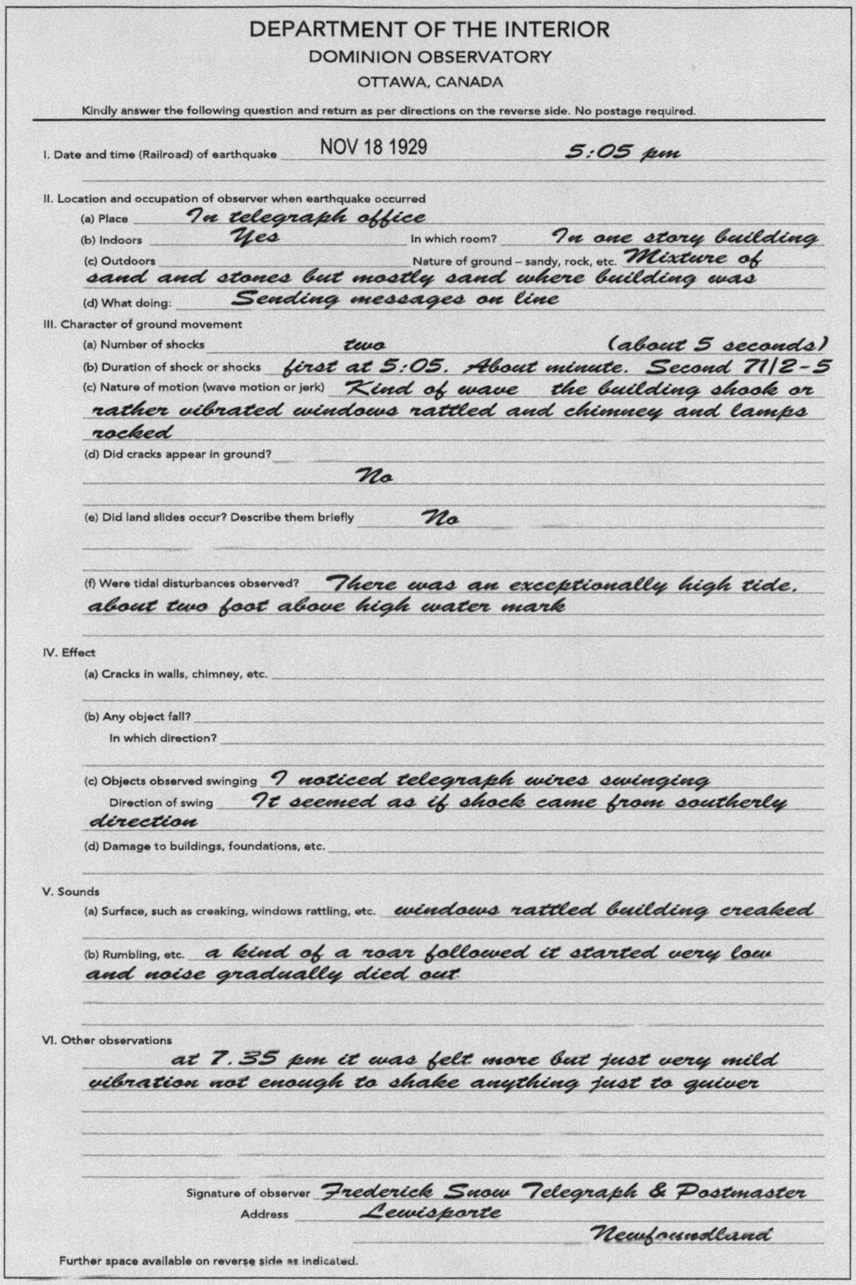

DEPARTMENT OF THE INTERIOR
DOMINION OBSERVATORY
OTTAWA, CANADA

Kindly answer the following question and return as per directions on the reverse side. No postage required.

I. Date and time (Railroad) of earthquake NOV 18 1929 5:05 pm

II. Location and occupation of observer when earthquake occurred
(a) Place In telegraph office
(b) Indoors Yes In which room? In one story building
(c) Outdoors Nature of ground – sandy, rock, etc. Mixture of sand and stones but mostly sand where building was
(d) What doing: Sending messages on line

III. Character of ground movement
(a) Number of shocks two (about 5 seconds)
(b) Duration of shock or shocks first at 5:05. About minute. Second 71/2-5
(c) Nature of motion (wave motion or jerk) Kind of wave the building shook or rather vibrated windows rattled and chimney and lamps rocked
(d) Did cracks appear in ground? No
(e) Did land slides occur? Describe them briefly No
(f) Were tidal disturbances observed? There was an exceptionally high tide, about two foot above high water mark

IV. Effect
(a) Cracks in walls, chimney, etc.
(b) Any object fall?
In which direction?
(c) Objects observed swinging I noticed telegraph wires swinging
Direction of swing It seemed as if shock came from southerly direction
(d) Damage to buildings, foundations, etc.

V. Sounds
(a) Surface, such as creaking, windows rattling, etc. windows rattled building creaked
(b) Rumbling, etc. a kind of a roar followed it started very low and noise gradually died out

VI. Other observations
at 7.35 pm it was felt more but just very mild vibration not enough to shake anything just to quiver

Signature of observer Frederick Snow Telegraph & Postmaster
Address Lewisporte
Newfoundland

Further space available on reverse side as indicated.

Figure 4.12
Sample intensity questionnaire response from Lewisporte, Newfoundland, following the 1929 Grand Banks earthquake.

Source: Reproduced with the permission of Natural Resources Canada 2014, courtesy of Earthquakes Canada. http://www.earthquakescanada.nrcan.gc.ca/historic-historique/events/images/19291118_1929resp.jpg.

LO2 Earthquakes of Canada's Pacific Coast

The descriptions of several significant earthquakes in Canada's history provide a glimpse of the interactions between Canadian society and its natural environment. Several of the descriptions presented in the next subsections are adapted from the Web pages of Natural Resources Canada (http://www.earthquakescanada.ca). Natural Resources Canada recognizes an earthquake as significant when its magnitude exceeds 6 on the Richter scale or when its modified Mercalli intensity is VI or stronger.

Nowhere in Canada are earthquakes more present in the collective minds of communities than along the Pacific coast. The people of British Columbia feel

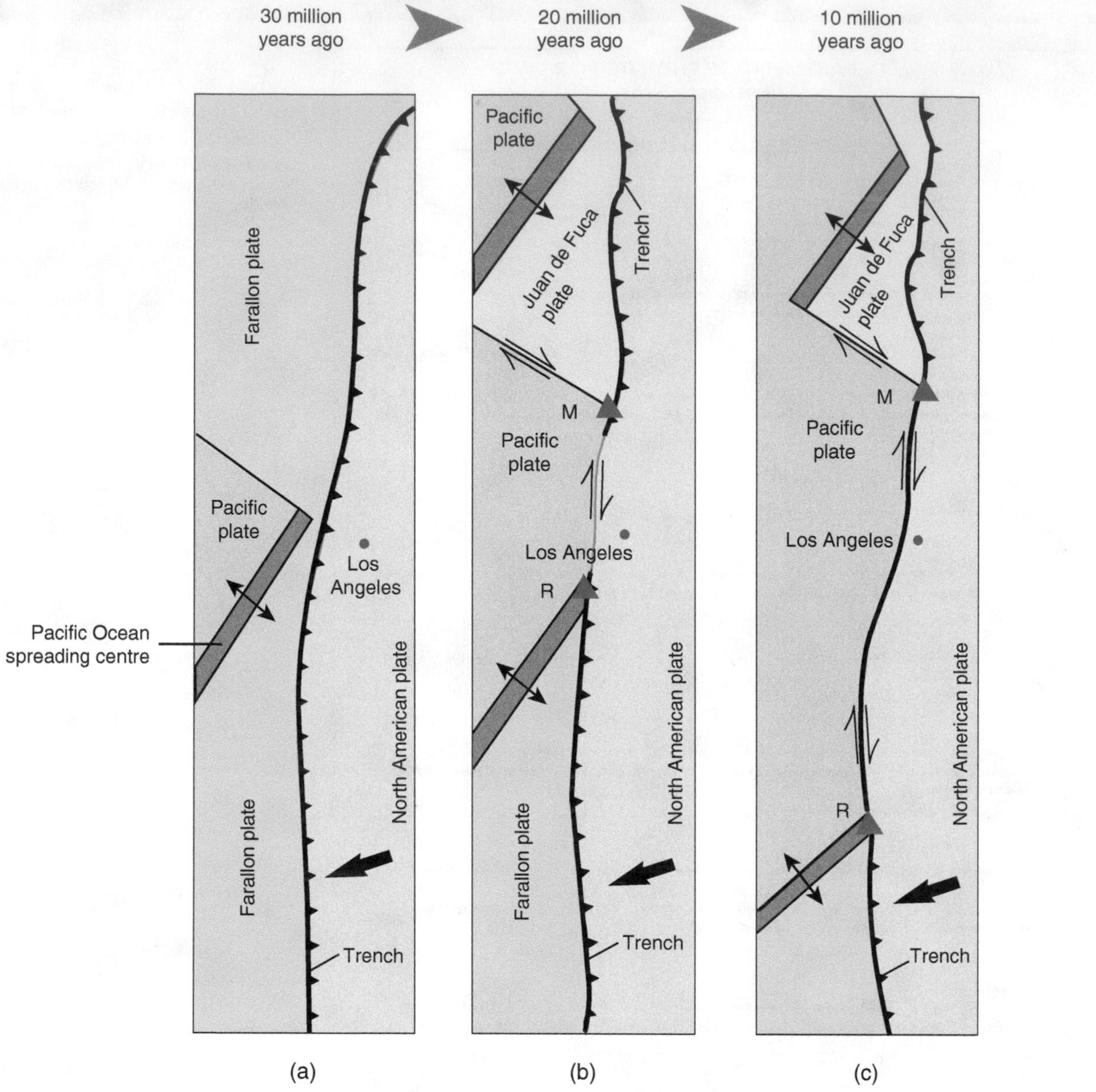

Figure 4.13

Subduction of the Farallon plate underneath the North American plate: (a) 30 million years ago—the Pacific Ocean spreading centre nears southern California, (b) 20 million years ago—the Farallon plate splits into two plates, (c) 10 million years ago—the transform fault connecting the two plates continues to grow. Interpretations based on work of Tanya Atwater.

Source: Kious, W. J., and Tilling, R. I., *This Dynamic the Earth.* United States Geological Survey, p. 77.

a strong connection with their circum-Pacific neighbours and know their geological environments share many similarities. They maintain a high level of awareness of events occurring around the "Ring of Fire" (Figure 1.12b).

The lives of the inhabitants of the West Coast of North America are affected by the fate of an ancient tectonic plate, the Farallon plate. Until 30 million years ago, the eastern edge of the Farallon plate was being destroyed by subduction underneath the North American plate. Approximately 28 million years ago, the Pacific Ocean spreading centre collided with North America near the site of the present-day city of Los Angeles (Figure 4.13). The collision segmented the Farallon plate into smaller plates, the Juan de Fuca plate to the north and the precursor of the Rivera and Cocos plates to the south. A transform fault, the ancestor of the San Andreas fault, connected the plates.

Figure 4.14 shows the present-day tectonic setting along the western edge of the North American plate. The northern fragment is now composed of three plates. The larger Juan de Fuca plate is located between the Explorer plate to the north and the Gorda plate to the south. These three plates are currently subducting underneath Vancouver Island and the northwestern United States along the Cascadia Subduction Zone at a rate of approximately 4 cm per year. Over the last tens of millions of years, this sustained subduction has triggered major earthquakes and produced an outpouring of vast quantities of lava, building the Cascade Range volcanoes (Figures 6.8, 6.9, and 6.10). North of the Cascadia Subduction Zone, the Queen Charlotte fault (see photo of chapter opener) accommodates the alongside movement of the Pacific and North American plates in a fashion similar to its southern cousin, the San Andreas fault, and has been the site of large earthquakes. Finally, the Queen Charlotte fault moves inland in the Alaska Panhandle and connects to the Aleutian Subduction Zone.

Let's take a closer look at the convergence between the oceanic Juan de Fuca plate and the continental North American plate (Figure 4.15), which is one of the science thrusts of the current NEPTUNE oceanographic research project (see In Greater Depth box: Project NEPTUNE: Revolutionizing Ocean Science, in Chapter 7). In this complex tectonic puzzle, different types of plate boundaries are present (subduction zone, transform fault, and spreading centre). All three types of subduction zone earthquake described in Chapter 3 (Figure 3.23) occur.

A cross-section reveals the megathrust fault that marks the contact between the two plates at a depth of approximately 30 km (Figure 4.16). Although a large megathrust earthquake shook the region in 1700, there seems to be a deficit of this type of earthquake in the Cascadia subduction zone compared to similar tectonic environments around the world. A likely hypothesis is that the megathrust fault is currently locked, refusing to slip to accommodate further movement. The Juan de Fuca plate, however, keeps moving east at a velocity of 3.7 cm per year. The enormous compression caused by the movement of this plate against the locked fault results in the shortening and uplift of Vancouver Island at a rate of 1 to 4 mm annually, which is directly measurable using the global positioning system (GPS) (Figures 4.17, 4.18 and 4.19). When stress exceeds the resistive forces locking the fault, the stored elastic energy will be released as seismic waves. The bulge will then collapse almost instantly and the seaward portion of the continent will spring back, possibly triggering a tsunami (Figure 4.17b) (see Chapter 7). The west coast of Vancouver Island, located directly in front of the subduction trench, would be subjected to intense shaking (Figure 4.20). Strong and long-duration shaking would also affect Vancouver due to amplification effects in the Georgia basin. Sheri Molnar, a doctoral student at the University of British Columbia who has studied the structure of the basin and its impact on ground motion describes the phenomenon as seismic waves sloshing and bouncing around within gelatin surrounded by a hard block of cheese.

Megathrust earthquakes are a considerable hazard affecting southern British Columbia. However, seismologists attribute the largest hazard not to these gigantic but infrequent events (return period approximately 600 years) but to intra-slab and crustal earthquakes associated with the deformation of the plates as they move toward each other. These deformation earthquakes can be quite large—there have been four earthquakes of magnitude 7 or higher in the past 130 years in southwestern British Columbia and northern Washington State. They occur frequently (return period of 30–50 years for intra-slab earthquakes of magnitude equal to or greater than 6; return period of 100 years for crustal earthquakes of magnitude equal to or greater than 6) and therefore represent the most serious hazard. Note how several shallow hypocentres originating from the North American plate (blue dots in Figure 4.21) lie directly beneath Victoria and Seattle.

LO3 1700 CASCADIA EARTHQUAKE, BRITISH COLUMBIA

At 9 p.m. on 26 January 1700, a gigantic megathrust earthquake—the largest seism in Canada since 1627—occurred in the Cascadia Subduction Zone. As a result of the convergence between the oceanic Juan de Fuca plate and the continental North American plate, the megathrust fault marking the contact between the two plates ruptured suddenly (Figures 4.15 and 4.16). The rupture affected the entire length of the subduction zone from Vancouver Island to northern California, leading to magnitude estimates of approximately 9. Stories told by Aboriginal groups vividly describe the event. They report that the shaking was so violent that people could not stand and so prolonged that it made them sick.

How do we know the exact date and time of the earthquake? A recent book, *The Orphan Tsunami of 1700—Japanese Clues to a Parent Earthquake in North America,* written by a group of American and Japanese scholars, presents converging lines of evidence like a scientific detective story. (1) Several Japanese magistrates, merchants, and peasants recorded in their diaries the arrival of tsunami waves on their shores in the early hours of 27 January 1700 (Figure 4.22). There are reports of damage and flooding at seven sites along the coast due to waves estimated to be one to five metres in height. Taking into account the travel time of the waves across the Pacific, this timing of events is consistent

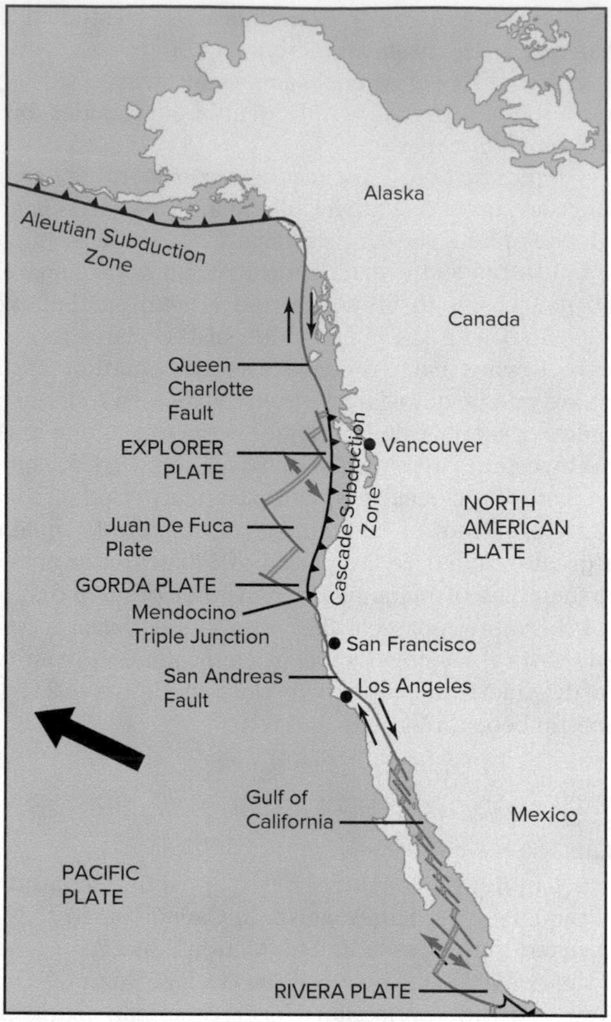

Figure 4.14
Present-day tectonic setting of western North America. The large black arrow shows the relative movement of the Pacific plate with respect to the North American plate.
Source: Claire Samson.

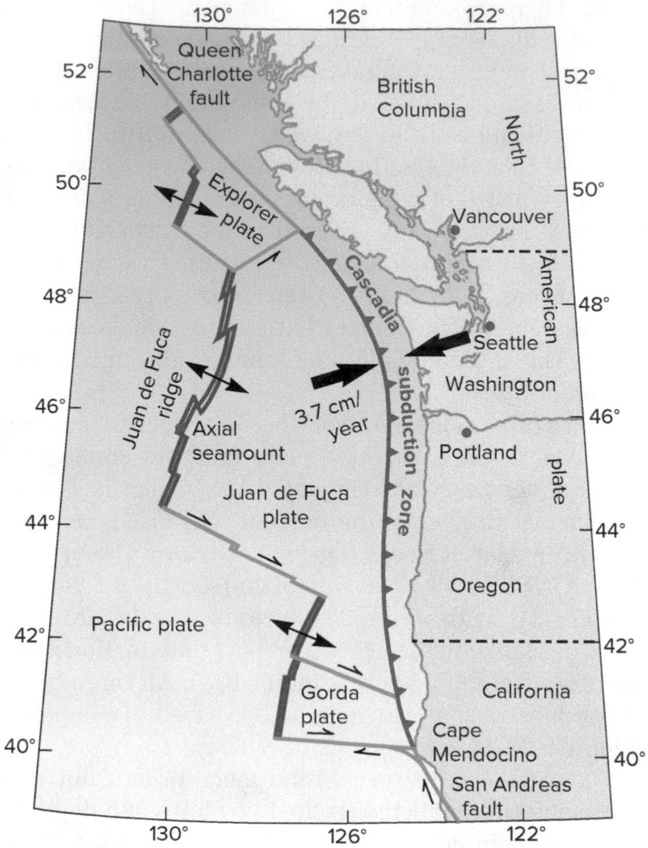

Figure 4.15
Map of the oceanic Juan de Fuca plate and its companions, the smaller Explorer and Gorda plates, being subducted beneath the North American plate along the Pacific coast. Red: subduction trench, blue: spreading centres, green: transform faults.

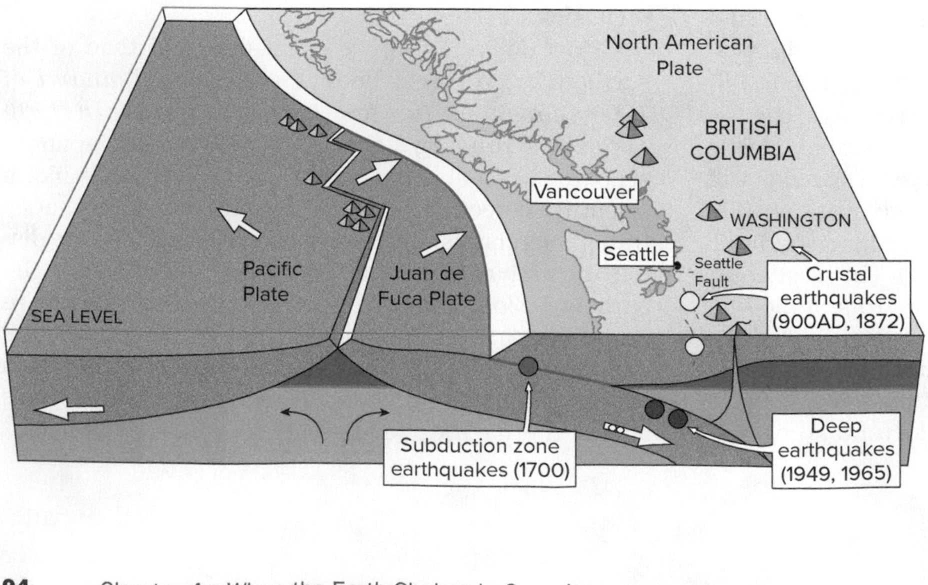

Figure 4.16
Cross-section view of the subduction of the Juan de Fuca plate underneath Vancouver Island and epicentres and hypocentres of major earthquakes. The Cascadia megathrust fault is drawn in red.
Source: Natural Resources Canada

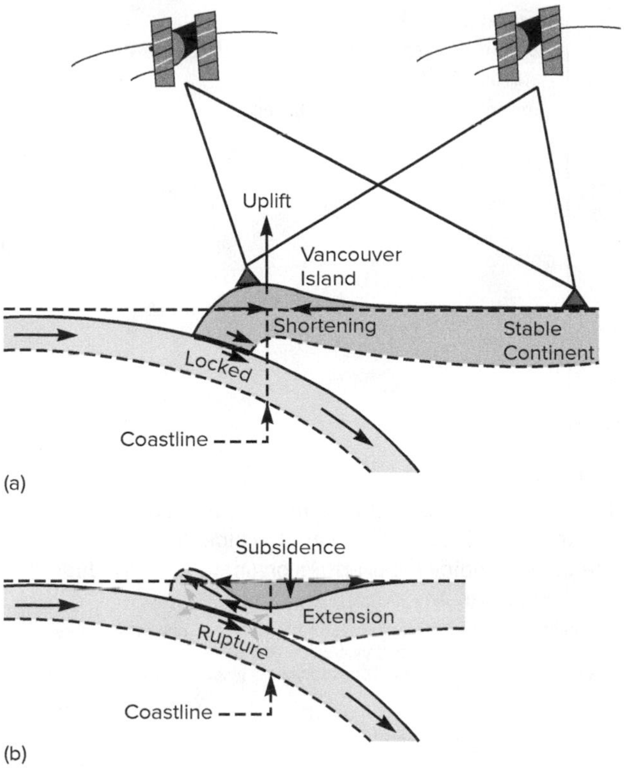

Figure 4.17
(a) The Cascadia megathrust fault is locked, causing the toe of the North American plate to be dragged down along the subduction trench offshore Vancouver Island, and the island itself to bulge up under the squeeze. These deformations can be measured directly using GPS. (b) When the Cascadia megathrust eventually ruptures, the North American plate will rebound violently, triggering an earthquake of magnitude 9 or greater and, possibly, a tsunami.
Source: Hyndman et al., Natural Resources Canada.

with a Cascadia earthquake the previous evening (Figure 4.23). (2) The discovery of ghost forests of desiccated red cedars and spruce stumps along the British Columbia, Washington, and Oregon coasts in the 1980s provided additional clues (Figure 4.24). Detailed examination of tree rings and radioactive carbon (C^{14}) dating of organic material helped to narrow the occurrence of the seism to a 10-month window between August 1699 and May 1700, between the end of one growing season and the beginning of the next one (Figure 4.25). Figure 4.26 shows the sequence of events near the coast before and after the 1700 Cascadia earthquake. The ground dropped by one or two metres during the earthquake and seawater reached the tree roots. The ensuing tsunami brought sand far onshore. Over the following many years, mud followed by peat were deposited over the sand layer. (3) The strong shaking that accompanied the earthquake triggered submarine mass movements (Figure 4.27).

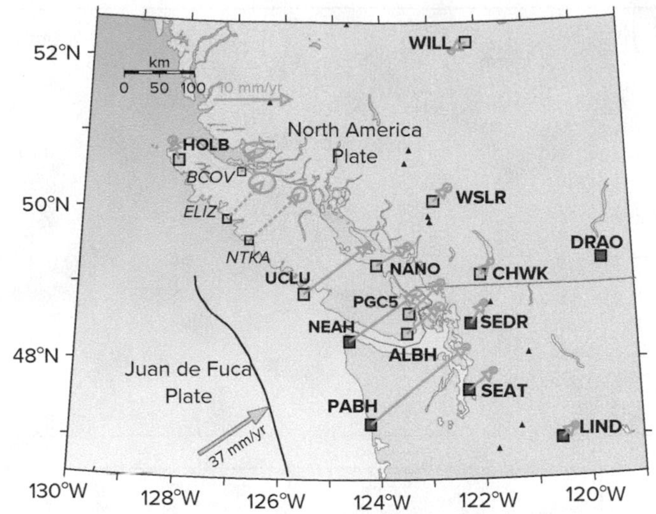

Figure 4.18
Lateral deformation of Vancouver Island. The Juan de Fuca plate moves northeastward at a velocity of 37 mm/yr. Since the Cascadia megathrust fault is locked, Vancouver Island is being compressed in that direction. Note how the GPS stations closest to the subduction trench (black line), on the west coast of the island (UCLU and NEAH, for example), move more rapidly (longer green arrows) than the GPS stations on the east coast (PGC5 and NANO, for example).
Source: Reproduced with the permission of Natural Resources Canada, 2014 (J.A. Henton et al).

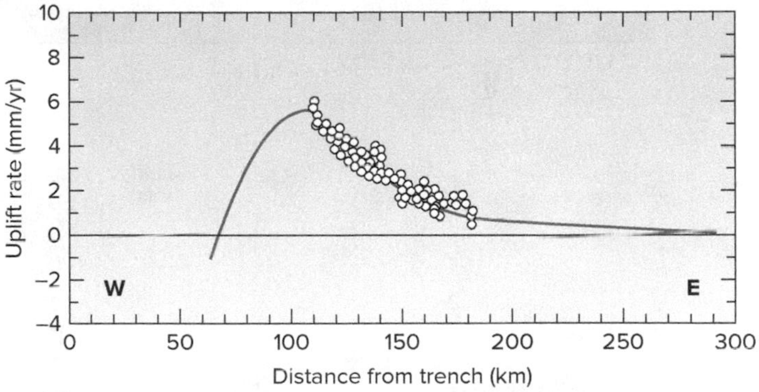

Figure 4.19
Vertical deformation of Vancouver Island. The uplift of the crust on Vancouver Island as a result of the subduction of the Juan de Fuca plate can be measured using GPS. Note how the uplift rate decreases moving east, away from the subduction trench.
Source: http://www.earthquakescanada.nrcan.gc.ca/zones/cascadia/megafig2-eng.php Reproduced with the permission of Natural Resources Canada, 2014 (Hyndman et al., 1995).

The 1700 Cascadia earthquake left unmistakable signatures in the geological record. The recognition of similar signatures tells us that the 1700 seism was not a unique event, but has been repeated many times at irregular intervals of hundreds of years

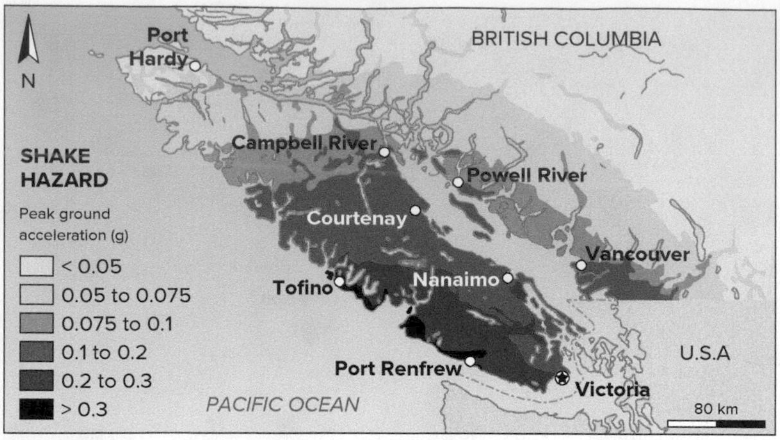

Figure 4.20
Shake hazard map of Vancouver Island and surrounding areas.
Source: Insurance Bureau of Canada

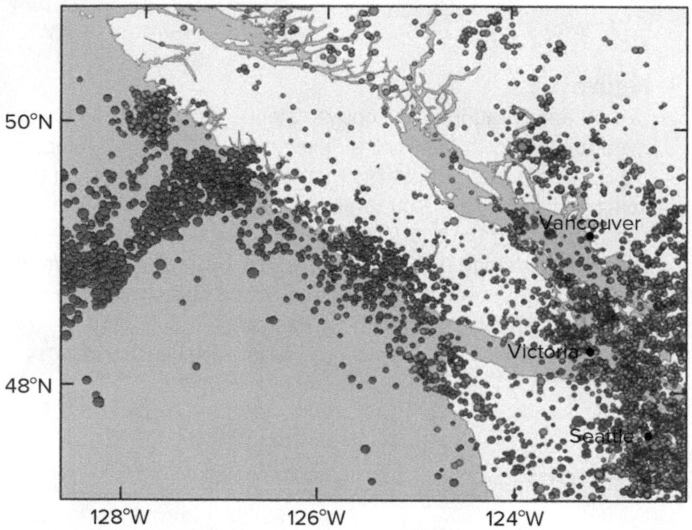

Figure 4.21
Epicentre locations in the vicinity of Vancouver Island between 1985 and 2000. Red and blue dots indicate that the corresponding hypocentres originate from the Juan de Fuca and North American plates, respectively.
Source: © 2014 Department of Natural Resources Canada. All rights reserved http://www.collectionscanada.gc.ca/webarchives/20071120073929/http://geoscape.nrcan.gc.ca/victoria/eq_e.php.

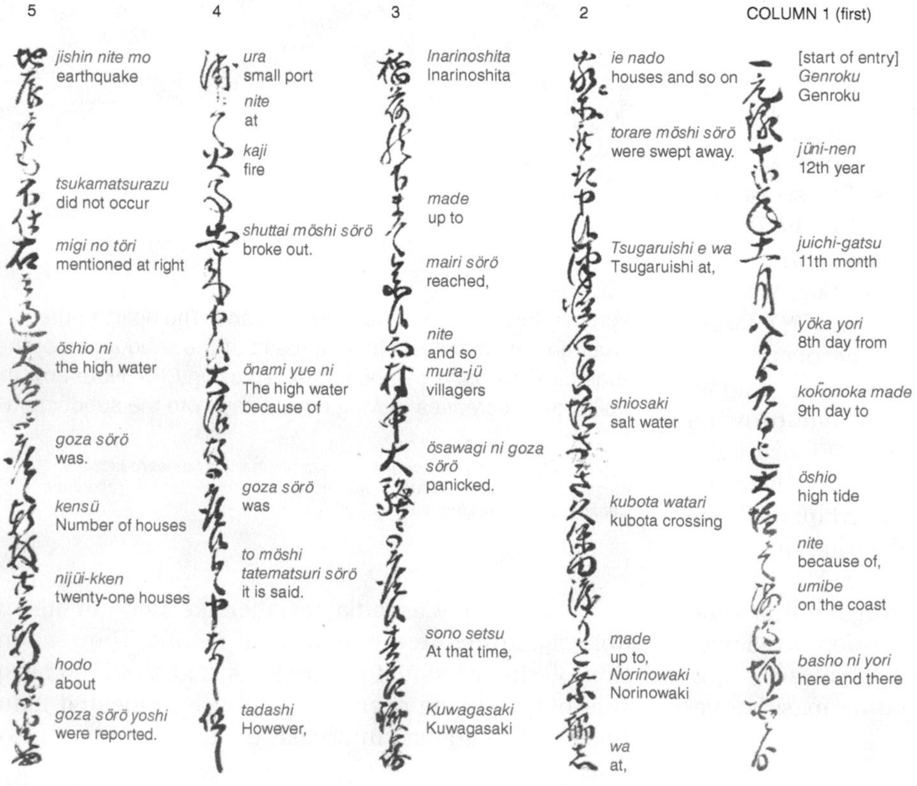

Figure 4.22
The diary of the Moriai family of Tsugaruishi, Japan. The characters read from top to bottom, right to left, starting at the top of the rightmost column.
Source: Brian F Atwater et al., 2005. *The Orphan Tsunami of 1700—Japanese Clues to a Parent Earthquake in North America.* Produced by the United States Geological Survey.

Figure 4.23
Simulation showing the tsunami hitting the coast of Japan 9 hours after the 1700 Cascadia earthquake.

Source: Simulation of 1700 tsunami. USGS/Japan Geological Survey.

(Figures 4.26 and 4.27). Geological evidence indicates that 13 great earthquakes have occurred in the last 6000 years in the Cascadia Subduction Zone. The average return period of large megathrust earthquakes in the region is in the order of 600 years. The last one occurred 300 years ago. Seismologists assign a 10% probability that the next "Big One" will occur in the next 50 years.

On 26 January 2011, on the anniversary of the 1700 Cascadia earthquake, more than 470 000 people from coastal British Columbia took part in the first "Great British Columbia ShakeOut," the largest earthquake drill ever conducted in Canada. Radio stations across the province joined in by sounding an alarm at 10:00 a.m. local time. Groups (schools, business, government, etc.) were encouraged to stage drills ranging from the very simple "Drop, cover, and hold on!" to complex simulations involving emergency response and recovery (Figure 4.28). Since then, the drill has become an annual event in British Columbia.

Figure 4.24
Ghost forest of Willapa Bay, Oregon.

Source: Brian F Atwater et al., 2005. *The Orphan Tsunami of 1700—Japanese Clues to a Parent Earthquake in North America.* Produced by the United States Geological Survey.

2012 HAIDA GWAII EARTHQUAKE, BRITISH COLUMBIA

Canada's largest earthquake (magnitude 7.7) of the twenty-first century occurred on 28 October 2012 off the coast of Haida Gwaii in northern British Columbia (Figures 4.7 and 4.12). The 2012 seism—like its

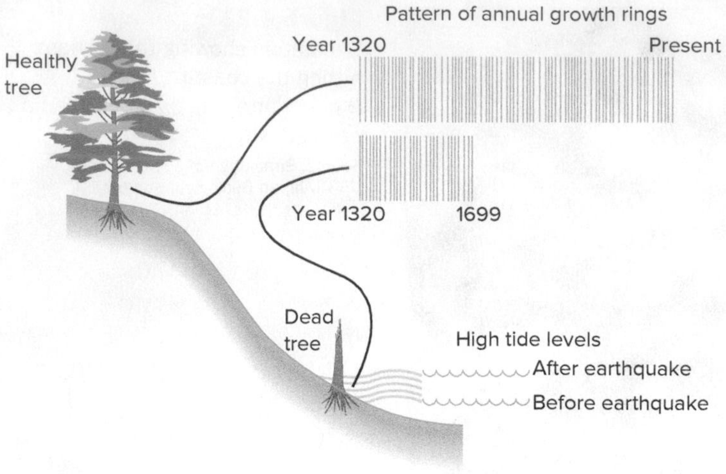

Figure 4.25
Annual growth rings in in long-lived tree species, such as the western red cedar and the sitka spruce, in the coastal forests of British Columbia, Washington, and Oregon. The spacing of rings in healthy trees is primarily a function of weather. In lower elevations, these forests also contain a number of dead trees still standing vertically, in growing position. Their rings reveal that these trees were growing vigorously until their sudden deaths, all at once, after the 1699 growing season. These observations concur with a sudden invasion of seawater that poisoned the trees. This rapid sea-level rise is thought to be a consequence of land dropping abruptly during a very large earthquake. If land subsidence had occurred at a slow pace, seawater invasion would have been a gradual process, and the trees would have died over several years.

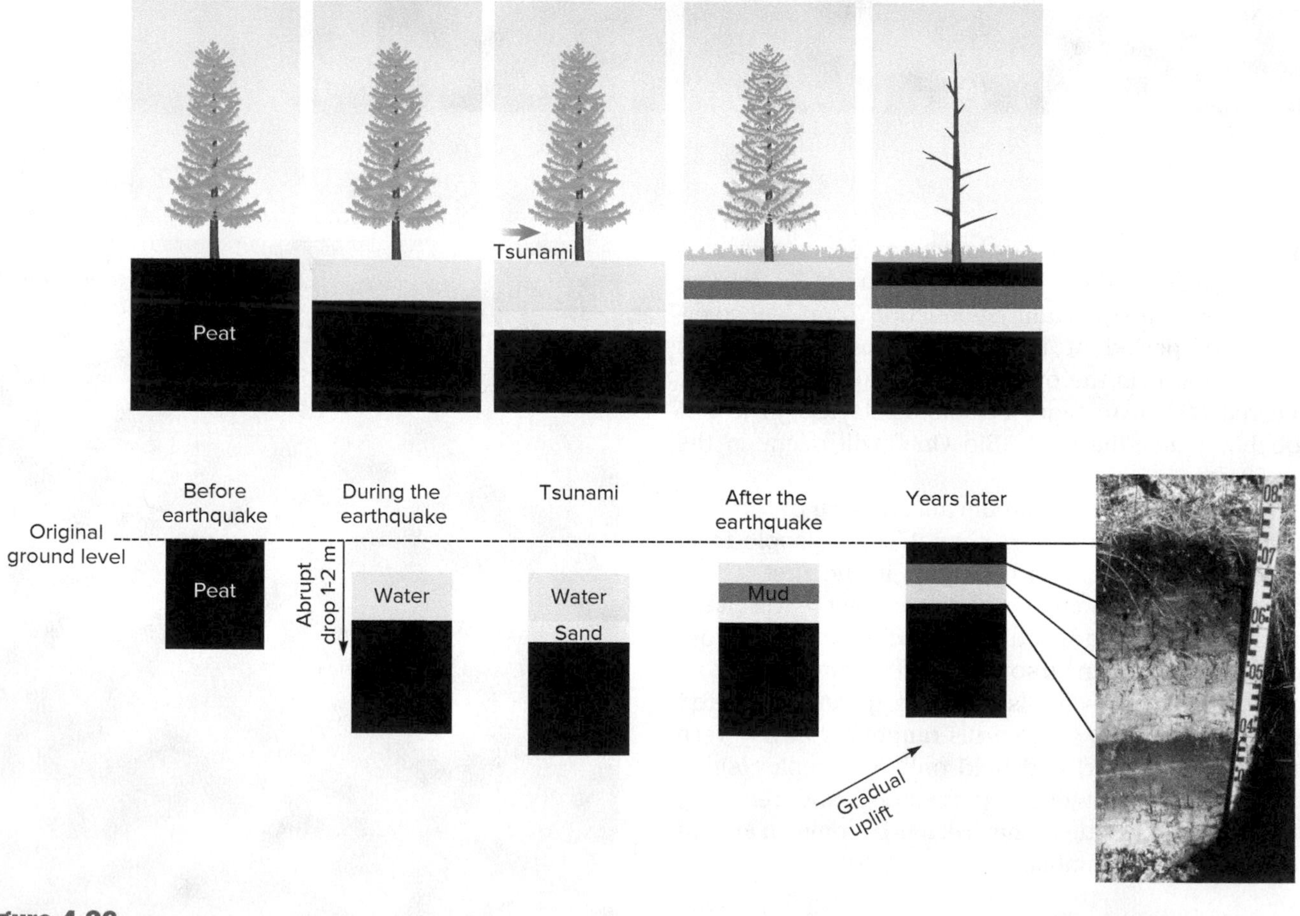

Figure 4.26
Repeating sequences of peat-mud-sand layers at coastal marshes. Peat is deposited when the marsh is above water. During an earthquake, the coast drops abruptly by one to two metres, submerging the marsh. The ensuing tsunami brings a layer of sand. Mud is deposited as long as the marsh remains underwater. Crustal uplift causes the marsh to gradually emerge. When the marsh is back above water, peat is deposited again, and the cycle repeats. Far right: Soil profile showing two cycles of peat-mud-sand deposition.

Source: Top row: modified from J. Clague, C. Yorath, and R. Franklin "At Risk: Earthquakes and Tsunamis on the West Coast". (e) Figure 5: Tidal Marsh Evidence (Clague and Bobrowsky, 1994a) http://earthquakescanada.nrcan.gc.ca/zones/cascadia/megafig-eng.php. Reproduced with the permission of Natural Resources Canada, 2014 (Clague and Bobrowsky, 1994a).

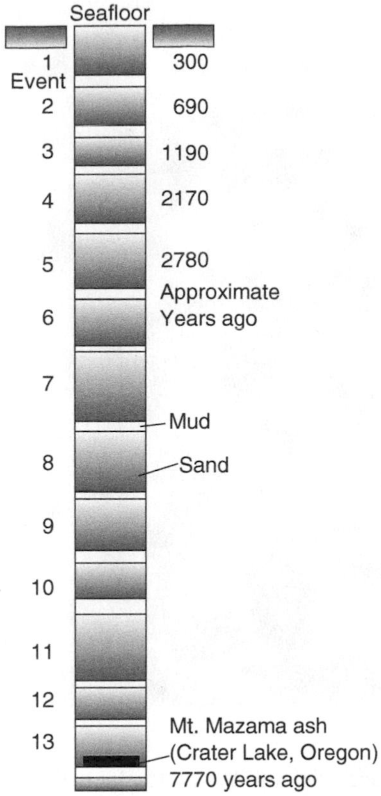

Figure 4.27
A core sample taken from the deep seafloor offshore British Columbia shows alternating mud and sand layers that can be dated. The sand layers are interpreted to have been deposited as a result of submarine mass movements triggered by great earthquakes. The most recent corresponds to the 1700 Cascadia earthquake, 300 years ago.

Source: Reproduced with the permission of Natural Resources Canada 2014, courtesy of the Geological Survey of Canada (J. Adams, 1990) http://earthquakescanada.nrcan.gc.ca/zones/cascadia/megafig-eng.php.

historical predecessors in 1929, 1949 (famous in seismology circles for having knocked cows off their feet!), and 1970—was a classic earthquake resulting from the abrasive movement of the Pacific and North American plates along the Queen Charlotte transform fault (Figure 4.14). Earthquakes along the Queen Charlotte fault share many similarities with their southern cousins, the San Andreas fault earthquakes. The Queen Charlotte fault, however, runs mostly offshore (see photo of chapter opener). Its earthquakes affect a largely unpopulated area and therefore present much less risk. Helicopter reconnaissance flights conducted a few days after the earthquake found no evidence of a tsunami but identified several fresh debris slides (Figure 4.29). These mass movements are thought either to have been triggered directly by the earthquake, or to have occurred during a rain storm a few days later because surfaces had been weakened by the earthquake.

LO4 Intraplate Earthquakes of Eastern Canada

Pushed by the ever-widening Atlantic Ocean, the landmass of Canada is drifting slowly to the west as part of the large North American plate. As predicted by plate tectonics, there is notable seismic activity on the edges of the plate: along Canada's Pacific coast to the west and along the spreading centres of the mid-Atlantic ridge to the east. Why is there then a cluster of **intraplate earthquakes** along the St. Lawrence River Valley and the Atlantic coast, regions that are thousands of kilometres away from plate boundaries (Figure 4.31)?

Figure 4.28
Basic safety precautions during an earthquake.

Source: Earthquake Country Alliance.

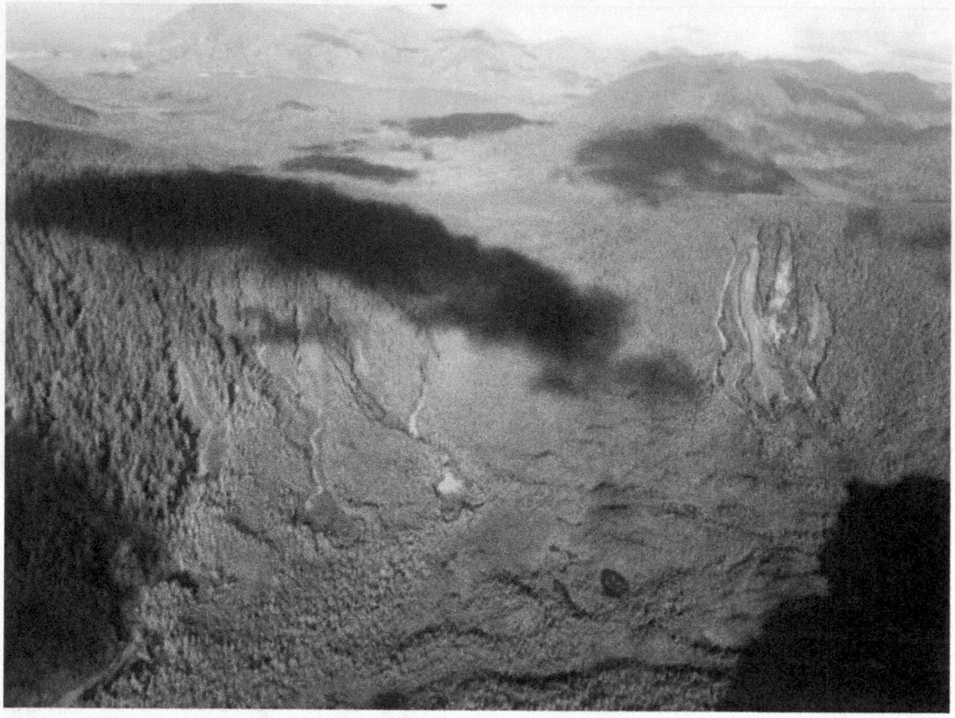

Figure 4.29
Cluster of debris slides south of Cowgala Bay (in background), Moresby Island, associated with the 2012 Haida Gwaii earthquake (except those outlined in red which predated the seism).
Source: Centre for Natural Hazard Research, Simon Fraser University.

The entire crust of the Earth is subjected to stresses (Figure 2.17) and the influence of deformation forces extends well into the interiors of continents. In these intraplate settings, ancient scars in the crust remain as zones of weakness where existing faults reactivate, fail due to current stress, and generate earthquakes. The geology of eastern Canada features several examples of processes weakening the crust locally, including rifting, impact cratering, and the **intrusion** of **igneous rocks** into the subsurface.

IMPACT AND EARTHQUAKES IN CHARLEVOIX

The present path of the St. Lawrence River follows an ancient tectonic structure related to the opening of the Atlantic ocean. Some 600 to 500 million years ago, a major rift valley extended through the region. This partially buried rift coincides with most of the large earthquakes in eastern Canada. Zooming in, the most active area along the rift is an 80 km by 35 km zone near Charlevoix, northeast of Quebec City. Here, earthquakes of magnitudes 6 to 7 occurred in 1663, 1791, 1860, 1870, and 1925. Why the concentration of large seisms in this one relatively small area? Charlevoix was the site of a meteorite impact some 350 million years ago. The northern half of the heavily eroded impact crater still stands out on a satellite image against the fabric of the Canadian Precambrian Shield (Figure 4.32). The southern half lies beneath the waters of the St. Lawrence River. When the epicentres for a 20-year period between January 1978 and September 1999 (including the epicentre of the 1992 earthquake we located in Figures 3.12, 3.13, and 3.14) are superimposed on the image, we can see clearly that the epicentres are not evenly distributed underneath the crater but follow the St. Lawrence River rift. The impact caused intensive fracturing of the area. The impact-caused fractures are probably being reactivated today under the stresses generated by the widening Atlantic Ocean (Figure 4.33).

EARTHQUAKES OF WESTERN QUEBEC

The western Quebec seismic zone is a cluster of intraplate earthquakes whose epicentres are located in a linear zone branching out from the St. Lawrence rift west of Montreal (Figure 4.31).

A speculative hypothesis proposes that the transform faults that offset the mid-Atlantic Ocean spreading centre continue northwestward as great

HUMAN FOCUS

John Cassidy, Research Scientist, Natural Resources Canada

I spent most of my childhood and youth in British Columbia "shaken" regularly by local earthquakes. In high school, I was interested in sciences so I took courses in all of them! I finally opted for physics for my undergraduate degree. One day, we were assigned homework on how to locate an earthquake near my hometown of Victoria. I found this application of physics very exciting, relevant to my everyday life and important to society. I decided to study earthquake seismology at the Master's degree level. This was followed by a Ph.D.at the University of British Columbia, where I investigated the structure and seismicity of the Cascadia Subduction Zone In detail. While writing my Ph.D. thesis I experienced a magnitude 5 earthquake with its epicentre just to the south in Washington State! This earthquake, and its many hundreds of aftershocks, reminded me of the importance of earthquake research.

A great deal has been accomplished in our understanding of the Cascadia subduction zone since my Ph.D. days. One theory at the time was that the Juan de Fuca plate was moving seamlessly under the North American plate without storing energy that could be released in a large earthquake. We now know, thanks to GPS and many other datasets, that the Juan de Fuca plate is "stuck", causing Vancouver Island to be squeezed horizontally and its west coast to rise. Energy is accumulating that eventually will be dissipated in a large subduction earthquake, with serious implications for public safety. People often do not realize that seismology is a young science. It really started in the late 1800s with the first recordings made with pendulum seismographs (Figure 3.4). When a large nearby earthquake struck, the pen would go off the scale and no data would be recorded! Seismology made a giant leap forward with the advent of digital recordings in the 1970s that allowed advanced mathematical analyses to be applied to the data. Another breakthrough was the addition of GPS data, which allowed scientists to measure deformation on the surface of the Earth directly.

I have travelled around the world to see damage from large earthquakes and how we can learn from these devastating events first hand. I visited San Francisco shortly after the 1989 Loma Prieta earthquake and witnessed damage related to local soil conditions. More recently, in 2010, I was in Chile a few days after the magnitude 8.8 Maule earthquake. The scale of the destruction was beyond my imagination: an area of 100 km by 500 km had been affected. What struck me most was the impact on people. Schools were closed. Businesses were damaged and people did not have jobs to go to anymore.

Large events that make the international news, such as the 2004 Indian Ocean and 2012 Tohoku, Japan earthquakes and tsunamis, are vivid reminders that there is no room for complacency and that British Columbia must maintain a high level of preparedness towards seismic hazards. I am determined to contribute to this goal and to make a difference. My current research focuses on the Georgia basin, which underlies metropolitan Vancouver. My work has shown that earthquake energy is amplified by the deep structure (kilometres below the surface) of the basin. The ground shaking is also affected by several interrelated variables such as bedrock topography, soil thickness, and local geology. I hope that furthering our knowledge of these complex phenomena will lead to improved building codes and reduced losses from future earthquakes.

Earthquake science, engineering, and disaster management are evolving rapidly. When I was attending grade school in British Columbia, there were no earthquake drills, there was little awareness of seismic risk, and seismic hazard maps were very basic. Now, we are seeing very substantial improvements both in national building codes that protect us from earthquakes, and in preparedness and awareness of earthquake hazards. Earthquake drills are now performed regularly, and schools in British Columbia are being retrofitted to withstand strong ground motion. Geophysicists, earth scientists, and engineers work as multidisciplinary teams with emergency managers and social scientists to bring a multifaceted approach to earthquake hazard mitigation. I am proud to contribute to these initiatives, and to serve as a scientist with Natural Resources Canada, working with universities, governments at all levels, and the private sector to help make our communities safer for generations to come.

Figure 4.30
John Cassidy, Research Scientist, Natural Resources Canada.
Source: Photo courtesy of John Cassidy, Natural Resources Canada

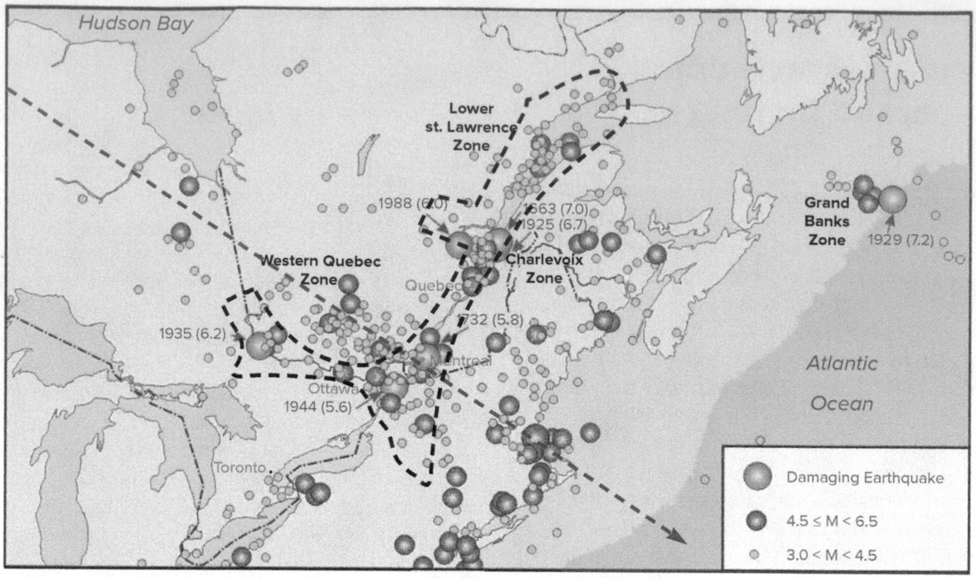

Figure 4.31
Seismicity map of eastern Canada (1568–1998). The black dashed line outlines the ancient St. Lawrence River Rift and its two failed arms, the Ottawa-Bonnechere and Saguenay graben. The red dotted line marks the track of the Great Meteor hot spot.
Source: Modified from Natural Resources Canada 2014.

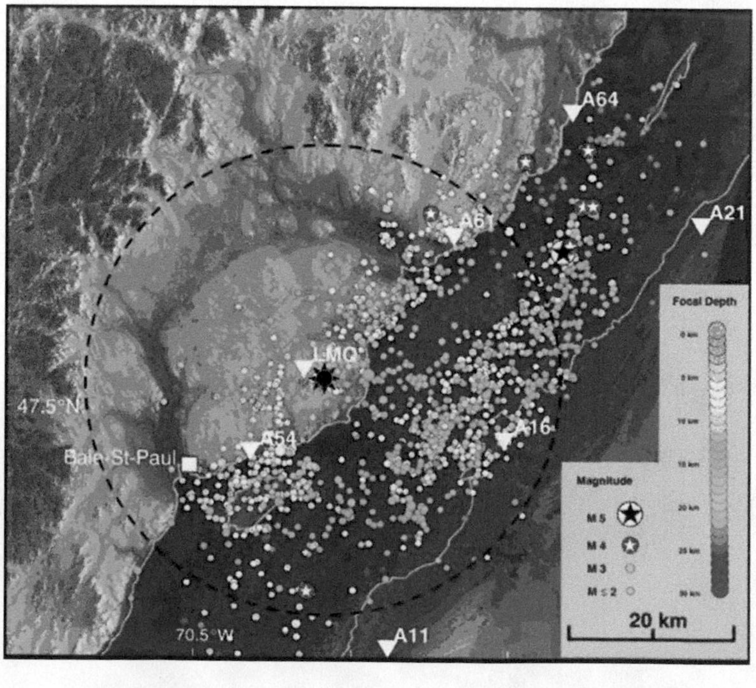

Figure 4.32
Earthquake epicentres from January 1978 to September 1999 superimposed on a satellite image of the Baie-St-Paul area in Charlevoix, Quebec. The black star represents the location of the meteoritic impact. The dashed circle represents the external boundary of the impact structure.
Source: Lamontage, M., Keating, P., and Toutin, T. Complex faulting confounds earthquake research in the Charlevoix Seismic Zone, Quebec. © Copyright 2000, 81, no. 26, p. 289–293. Reproduced by permission of American Geophysical Union.

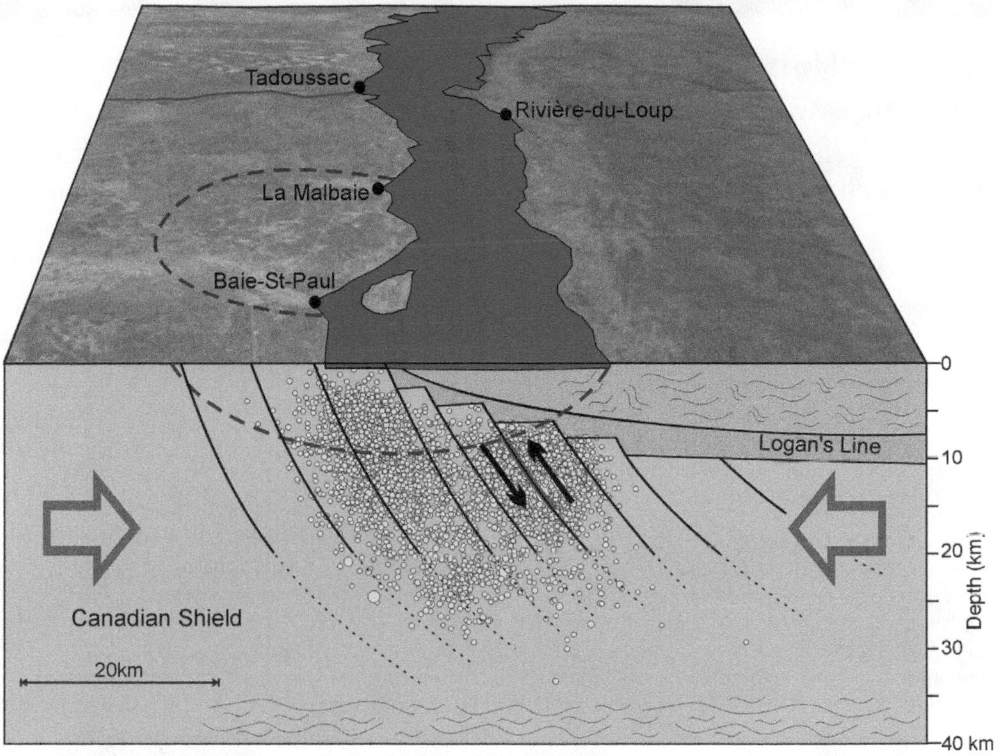

Figure 4.33
Three-dimensional view of the Charlevoix area. Hypocentres (yellow circles) cluster along pre-existing faults (oblique lines) associated with rifting and the opening of the Atlantic Ocean rather than along crater faults (dashed line).
Source: Lamontagne, M. © Her Majesty the Queen in Right of Canada 2014.

fracture zones beneath the North American continent, creating linear trends of crustal weakness. In Figure 4.35, notice how the northernmost fracture zone lines up with the epicentre of the 1929 Grand Banks earthquake. The southernmost fracture zone lines up with the epicentre of the 1886 Charleston, South Carolina, earthquake. The central fracture zone projects toward the New England seamounts and the western Quebec seismic zone.

An alternative hypothesis is that western Quebec earthquakes, the Monteregian Hills, and the New England seamounts are remnants of the passage of the North American plate over the Great Meteor hot spot. The Great Meteor hot spot is a long-lived thermal anomaly over which the westward drifting North American plate has been migrating, just as the Pacific plate migrates over the Hawaiian hot spot (Figure 2.32). Some 150 million years ago, the Great Meteor hot spot was underneath the present-day Ottawa River Valley. Molten rocks rose from deep in the mantle, were trapped in the crust, and crystallized in the subsurface. Several fractures developed in the crust to accommodate the intrusive bodies, creating local zones of weakness. These fractures might be reactivating and controlling present-day seismicity in the area. Since then, erosion has gradually removed the rocks surrounding several of these intrusive bodies, leaving them exposed. They form a chain of small mountains, the Monteregian Hills, the most famous being Mount Royal, after which the city of Montreal has been named (Figure 4.36). Approximately 100–80 million years ago, the plate continued its migration and molten material from the hot spot punctured the ocean floor to form the New England seamounts. The process continues today at the Great Meteor seamount in the Atlantic Ocean, south of the Azores.

HUMAN FOCUS

Marie de L'Incarnation and the 1663 Charlevoix Earthquake

Mother Marie de L'Incarnation, (1599–1672) (Figure 4.34) spent most of her life cloistered in the Ursuline monastery in Quebec City, yet she was one of best informed leaders of New France. Her writings are an invaluable source of information about the bourgeoning colony.

Marie de L'Incarnation (née Marie Guyart) joined the Ursuline religious order after becoming a widow. Answering a call from God, she embarked for New France to found a new convent, leaving her son Claude behind in France. Over the years, she would send him letters describing the challenges of her new life to foster his spiritual development.

The 1663 Charlevoix earthquake was felt all over eastern North America, an area of two million square kilometres. Marie de L'Incarnation wrote a vivid account of the magnitude 7 earthquake, in which religious references and concrete descriptions are intermingled:

> Thick dust flew from all sides. Doors opened of themselves. Others, which were open, closed. The bells of all our churches and the chimes of our clocks pealed quite alone, and steeples and houses shook like trees in the wind—all this in a horrible confusion of overturning furniture, falling stones, parting floors, and splitting walls. Amidst all this the domestic animals were heard howling. Some ran out of their houses; others ran in. In a word, we were all so frightened we believed it was the eve of Judgement, since all the portents were to be seen.

About the St. Lawrence River, she writes: ". . . nothing astonished us more, I say, than to see this river change and assume the colour of sulphur and retain it for a week." This coloration is probably the result of numerous landslides on the river banks. Traces of the 1663 landslides are still visible today, for example in St-Jean-Vianney, Quebec, which was to be the site of another spectacular mass movement two centuries later (Figure 13.23).

The earthquake struck on 5 February, a day before Shrove Tuesday. In Roman Catholic societies, this is a time of merrymaking when people celebrate carnival. Marie de l'Incarnation asks herself if the earthquake is not a sign from God to boisterous youth: "So unexpected a calamity, when the young people were preparing to spend the carnival season in excesses, was a clap of thunder on everyone's head, they expecting nothing less." She notes that, in his mercy, God did not punish humankind but merely issued a warning: "But the wondrous thing is that amidst so great and universal a wreckage, no one has perished or even been injured. This is a quite visible sign of God's protection of his people, which gives us just cause to believe that he is angry with us only to save us."

Dr. Anne Trépanier of Carleton University, who has studied in detail the writings of Marie de L'Incarnation, goes further. She notes that Marie de L'Incarnation distinguished between the French traders, accusing them of corrupting the First Nations people by trading alcohol, and the more virtuous Canadians (first generation of settlers born in Canada). In that respect, Marie de L'Incarnation captured a nascent sense of national identity. The 1663 earthquake was followed by a peak of religiosity in the local population, which Marie de L'Incarnation interpreted as a collective will for rebuilding New France as a more righteous society.

Figure 4.34
Statue of Marie de L'Incarnation who dedicated her life to First Nations girls' education. She was proclaimed a saint by Pope Francis in 2014.
Source: © Claire Samson.

IN GREATER DEPTH

Documenting the First Direct Casualties of a Canadian Earthquake

As of 2014, no loss of life has been attributed directly to an earthquake in Canada. A direct loss of life is defined as a death caused by the consequences of seismic ground motions or by surface rupture of a fault. Examples of events causing direct losses of life are partial or total collapses of buildings, and mass movements such as rockfalls, mudslides, and avalanches. Indirect losses of life are those related to physical, technological, or human consequences derived from earthquakes. The best Canadian example of an earthquake causing indirect loss of life is the 1929 Grand Banks earthquake, which sent a tsunami to the southern coast of Newfoundland.

In a letter describing the 1732 Montreal earthquake, Mother Duplessis of St. Helen from Quebec City mentions that one girl was killed in the event. Since there was no casualty reported by hospitals in Montreal, historians consider the remark an unfounded rumour.

According to recent investigations by Maurice Lamontagne, seismologist at Natural Resources Canada, the 20 October 1870 magnitude 6.5 earthquake, centred in the Charlevoix region of Quebec, may indeed have caused direct casualties.

Quebec City's *Quebec Daily Mercury* of 22 October 1870 reported: "At Éboulements, ten houses were completely thrown down, besides that of Mr. Clement, M.P.P., for Charlevoix, and Dr. Laterriere. Two children are reported killed in this parish, but a letter from there today does not mention the fact. It appears that all the houses within an area of a mile, in this locality, were more or less damaged and there would have been great loss of life had not the people hurriedly quitted their residences."

Quebec City's *Morning Chronicle—Commercial and Shipping Gazette* of 22 October 1870 reported: "At les Éboulements the church and ten houses were injured, and two children killed." The newspaper *Le Canadien* of 24 October 1870 says of the village Les Éboulements: *"Il y a eu deux enfants de tués en cet endroit.* [There were two children killed at that place]."

The parish registry of Les Éboulements reports two deaths of children on 24 October 1870. The first is Joseph Tremblay, 6 years old, *"mort l'avant veille* [who died the day before yesterday]," which would mean on 22 October. The other is Marie-Élizabeth Miville, 4 months old, *"décédée depuis quatre jours et déjà inhumée* [dead for four days and already buried]." The latter would have died on 20 October 1870, the date of the earthquake. The causes of the deaths are not mentioned. There are no other sources of information in existence.

From a lack of text explicitly mentioning the causes of the deaths of these two children, we cannot be certain that the earthquake was really to blame. In fact, deaths of children in their early years were quite common in those days. On the other hand, the severity of the earthquake in Les Éboulements (landslide, soil liquefaction, and damage to most houses, including complete destruction of some dwellings) makes it a likely cause of the deaths of these two children. As a footnote, it is interesting to note that the village name "Les Éboulements" translates to "landslides". Les Éboulements acquired its name when a huge landslide was triggered by the 1663 Charlevoix earthquake. The debris flow is still visible today as a tongue of earth advancing into the St. Lawrence River.

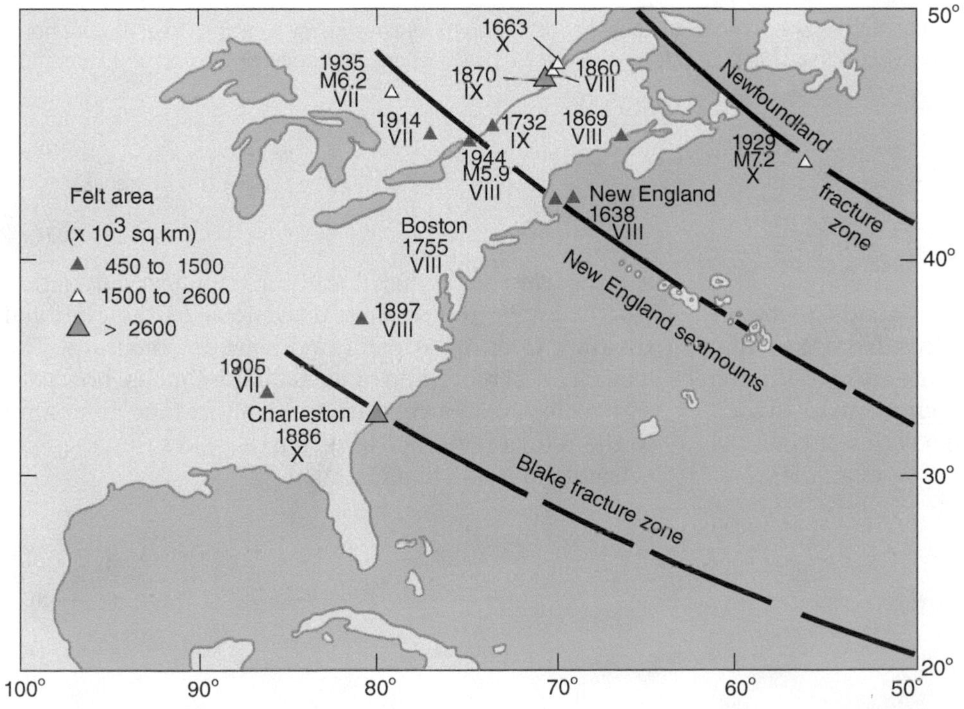

Figure 4.35
Location of earthquake epicentres in eastern North America and extensions of transform faults from the mid-Atlantic spreading centre.

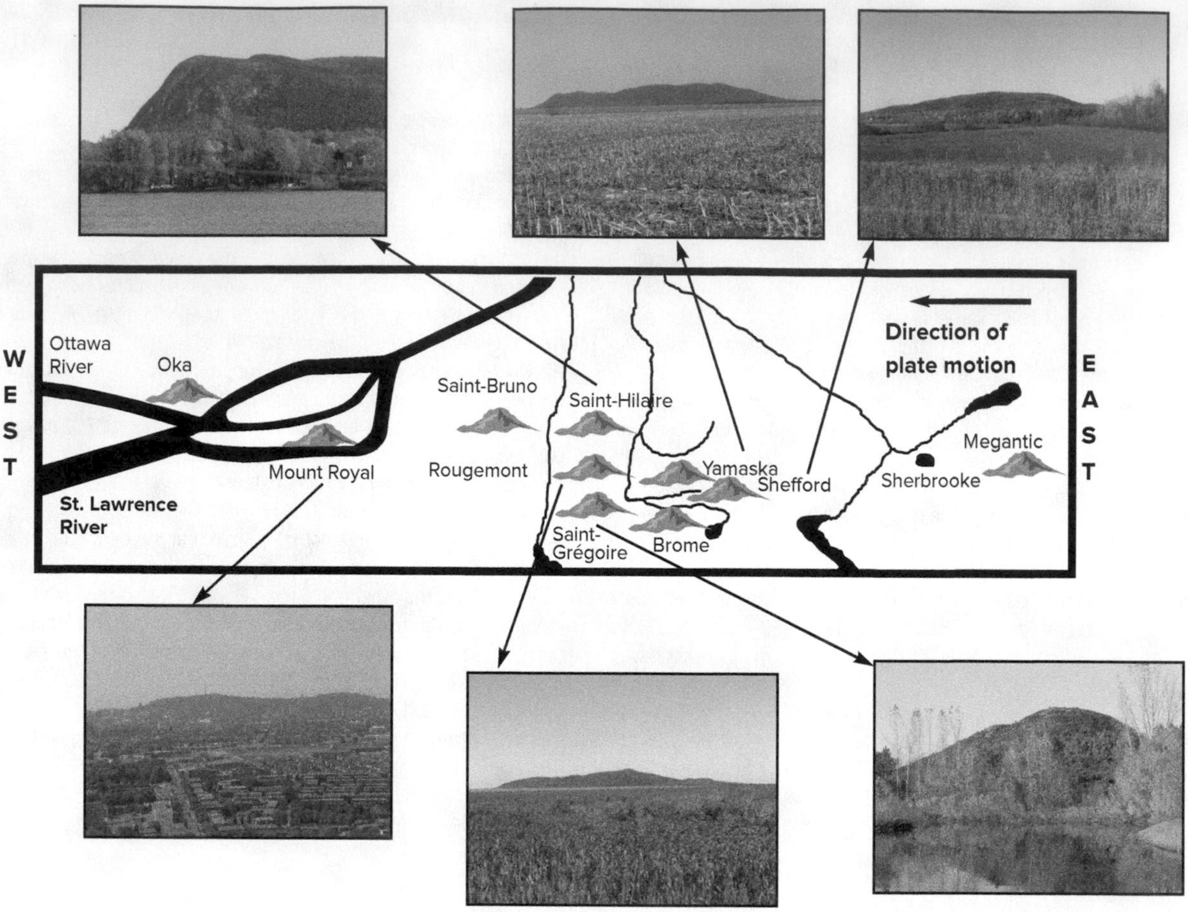

Figure 4.36

The ten Monteregian Hills of Ontario and southern Quebec formed by the passage of the North American plate over the Great Meteor hot spot 150 million years ago. Can you infer which hill is the oldest? Check your answer in the Questions for Review at the end of the chapter.

Source: © Claire Samson.

A Lot Still to Be Learned . . .

Significant efforts are deployed in Canada to better understand and assess seismic hazards, from the maintenance of a complex infrastructure of monitoring instruments to geological fault mapping. Canadian society is addressing seismic risk using a series of concrete measures for short-term response (for example, alert services and shakemaps) and for long-term mitigation (for example, the seismic provisions of the National Building Code of Canada and seismic zonation). The instrumental recording of earthquake signals, however, started less than a century ago, a short time compared to the return period of large earthquakes. Earthquake seismology is still in its infancy.

IN GREATER DEPTH

Seismicity Induced by Human Activities

Several engineering activities can produce earthquakes—some of them large enough to cause concerns—blurring the distinction between natural and human-made disasters.

Seismicity Related to Oil and Gas Production

As our energy-hungry society looks for new sources of fuel, the extraction of oil and gas from unconventional sources such as heavy crude oil and shale rocks increases. The hydrocarbons in both heavy oil and shales are difficult to extract. Heavy crude oil from tar sands often requires steam injection in order to flow. In the case of shale gas, an effective production strategy is to create a network of fractures in the subsurface to ease flow, a process known as hydraulic fracturing or "fracking". In a few cases, both steam injection and hydraulic fracturing have caused inactive faults to slip, generating earthquakes (Figure 4.37). World-wide, the largest earthquake induced by hydraulic fracturing was the magnitude 3.8 event of 19 May 2011 in the Horn River Basin of northeastern British Columbia. The earthquake was felt but did not cause any damage. To address public concerns, new technology has been developed to monitor seismicity related to oil and gas production. Sensors are deployed on the surface of the ground and in observation wells drilled near production boreholes (Figure 4.38).

Mining-Induced Seismicity

As mining progresses to ever-deeper levels (Canada's deepest underground mine, the Kidd Creek copper and zinc mine, currently extends to approximately 3 km below the surface), tunnels are driven through rock subjected to enormous stress. Over time, tunnel walls deform under pressure. On rare occasions, rocks fail abruptly and generate small earthquakes, which are especially dangerous since they occur underground (Figure 4.39). For instance, Kidd Creek mine experienced a serious magnitude 3.8 rock burst in 2011. As part of due diligence to protect miners, Canadian mines are equipped with seismic monitoring networks. If an area becomes abnormally active, work is stopped. Detailed re-entry protocols dictate when it is safe to resume operations.

Seismicity and Large Water Reservoirs

Building a large dam and impounding a deep reservoir of water may trigger earthquakes. Contrary to our intuition, the weight of the water in the reservoir is not the main trigger of these earthquakes. The earthquakes

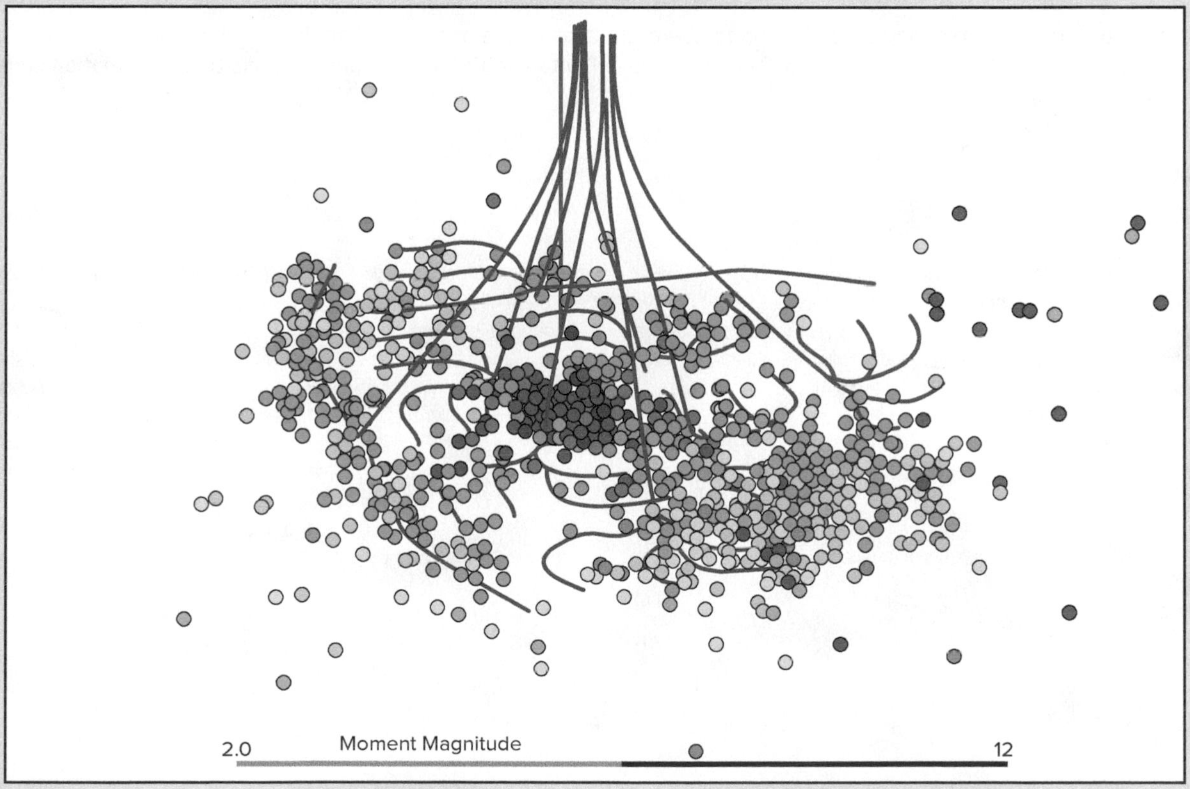

Figure 4.37

Small earthquakes (dots coloured according to magnitude) detected in the vicinity of production wells (blue solid lines).

Source: Engineering Seismology Group.

continued

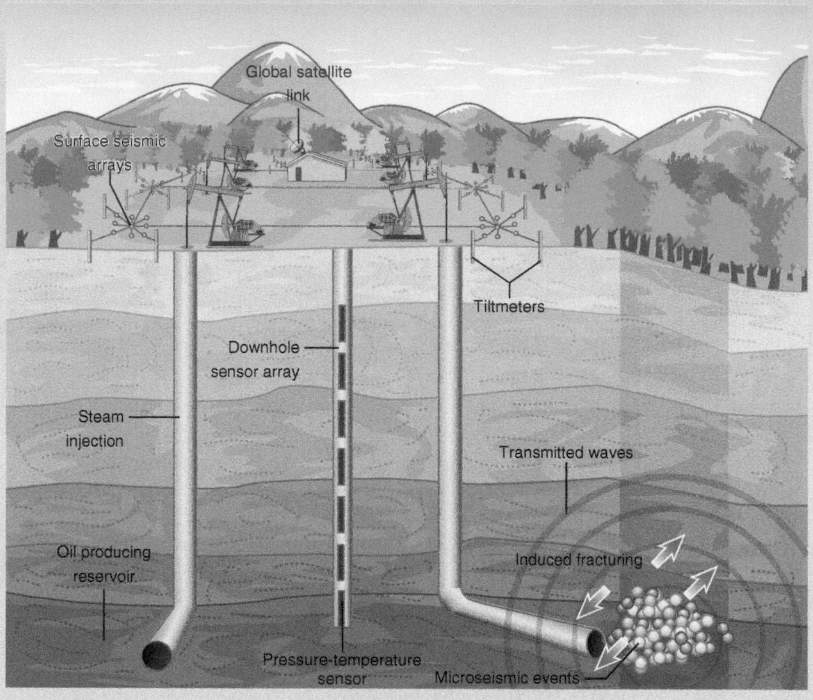

Figure 4.38

Sensitive borehole seismometers and pressure and temperature sensors are deployed in an observation well (centre) to monitor seismic activity generated by steam injection (left) and hydraulic fracturing (right). Additional seismic and deformation sensors are deployed on the surface.

Source: Engineering Seismology Group.

are primarily associated with water seeping through the floor of the reservoir and flowing slowly underground, pushed by the large body of reservoir water above it. The underground water moves downward and outward as an advancing front of high pressure along pre-existing faults or fractures. When the shear resistance is sufficiently low, the sides of the fault move abruptly, giving rise to an earthquake.

The province of Quebec, with its large hydroelectric infrastructure, has experienced many cases of reservoir-induced seismicity. The first case was reported in 1975 under the reservoir created by the Manic-3 dam. The earthquake had a magnitude of 4.1 on the Richter scale and caused quite a surprise. In months to follow, hundreds of smaller shocks occurred, closely monitored by portable seismographs. Later, a permanent seismograph station was added to monitor the activity, which eventually died down. Most earthquakes were shallow (about 1 km deep) and located along one of the numerous fractures of the Canadian Precambrian Shield in the area. Surprisingly, a much larger reservoir upstream from the Daniel-Johnson dam (formerly the Manic-5 dam; Figure 4.40), which made the Manicouagan crater visible from space (Figure 14.3), did not cause any reservoir-induced seismicity. Other cases were observed in other large reservoirs in Quebec, but none approached the magnitude of the earthquake recorded at Manic-3. The small magnitude of most reservoir-induced seismicity makes it a minor risk to large dams.

continued

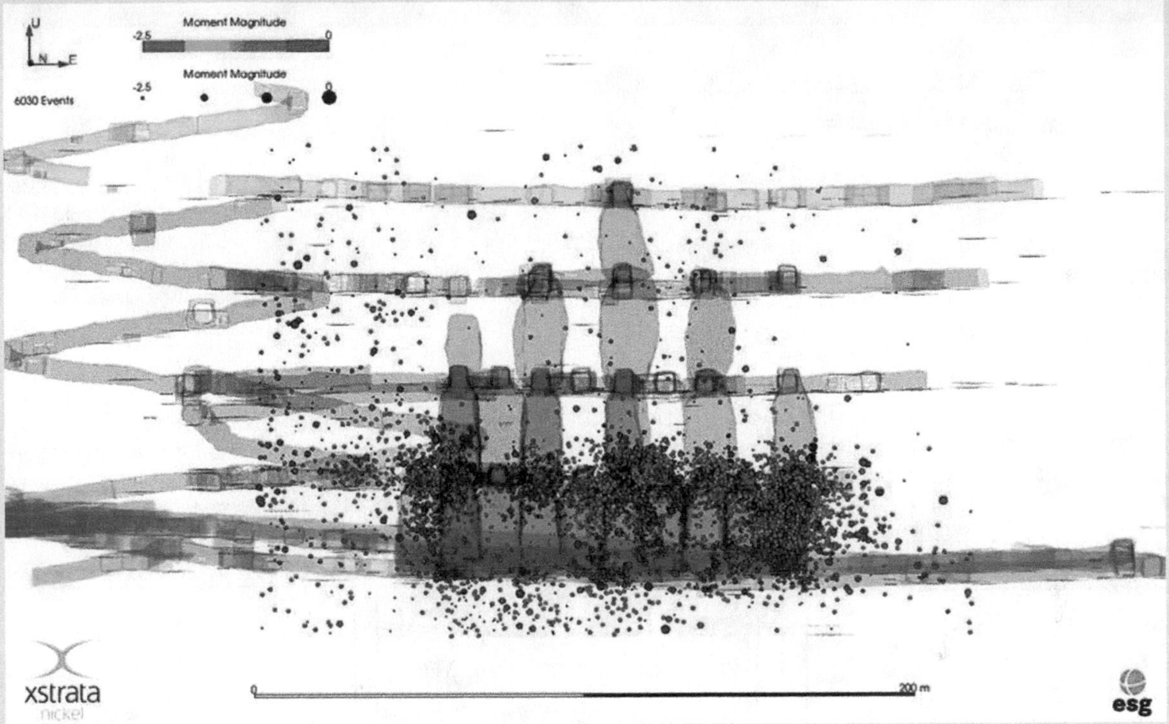

Figure 4.39
Cross-section view of an underground mine model with a spiral ramp (left) and 5 horizontal tunnels. Ore has been removed from the areas shown in blue. Dots correspond to the epicentres of very small earthquakes induced by mining activities. Epicentres tend to cluster near the most recent active mining area, in this example, along the two deepest tunnels.
Source: Glencore Canada.

Figure 4.40
The Daniel-Johnson dam on the Manicouagan River, Quebec. The dam, the largest multiple-arch-and-buttress dam in the world, was completed in 1968.
Source: Hydro-Quebec.

IN GREATER DEPTH

What to Do Before, During, and After an Earthquake

Before

We have seen that earthquakes don't kill us: it is our own buildings and belongings that fall when the Earth shakes that harm us. What should you do to prepare for an earthquake? *First,* walk into each room of your home, assume strong shaking has begun, and carefully visualize what might fall (for example, ceiling fan, chandelier, mirror, china cabinet, gas water heater). Now reduce the risk. Nail them. Brace them. Tie them. Velcro™ them. Lower them. Remove them.

Second, walk outside, assume strong shaking, and visualize what might fall (for example, trees, power lines, brick chimneys). Now reduce the risk, where possible. Trim them. Chop them. Replace them.

Third, repeat the visits inside and outside your home. This time, locate safe spots where protection exists, for example, under a heavy table, beneath a strong desk, or under a bed. Remember these safe spots so you can use them quickly when shaking begins.

During

After examining your home, prepare yourself to stay composed during the shaking. Drop, cover, and hold on (Figure 4.28 and Figure 4.41a). Remember that the severe shaking probably will last only 5 to 60 seconds. So, be calm and protect yourself for one minute. In most places, if you are inside, you should stay inside; if you are outside, stay outside.

After

Expect aftershocks. If you feel aftershocks, stay where you are until they stop.

Do a safety check around your home. Check for fire hazards such as gas leaks and damaged electrical wiring (Figure 4.41b). Check for structural damage to your home. Approach chimneys with caution. Turn on a battery-powered radio for information and damage reports (Figure 4.41c).

(a) (b) (c)

Figure 4.41
Simple earthquake safety steps.
Source: Reproduced with the permission of Natural Resources Canada, 2014.

SUMMARY

- A seismicity map reveals that Canada can be divided into a stable central region, flanked by seismically active regions to the west, north, and east.
- The seismically active western region coincides with active tectonic environments. The subduction of small oceanic plates underneath the North American plate has triggered several megathrust earthquakes in the Cascadia Subduction Zone in the last few thousand years. Vancouver is the Canadian city where seismic risk is highest. In northern British Columbia, the alongside movement of the Pacific and North American plates along the Queen Charlotte fault has produced several transform fault earthquakes in the past. These large earthquakes, however, affect a largely unpopulated area.
- The earthquakes of the seismically active eastern region occur far from plate boundaries. The causes of these intraplate earthquakes are more enigmatic. The seisms seem to be related to pre-existing zones of weakness in the crust that are reactivated under current stresses. Ancient rifting, the Charlevoix

meteoritic impact, and intrusions have left scars in the crust where rocks are more susceptible to fail. The continued opening of the Atlantic Ocean has been invoked as the source of present-day regional stress.

- Seismicity patterns, seismic wave propagation data, and geological trends are integrated to produce a national seismic hazard map for Canada. At the local level, several cities are compiling maps of local soil conditions to identify zones more vulnerable to seismic amplification effects.
- In Canada, seismic risk is mitigated in the long term by the design of a better earthquake-resistant infrastructure. In the event of an earthquake, automated alert services and shakemaps could contribute to an effective short-term response.

Terms to Remember

accelerograph
fracture zone
igneous rock
intraplate earthquake
intrusion
seismicity
seismic zonation
shakemap

Questions for Review

Ans. In Figure 4.36, the oldest Monteregian hill is Oka.

1. Sketch a plate-tectonic map of western North America from Alaska through Mexico. Label the spreading centres, subduction zones, and transform faults. What types of earthquakes are expected along the coastal zones?
2. Where do earthquakes occur in Canada? Where do megathrust earthquakes occur? Why?
3. Do damaging earthquakes occur in Canada?
4. What are the similarities between the Queen Charlotte faults of northern British Columbia and the San Andreas fault of California?
5. What is the largest earthquake ever felt in Canada? The largest ever recorded?
6. What other natural disasters can be associated with earthquakes?

Questions for Further Thought

1. On the basis of the map presented in Figure 4.9, where in Ottawa would you build bungalows? High-rise apartment buildings?
2. Which would be the better of two bad choices for the Vancouver area: a magnitude 6.5 to 7 earthquake every 15 years or a magnitude 8 earthquake every century?
3. How earthquake safe is your home or school? Where are the nearest faults? What kind of earth materials is your home or office built upon? How will your building size, shape, and materials react to shaking? What hazards exist inside your home?
4. If the return period of magnitude 7 earthquakes in a particular urban area is 1000 years, which buildings should be built to withstand it? For example, should we go to a lot of expense to make houses withstand it? Nuclear power plants? Refineries? Schools? Explain in each case why or why not.
5. How should the Canadian federal government split limited funds for seismic risk analysis and mitigation between western and eastern Canada?

Interesting Websites

- Earthquakes Canada, Natural Resources Canada
  http://earthquakescanada.nrcan.gc.ca
- See the shaking! Live seismogram viewer, Earthquakes Canada
  http://www.earthquakescanada.nrcan.gc.ca/stndon/wf-fo/index-eng.php
- Prepare Now for an Earthquake in British Columbia, Provincial Emergency Program, British Columbia
  http://www.pep.bc.ca/hazard_preparedness/prepare_now/prepare.html

- The Great British Columbia ShakeOut Earthquake Drill
  http://www.shakeoutbc.ca
- ShakeMap Atlas, United States Geological Survey
  http://earthquake.usgs.gov/earthquakes/shakemap/atlas.php
- Interactive seismic zonation map of Ottawa
  http://http-server.carleton.ca/~dariush/Microzonation/vs30-map/google_map.html

CHAPTER FIVE

5

Volcanic Eruptions and Landforms

View over the harbour city of Catania, Sicily, toward Mount Etna. The city has been buried seven times by lava from Etna. Each time, the city has been rebuilt on top of its predecessor to await its turn to be buried.

Source: © Pat Abbott.

"History teaches everything, including the future."

—Alphonse de Lamartine

Outline

LO1 List the magma characteristics that control peaceful versus explosive eruptions.

LO2 Explain how energy is released during a volcanic eruption.

LO3 Describe various volcanic materials.

LO4 Explain the three Vs of volcanology and relate them to eruptive style and landforms.

LO5 Use the volcanic explosivity index.

Volcanoes produce overwhelming doses of energy no human can survive. The dangers of volcanic eruption are obvious, but the quiet spells between active volcanism are seductive. Some people, including many who should know better, are lured to volcanoes like moths to a flame. On 14 January 1993, volcanologists attending a workshop in Colombia, as part of the international decade of natural disaster reduction, hiked into the summit **crater** of Galeras Volcano to sample gases. They were looking for ways to predict imminent eruptions. The volcano had been quiet since July 1992, but during their visit, an unexpected, gas-powered secondary eruption killed six in the scientific party—four Colombians, a Russian, and a Briton. Unfortunately, deaths such as these have not been unusual events (Table 5.1). The early 1990s saw an increase of fatalities, which prompted the International Association of Volcanology and Chemistry of the Earth's Interior (IAVCEI) to issue safety recommendations for volcanologists and the general public. Since then, encouragingly, only one fatal incident has occurred.

The statistics shown in Table 5.1 serve as a small-scale example of the larger drama played out when a volcano suddenly buries an entire city. People commonly speculate about whether an individual volcano is active, dormant, or extinct. The word "dormant" is derived from the French verb *dormir*, which means "to sleep." Because of the strong hope that it is an **extinct volcano** and the nearby land is thus available for use, many **dormant volcanoes** are misclassified. During long periods of volcanic quiescence, people tend to build cities near volcanoes. For example, today 400 000 people live on the flanks of Galeras Volcano, defying the inevitability of a large eruption. But consider this: A subduction zone commonly lasts for tens of millions of years, and its province of volcanoes is active for the entire time. An individual volcano may be active for millions of years, but its eruptive phases are commonly separated by centuries of inactivity, lulling some into a false sense of security. As a general rule, if a volcano has a well-formed and aesthetic conical shape, it is active. A pretty shape is dangerous (Figure 5.30).

Several Canadian volcanoes are dormant (they are indicated by stars in Figure 6.14). Three were active in the eighteenth and nineteenth centuries. They might only be taking a short nap.

TABLE 5.1

People Killed by Eruptions (1951–2014)

Year	Volcano	Total Deaths	Volacanologists' Deaths
1951	Kelut, Indonesia	7	3
1952	Myojin-sho, Japan	31	9
1979	Karkar, Papua New Guinea	2	2
1980	Mount St. Helens, United States	62	2
1991	Unzen, Japan	44	3
1991	Lokon-Umpong, Indonesia	1	1
1993	Galeras, Colombia	9	6
1993	Gaga Pichincha, Ecuador	2	2
2000	Semeru, Indonesia	2	2
2014	Mount Ontake, Japan	51	0

A Classic Volcano: Vesuvius

The most famous of all volcanoes is probably Vesuvius in Italy. Vesuvius has been a source of both fear and wonder over its 6000 years of coexistence with local humans (Figure 5.1). Vesuvius began as a submarine volcano in the Bay of Naples. It grew greatly in size, and its rocky debris filled in the waters that once separated it from mainland Italy. What is the cause of the volcanism at Vesuvius and the neighbouring volcanoes of Stromboli, Vulcano, Etna, and others? It is the subduction of Mediterranean seafloor beneath Europe to make room for the northward charge of Africa.

The eruption of Vesuvius in 3780 **BCE** has been studied in detail by Giuseppe Mastrolorenzo and coworkers. The pre-historic eruption sterilized the plain surrounding the volcano with ash and steam, leading to the desertification of the natural environment,

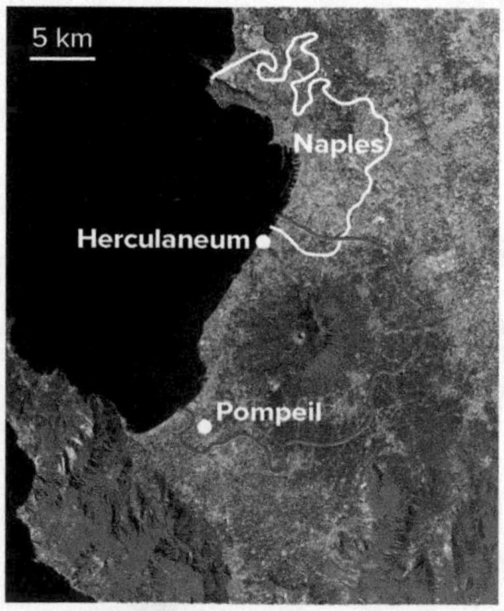

Figure 5.1
Mount Vesuvius is surrounded by a densely populated urbanized region, including the city of Naples, whose limits are delineated by a white line. The red line marks the zone that will be evacuated ahead of an eruption.
Source: NASA.

social-demographic collapse and the abandonment of the area for centuries (Figure 5.2). Mastrolorenzo and his team of earth scientists and anthropologists speculate that the event represents a worst-case scenario for a future eruption.

Vivid accounts of a Vesuvius eruption are found in the classic texts of Pliny the Younger, a survivor of the eruption that destroyed much of Pompeii and caused serious damage in Herculaneum and Neapolis (Naples):

> And now came the ashes, but at first sparsely. I turned around. Behind us, an ominous thick smoke, spreading over the earth like a flood, followed us. "Let's go into the fields while we can still see the way," I told my mother—for I was afraid that we might be crushed by the mob on the road in the midst of darkness. We had scarcely agreed when we were enveloped in night—not a moonless night or one dimmed by cloud, but the darkness of a sealed room without lights. To be heard were only the shrill cries of women, the wailing of children, the shouting of men. Some were calling to their parents, others to their children, others to their wives—knowing one another only by voice. Some wept for themselves, others for their relations. There were those who, in their very fear of death, invoked it. Many lifted up their hands to the gods, but a great number believed there were no gods, and that this was to be the world's last eternal night.

Small earthquakes had been a common occurrence during the 17 years preceding the eruption. Finally, on 24 August 79 CE, Vesuvius began erupting and most residents fled Pompeii. Those who stayed first experienced volcanic ash clouds dropping **pumice** up to three metres deep. It is thought that about 60% of the people who remained in Pompeii survived the first flows of ash and pumice. About half of the survivors then fled, but many of them died when they were caught outside during later flows of ash and pumice. The people still inside houses remained alive only to suffocate from breathing hot particles and gases seeping out of the volcanic debris. Death was not always quick. Some bodies were found inside houses on top of thick layers of pumice—evidence of hours of struggle by people fighting to stay alive and holding cloths over their mouths to avoid asphyxiation. The volcano then entered a second eruptive phase, in which it blew immense volumes of volcanic material up to 32 km high into the atmosphere. The height of the eruption column varied as the volcanic energy waxed and waned. At intervals, the great vertical column of ash would temporarily collapse, sending **pyroclastic flows** down the volcano slopes. These flows finished off the surviving Pompeiians.

In the coastal city of Herculaneum, 300 skeletons were found in life-like positions in boat chambers at the beach. The skeletons of these people killed by the eruption testify to the lethal energy they experienced. The people had not been battered or suffocated; they did not display any voluntary self-protection reactions or agony contortions. In other words, their vital organs stopped functioning in less than a second, in less time than they could consciously react. The types of bone fractures, tooth cracks, and bone coloration indicate the victims were covered by volcanic material at a temperature of about 500°C (Figure 5.3).

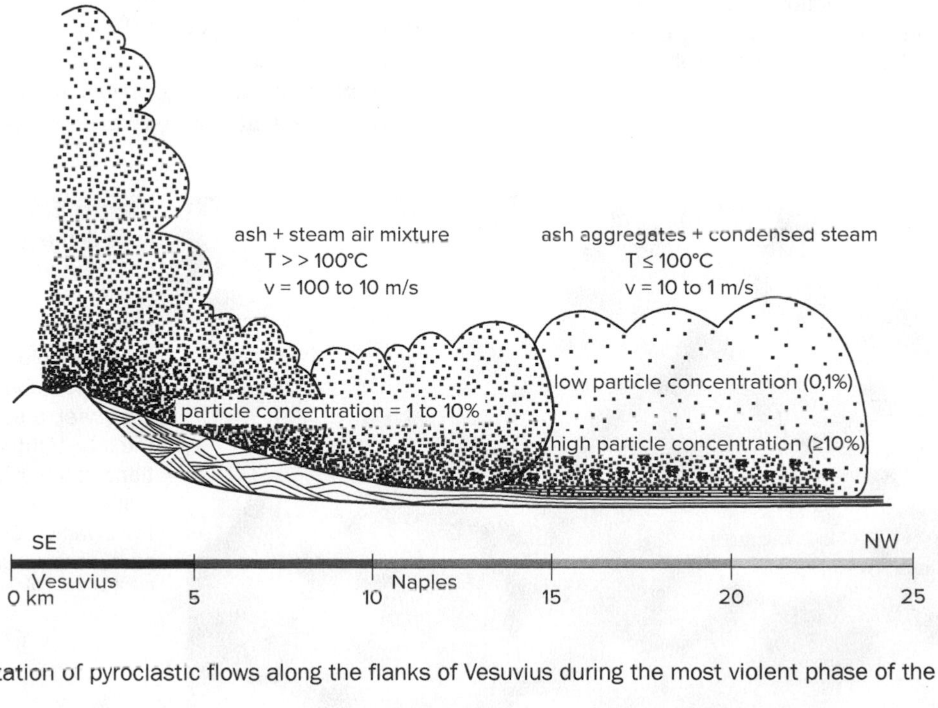

Figure 5.2
Schematic representation of pyroclastic flows along the flanks of Vesuvius during the most violent phase of the 3780 BCE eruption.
Source: Modified from Mastrolorenzo et al., 2006.

Figure 5.3
Feet of a child killed by an eruption from Vesuvius in 79 CE. The flexed toes and feet were an involuntary contraction when surrounded by 500°C volcanic material. Death was instantaneous.

Source: © Mastrolorenzo, G., Petrone, P., Pagano, M., Incoronato, A., Baxter, P., Canzanella, A., Fatore, L., in *Nature,* 410:769,2001.

After 79 CE, large eruptions occurred more often: in 203, 472, 512, 685, 993, 1036, 1049, and 1138–1139 CE. Then nearly 500 years passed; time to forget the past and recolonize the mountain. But in 1631, Vesuvius poured out large volumes of lava that destroyed six towns; mudflows ruined another nine towns, and about 4000 people perished. Between 1631 and 1944, there were 18 eruption cycles; each lasted from 2 to 37 years with quiet intervals ranging from 0.5 to 6.8 years (Figure 5.4).

Since 1944, Vesuvius has been quiet. Is this interval of calm setting the stage for another major eruption? It is not known for sure, but consider that almost three million people live within reach of Vesuvius today, including about one million people living on the slopes of the volcano. Italy's civil protection agency has formulated an elaborate emergency plan in case of an eruption. The plan defines a "red zone" surrounding Vesuvius where half a million people will be evacuated before an eruption takes place (Figure 5.1). The key variable here is time. When exactly will the authorities give the evacuation signal? How much time will people have to leave safely? Is this realistic?

Chemical Composition of Magma

Plate tectonics has given us great insight into the relationship between volcanoes and tectonic environments (Figure 2.42). From a disaster perspective, the differences between volcanoes in different tectonic environments are clear. Oceanic volcanoes are relatively peaceful, whereas subduction-zone volcanoes are explosive and dangerous. Ironically, humans tend to congregate at the seaward edges of the continents,

Figure 5.4
Lava dome growing in the crater of Mount Vesuvius, a few weeks before the eruption of 1767. This fascinating illustration is one of 54 hand-coloured plates by artist Pietro Fabris found in *Campi Phlegraei,* a scientific treatise on the late-eighteenth-century eruptions of Vesuvius written by Sir William Hamilton, Britain's envoy to the Spanish Court at Naples.

Source: Glasgow University Library, Department of Special Collections.

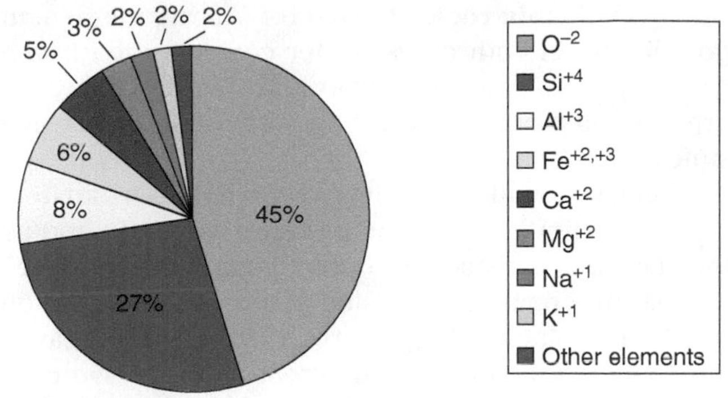

Figure 5.5
Common elements in the Earth's crust (percentage by weight).

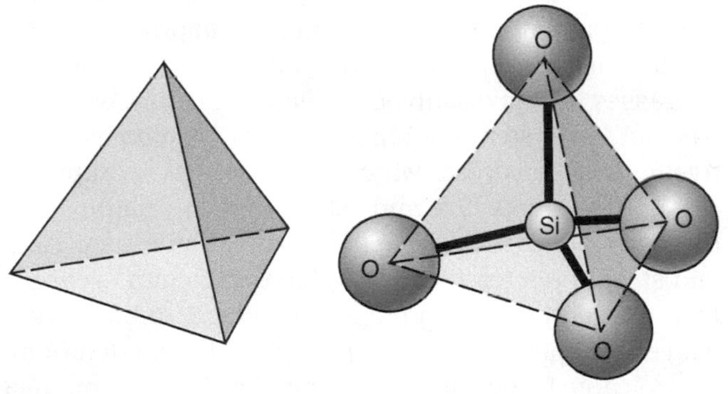

Figure 5.6
A silicon atom with +4 charge is linked to four oxygen atoms each with a −2 charge.

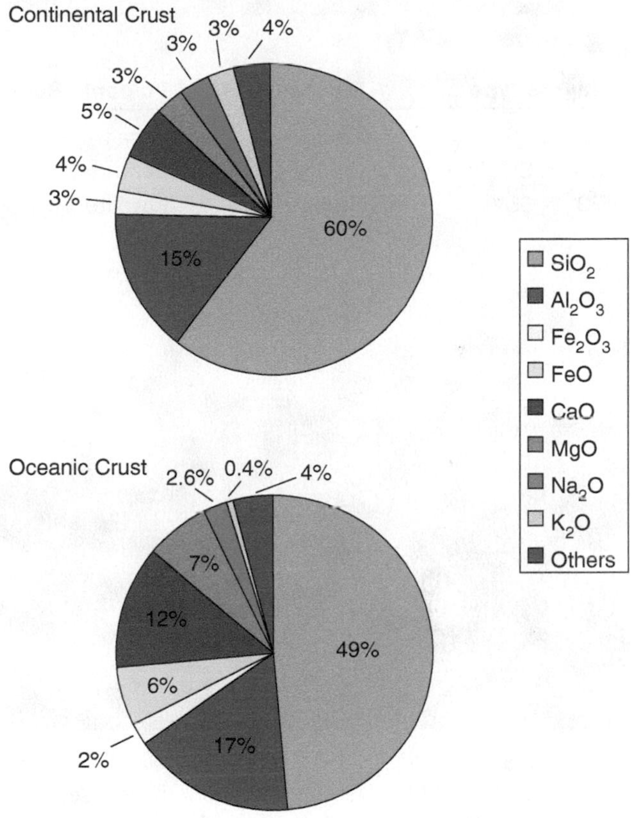

Figure 5.7
Crustal oxides (percentage by weight).

where the most dangerous volcanoes operate. Why do spreading-centre volcanoes have relatively peaceful eruptions? And why do subduction-zone volcanoes explode violently? The answers to these questions can be found by learning how different **magma** behaves. Although there are 92 naturally occurring elements, a mere 8 make up more than 98% of the Earth's crust (Figure 5.5). Oxygen and silicon are so abundant that their percentages dwarf those of all other elements. Oxygen atoms carry negative charges (−2), while silicon atoms are positively charged (+4). As magma begins cooling, some silicon and oxygen atoms bond. A central silicon atom (+4) links up with four oxygen atoms ($4 \times -2 = -8$) to form the silicon-oxygen tetrahedron (SiO_4) (Figure 5.6). The SiO_4 tetrahedron is particularly stable; the bond between silicon and oxygen atoms is the strongest of all the different oxides commonly present in the earth's crust (Figure 5.7). The SiO_4 tetrahedron presents a −4 charge on its exterior that attracts positively charged atoms. After negatively charged oxygen, the seven elements of greatest abundance in the Earth's crust are all positively charged (Figure 5.5); they are attracted to, and bound up with, oxygen. This process is so common that elemental abundances in the crust are usually listed in combination with oxygen (as oxides). The percentages of elements by weight are quite different in continental crust versus oceanic crust (Figure 5.7). These marked differences in oxide percentages produce magma of variable composition and behaviour.

LO1 Water Content, Viscosity, and Temperature of Magma

Volcanic behaviour can be understood by considering the properties of three types of magma and the volcanic rocks they become—**basalt, andesite,** and **rhyolite** (Table 5.3). The rock types are based on their silicon and oxygen (SiO_2) percentages (Table 5.2). If magma cools and solidifies below the surface, it crystallizes as **plutonic rocks,** named for Pluto, the Greek god of the underworld. If magma reaches the surface,

TABLE 5.2

Igneous Rock Types

Magma Type	Plutonic Rock	Volcanic Rock
$SiO_2 < 55\%$	Gabbro	Basalt
$55\% \leq SiO_2 \leq 65\%$	Diorite	Andesite
$SiO_2 > 65\%$	Granite	Rhyolite

Figure 5.8
Peaceful eruption of low-viscosity magma with easy separation of volatiles from magma, Surtsey, Iceland.
Source: © Pat Abbott.

it forms **volcanic rocks**, named for Vulcan, the Roman god of fire. In both cases, water concentration in the magma plays a controlling role, and viscosity a secondary role, in determining a peaceful versus explosive style of eruption.

Magma contains dissolved gases held as **volatiles;** their solubility increases as pressure increases and as temperature decreases. You can visualize the pressure–temperature relationship using a carbonated beverage in a bottle as an analogy. Carbon dioxide (CO_2) gas is dissolved in the beverage and kept under pressure by the bottle cap. Pop the cap off the bottle, reducing pressure, and some volatiles escape. As the uncapped bottle warms, more volatiles are lost.

In magma, water is the most abundant dissolved gas. Water lowers the melting point of rock, causing it to partially liquefy and start to migrate upward. As magma rises toward the surface and pressure decreases, water dissolved in the hot magma becomes gas and forms steam bubbles. Basaltic magma has relatively little dissolved water, helping make eruptions peaceful (Figures 5.8 and 5.9). Rhyolitic magma, on the other hand, is up to 6% dissolved water; as it rises and steam bubbles form, they have difficulty escaping from the high-viscosity magma and have to burst their way out (Figure 5.10). The greatest factors in determining volcanic hazard are how much gas is in the magma and how easily the dissolved gases can escape from

Figure 5.9
Volcano viewing is a spectator's sport in Hawaii! You can safely stay close to slowly advancing lava flows during a peaceful eruption.
Source: © Leigh Hilbert.

Figure 5.10
Explosive eruption of high-viscosity magma and trapped volatiles, Paricutin Volcano, Michoacan, Mexico.
Source: © United States Geological Survey.

the magma. As Frank Perret stated: "Gas is the active agent, and magma is its vehicle."

Liquids vary in how they flow; some flow quickly, some flow slowly, and some barely flow at all. A liquid's internal resistance to flow is measured by its viscosity; viscosity may be thought of as a measure of fluid friction. The lower the viscosity, the more fluid the behaviour. For example, tilt a glass of water and watch it flow quickly; water has low viscosity. Now tilt a glass filled with honey and watch the slower flow; honey has higher viscosity. Low-viscosity magma flows readily. High-viscosity magma barely flows.

The viscosity of magma is changed by various means.

1. A higher temperature lowers viscosity; it causes atoms to spread farther apart and vibrate more vigorously, thus atomic bonds break and deform more, resulting in increasing fluidity. Consider the great effect of temperature on magma: at 600°C, magma viscosity is 100 000 times higher than at 900°C.
2. Silicon and oxygen (SiO_2) increase the viscosity of magma because they form abundant silicon–oxygen tetrahedra (Figure 5.6) that link up in chains, sheets, and networks, creating more joints and bonds between atoms, which in turn make flow more difficult.
3. Magma is a mixture of liquid and solid minerals that have crystallized from the liquid fraction. A higher concentrations of **mineral** crystals increases viscosity.

Basalt is mainly composed of dark minerals that crystallize first in a cooling magma; andesite is the intermediate case; rhyolite is mainly formed of the light-coloured minerals that crystallize last. Notice that the highest temperatures and lowest SiO_2 contents occur in basaltic magma, giving it the lowest viscosity and easiest fluid flow. The lowest temperatures and highest SiO_2 contents occur in rhyolitic magma, material so viscous that it commonly does not flow. Table 5.3 also states that about 80% of the magma reaching Earth's surface

TABLE 5.3

Comparison of Three Types of Magma

	Volcanic Rock Types		
	Basalt	**Andesite**	**Rhyolite**
Rock description	Black to dark grey	Medium to dark grey	Light-coloured
Volume at Earth's surface	80%	10%	10%
SiO_2 content	45–55%	55–65%	65–75%
	increasing SiO_2 →		
Temperature of magma	1000–1300°C	800–1000°C	600–900°C
	← increasing temperature		
Viscosity	Low		High
	increasing viscosity →		
Water dissolved in magma	~0.1–1 wt. %	~2–3 wt. %	~4–6 wt. %
	increasing water →		
Gas escape from magma	Easy		Difficult
	increasing difficulty →		
Eruptive style	Peaceful		Explosive
	increasing explosiveness →		

is basaltic, with only about 10% andesitic and 10% rhyolitic. Why the difference? Basaltic magma is produced in great abundance by partial melting of the mantle. The lower viscosity of basaltic magma helps it reach the surface, especially at spreading centres. Much basaltic magma is also produced at subduction zones, but as magma at these zones rises through continents, its composition changes as it incorporates continental rock with a high SiO_2 content, and it becomes more andesitic or rhyolitic. The more viscous rhyolitic magma is so sluggish that it tends to be trapped deep below the surface where it cools, solidifies, and grows into the large mineral crystals of plutonic rocks, such as granite.

ERUPTIVE STYLES AND PLATE-TECTONIC SETTING

Knowing about magma viscosity and volatile content allows us to revisit the questions posed earlier about plate tectonics and volcanism. Why does the vast majority of Earth's magma pour out at spreading centres in relatively peaceful eruptions? And why does the magma above subduction zones often explode violently? Spreading centres operate in oceanic crust, and subducting plates are commonly pulled beneath continental crust. The chemical compositions of oceanic crust and continental crust are different (Figure 5.7), their magmas are different, and their volcanic behaviours are different.

Spreading centres are ideal locations for volcanism because (1) they sit above the high-temperature asthenosphere, (2) the asthenosphere rock has low percentages of SiO_2, and (3) the oceanic plates pull apart, allowing hot asthenosphere rock to rise, experience lower pressure, and change to magma that continues to rise. This magma is high-temperature, low-SiO_2, low-volatile-content, low-viscosity basalt that allows gases to escape easily. Spreading centres combine all the factors that promote the peaceful eruption of magma.

When a subducting oceanic plate reaches a depth of about 100 km, magma is generated and rises toward the surface. The subducting plate stirs up the mantle, causing the hotter rock at depth to rise and then melt as pressure decreases. A significant reason that magma forms here is that the subducting plate carries a cover of sediment, water, and hydrated minerals down with it. Water, even in slight amounts, promotes partial melting by lowering the temperature necessary for rock to melt. As this partial melted rock rises upward, it in turn melts part of the overlying crust to produce magma of highly variable compositions (Figure 5.11). Magma composition depends on the amount of crustal rock melted and incorporated into the rising magma. In general, in the subduction-zone setting, magma temperature decreases while SiO_2, water content, and viscosity increase. All these changes in magma add to its explosive potential.

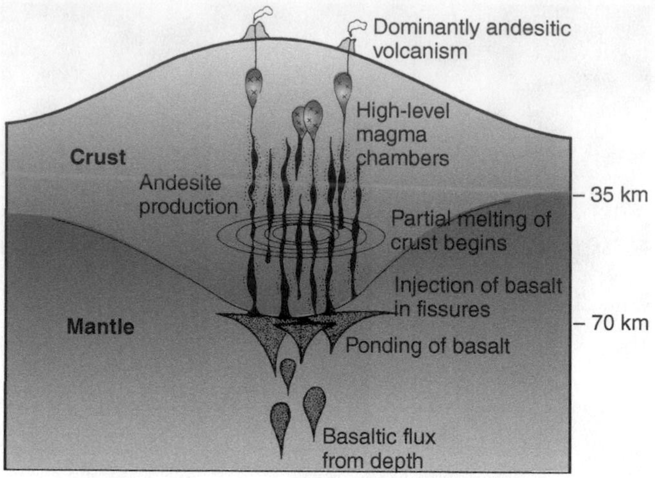

Figure 5.11
Schematic cross-section of magma rising and being contaminated en route.

LO2
How a Volcano Erupts

The Earth's internal energy flows outward as heat (see Chapter 2). Volcanic eruptions allow Earth to expel some of its internal heat rapidly.

A volcanic eruption begins with heat at depth. Superheated rock rises to levels with lower pressure, allowing the rock to expand. Some solid rock may change phase to liquid magma, leading step by step to eruption.

Magma is generated when solid rock melts. Rock may melt when (1) the pressure it experiences is reduced, (2) its temperature is raised, or (3) its water content is increased.

Most magma is generated by decreasing the pressure on hot rock. For example, as the solid, but mobile, hot rock of the mantle rises upward, it experiences progressively less pressure and spontaneously melts, without the addition of more heat. Melting caused simply by a decrease in pressure is called **decompression melting.** The process of decompression melting is so important it is worth restating: most of the rock that melts to form magma does so because the pressure on it decreases, not because heat is added.

The largest nearby reservoir of superhot, ready-to-melt rock exists in the nearly molten asthenosphere; this rock, hot enough to flow without being liquid, is the main source of magma. As this superheated rock rises, the pressure on it decreases, allowing some rock to melt. The hot, rising rock-magma mixture raises the temperature of rock it passes through, thus melting portions of the overlying rocks.

If pressure in the asthenosphere or lithosphere is decreased, some rock melts and expands, causing overlying rocks to fracture. The fractures allow more material to rise to lower pressure levels, causing more rock to liquefy. For example, at a depth of 32 km, basaltic rock melts at 1430°C, but this same rock will melt at only 1250°C at Earth's surface.

Magma at depth does not contain gas bubbles because the high pressure at depth keeps volatiles dissolved in solution. But as magma rises toward the surface, pressure continually decreases, and gases begin to come out of solution, forming bubbles that gradually expand (Figure 5.12). The low density of gas bubbles helps propel magma upward through fractures. Gas bubbles continue increasing in number and volume as magma keeps rising upward to lower pressures. Eventually, the gas overwhelms the magma, fragmenting it into pieces that are carried up and out by a powerful gas jet. Upon escape from the volcano, the gas jet draws in air, which adds to the buoyancy of the turbulent, rising plume (Figure 5.12).

There are several types of volcanic eruption. This classification illustrated in Figure 5.13 is for general purposes; individual volcanoes can vary in eruptive behaviour over time. Non-explosive eruptions are commonly subdivided into *Icelandic* and *Hawaiian* types. *Strombolian* types are somewhat explosive. Explosive eruptions can be described as *Vulcanian* or *Plinian.* Some scientists add to this list an ***ultra-Plinian*** type to describe a particularly collosal **Plinian eruption**.

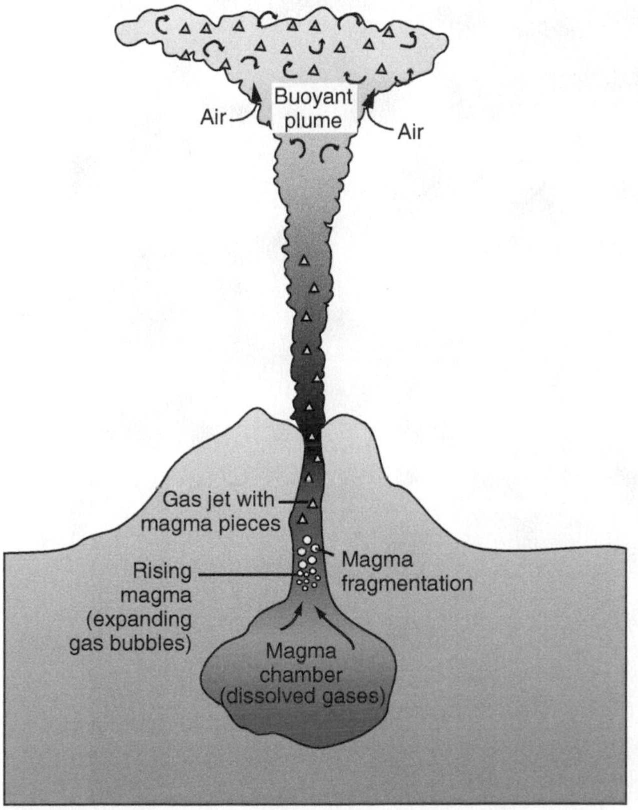

Figure 5.12

Mechanics of an eruption. As magma rises to levels of lower pressure, gas comes out of solution, forming bubbles that overwhelm magma and create a gas jet, leading to a buoyant plume.

LO3 VOLCANIC GASES AND MATERIALS

The dominant elements in volcanic gases are hydrogen (H), oxygen (O), carbon (C), sulphur (S), chlorine (Cl), and nitrogen (N). These gaseous elements combine at Earth's surface to make water (H_2O), carbon dioxide

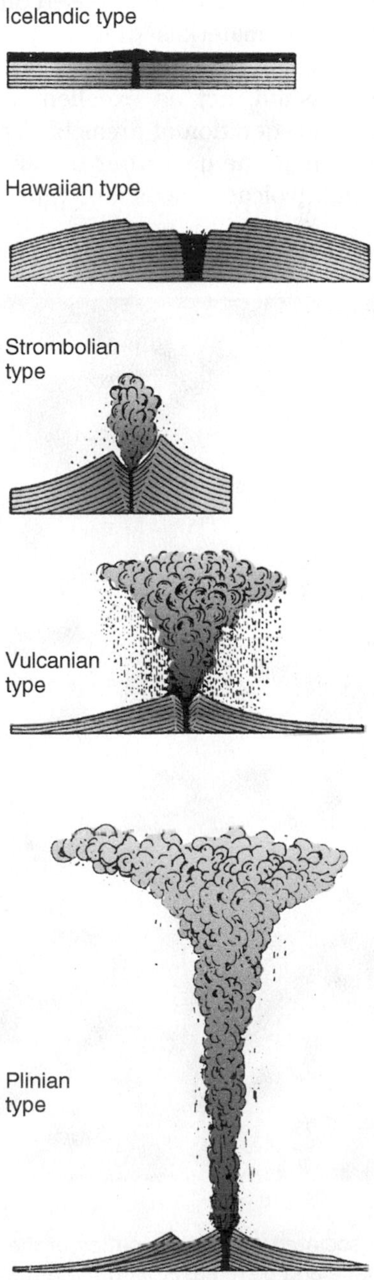

Figure 5.13

Types of volcanic eruptions (not to scale).

(CO_2), sulphur dioxide (SO_2), hydrogen sulfide (H_2S) with its rotten-egg smell (Figure 5.14), carbon monoxide (CO), nitrogen (N_2), hydrogen (H_2), hydrochloric acid (HCl), methane (CH_4), and numerous other gases. The dominant volcanic gas is water vapour; it commonly represents more than 90% of total gases.

Magma (from the Greek word "ointment") changes its name to **lava** (from the Latin verb "to wash," becoming "torrent" in Italian) when it reaches the Earth's surface. Magma is rich in magnesium and iron from its origin deep in the asthenosphere. On its way up, it becomes enriched in the elements that are abundant in the crust such as aluminum, calcium, potassium, and sodium (Figure 5.7). When exposed on the surface of Earth, volcanic materials gradually break down, releasing these elements into the ground where they, especially potassium, act as excellent fertilizers. In tropical areas, revegetation of areas buried under lava can begin less than one year after the eruption, given enough rainfall. Volcanic soils are among the most fertile on the planet, and have nurtured civilizations for thousands of years (Figure 5.34).

Lava flows are especially typical of basaltic magma and exhibit a variety of textures (Table 5.4). Highly liquid lava may cool with a smooth, ropy surface called **pahoehoe** (Figure 5.15). Slower-flowing, more viscous lava commonly has a rough, jagged texture called **aa** (Figure 5.16). The top surface of aa lava flows is often covered with holes formed by escaping gases (Figure 5.17). You can walk on pahoehoe wearing flip-flops but will need sturdy footwear to venture on aa!

Gas blasting into the atmosphere takes along chunks of magma and older rock known collectively as **pyroclastic** debris (*pyro* = fire; *clastic* = fragments). Pyroclastic debris exhibits a wide range of sizes from dust to huge blocks and bombs (Table 5.4; Figures 5.18 and 5.19). Airborne pyroclasts have their coarsest grains fall from the atmosphere first, closest to the volcano, followed by progressively finer material at greater distances.

Figure 5.14

Deep faults associated with the formation of the Kilauea caldera (Figure 5.32) provide pathways for sulphur dissolved in magma to reach the surface and be released into the atmosphere.

Source: © Claire Samson.

TABLE 5.4

Volcanic Materials

Lava	Aa	Rough, blocky surface
	Pahoehoe	Smooth, ropy surface
	Pillow	Ellipsoidal masses formed underwater
Pyroclastic debris	Air-fall fragments	
	Fine ash (dust)	Flour-sized particles
	Coarse ash	Sand-sized particles
	Cinders	Marble- to golf-ball-sized particles
	Blocks	Large angular fragments, solid while airborne
	Bombs	Large fragments often aerodynamic, liquid while airborne
	Volcanic tuff	Rock made of smaller fragments, e.g., deposit of a hot, gas-charged flow
	Volcanic breccia	Rock made of coarse, angular fragments, e.g., deposit of a water-charged debris flow
Glass	Obsidian	Non-porous glass
	Pumice	Porous froth

Figure 5.15
Pahoehoe near Kilauea, Hawaii.
Source: © Claire Samson.

Figure 5.16
Aa flow in Hawaii.
Source: © Pat Abbott.

Figure 5.18
Volcanic ash covers a house near Mount Pinatubo in the Philippines, June 1991.
Source: © R. P. Hoblitt, United States Geological Survey.

Figure 5.17
Freshly solidified lava from Hawaii whose surface is covered by abundant vesicles from which gas escaped, giving the sample a jagged texture.
Source: © Claire Samson.

(a)

Figure 5.19
(a) A large blob of magma cooled while airborne and fell as a pyroclastic bomb, Irazu Volcano, Costa Rica. (b) A more modest-sized volcanic bomb from Hawaii exhibits aerodynamic flow lines.
Source: (a) © Pat Abbott; (b) © Claire Samson.

(b)

An air-fall deposit can be recognized by its layering and the sorting of pyroclasts into layers of different sizes. On the other hand, pyroclastic debris is also blasted out over the ground surface as high-speed, gas-charged flows that dump material quickly, producing indistinct layering and little or no sorting of the various-size particles.

Magma reaching the surface can solidify so quickly that **crystallization** cannot take place because there is no time for atoms to arrange themselves into the ordered atomic structures of minerals. When magma cools this quickly, it produces glass (Table 5.4). Cooled volcanic glass is known as **obsidian** (Figure 5.20a).

Obsidian is a valued product, sought after and traded extensively throughout the ages (Figure 5.21). People from early civilizations broke obsidian into sharp fragments to make arrowheads and sword blades. They polished it to make mirrors. Obsidian was also used as a gemstone, a tradition that continues today.

When gas escapes quickly and violently from lava, it may produce a frothy glass full of holes left by former gas bubbles; this porous material, known as pumice, contains so many holes that it can float on water (Figure 5.20b).

LO4 The Three Vs of Volcanology

We can understand volcanoes anywhere in the world using *the three Vs of volcanology: viscosity, volatiles,* and *volume. Viscosity* may be low, medium, or high; and it controls whether magma flows away or piles up. *Volatile* content may be low, medium, or high; and volatiles may ooze out harmlessly or blast out explosively. *Volume* of magma may be small, large, or very large. Volume correlates fairly well with eruption

(a)

(b)

Figure 5.20

Volcanic glass. (a) Obsidian—glassy and dark. (b) Pumice—porous and light. Pumice is used in foot care, to scrub calluses away.

Source: © Dave Melanson.

Figure 5.21
Painting from a shrine in the ruins of the Stone Age town of Çatal Hüyük in Turkey (top: reconstruction drawing; bottom: original wall-painting). The painting, which features volcano Hasan Da with stylized houses in the foreground, is the earliest known depiction of a volcanic eruption. Abundant obsidian has been found at this archeological site, which suggests that Çatal Hüyük had the monopoly of the obsidian trade within a large region reaching as far as Cyprus and the Middle East.
Source: J. Mellaart, *Early Civilizations of the Near East,* 1965.

intensity; the greater the volume, the more intense the eruption.

Consider the five eruption types in Figure 5.13 in terms of volatile content and viscosity (Table 5.5). The lower the volatile content and the viscosity, the more peaceful the eruption.

Applying what we have learned about magma allows us to see links between eruptive behaviours and the landforms built by volcanic activity. By mixing and matching the values among the three Vs, we can define volcanic landforms (Table 5.6) and forecast the eruption types that occur at each of them.

SHIELD VOLCANOES: LOW VISCOSITY, LOW VOLATILES, LARGE VOLUME

The rocks of **shield volcanoes** are formed mostly by the solidification of basaltic lava flows. These lava flows have large volumes, contain less than one percent volatiles by weight, and have such low viscosity that they travel for great distances, somewhat analogous to pouring pancake batter on a griddle. Each basaltic flow cools to form a gently dipping, relatively thin volcanic rock layer. Many thousands of these lava flows must cool on top of each other over a long time to build a large volcano. A shield volcano, such as Mauna Loa in Hawaii, has a great width compared to its height, whereas a volcano built of high-viscosity magma, such as Mount Baker in northern Washington State, has a great height compared to its width (Figure 5.22).

Hawaiian-Type Eruptions

As with virtually all volcanic eruptions, Hawaiian-type eruptions are commonly preceded by a series of earthquakes as rock fractures to accommodate expanding magma (Figure 3.31). When these fractures split the ground surface, they reduce pressure suddenly, allowing gas to escape from the top of the magma body. After the initial venting of gas, great quantities of basaltic lava spill out of the **fissures** and flow down the mountain slopes as red-hot rivers (Figure 5.23).

TABLE 5.5

Eruptive Styles, Eruption Types, and Explosiveness

Eruptive Style and Eruption Type	Magma Characteristics: Composition			Volatile Content			Viscosity			Volcanic Explosivity Index
	Basalt	Andesite	Rhyolite	Low	Medium	High	Low	Medium	High	
Peaceful: Icelandic	√			√			√			0–1
Peaceful: Hawaiian	√			√			√			0–1
Explosive: Strombolian	√	√			√		√	√		1–2
Explosive: Vulcanian	√	√	√		√	√		√	√	2–4
Explosive: Plinian and Ultra-Plinian		√	√			√			√	3–8

TABLE 5.6

Volcanism Control by the Three Vs (Viscosity, Volatiles, Volume)

Viscosity +	Volatiles +	Volume =	Volcanic Landforms
Low	Low	Large	Shield volcanoes
Low	Low	Very large	Flood basalts
Low/medium	Medium/high	Small	Scoria cones
Medium/high	Medium/high	Large	Stratovolcanoes
High	Low	Small	Lava domes
High	High	Very large	Calderas

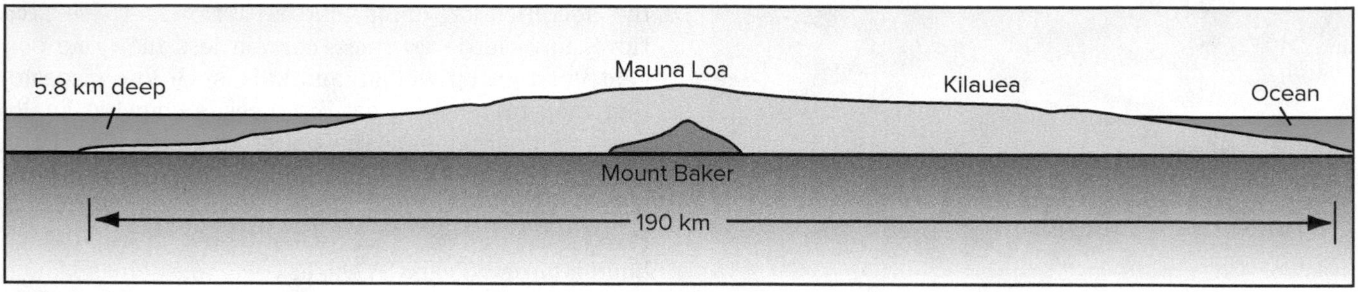

Figure 5.22
A shield volcano, such as Mauna Loa in Hawaii, has a great width compared to its height. A stratovolcano, such as Mount Baker in northern Washington State (Figure 6.23), has a great height compared to its width.
Source: © Modified fromTilling, R. I., et al., *Eruptions of Hawaiian Volcanoes*, United States Geological Survey, 1987.

These eruptions may last from a few days to a year or more. Although few lives are lost to Hawaiian volcanism, the ubiquitous lava flows engulf and incinerate buildings, bury highways, cause drops in property value of homes near the latest flow, and cause some homeowners to lose their peace of mind (Figure 5.24).

Kilauea on the island of Hawaii is the only volcano of the Hawaiian chain currently erupting. Since 1983, voluminous amounts of lava have continued to pour out of the Pu'u 'O'o vent, located on the volcano's eastern flank (Figure 5.25). The island-to-be Loihi is located about 30 km off the southeastern shore of Hawaii (Figure 5.23). Loihi's peak is currently about 969 m below sea level, and the weight of the overlying ocean water suppresses the explosiveness of the eruptions for now, but the volcano is building upward impressively.

Icelandic-Type Eruptions

The most peaceful eruptions are the Icelandic type. They are referred to as fissure eruptions because lava pours out of linear vents or long fissures (cracks) up to 25 km long. Eruptions can be beautiful to watch as an elongated "curtain of fire" shoots upward with varying intensity and height (Figure 5.26). Over time, the low-viscosity, low-volatile water-like lava flows create wide volcanic plateaus of nearly horizontal volcanic rock layers.

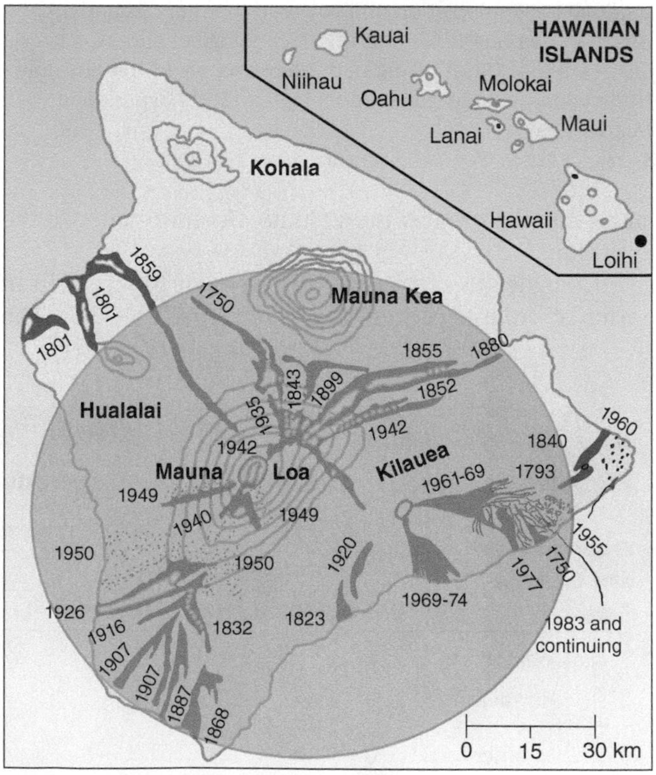

Figure 5.23
Map of Hawaii showing some historical lava flows. Colour overlay shows the boundaries of the mantle plume rising from the hot spot at depth.

Figure 5.24
Lava flows caused the Wahalua Visitors' Center in Hawaii Volcanoes National Park to burn to the ground in 1989.
Source: © J. D. Griggs, United States Geological Survey.

Figure 5.26
Fissure eruption generating a "curtain of fire" on Kilauea Volcano, Hawaii, in 1992. Icelandic-type eruptions do not occur only in Iceland!
Source: Kilauea East Rift Zone Eruption, 1983-1, FIG0182.jpg USGS.

Figure 5.25
Volcanic gases escape from the crater floor of the Pu'u 'O'o vent at Kilauea volcano on the island of Hawaii. The crater is approximately 400 m in diameter.
Source: -© Deanne Van Rooyen.

IN GREATER DEPTH

LO5 Volcanic Explosivity Index (VEI)

Combining the historical record with the geological information stored in the rock record, the major volcanic eruptions occurring between the years 1500 and 1980 were studied to develop a semiquantitative estimate of their magnitude, the volcanic explositivity index (VEI). Factors evaluated included (1) volume of material erupted, (2) height of the eruption column, and (3) duration of the major eruptive blast (Table 5.7). The VEI ranges from 0 to 8. Plinian and ultra-Plinian-type eruptions have the highest VEI values.

TABLE 5.7

Volcanic Explosivity Index (VEI)

	VEI								
	0	1	2	3	4	5	6	7	8
Volume of ejecta (m^3)	$<10^4$	10^4–10^6	10^6–10^7	10^7–10^8	10^8–10^9	10^9–10^{10}	10^{10}–10^{11}	10^{11}–10^{12}	$>10^{12}$
Eruption column height (km)	<0.1	0.1–1	1–5	3–15	10–25	>25			
Eruption style	←Hawaiian→			← Vulcanian →					
	←Icelandic→								
			← Strombolian →		← Plinian →				
								← ultra-Plinian →	
Duration of continuous blast (hours)		← <1 →		← 1–6 →				← >12 →	
				← 6–12 →					

Source: Based on United States Geological Survey http://www.volcano.si.edu/world/eruptioncriteria.cfm#VEI

How frequent are eruptions at specific VEIs? Somewhere on Earth, a VEI 2 event occurs every few years, a VEI 3 event occurs about once per decade, a VEI 4 event happens every 40 years or so and a VEI 5 event blasts forth once a century. The bigger the eruptions, the less frequently they occur, another example of the inverse relationship between magnitude and frequency. This trend has been confirmed for the past 10 000 years (Table 5.8).

The energy released during a volcanic eruption increases linearly as a function of VEI. The additional amount of energy released when the VEI increases from 2 to 3 is the same as between 3 and 4, 4 and 5, and so forth. Does the energy released correlate well with the number of deaths? Not necessarily. Table 5.9 lists VEIs for some of the deadly events we will be discussing in Chapter 6. Some had low VEIs but nevertheless killed thousands with **lahars** (Nevado del Ruiz) or gas (Lake Nyos).

TABLE 5.8

Frequency and Average Energy Release of Volcanic Eruptions

VEI	Number of Eruptions in Past 10 000 Years	Thermal energy flux (Watt x 10^9)
7	4	10.0
6	39	8.7
5	84	7.2
4	278	5.9
3	868	4.9
2	3477	3.9

Source: Based on U.S. Geological Survey http://volcanoes.usgs.gov/images/pglossary/vei.php and D.M. Pyle "Mass and energy budget of explosive volcanic eruptions (1995).

continued

FLOOD BASALTS: LOW VISCOSITY, LOW VOLATILES, VERY LARGE VOLUME

Flood basalts are the largest volcanic events known on Earth. All have occurred in the distant geological past. Two important features of these events are (1) the immense amounts of mass and energy they pour onto Earth's surface, and (2) the geologically brief time over which eruptions occurred—only one to three million years. The volumes of magma that erupted and the surface areas buried with lava are so large they are hard to visualize. For example, over one billion years ago, a failed rift developed in the mid-continent region of North America, accompanied by flood basalt eruptions. It is estimated that 1.3 million km^3 of basalt flowed out along a long network of fissures, extending from Kansas to Lake Superior. There are more than 15 km of basalt beneath the centre of Lake Superior, the thickest accumulation of volcanic rock anywhere on the planet. Some of these rocks are exposed on the lake's shore (Figure 5.27).

TABLE 5.9

VEIs of Notable Volcanic Disasters

VEI	Fatalities	Volcanic disaster	Date	Location
8	—	Yellowstone	600 000 years ago	U.S.A
7	92 000	Tambora	1815	Indonesia
7	Unknown	Santorini	1628 BCE	Greece
6	700	Pinatubo	1991	Philippines
6	36 000	Krakatau	1883	Indonesia
6	18 000	Vesuvius	79	Italy
5	57	Mount St. Helens	1980	U.S.A
4	29 000	Pelee	1902	Martinique, France
4	3	Paricutin	1943	Mexico
4	0	Eyjafjallajökull	2010	Iceland
3	24 000	Nevado del Ruiz	1985	Columbia
3	1	Vestmannaeyjar	1973	Iceland
2	9	Galeras	1993	Columbia
1	—	Stromboli	Daily eruptions	Italy
0	1 700	Lake Nyos	1986	Cameroon
0	—	Kilauea	Current eruption	U.S.A

Figure 5.27
Precambrian flood basalts from eastern Lake Superior display pahoehoe texture (compare this photo with Figure 5.15).
Source: © Claire Samson.

SCORIA CONES: MEDIUM VISCOSITY, MEDIUM VOLATILES, SMALL VOLUME

Scoria cones (Figures 5.28 and 6.18) are conical hills, typically of low height, formed of basaltic to andesitic pyroclastic debris piled up next to a volcanic vent. Scoria cones are commonly produced during a single eruptive interval lasting from a few hours to several years. The scoria cone has a summit crater that may hold a lava lake during eruption. After the excess gas has been expelled from the magma body, the lava may drain and emerge from near the base of the cone. When eruption ceases, scoria cones usually do not erupt again. Being made of poorly consolidated debris, they degrade rapidly when subjected to rain and wind.

Strombolian-Type Eruptions

Scoria cones are built mainly by Strombolian-type eruptions. Strombolian eruptions are not strong enough to break the cones. The volcano Stromboli, offshore from southwestern Italy, has had almost daily eruptions for millennia. Its central lava lake is topped by a cooled crust. Even the tidal cycle disrupts the lava-lake crust, thus triggering eruptions. Gas pressure builds quickly beneath the crust, and eruptions occur as distinct and separate bursts up to a few times per hour. Each eruption tosses pyroclasts tens to hundreds of metres into the air. For many centuries, tourists have climbed Stromboli to thrill at the explosive blasts, but almost every year, a few of those tourists die when hit by large pyroclastic bombs.

On 20 February 1943, a new volcano was born as eruptions blasted up through a corn field near the village of Paricutin in the state of Michoacan, Mexico. Farmer Dionisio Pulido was first to witness the event:

> At four o'clock in the afternoon, I had left my wife Paula beside the fire in the kitchen when I noticed a fissure had opened in the ground, in one of the corrals of my farm. The fissure was only half a metre deep. I looked around again when I heard what sounded like loud thunder. The trees were shaking and I turned back to talk to Paula. It is at this moment that I saw the ground in the hole swell and rise by 2 or 2.5 m. A fine, grey powder, like ash, was starting to come out of a portion of the fissure I had not seen until then. Smoke continued to come out with a whistling noise. It smelled like sulphur. I was very frightened . . .

Figure 5.28
Scoria cone on the flank of Kilauea Volcano on the island of Hawaii, with aa lava flows in the foreground.
Source: © Claire Samson.

Over the following weeks, a scoria cone grew at an amazing rate, reaching 30 m in the first day, 60 m after 3 days, 120 m after a week, and 150 m after a month. The volcano erupted for nine years, reaching a final height of 450 m above the plain and developing a secondary cone on its northeast flank. Pyroclastic debris and lava flows buried about 260 km^2 of land and destroyed the towns of San Juan de Parangaricutiro and Paricutin, where only the facade of the church survives today (Figure 5.29). No lives were loss in the initial phase of the eruption but three people died later of heart and respiratory problems.

STRATOVOLCANOES: HIGH VISCOSITY, HIGH VOLATILES, LARGE VOLUME

Stratovolcanoes are commonly steep-sided, symmetrical volcanic peaks built of alternating layers of pyroclastic debris successively overlain by high-viscosity andesitic to rhyolitic lava flows. Stratovolcanoes may show marked variations in their magma compositions from eruption to eruption, and their eruption types include Vulcanian and Plinian. Some of Earth's most beautiful mountains are stratovolcanoes, for example, the Popocatepetl in Mexico, Mount Kilimanjaro in Tanzania, and Mount Fuji in Japan (Figure 5.30).

Vulcanian-Type Eruptions

All volcanoes take their name from Vulcan, the Roman god of fire and the blacksmith for the gods. The prototypical volcano is one of the Aeolian Islands in the Tyrrhenian Sea north of Sicily. The fire and smoke emitted from the top of the mountain reminded observers of the chimney of Vulcan's forge, so the mountain was named Vulcano. Vulcanian-type eruptions alternate between thick, highly viscous lava and masses of pyroclastic material blown out of the volcano. Some Vulcanian-type eruptions are more violent blasts of high-viscosity magma loaded with trapped gases. The material blown out during eruptions covers wide areas. A Vulcanian-type eruption commonly corresponds to the early phase of an eruptive sequence leading to a Plinian-type eruption. In this case, the volcano merely "clears its throat" during the Vulcanian-type eruption before emitting a larger eruption.

Figure 5.29
The facade of the church of Paricutin, engulfed in a field of aa lava flows. Paricutin Volcano and its secondary Sapichu cone are seen in the background.
Source: © Dr. Alana Hinchey.

Figure 5.30
Mount Fuji, a symmetrical stratovolcano rising 3776 m above sea level, Honshu, Japan. Last major eruptions were in 1707–1708.
Source: © CORBIS.

Figure 5.31
Novarupta lava dome formed as hardened magma plugged the central magma pipe of the 1912 eruption of Mount Katmai in southern Alaska, the biggest eruption of the twentieth century. The dome is 244 m across and 61 m high.
Source: © United States Geological Survey.

Plinian-Type Eruptions

In Plinian eruptions, the volcano's "throat is now clear," and incredible gas-powered vertical eruption columns carry pyroclastic debris, including large quantities of pumice, up to 50 km into the atmosphere. The Plinian eruption is a common final phase in a major eruptive sequence.

LAVA DOMES: HIGH VISCOSITY, LOW VOLATILES, SMALL VOLUME

A common pattern for a major eruptive episode is that gas-rich materials shoot out first as a Vulcanian blast, quickly followed by a longer-lasting, gas-driven Plinian eruption. When the gas is depleted, gas-poor, high-viscosity magma slowly oozes out to build a **lava dome,** forming a plug in the throat of the volcano. The volcanic sequence could be described as a Vulcanian precursor, a Plinian main event, and a lava dome conclusion.

Lava domes form when high-viscosity magma with a low-volatile content cools quickly, producing a hardened dome or plug a few metres to several kilometres wide and a few metres to one kilometre high (Figure 5.31). Lava domes can form in as little as a few hours, or they may continue to grow for decades.

Lava domes can provide spectacular sights. After the 1902 eruptions of Mont Pelée in the Caribbean killed more than 30 000 people (see Chapter 6), a lava dome formed as a great spine that grew about 10 m per day and rose above the top of the volcano. The spine of hardened magma was forced upward by the pressure of magma below until it stood over 300 m higher than the mountaintop, like a giant cork rising out of a bottle.

Lava domes were responsible for 129 deaths in the 1990s: 19 at Soufriere Hills Volcano on Montserrat in 1997, 66 at Mount Merapi in Indonesia in 1994, and 44 at Mount Unzen in Japan in 1991. The hardened lava dome rock can fail in a gravity-pulled mass movement, or magma trapped below the brittle lava dome can break out in a violent eruption.

CALDERAS: HIGH VISCOSITY, HIGH VOLATILES, VERY LARGE VOLUME

Caldera-forming ultra-Plinian eruptions are the largest of the explosive volcanic behaviours. Calderas are large volcanic depressions formed by roof collapse into partially emptied magma reservoirs. Both craters and calderas are topographic depressions, but a crater is less than 2 km in diameter and forms by *outward explosion*. Calderas range from 2 to 75 km in diameter and form by *inward collapse* (Figure 5.32; compare with Figure 5.25).

Figure 5.32
Kilauea caldera, Hawaii, has a diameter of approximately four kilometres.
Source: © Claire Samson.

Santorini and the Lost Continent of Atlantis

As the Mediterranean oceanic plate subducts beneath Europe, it causes numerous volcanoes. One of the biggest is the stratovolcano Santorini in the Aegean Sea. Today, Thera is the largest island in a circular group centred on the new volcanic cone Nea Kameni and marking the sunken remains of Santorini (Figures 5.33 and 5.34).

Akrotiri was an important Bronze Age city, a part of the sophisticated Minoan civilization based in Crete. It had three-storey houses; paved streets with stone-lined sewers beneath them; stylish ceramic and jewellery work; and colourful wall frescoes that depicted the inhabitants' wealthy and comfortable lifestyles. Around 1628 BCE, Santorini underwent an explosive series of eruptions that buried Akrotiri to depths of 70 m, culminating in a caldera collapse triggering a large tsunami.

The dramatic collapse of Akrotiri must have made an indelible impression on the people of that time. In fact, this may be the event passed down to us by Plato as the disappearance of the island empire of Atlantis, which after violent earthquakes and great floods "in a single day and night disappeared beneath the sea." Plato lived in Greece from 427 to 347 BCE. He told the tale in the dialogues of Critias, the historian, who recounted the visit of Solon to Egypt where he had heard the account of Atlantis from Egyptian priests in their oral histories. About 1200 years after the event, Plato wrote a reasonably good description of a caldera-forming collapse with attendant earthquakes and floods (steam surges or tsunamis). Historians also note that the Minoan civilization declined some 150 years after the Santorini eruption, and was gradually replaced by the Mycenaean culture from mainland Greece with no sign of hostilities. They speculate that the Minoans suffered a loss of collective knowledge when skilled people living near the sea—sailors, shipwrights, sailmakers—died in the tsunami. Over a few generations, this loss caused a deterioration of their commercial fleet and undermined their domination of Mediterranean trade routes.

In 2011 and 2012, residents of Santorini experienced a swarm of small earthquakes. GPS data confirmed that the magma chamber beneath the volcano is swelling. "It is a reminder that Santorini is an **active volcano**," said Dr. Nomikou Paraskevi, geologist at the University of Athens, to the press.

Figure 5.33
The dark silhouette of the reborn volcano Nea Kameni, meaning "New Burnt," in the centre of the Santorini caldera. Nea Kameni has raised 450 m from the seafloor in the last 3000 years.
Source: © Claire Samson.

Figure 5.34
Terraced gardens in Santorini, Greece. Note the dark colour of the soil, enriched with volcanic ash.
Source: © Claire Samson.

The Yellowstone Continental Caldera

A **resurgent caldera** exists above a hot spot in Yellowstone National Park, Wyoming, United States. The hot spot occupies a relatively fixed position above which the North American plate moves southwestward about two to four centimetres per year. Plate movement over the hot spot during the last 15 million years is recorded by a trail of surface volcanism. At present, Yellowstone National Park sits above the hot spot, and a large body of rhyolitic magma lies about 5 to 10 km beneath the surface.

In the last two million years, three catastrophic ultra-Plinian eruptions have occurred at Yellowstone: 2 million, 1.3 million, and 0.6 million years ago. Such mega eruptions do not come often, but in a few short weeks, they pour forth almost unimaginable volumes of rhyolitic magma, mostly as pyroclastic flows. The oldest event erupted 2500 km^3 of magma, the middle one ejected 280 km^3, and the youngest ejected 1000 km^3, creating a giant caldera 75 km long and 45 km wide.

These giant caldera-forming eruptions go through a characteristic sequence. They begin when a very large volume of rhyolitic magma rises to a few kilometres below the surface, bowing the ground upward (Figure 5.35a). The magma body accumulates a cap rich in volatiles and low-density components such as SiO_2.

After a few hundred thousand years, a mega-eruption begins with a spectacular circular ring of fire as Plinian columns jet up from circular to ovoid fractures surrounding the magma body (Figure 5.35b). The escaping magma erodes the fractures, thus increasing the size of the eruptive vents so more and more magma escapes.

As greater volumes of gas experience the lessening pressure, the magma begins gushing out of the fractures in mind-boggling volumes (Figure 5.35c). The outrushing magma is too voluminous to all become airborne, so most just pours away from the vents as pyroclastic flows, the fastest way to remove gas-laden, sticky magma.

As the subsurface magma body shrinks, the land surface sinks as well, like a piston in a cylinder, creating a giant caldera (Figure 5.35d). The removal of 1000 km^3 of magma creates a void—an isostatic imbalance—that is filled by a new mass of rising magma that bows up the caldera floor to create **resurgent domes**. Resurgent domes may be viewed as the reloading process whereby magma begins accumulating toward the critical volume that will trigger the next eruption.

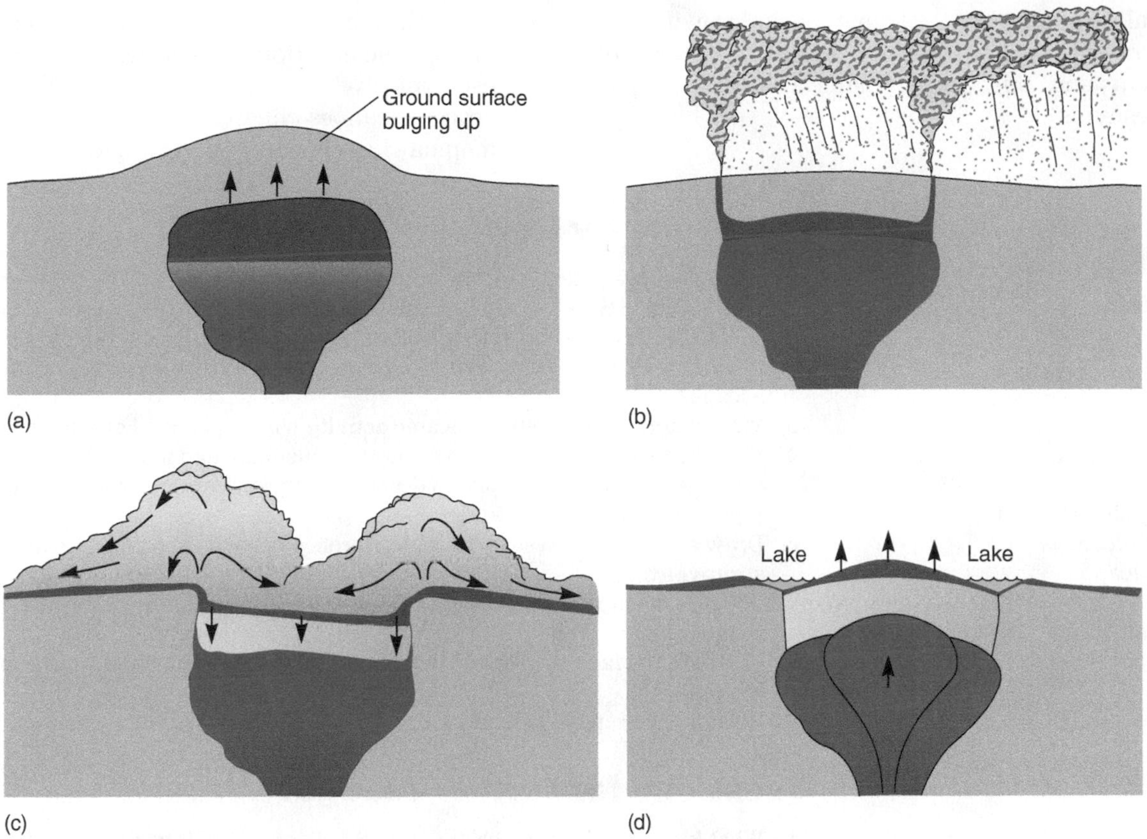

Figure 5.35
Stages in formation of a giant continental caldera. (a) Rising mass of magma forms low-density cap rich in SiO_2 and gases, bulging the ground surface upward. (b) Plinian eruptions begin from circular fractures surrounding the bulge. (c) Magma pours out in pyroclastic flows of tremendous volume, causing the ground surface to sink into a giant caldera. (d) Removal of magma decreases the crustal pressure, causing new magma to bulge up the caldera floor.

SUMMARY

- Volcanism is a rapid mechanism by which the Earth dissipates its internal energy. Hot rock at depth rises buoyantly. This rock may melt and become magma due mainly to decreased pressure and/or increased water content, and to a lesser extent due to increased temperature. When magma nears the surface, gases come out of solution and help its upward progression.
- Viscosity is an important property controlling magma behaviour and therefore eruptive style. Factors affecting viscosity are temperature, the percentage of SiO_2, and mineral content.
  - Beneath the ocean basins, magma is basaltic in composition, with low contents of SiO_2 and water and high temperatures producing low viscosity lava, easy escape of volatiles, and peaceful eruptions.
  - Beneath continents, rising basaltic magma is contaminated by melting continental-crust rocks, thus altering magma compositions. The resultant andesitic-to rhyolitic magma has high contents of SiO_2 and water, and relatively low temperatures, producing high viscosity lava, difficult escape of volatiles, and explosive eruptions.
- Magma viscosity, volatiles, and volume determine the shape of volcanic landforms.
  - Low-viscosity lava flows may build shield volcanoes much wider than they are tall (for example, the Hawaiian volcanoes).
  - If the concentration of gas trapped in magma is high, explosions may blast pyroclastic debris into the air. This debris accumulates around the volcanic vent, gradually building up a scoria cone (for example, Paricutin).

- Tall symmetrical volcanic peaks are usually stratovolcanoes built of alternate layers of lava and pyroclastic material (for example, Vesuvius).

- The volcanic explosivity index (VEI) measures size of volcanic eruptions on a scale of 0 to 8. The largest explosive eruptions (VEI = 7–8) occur when stratovolcanoes collapse into their rapidly emptied magma chambers, creating calderas.

Terms to Remember

aa
active volcano
andesite
basalt
BCE
caldera
crater
crystallization
decompression melting
dormant volcanoes
extinct volcano
fissure
flood basalt
lahar
lava
lava dome
magma
mineral
obsidian
pahoehoe
Plinian eruption
plutonic rock
pumice
pyroclastic
pyroclastic flow
resurgent caldera
resurgent dome
rhyolite
scoria cone
shield volcano
stratovolcano
ultra-Plinian
volatile
volcanic rock

Questions for Review

1. What changes in temperature, pressure, and water content will cause hot rock to melt? What is the most effective melting agent?
2. What are the differences between basaltic, andesitic, and rhyolitic magma in terms of SiO_2 percentage, water content, temperature, viscosity, and mode of gas escape?
3. What determines whether volcanic activity will be peaceful or explosive?
4. Play the three Vs game. Pick various low, medium, and high values for viscosity, volatiles, and volume, and then describe the resultant eruptive styles, eruption types, and volcanic landforms.
5. Draw a cross-section showing the difference between a shield volcano and a stratovolcano.
6. Which volcanic landform degrades faster due to erosion: a scoria cone or a stratovolcano? Why?
7. What are the factors controlling the volcanic explosivity index (VEI)? Explain each.
8. What is the eruptive behaviour of a hot spot–fed volcano on a continent?

Questions for Further Thought

1. What kind of volcanic rocks are found in your area? How old are they? How did they form?
2. Why do people keep rebuilding cities in the vicinity of an active volcano, such as Vesuvius?
3. List the beneficial aspects of volcanoes and volcanism.
4. How do volcanoes change the landscape?
5. When will the Atlantic ocean floor start to subduct underneath eastern North America? What kind of volcanoes will be created by this process?
6. Have major volcanic eruptions changed the course of history? If so, how?

Interesting Websites

- Photo Glossary of Volcanic Terms, United States Geological Survey
  http://volcanoes.usgs.gov/images/pglossary/index.php

- How Volcanoes Work, Dept. of Geological Sciences, San Diego State University
  http://www.geology.sdsu.edu/how_volcanoes_work

- International Association of Volcanology and Chemistry of the Earth's Interior
  http://www.iavcei.org/

- Global Volcanism Program, Smithsonian National Museum of Natural History
  http://www.volcano.si.edu

- Hawaiian Volcano Observatory, United States Geological Survey
  http://hvo.wr.usgs.gov

CHAPTER SIX

6

Volcano Case Histories: Killer Events

High-temperature pyroclastic flow rolling down the side of Mount St. Helens, 7 August 1980.

Source: © United States Geological Survey.

"An incredible black cloud was cascading down the mountain-side, fed by the billowing columns soaring upwards into a huge mushroom cloud. 'Nuée ardente' immediately came to mind as it became obvious nothing would stop it—not even the deep river valley that lay between us and the mountain."

—Canadian volcanologist Catherine Hickson, eyewitness to the 1980 Mount St. Helens eruption

Excerpt from her book Mt. St. Helens—Surviving the Stone Wind

Outline

- Volcanism at Spreading Centres
- Volcanism at Subduction Zones
- Volcanism at Hot Spots
- Canada's Sleeping Volcanoes
- Killer Events and Processes
- Volcano Monitoring and Warning
- Summary

LO1 Describe volcanic eruptions in different plate-tectonic settings.

LO2 List the characteristics of Canadian volcanoes.

LO3 Explain the leading causes of death by volcanoes.

LO4 Read the signs of an impending volcanic eruption.

In this chapter, we tour the world, describing volcanism in different tectonic environments, and discover that Canada has examples of almost every type of volcano found on the planet. We then examine the historical record of volcano-related fatalities to understand the processes that kill people and affect the environment. Lastly, we look at issues in volcano monitoring and warning.

LO1 Volcanism at Spreading Centres

Most of the volcanism on Earth takes place along the oceanic ridge systems where seafloor spreading occurs. Solid, but hot and ductile, mantle rock rises upward into regions of lower pressure, where up to 30 to 40% of the rock melts and flows as basaltic magma. Virtually all of this volcanic activity takes place below sea level and is thus difficult to view. Recently, project NEPTUNE (see In Greater Depth box: Project NEPTUNE: Revolutionizing Ocean Science, in Chapter 7) has provided us with an exceptional glimpse of the processes taking place on the seafloor. Photographs from Endeavour Ridge taken 2000 m below sea level show cracked seafloor stretched under tension (Figure 6.1) and hydrothermal vents (Figure 6.2). The worldwide rifting process releases enough magma to create 20 km^3 of new basaltic oceanic crust each year. We see and are impressed by the tall and beautiful volcanic mountains on the edges of continents, but the volume of magma they release is small compared to that of spreading centres.

ICELAND

Iceland is a volcanic plateau built of basaltic lava erupted from a hot spot below the mid-Atlantic spreading centre (Figures 6.3 and 6.4). One theory for the formation of the Atlantic Ocean is that a series of triple junctions formed over hot spots. From each triple junction, two arms lined up and joined two arms of the adjacent hot spot. These linked arms opened up to become the Atlantic Ocean; the third arms became failed rifts.

Approximately 13% of Iceland's surface is covered by glaciers, and one-third is comprised of active volcanoes. During the nearly 1000 years of human records, volcanic eruptions have occurred every five years on average. Most Icelandic eruptions do not cause deaths, but exceptions do occur (see description of the famine of 1783 later in this chapter).

Figure 6.1
Seafloor spreading at Endeavour Ridge, offshore Vancouver Island.
Source: NEPTUNE Canada/CSSF

Figure 6.2

Hydrothermal vents at Endeavour Ridge indicate the proximity of hot magma in the subsurface.

Source: NEPTUNE Canada.

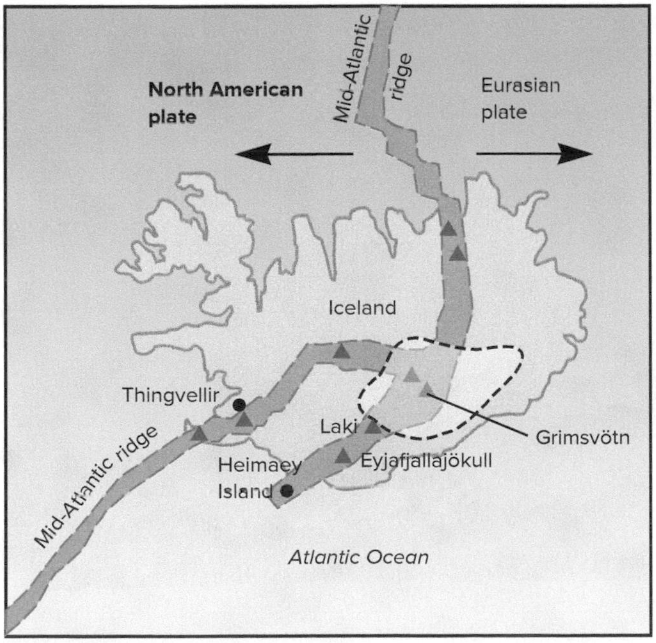

Figure 6.3

Iceland sits on top of a hot spot and is being pulled apart by spreading along the mid-Atlantic ridge. Triangles mark sites of some active volcanoes. The dotted line delineates the extent of the Vatnajökull glacier.

Figure 6.4

Rift valley at Thingvellir, Iceland, pulled apart in an east-west direction by the continuing opening of the Atlantic Ocean. The actual expression of the spreading centre is an elongated, generally flat, slightly depressed valley, several kilometres across. Because of the extension, there are several fissures on the ground.

Source: © Stan Dosso.

Lava Flows of 1973

The recent story of Iceland shows that humans can make enough adjustments to live profitably and happily next to active basaltic volcanism. The 1973 eruptions on the small island of Heimaey on the southern coast of Iceland illustrate the "peaceful" nature of this type of eruption. The town of Vestmannaeyjar is built next to the premier fishing port in Iceland. The safe harbour is itself a gift of volcanism; it was formed between ancient lava flows. On 23 January 1973, a fissure opened up only one kilometre from the town of 5300 people (Figure 6.5). By early July, the eruption had emitted 230 million cubic metres of lava (Figure 6.6) and 26 million cubic metres of pyroclastic material. The lava flows increased the size of the island by 20%. Gases vented during the eruptive sequence, other than water vapour, were dominantly CO_2 with lesser amounts of H_2, CO, and CH_4. The only fatality was a person asphyxiated in a gas-filled building.

The early lava flows on Heimaey began filling in the harbour and destroyed about 300 buildings; pyroclastic fallout buried another 70 buildings. But the volume of lava was not overwhelming, so the Icelanders took charge. Pyroclastic material was bulldozed to create barriers that diverted the flow of lava and even controlled the flow paths of the dense volcanic gases. To save their harbour and economic livelihood, the Icelanders sprayed seawater on the lava flows, hardening them into wall-like features that forced the lava to flow off in another direction (Figures 6.6 and 6.7). This heroic action prevented the harbour from being filled and closed. Now, with its new shape and larger size, the harbour is better than before the 1973 eruptions (Figure 6.5).

When the eruptions stopped, the people set up a pipe system that poured water into the 100 m thick mass of slowly cooling lava. Return pumps were installed to bring the water, which had been heated to 91°C, back to the surface and into town, where it was used to heat buildings. Basaltic eruptions do not have to be killers. Humans and volcanoes can coexist in harmony, with luck and with some exceptions.

Jokulhlaup of 1996

An earthquake episode began in southeastern Iceland on 30 September 1996 as a fissure opened along the mid-Atlantic spreading centre beneath the thick Vatnajökull glacier, which covers 10% of Iceland. In two days, magma rising through the fissure melted through the 600 m thick icecap, sending steam and other gases several kilometres into the atmosphere. Meltwater

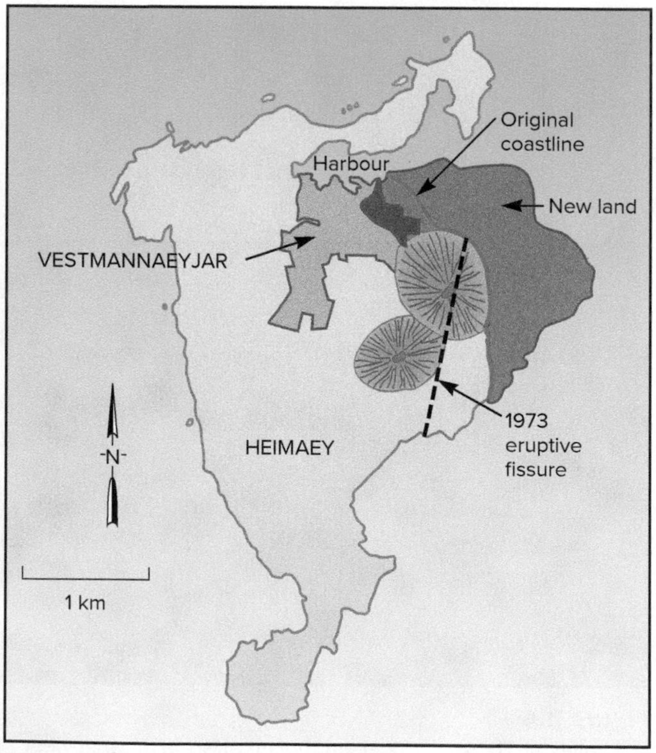

Figure 6.5
The island of Heimaey with the old coastline shown as an orange line. Dark-grey area is new land formed by the 1973 lava flows. Note that the new harbour is bigger and better protected.
Source: Williams, R.S., Jr., and Moore, J.G.

Figure 6.6
Seawater is being sprayed on the lava front to cool and harden it, and to stop it from closing off Vestmannaeyjar harbour, 4 May 1973.
Source: © United States Geological Survey.

Figure 6.7
The toe of the 1973 lava flows at the edge of Vestmannaeyjar harbour, Iceland, partially crushing a concrete water tank.
Source: © Brian Cousens.

flowed under the glacier to the ice-covered Grimsvötn Volcano, where it accumulated in the volcano caldera. The meltwater volume reached an estimated 4 km^3, but on 5 November, the rising water lifted the glacier and poured forth as an enormous **jokulhlaup,** a flood flowing at 45 000 m^3/s. For two days, the water flowed as the second largest river in the world, behind only the Amazon River, and then it died out, stranding blocks of ice weighing up to 1000 tonnes on the bed of the short-lived stream. The jokulhlaup water and ice blocks destroyed Iceland's longest bridge, telephone lines, and a road.

Volcanism at Subduction Zones

Through newspapers and television, we learn of death-dealing volcanic eruptions such as those at Galeras Volcano in Colombia, Mount Unzen in Japan, Mounts Pinatubo and Mayon in the Philippines, and Soufriere Hills on Montserrat. These are all subduction-zone volcanoes. Worldwide, many of the regions around subduction-zone volcanoes are heavily populated and feel the wrath of the eruptions. Also, because these volcanoes erupt directly into the atmosphere, they can affect weather worldwide.

A similar situation exists in southern British Columbia, where Canada's most explosive volcanoes—Mount Garibaldi and Mount Meager— are found at the northern end of a **volcanic belt** extending along the Pacific coast all the way to northern California, the Cascade Range.

CASCADE RANGE, SOUTHERN BRITISH COLUMBIA AND NORTHWESTERN UNITED STATES

Explosive eruptions are frequent events at the numerous volcanoes in southern British Columbia and in the Pacific Northwest region of the United States (Figure 6.8). The plate-tectonic process responsible for these volcanoes is identical to the process responsible for the

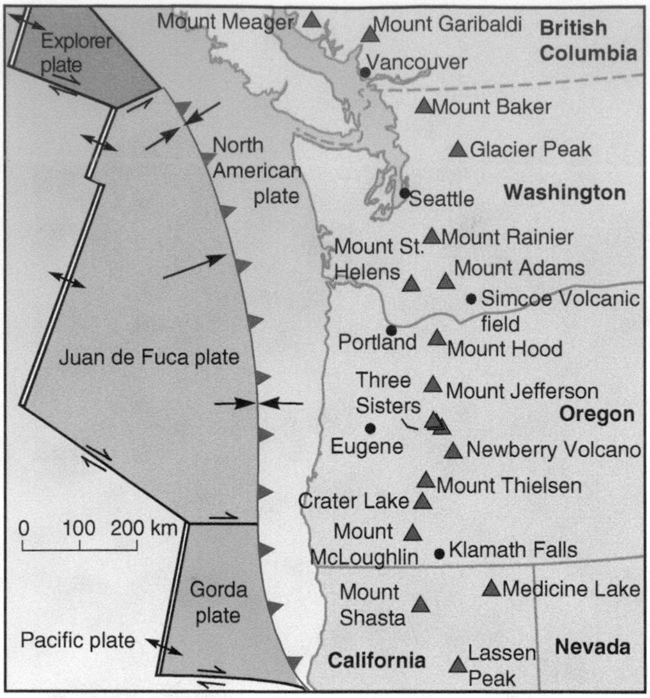

Figure 6.8
Tectonic map of Cascade Range volcanoes, indicated by red triangles. Volcanoes align along an axis parallel to the subduction zone and are spaced somewhat regularly.

region's great earthquakes—subduction. The melting of part of the asthenosphere wedge above the subducting plate is aided by water released from sediment on top of the subducting plate. The rising basaltic magma partially melts overlying crustal rock, increasing its contents of SiO_2. Much of the magma changes its composition to andesite or rhyolite and increases its viscosity as it rises (Figure 6.9). Some collects in great pods and cools underground, forming plutonic rocks, but some erupts explosively at the surface.

How often do major eruptions occur? Forty-nine eruptions have been documented in the Cascade Range in the past 4000 years (Figure 6.10). Basically, the volcanoes are all the same age; they sit above subducting plates and are active now. Volcanoes built above hot spots also line up, for example, in Hawaii (Figure 2.32). In contrast to subduction-zone volcanoes, however, chains of hot-spot volcanoes range from young to old in an orderly progression.

Note the exceptional activity of Mount St. Helens, which has experienced major eruptions every century or two and has never been free from major volcanism for longer than 500 years (Figure 6.10). In their 1975 study, Dwight Crandell and colleagues stated, "Although dormant since 1857, St. Helens will erupt again, perhaps before the end of this century." Their geological analysis was prophetic (Figure 6.11).

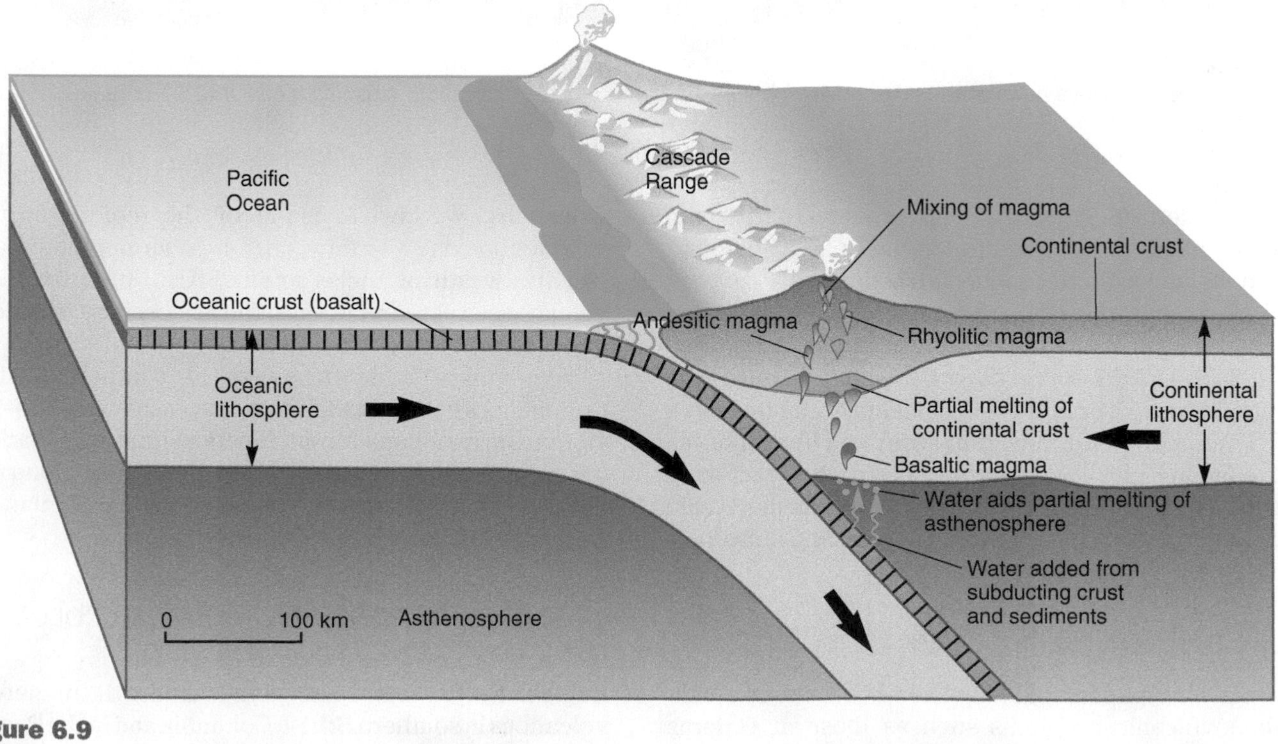

Figure 6.9
Subduction-zone volcano factory. Basaltic magma forms in upper asthenosphere where water from the subducting plate aids partial melting. Rising magma partially melts some continental crust, forming water-rich andesitic to rhyolitic magmas that erupt explosively.

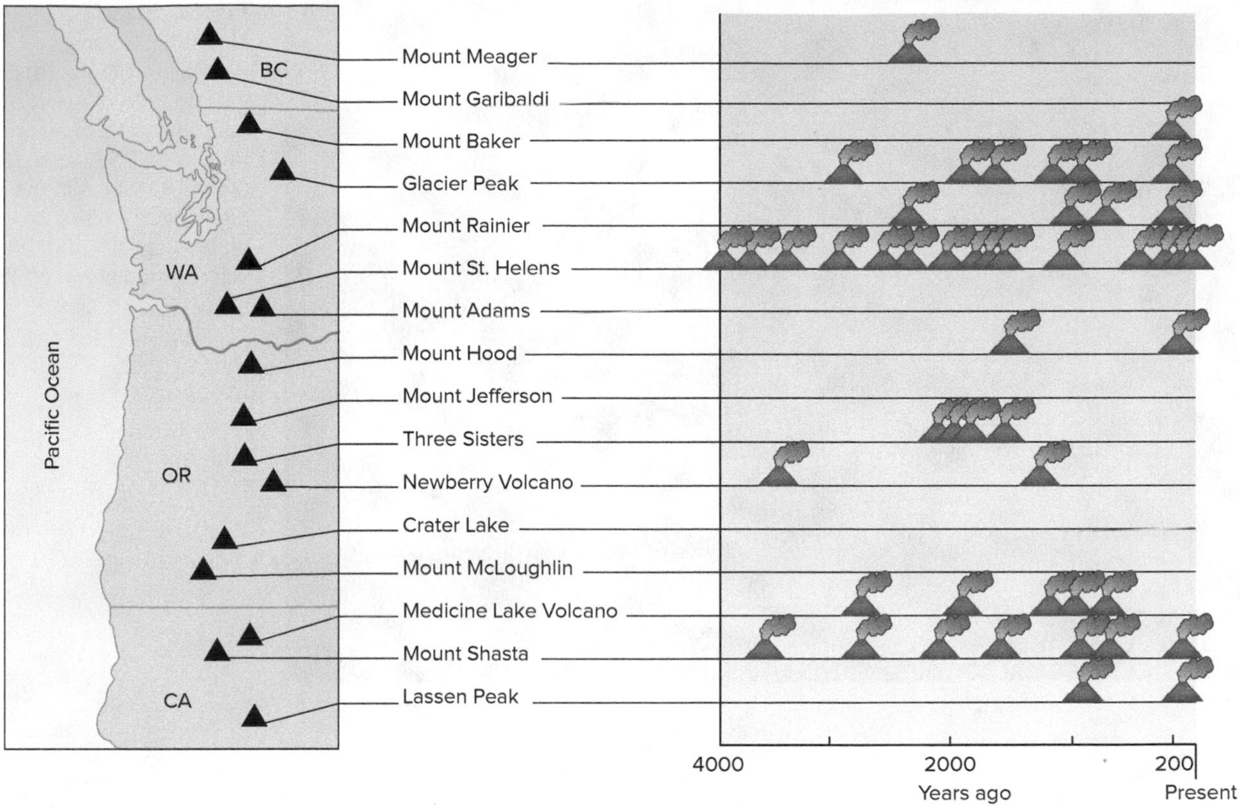

Figure 6.10
Eruption histories of Cascade Range volcanoes.

Mount St. Helens, Washington State, 1980

In late March 1980, Mount St. Helens awoke from a 123-year-long slumber. The spectacle of an erupting volcano was a tremendous lure for sightseers. People flocked to Mount St. Helens. The weekend traffic was so jammed that it reminded people of rush hour in big cities. The governor of Washington ordered blockades placed across the roads to Mount St. Helens to keep people a safe distance from the volcano; her action was unpopular. Then, on 18 May 1980, the volcano blew off the top 400 m of its cone during a spectacular blast with a power equivalent to approximately 100 times that of all electrical power plants in the United States combined. Most of the 62 people killed had found ways around the barricades to get a better view of an erupting volcano.

A look at the eruptive sequence provides a good example of how an explosive volcano operates (Figure 6.12). Mount St. Helens achieved its beautiful conical shape during the mid-1800s (Figure 6.12a). In 1980, rising magma began changing the shape of the volcano (Figure 6.12b). Dozens of magnitude 3 earthquakes occurred each day as magma pushed its way toward the surface. By 12 April, a 2 km^2 area on the north flank had risen upward and outward by 100 m.

At 8:32 a.m. on 18 May 1980, a magnitude 5.1 earthquake rocked the volcano. It triggered a gigantic landslide as a roiling mass of fragmented rock, combined with ice blocks, snow, magma, soil, and broken trees, fell away at speeds up to 250 km/h (Figure 6.12c). At the same time, lahars were forming and coming down the river valleys. These slurries flowed long distances at speeds up to 40 km/h for many hours after the eruption began, with a consistency like wet concrete. As the landslide began to pull away, the dramatic drop in pressure on the gaseous magma and super-heated groundwater caused the release of a pyroclastic flow (Figure 6.12d). This menacing cloud of rock fragments and swirling gases at approximately 300°C is what Dr. Catherine Hickson, an earth science student at the University of British Columbia at the time, describes as the "stone wind" (see quotation of chapter opener). Caught directly in the turmoil of the eruption, she was fleeing for her life, driving through a maze of back roads in very poor visibility. This experience was clearly a defining moment for Dr. Hickson, who has since then devoted her professional career to the study of volcanoes.

(a)

(b)

Figure 6.11
Mount St. Helens, Washington State. (a) *Before:* View to the northeast of the beautiful cone of Mount St. Helens on 25 August 1974. Mount Rainier is in the distance. (b) *After:* Same view on 24 August 1980, after the volcano had blown off its top.
Source: © John S. Shelton.

The big blast exposed the effervescing magma body. Rapidly escaping gases blew upward, carrying small pieces of magma to heights greater than 20 km during the Plinian phase, which lasted about nine hours (Figure 6.12e). About 0.25 km^3 of ash was blown across the United States and Canada by westerly wind systems. Mount St. Helens looks very different these days (Figure 6.11b). The volcano is slowly repairing the damage done as it builds a new SiO_2-rich lava dome (Figure 6.12f).

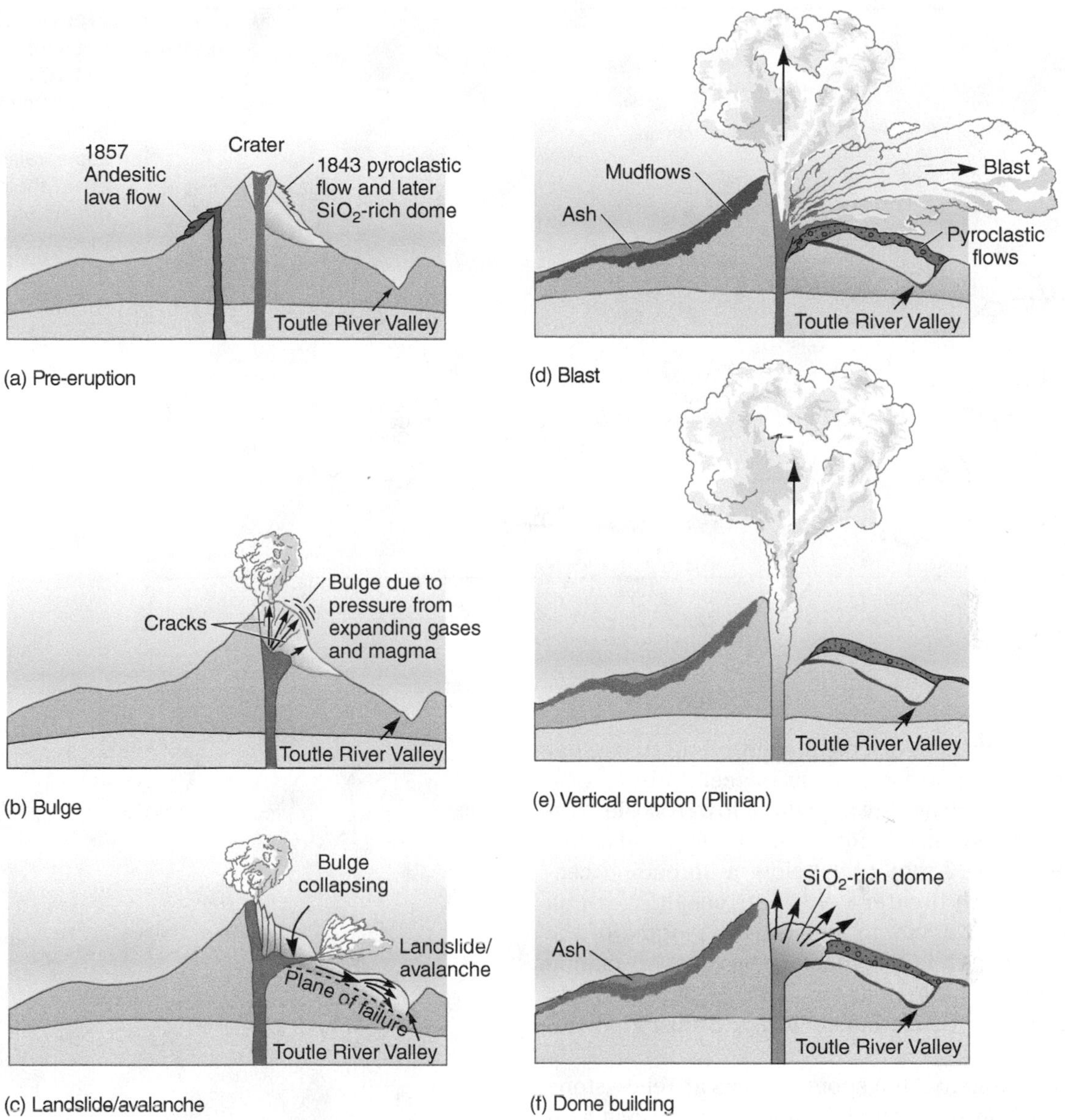

Figure 6.12
Eruptive sequence (VEI = 5) of Mount St. Helens in 1980. (a) The symmetrical volcanic cone was shaped in 1843 and 1857. (b) In late March 1980, rising magma and expanding gases caused a growing bulge on the north side. (c) On 18 May 1980, a magnitude 5.1 earthquake caused the bulge to fail in a massive landslide/avalanche. (d) The landslide released pressure on the near-surface body of magma, causing an instantaneous blast of fragmented rock and magma. (e) The "throat" of the volcano was now clear, and the vertical eruption of gases and small blobs of magma shot up to heights of more than 20 km for nine hours. (f) Today, the mountain is slowly rebuilding with a volcanic dome of low-water-content, SiO_2-rich magma.

Volcanism at Hot Spots

Hot spots are plumes of slowly rising mantle rock that create volcanism on the Earth's surface. The temperature of the rising rock is hotter than the surrounding rock by about 300°C in the plume centre and by 100°C along the outer margin of the plume head. This temperature difference lowers viscosity enough to start the rise of magma toward the surface.

Most hot spots operate for about 100 million years. They do not move as much as tectonic plates and are used as static reference points to help chart plate movements (Figures 2.32 and 4.36). They occur under the oceans and under the continents, in the centre of plates, and as part of spreading centres (Figure 6.13). There is only one hot spot currently in Canadian territory, the Anahim hot spot, fuelling volcanism in central British Columbia.

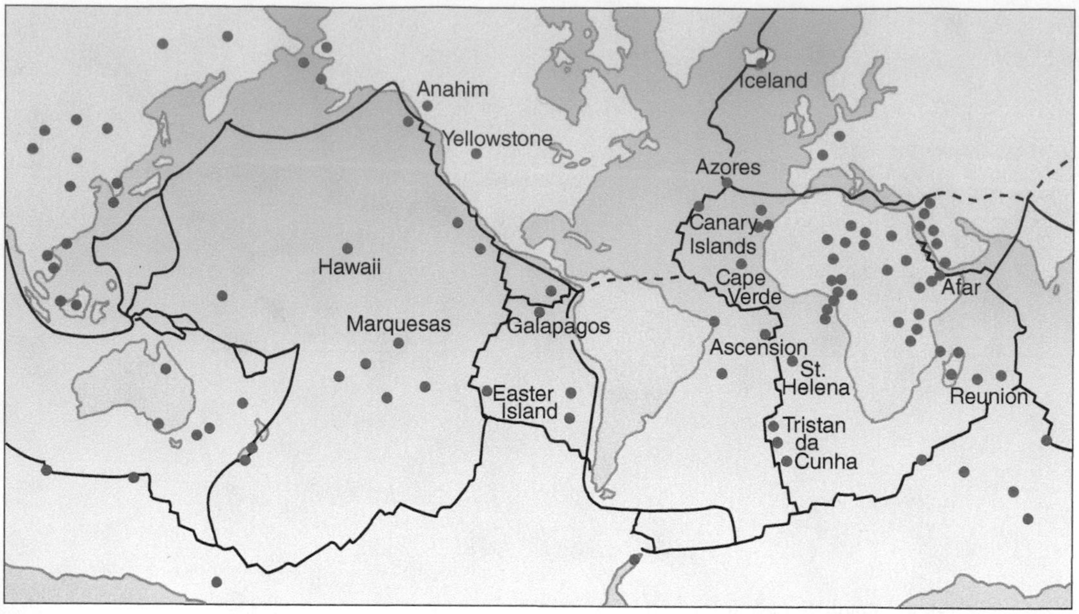

Figure 6.13
Hot spots active in the last 10 million years. Antarctica is not shown but lies above 11 hot spots, raising questions about the possible effects of melting massive volumes of ice.

The explosiveness of volcanic eruptions above hot spots varies. They are relatively peaceful above oceanic hot spots, such as Hawaii, where low-volatile, low-viscosity, large-volume magma flows easily and builds shield volcanoes. A hot spot below a spreading centre means a much greater volume of basaltic magma can erupt. For example, in Iceland, the magma of the spreading process is augmented by deeper mantle magma to create an immense volume of basaltic rock. The mantle plume beneath Iceland is the most vigorous on Earth today.

Above continental hot spots, such as at Yellowstone National Park in the United States, the eruptions may be incredibly explosive. These mega-eruptive centres occur where large volumes of basaltic magma intrude upward to shallow depths. While rising, they encounter continental rocks that melt at lower temperatures. The resultant mixture of melts creates magmas with lower temperatures, higher percentages of SiO_2, high viscosity, and high contents of volatiles. The buoyant, sticky magma accumulates as very large masses a few kilometres below the surface.

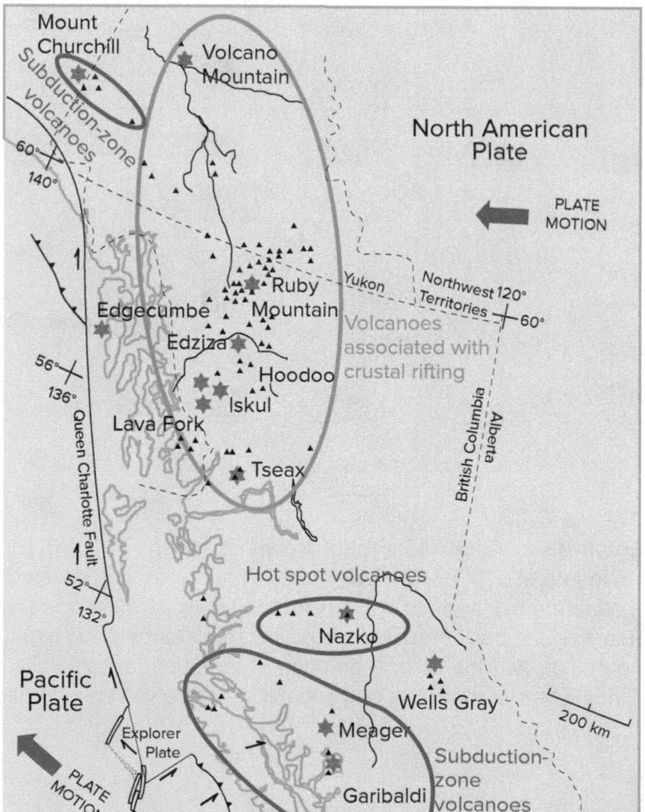

Figure 6.14
Map of Canadian volcanoes. Stars indicate young volcanoes that have erupted in the past 12 000 years, and triangles correspond to older volcanoes that erupted between 12 000 and 1.8 million years ago.

Source: Reproduced with the permission of Natural Resources Canada 2014, courtesy of the Geological Survey of Canada (GSC Bulletin 548).

LO2 Canada's Sleeping Volcanoes

Although there are currently no volcanic eruptions in Canada, there are more than 200 dormant volcanoes in the country, 49 of which have erupted in the past 12 000 years.

Figure 6.15
Table Mountain (foreground) and Garibaldi Volcano (background), southern British Columbia.
Source: © Old Goat/Flickr.

Canada's volcanoes are concentrated in British Columbia and Yukon. Within these regions, a large variety of volcanic landforms exists and three tectonic environments are represented (Figure 6.14). There are subduction zone volcanoes in southern British Columbia and southwestern Yukon due to the subduction of the Pacific plate beneath the North American plate. In central British Columbia, the alignment of several volcanoes along an east-west trend is the surface expression of the Anahim hot spot track. Finally, in northern British Columbia and Yukon, the Earth's crust is subjected to stretching and thinning in association with the development of a continental rift. Several volcanoes lie in this zone of weakened crust, including the three Canadian volcanoes that have erupted in historical times: Lava Fork (1750 ± 100), Tseax Cone (1730 ± 150) and Ruby Mountain (1898?).

GARIBALDI VOLCANO, SOUTHERN BRITISH COLUMBIA

The Garibaldi volcanic belt, the northern extension of the Cascade Range into Canada, contains the most explosive volcanoes in the country: Garibaldi Volcano and Mount Meager, both uncomfortably located in the shadow of the Vancouver metropolitan area. Consider that only 2350 years ago, Mount Meager experienced an eruption similar to that of Mount St. Helens in 1980 (VEI = 5).

Garibaldi Volcano itself formed 300 000 years ago. The stratovolcano is a complex structure, damaged and rebuilt several times in a succession of violent eruptions (Figure 6.15). The rugged volcanic landscape at Garibaldi Volcano has been sculpted by fire and ice. The most recent eruption, 13 000 years ago, coincided with the final stages of the last glaciation. Rapid melting of glaciers surrounding the volcano left it without lateral support and caused a catastrophic collapse of its western flank. At approximately the same time, two lava flows erupted from Mount Price, to the north. They were blocked in their progression by glaciers, causing them to pool and gradually solidify behind a wall of ice up to a thickness of 250 m. The resulting steep cliff of crumbly volcanic rocks, called "The Barrier" (Figures 11.28, 11.29, and 11.30, respectively), has been the site of several mass movements, most recently in 1855–1856. The small village of Garibaldi located at the foot of the cliff has been closed permanently as a preventive measure. Table Mountain, a classic **tuya,** dates from the same time. A tuya is a subglacial volcano with a characteristic flat top (Figures 6.16 and 6.17).

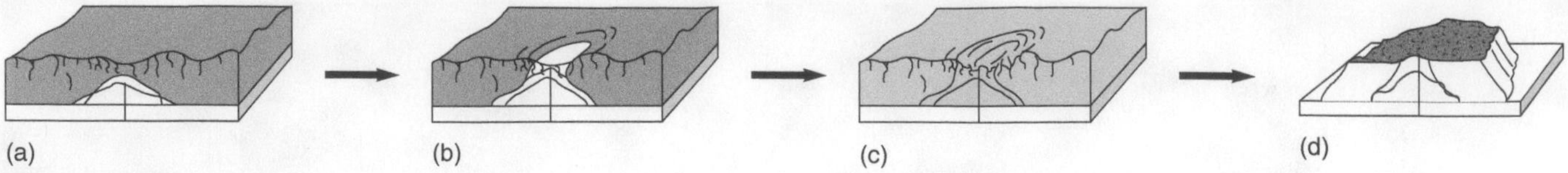

Figure 6.16

Development of a tuya. The eruption occurs (a) initially below the ice, and (b) then subaerially. (c) Lava pools and solidifies on the surface of the ice. (d) The ice later melts, exposing a volcano with a distinctive flat top.

Source: Reproduced with the permission of Natural Resources Canada 2014, courtesy of the Geological Survey of Canada (GSC Bulletin 548).

NAZKO CONE, CENTRAL BRITISH COLUMBIA

The Anahim hot spot is believed to have been active for over 23 million years. As the North American plate moves westward relative to the Anahim hot spot, a chain of volcanoes, progressively younger to the east, have been created along its track. The two oldest volcanoes, heavily eroded, lie on the Pacific coast. The youngest volcano, Nazko Cone, created 340 000 years ago, occupies a central location in British Columbia (Figure 6.18). Nazko Cone has had a mixed eruptive history, including quiet lava eruptions and explosive pyroclastic eruptions. The last eruption at Nazko Cone, some 7200 years ago, may have started forest fires. Charcoal can be found within pyroclastic deposits at the site. Today, some of the unconsolidated pyroclastic material from the volcano is mined for landscaping and agricultural applications.

On 9 October 2007 seismometers started to detect signals from a swarm of small earthquakes whose epicentres were located 20 km west of Nazko Cone in central British Columbia. Eight earthquakes of magnitude 2–3 occurred the following day. Was Nazko Cone reawakening? State-of-the-art equipment was rapidly deployed to monitor the situation from

Figure 6.17

A field geologist and his companion dog take a break at the foot of the tuya at Mount Llangorse in northern British Columbia.

Source: Donald Francis.

Figure 6.18
The Nazko cinder cone shines in the sunset on a winter's day.
Source: Reproduced with the permission of Natural Resources Canada 2014, courtesy of the Geological Survey of Canada (GSC Bulletin 548, Photograph by C.J. Hickson).

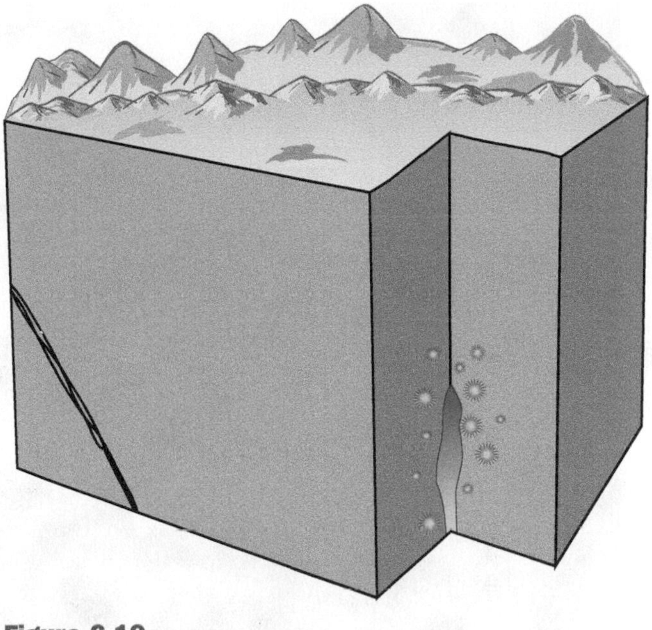

Figure 6.19
Sketch showing how a rising plume of magma at the base of the crust beneath Nazko Cone is accompanied by small earthquakes (stars indicate epicentre locations).
Source: Reproduced with the permission of Natural Resources Canada 2014

different perspectives. Nine portable seismograph stations were installed to gather the data necessary to pinpoint the hypocentres with enhanced accuracy. To complement the seismic recordings, an infrasound station was put in place to capture pressure waves, which have a higher frequency content than seismic waves but are still below the threshold of human hearing. Geologists also measured concentrations of carbon dioxide that might be linked to subsurface magmatic activity. Analysis of the data indicated that the seismic activity was probably caused by magma movement some 25 km below the surface (Figure 6.19). Earth scientists from Natural Resources Canada concluded, "There is no evidence at this time to suggest that a volcanic eruption is likely. It is possible that magma intruding at depth may stall without immediately rising towards the earth's surface, and swarms of small magmatic earthquakes may occur at volcanoes without being followed by eruptive activity." After a swarm of more than 1000 small earthquakes over a few months, seismic activity in the area ceased—at least for the time being.

TSEAX CONE, NORTHERN BRITISH COLUMBIA

The weakened crust of northern British Columbia and southern Yukon is host to the largest concentration of volcanoes in Canada. There are more than 100 volcanoes in the area, most of them small cinder cones erupting basaltic lavas (Figure 6.20).

The very young Tseax Cone is of particular significance because it was the cause of Canada's worst natural disaster. Its eruption in the 18th century caused the death of 2000 people of the Nisga'a First Nation by asphyxiation, most likely from carbon dioxide (CO_2). This tragedy represents the highest death toll for any geological disaster in North America (Figures 6.21 and 6.22).

The oral tradition of the Nisga'a tells of a prolonged period of disruption by the volcano, and includes reference to earthquakes, rivers of molten rock glowing red, and poisonous smoke. A well-known legend mentions that children had shown disrespect to the life-giving salmon by putting stones and burning sticks on their backs. The elders warned the children repeatedly to stop but they did not listen. Soon the ground began to rumble. The volcano erupted and lava flows covered the valley bottom, redirected a river, and destroyed two villages.

MOUNT CHURCHILL, YUKON AND ALASKA

Mount Churchill is a massive volcano sitting at the boundary between Yukon and Alaska. It last erupted violently some 1250 years ago, covering a vast area with a thick layer of pumice. Recent archeological

Figure 6.20
The Volcano Mountain cinder cone, Yukon, which last erupted a mere 3000 years ago.
Source: Donald Francis.

evidence suggests that the eruption might have influenced the early settlement of North America.

The Navajos (who call themselves Diné) of the American Southwest and the Dene of the Northwest Territories are separated by thousands of kilometres but speak a common parent language and share a genetic signature inherited from a small group of people. For millennia, Denes traditionally hunted caribou with stone-tipped darts. Some 700 years ago, however, spruce arrows suddenly became the

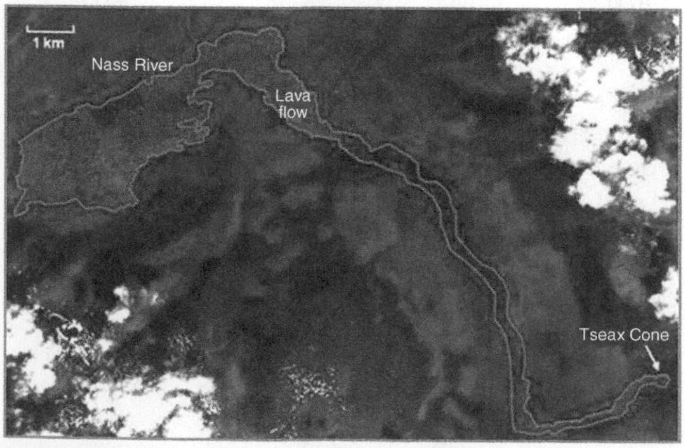

Figure 6.21
Lava flows travelled as far as 22 km from Tseax Cone, northern British Columbia, as shown on this satellite image.
Source: Reproduced with the permission of Natural Resources Canada 2014, courtesy of the Geological Survey of Canada (Photograph by C.J. Hickson).

Figure 6.22
Lava flows from Tseax Cone, northern British Columbia, covered a large plain and transformed the landscape into barren lands, forcing people to relocate.
Source: Reproduced with the permission of Natural Resources Canada 2014, courtesy of the Geological Survey of Canada (Photograph by C.J. Hickson).

weapon of choice. Archeologists speculate that this abrupt break in tradition resulted from a traumatic event. The discovery of moccasins from the same period with a typical Dene design in a cave in Utah implies a long trek across the continent. What could have caused such a hurried migration? Timing points to the eruption of Mount Churchill which must have profoundly disturbed the ecosystem of the Dene homeland, prompting some of them to venture south.

Figure 6.23
Mount Baker (where snowboarding was invented!), northern Washington State, is visible from Victoria, British Columbia, on a clear day.
Source: © Daves Photography.

VOLCANIC HAZARDS IN CANADA

With several dormant subduction-zone volcanoes in the Cascade Range, an explosive volcanic eruption is a significant hazard in British Columbia. The densely populated Vancouver and Victoria areas are most at risk from Mount Baker, Washington State, located very close to the international border (Figure 6.23). Mount Baker, which last erupted in 1880, is handsomely capped by a thick blanket of glacial ice and snow. Volcanic activity could induce a meltdown and send lahars reaching all the way to the Fraser River Valley. Mount Baker could also produce large quantities of volcanic ash. Southwestern British Columbia experiences significant accumulations of ash every few hundred years (Figure 6.24). The Geological Survey of Canada estimates that the threat of airborne ash in Canadian airspace constitutes the most important

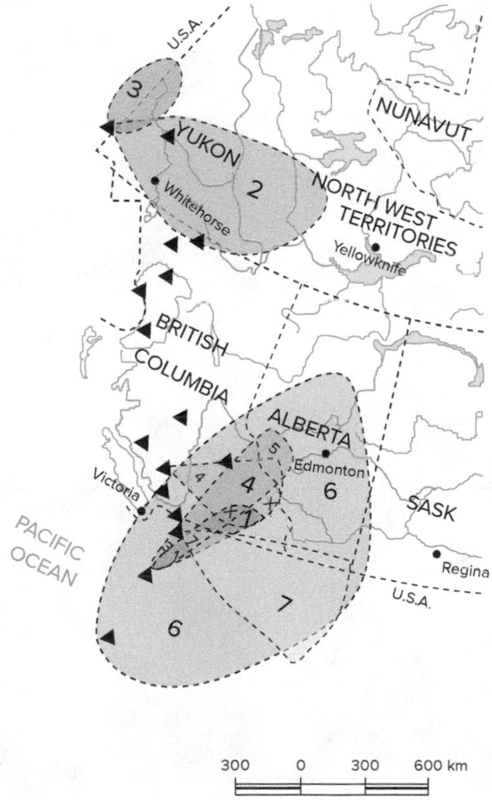

	Volcano	Eruption Date
1	Mount St Helens, Oregon	508 years ago
2	White River, Alaska	1200 years ago
3	White River, Alaska	1500 to 1900 years ago
4	Bridge River, British Columbia	2360 years ago
5	Mount St Helens, Oregon	3400 years ago
6	Mazama, Washington	6800 years ago
7	Glacier Peak, Washington	11 200 years ago

Figure 6.24
Significant accumulations of volcanic ash in western Canada. Cones represent volcanoes less than 12 000 years old.
Source: Reproduced with the permission of Public Safety Canada, 2014.

IN GREATER DEPTH

Volcanic Ash: A Challenge to Air Traffic Safety

The 2010 spring tourist season in Europe started with scenes of chaos. Hundreds of flights cancelled for six consecutive days in northern Europe created a domino effect, leaving millions of people stranded in airports all over the world. Security alert? A late blizzard? Labour strikes? No, a single Icelandic volcano, with complicated spelling—the Eyjafjallajökull (dubbed "E16" for simplicity by the North American media!) was the source of all this disruption.

The otherwise moderate (VEI = 4) Eyjafjallajökull eruption of 14 April 2010 produced exceptionally abrasive glass-rich volcanic ash (Figure 6.25). Because the Eyjafjallajökull was situated directly under a particularly stable jet stream at the time, most of the 250 million cubic metres of ash ejected out of the volcano were transported efficiently and consistently over

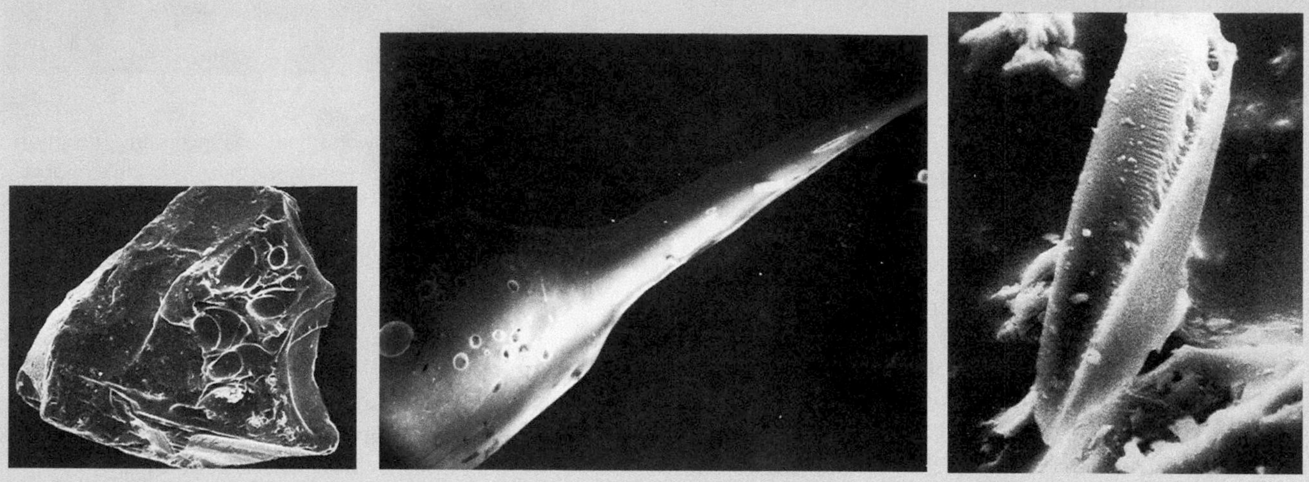

(a) (b) (c)

Figure 6.25
Volcanic ash under the high magnification of a scanning electron microscope (SEM) appears as sharp, jagged, angular pieces of glass and rock. (a) Broken glass droplet from Mount Etna, Sicily (size ≈ 2 microns); (b) Tail of cooled droplet from Kilauea, Hawaii (size ≈ 10 microns); (c) Angular glass fragment, Mount Mayon, Philippines (size ≈ 10 microns).
Source: © SEM photos from Grant Heiken, *Atlas of Volcanic Ash*, Smithsonian Press.

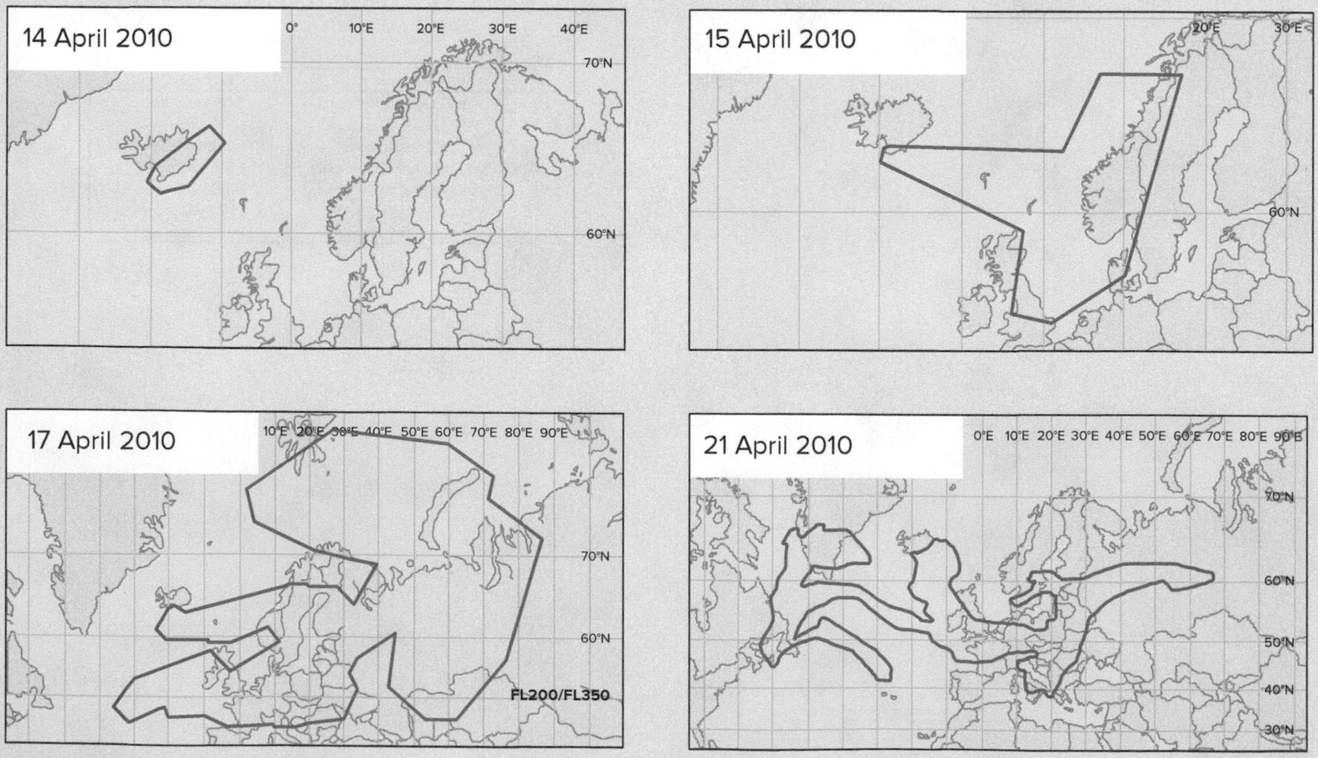

Figure 6.26
The Eyjafjallajökull ash cloud caused the closure of most of the European airspace from 15 to 21 April 2010.
Source: Met Office, United Kingdom.

continued

northern Europe (Figure 6.26). Some dispersed ash even reached Newfoundland where a few flights were cancelled.

Why are aircraft engines sensitive to volcanic ash (Figure 6.27)? They are two main reasons. First, the melting point of volcanic ash is typically between 600 and 800°C, some 200°C lower than the internal temperature of the combustion chamber of a typical gas turbine engine. Ash can melt and later solidify on turbine blades, causing the engine to stall. Second, volcanic ash is abrasive and can cause erosion damage on the blades, accelerating the normal aging of an engine. Other dangers include contamination of the air in the aircraft cabin, accumulation of ash on sensors recording vital data for navigation, and abrasion of the windshield, lowering visibility for the pilot.

Nine Volcanic Ash Advisory Centres around the world—including one in Montreal, which is responsible for all of Canada and the North Atlantic as far east as 30 degrees west longitude—are responsible for monitoring the extent and trajectories of ash clouds. The International Civil Aviation Organization (ICAO), headquartered in Montreal, has developed colour codes to inform pilots and air-traffic controllers about volcanic-ash hazards (Table 6.1). Depending on the circumstances, flights are rerouted, planes are supplied with extra fuel, or higher vigilance is recommended. As there is room for interpretation, an uneasy relationship can develop between the aviation authorities, who are empowered to close or open airspace and tend to be very conservative, and the airlines, which suffer the economic consequences of those decisions.

Figure 6.27
Photograph of turbine blades from the British Airways Boeing 747 that flew through the ash cloud of the Mount Galunggung volcano, Indonesia, on 24 June 1982. The image shows the dangerous accumulation of volcanic ash melted in the combustion chamber of the engine as well as local erosion damage from the ash particles. All four engines failed in flight; after gliding out of the ash cloud they were restarted, enabling the aircraft with 247 passengers on board to land safely in Jakarta.
Source: © Captain Eric Moody

TABLE 6.1

International Colour Codes for Volcanic Ash Hazards to Aviation

GREEN	**Volcano is in normal, non-eruptive state.** *or, after a change from a higher level:* **Volcanic activity considered to have ceased, and volcano reverted to its normal, non-eruptive state.**
YELLOW	**Volcano is exhibiting signs of elevated unrest above known background levels.** *or, after a change from a higher level:* **Volcanic activity has decreased significantly but continues to be closely monitored for possible renewed increase.**
ORANGE	**Volcano is exhibiting heightened unrest with increased likelihood of eruption,** *or,* **Volcanic eruption underway with no or minor ash emission** *[specify ash-plume height if possible].*
RED	**Eruption is forecast to be imminent with significant emission of ash into the atmosphere likely.** *or,* **Eruption is underway with significant emission of ash into the atmosphere** *[specify ash-plume height if possible.]*

Source: http://volcanoes.usgs.gov/activity/alertsystem/

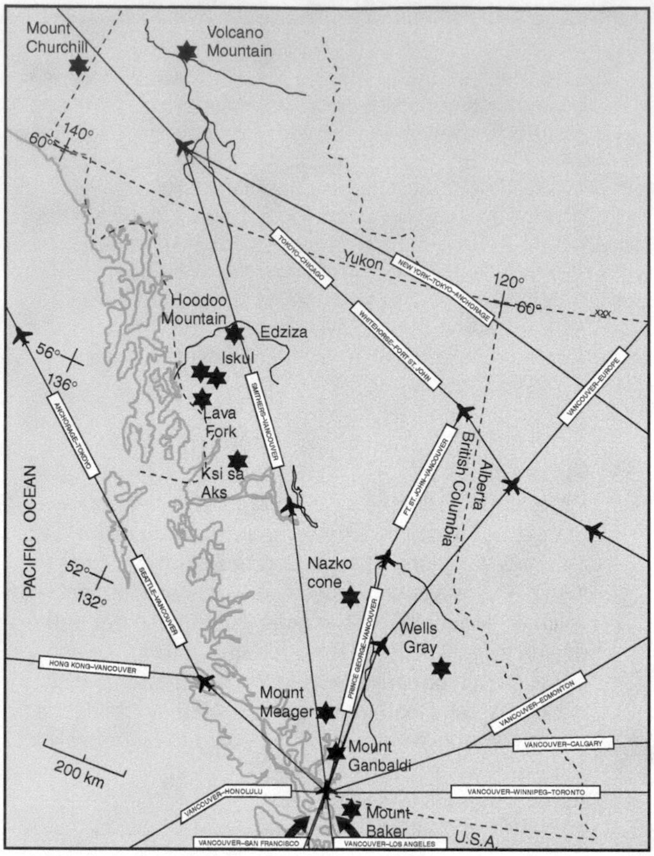

Figure 6.28

Several major air routes over western Canada could potentially be affected by volcanic ash.

Source: : Reproduced with the permission of Natural Resources Canada 2014, courtesy of the Geological Survey of Canada (GSC Bulletin 548)

short-term impact of volcanoes on the Canadian public (Figure 6.28). Ash fallout would also cause respiratory problems for people and disrupt technological systems.

LO3 Killer Events and Processes

Volcanoes exist all around the world. How many people do they kill? Which volcanic processes claim the most lives? The lack of written records for some time intervals and in some parts of the world makes these questions difficult to answer. Volcanologists Tom Simkin, Lee Siebert, and Russell Blong have studied the questions and made approximate answers. About 275 000 people have been killed by volcanic action during the last 500 years (Figure 6.30). A dozen or so volcanic processes have been responsible for these deaths (Figure 6.31 and Table 6.2).

The United States has developed a simple visualization tool, combining pictograms and the aviation colour codes (Table 6.1), to characterize the level of unrest at volcanoes and keep the public informed about related hazards (Figure 6.32). Furthermore, volcanic hazards can be labelled as primary, secondary, and tertiary to provide a framework for discussion (Table 6.3). Primary hazards are the direct consequences of an eruption and are thus tend to be intense and short lived. Secondary hazards result from the environment created by the volcano and can persist long after the eruptive phase is over. On an even longer term, tertiary hazards result from the destabilizing effects of the volcanic eruption on society.

PYROCLASTIC FLOWS

Few events on Earth are as frightening as having a super-hot, turbulent cloud of ash, gas, and air come rolling toward you at high speed. **A pyroclastic flow** can begin in a variety of ways (Figure 6.33). History records numerous instances of pyroclastic flows, killing thousands of people at each event.

Mont Pelée, Martinique, 1902

The Caribbean island of Martinique was colonized by the French in 1635. The tropical climate was superb for growing sugar cane to help satisfy the world's growing appetite for the sweetener. On the north end of Martinique stands a volcano 1350 m tall with a pronounced peak. The French called the volcano Pelée, meaning "peeled" or "bald," to describe the bare area where volcanism had destroyed all plant life during the eruptions of 1792 and 1851. By coincidence, the pronunciation of the French word *Pelée* is the same as the Polynesian word *Pele,* the Hawaiian goddess of volcanoes and fire.

In early spring of 1902, volcanic activity began. The crater atop Mont Pelée began filling with extremely viscous magma, which kept plugging the crater. At times, superhot pyroclastic flows would gush out of the crater; at other times, they would blast out. By late April, it was obvious to most people that this trouble might worsen. About 700 rural people migrated each day into St. Pierre, a nearby city normally home to 25 000 residents. Another 300 people a day were leaving St. Pierre, which lay only 10 km from Mont Pelée. But there was an election coming up on 10 May, and Governor Mouttet did not want everyone scattered from the island's largest city; that would be likely to change the election results. He ordered to the militia to halt the exodus of fleeing people.

Bad decision. There was to be no election on 10 May; all the voters, including the governor, died on 8 May (Figure 6.34).

HUMAN FOCUS

John Stix, Volcanologist, McGill University

My graduate studies in geology took me to northwestern Ontario to study the very old rocks of the Canadian Precambrian Shield. I was working hard in the field, in all weather and at the mercy of voracious black flies, trying to make sense of the rocks surrounding me. They were all volcanic in origin but had been altered over time. I did not understand them. In the spirit of Sir Archibald Geikie, who coined the phrase "The present is the key to the past", I decided to look at younger volcanic rocks as analogues. I became interested in progressively younger and younger volcanic rocks until, as I started my career as an academic (Figure 6.29), I made the conscious decision to study active volcanism.

Our world is volcanic! My career as a volcanologist has taken me all over the world, from the active volcanoes of central America to the geothermal Phlegraean fields of Italy and the extinct ancestral Cascade volcanoes of the American southwest. At small scale, my research focuses on the role of gases dissolved in magma, and at much larger scale, on the development of calderas. This is my contribution to a research direction that is currently receiving much attention in the scientific community—the development of a better understanding of very large explosive eruptions. What are the processes taking place in the magma chamber leading to such events? What are the precursor signs? This information is of critical importance for the safety of millions of people living dangerously close to calderas in places such as Italy, Papua New Guinea, and Indonesia.

In my career, I have seen several new technologies revolutionize the monitoring of active volcanoes. The number of sensors deployed and the power of modern computers have also increased dramatically. This powerful combination allows volcanologists to "take the pulse" of volcanoes in unprecedented detail. The Cascade volcanoes located north of Vancouver (Figure 6.10) represent the most hazardous volcanic situation in the country with potential risks of lahars and ash falls. While they are dormant, it is of primary importance to record background measurements with all the technology available. Since the essence of volcano monitoring is early detection of departure from the norm, the characterization of this base level is essential. I would advocate for a comprehensive and systematic program of acquisition of data related to Canadian volcanoes. This would include investigating the little-known volcanoes of the Canadian North. Maybe in the near future, we might even see an emerging ecotourism industry offering trips to see them in their untouched natural environment.

Figure 6.29
John Stix, Professor at McGill University, in front of Kirishima volcano, Japan.
Source: John Stix

On the morning of 8 May 1902, a massive volume of gas-charged, ultra-sticky magma had risen to the top of the crater. At about 7:50 a.m., sharp blasts sounded like thousands of cannons being fired as trapped gas bubbles exploded and shattered magma into fine pieces. This spectacular pyroclastic flow moved as a red-hot avalanche of incandescent gases and glowing volcanic fragments

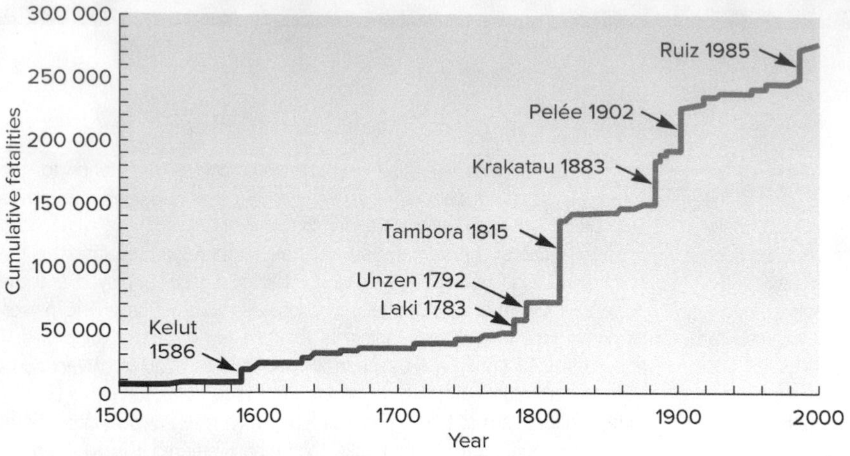

Figure 6.30
Cumulative fatalities from volcanoes during 500 years, 1500–2000.

Source: © Simkin, T., Siebert, L., and Blong, R., "Volcano Fatalities" in *Science,* 291:255, 2001.

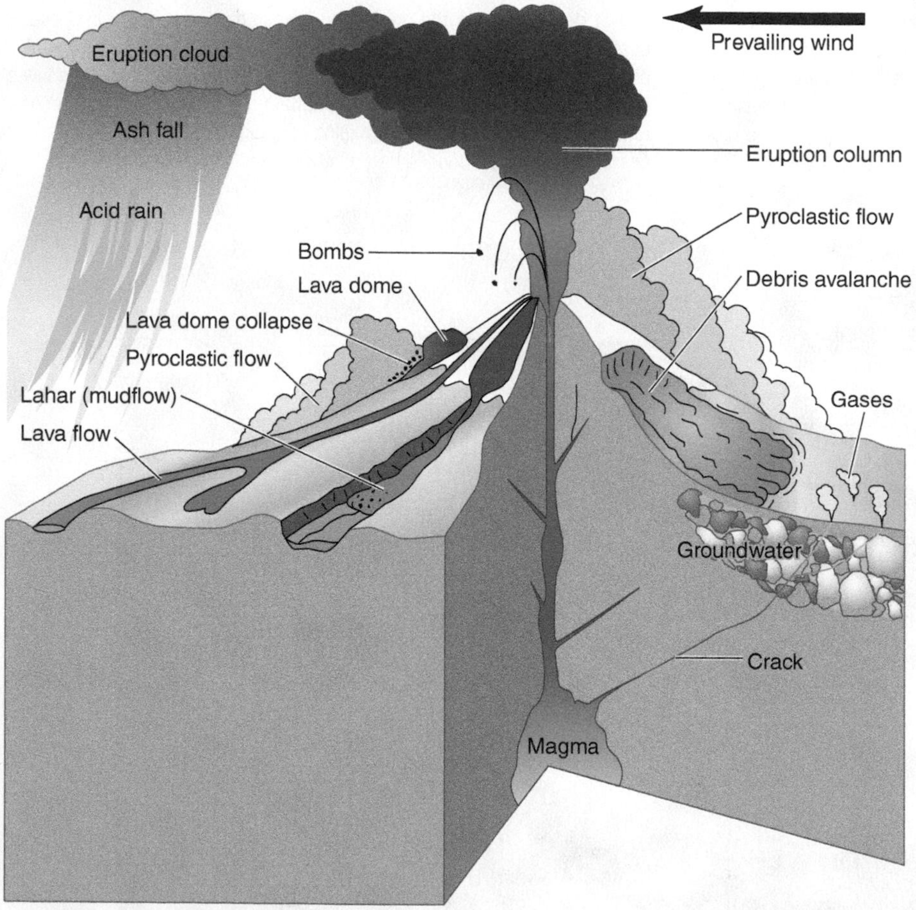

Figure 6.31
Volcanoes create many life-threatening natural hazards.

(then called ***nuée ardente,*** which is French for "glowing cloud"). The mass moved as solid particles of magma suspended in gas. Its energy came from (1) the initial blast, (2) gravity, and (3) gas continuing to escape from the pieces of airborne magma, creating a "popcorn" effect. The pyroclastic flow moved with hurricane wind speeds of about 190 km/h, but it was much denser than a hurricane because it contained solid ash. The flow lifted roofs, knocked down most walls perpendicular to its path, twisted metal bars, and wrapped sheets of metal roofing around the scorched trunks of trees. Within the space of a couple of minutes, St. Pierre turned from a verdant tropical city to burned-out ruin covered by a foot of grey ash.

Death was quick and came from three causes: (1) physical impact, (2) inhaling superhot gases, and (3) burns. The refugee-swollen population of St. Pierre at the time was more than 30 000; only two people are known to have survived. One was Auguste Ciparis, a 25-year-old murderer locked in a stone-hut jail without windows and with only a small barred grating in his door. When hot gases entered his cell, he fell to the floor,

TABLE 6.2

Volcanic Causes of Deaths

	275 000 Deaths	530 Volcanic Events
Pyroclastic flow	29%	15%
Tsunami	21%	5%
Lahar	15%	17%
Indirect (famine)	23%	5%
Gas	1%	4%
Lava flow	<1%	4%
Pyroclastic bombs	2%	21%
Debris avalanche	2%	3%
Flood	1%	2%
Earthquake	<1%	2%
Lightning	<1%	1%
Unknown	7%	20%

Source: © Simkin, T., Siebert, L., and Blong, R., "Volcano fatalities" in *Science*, 291:255, 2001.

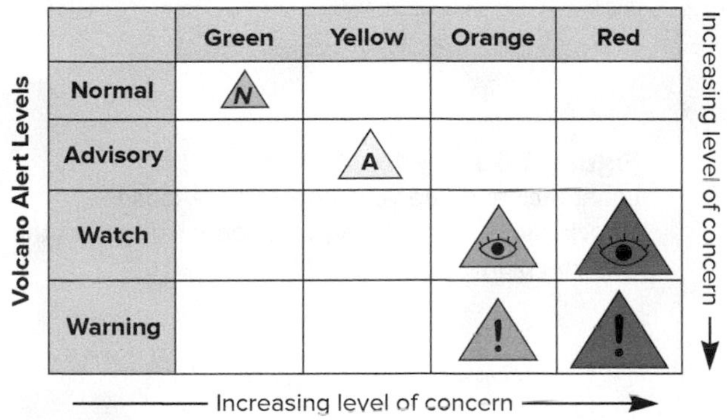

Figure 6.32
Volcanic activity alert-notification system
Source: United States Geological Survey

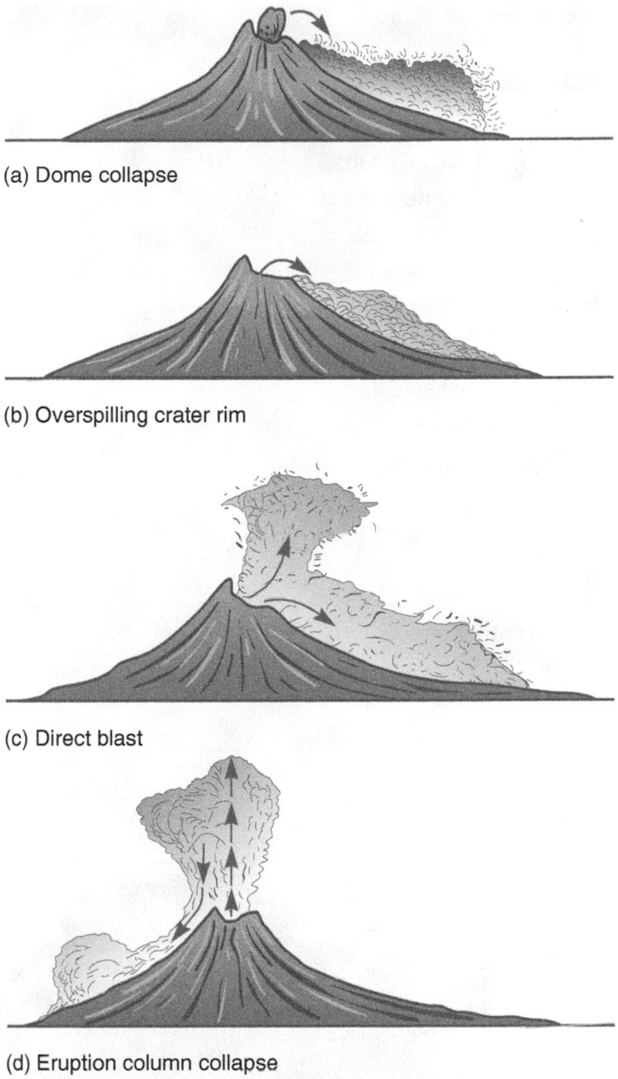

Figure 6.33
Ways of generating a pyroclastic flow. (a) Dome collapse as at Mount Unzen, 1991; (b) Overspilling of crater rim as at Mont Pelée, 1902–1903; (c) Direct blast as at Mount St. Helens, 1980, and Mount Pinatubo, 1991; (d) Eruption column collapse as at Mount Mayon, 1968.

suffering severe burns on his back and legs. Four days later, he was rescued; he then spent the rest of his life showing his scarred body at circus sideshows as "the prisoner of St. Pierre." The other survivor was a man inside the same house where his family members died.

TSUNAMIS

Can a pyroclastic flow or lava-dome avalanche cause a tsunami? Yes. On 21 May 1792, an earthquake triggered a collapse from the lava dome on Mount Unzen. The avalanche volume of 0.3 km^3 was not impressively large. However, after it flowed 6.4 km to the sea, it hit the water with enough impact to create a tsunami that killed 15 000 people in the surrounding region. The tragedy inspired the construction of the Anyoji Temple and Buddhist sanctuary in memory of those killed. In 1991, the temple served as a temporary morgue for the 44 people slammed and burned to death by the 3 June pyroclastic flow, including the famed French volcano photographers Maurice and Katya Krafft.

LAHARS

Any mass movements of muddy volcanic debris pulled by gravity are known as lahars, an Indonesian word (Figure 6.35). Lahars can be classified as both primary and secondary hazards (Table 6.3). Viscous lahars may accompany an eruption and cause immediate deaths and major damages. They may also be triggered during a period of quiescence.

TABLE 6.3

Volcanic Hazards

Secondary	Primary	Blasts
		Jokulhlaups
		Lahars
		Lava flows
		Pyroclastic bombs
		Pyroclastic flows
		Tsunami
	Mass movements	
	Volcanic ash	
	Volcanic gas	
Tertiary	Disease	
	Famine	
	Socio-economic decay	
	Weather effects	

Figure 6.34
The pyroclastic flow-charred remains of St. Pierre, May 1902. Mont Pelée is in background.
Source: © Underwood and Underwood, Courtesy of the Library of Congress.

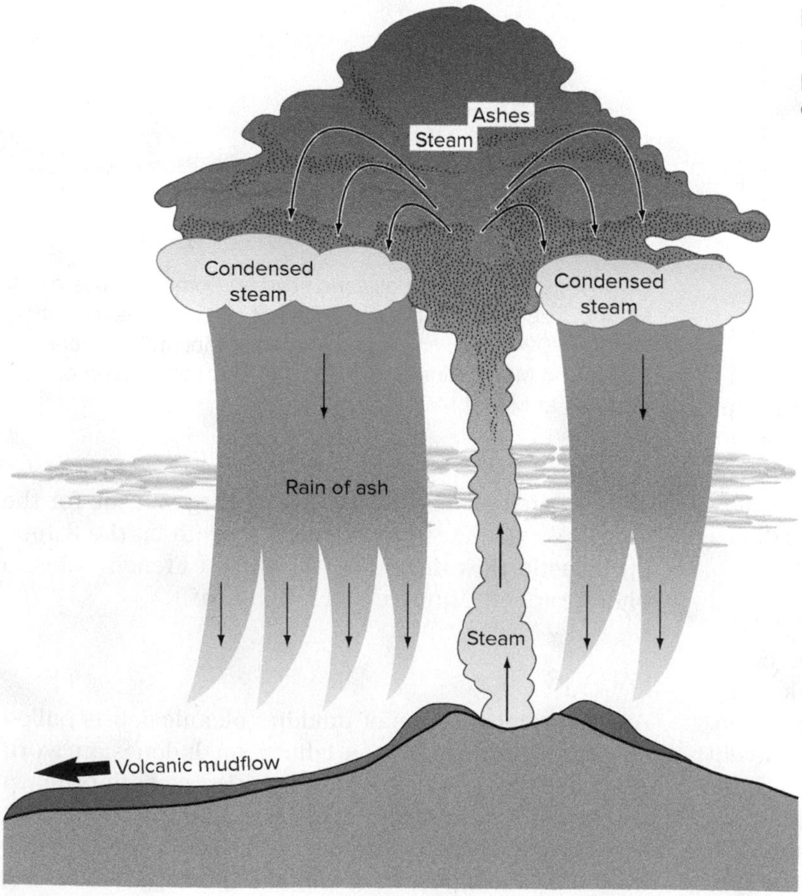

Figure 6.35
Lahar recipe: steep volcano slopes + loose pyroclastic debris + heavy rain condensing from the eruption plume.

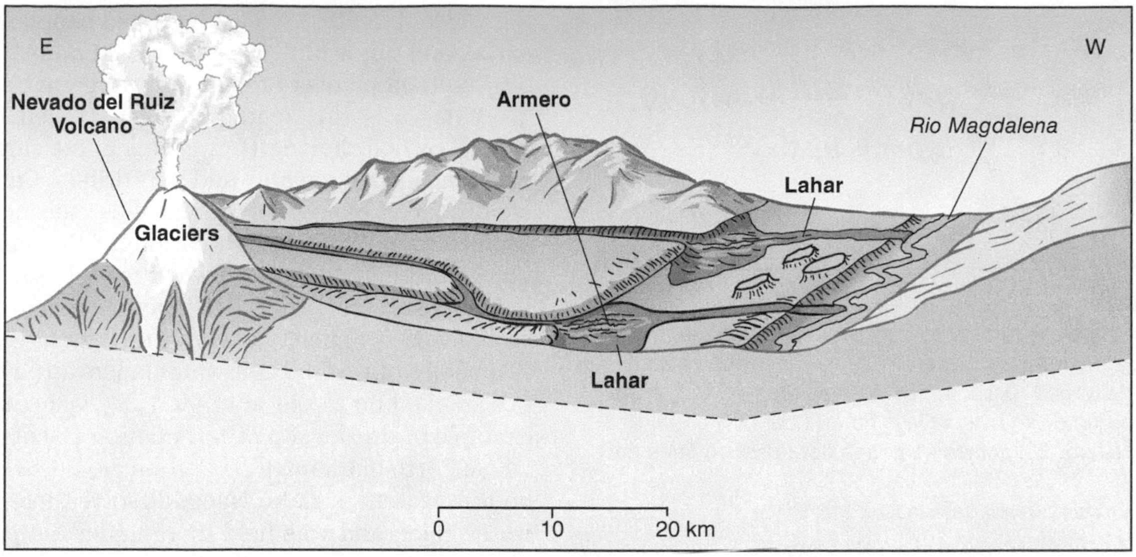

Figure 6.36
Eruption of Nevado del Ruiz in 1985 dropped hot pyroclastic debris onto glaciers, resulting in lahars (shown in brown).
Source: © United States Geological Survey.

Nevado del Ruiz, Colombia, 1985

Is a huge eruption required to kill a lot of people? Consider this story. Nevado del Ruiz rises to an elevation of 5400 m. The Spanish word *nevado* means snow-covered, and indeed a 19 km^2 area on top of the mountain is covered year-round by an ice cap 10 to 30 m thick with a volume of about 337 million cubic metres. In November 1984, the volcano awoke with small-scale activity.

A year later, on 10 November 1985, a swarm of small earthquakes foretold a coming eruption. At 9:37 p.m., a Plinian column rose several kilometres high. Hot pyroclastic debris began melting the ice cap. By 10 p.m., condensing volcanic steam, ice melt, and pyroclastic debris combined to send lahars down the east slopes, destroying homes and killing 1800 people.

But the worst was yet to come. Increasing eruptive activity melted more ice, sending even larger lahars flowing down the canyons to the west and onto the floodplain of the Rio Magdalena (Figure 6.36). At 11 p.m., the first wave of cool lahars reached the town of Armero and its 27 000 residents. These lahars had travelled 45 km from the mountaintop, dropping over 5000 m in elevation. A few minutes later, roaring noises announced the approach of successive waves of warm to hot lahars. Most of Armero, including 22 000 of its residents, ended up buried beneath lahars 8 m thick (Figure 6.37). The 22 000 unlucky people were either crushed or suffocated.

But 5000 people did escape. How? They were higher on the slopes. A memorable video showed a man's talking head, which appeared to be resting on top of the mudflows; the man was caught by lahars and buried to his chin as he tried to escape upslope. One step slower and he would have been completely buried and suffocated. But with a bit of digging, he was freed, shaken but unharmed.

The volcanic eruption at Nevado del Ruiz was actually rather minor. Had there not been an ice cap to melt, no harm would have been done. Danger was well known from historical records. In fact, a hazards map published just one month before the tragic events

Figure 6.37
Most of the town of Armero, Colombia, and 22 000 of its residents lie beneath lahars up to 8 m thick.
Source: © United States Geological Survey.

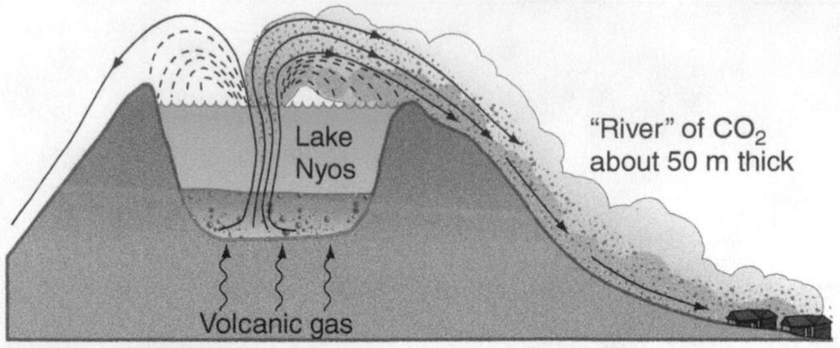

Figure 6.38

Schematic cross-section of Lake Nyos. Volcanic gas is absorbed by a deep water layer. In 1986, when the bottom water was disturbed, 0.15 km^3 of CO_2 gas erupted out of the lake and poured down river valleys for an hour or more in a 50 m thick cloud. Solid lines show gas flow; dashed lines are water drops.

Source: Diagram after Y. Zhang, 1996, *Nature,* 379, 57–59.

of November 1985 clearly indicated the potential danger for the town of Armero. The 1985 lahars were a virtual rerun of the events of 1845, themselves a repeat of those of 1595. The same places were buried by the same types of lahars. In 1845, the death toll was about 1000, but because Colombia's population has grown, the dead in 1985 numbered about 24 000. Faced with pressing demands for basic needs such as health services and education, poor countries often do not prioritize mitigation against natural hazards.

GAS

It is not just gas-powered magma that kills; gas can be deadly by itself.

Killer Lakes of Africa

Tragedy at Lake Nyos in 1986 uncovered a new volcanic hazard, "killer lakes."

Cameroon sits near the equator in western Africa. It hosts a string of crater lakes running in a northeasterly trend. Lake Nyos is one of these crater lakes, and is filled with beautiful, deep blue water. This topographically high crater is only several hundred years old. It was blasted into bedrock by explosions of volcanic gases and is 1925 m across at its greatest width and as deep as 208 m.

At about 9:30 p.m. on 21 August 1986, a loud noise rumbled through the Lake Nyos region as a gigantic volume of gas belched forth from the crater lake and swept down the adjacent valleys (Figure 6.38). The dense, "smoky" rivers of gas were as much as 50 m thick and moving at velocities up to 70 km/h. The ground-hugging cloud swept outward for 25 km. Residents of four villages overwhelmed by the gaseous cloud felt fatigue, light-headedness, warmth, and confusion before losing consciousness. Several hours later, about half a dozen people awoke from their comas to find themselves in the midst of death: 1700 asphyxiated people; 3000 dead cattle; and not a bird, insect, or wild animal alive. Yet the luxuriant plants of the region were unaffected.

What was the deathly gas? It turned out to be simply carbon dioxide (CO_2). This is the same gas we drink in sparkling water and soft drinks. Carbon dioxide displaced oxygen in the air, thus causing death by asphyxiation. What was the origin of the gas? It had a volcanic origin, leaking upward from basaltic magma in the subsurface. How did the gas accumulate into such an immense volume? Lakes by their nature are stratified bodies of water. Their water layers differ in density, one stacked on top of another. (This is a smaller-scale example of the density differentiation discussed for the whole Earth in Chapter 2.) Carbon dioxide rose into the bottom waters of Lake Nyos, dissolved into the lower water layer, and was held there under the pressure of the overlying water. As the amount of CO_2 in the lake-bottom water increased, the arrangement became more unstable. When CO_2 bubbles form, they rise with increasing speed, setting off a positive feedback chain of events leading to more and more bubble formation and rise. Volcanologist Youxue Zhang calculated that the gas eruption was moving about 325 km/h when it reached the lake surface. The event of 21 August 1986 released about 0.15 km^3 of gas in about one hour. It was like a large-scale erupting champagne bottle, where removal of the cork causes a decrease in pressure, allowing CO_2 to gush out. About 66% of the dissolved gases escaped. After the event, the lake level was one metre lower, and the water was brown from the mud and dead vegetation stirred up from the bottom (Figure 6.39).

What triggered the gas release? Many suggestions have been made, including volcanic eruption, mass movement, earthquake, wind disturbance, or change in water temperature with resultant overturn of lake-water layers. It is interesting to note that a similar event had occurred two years earlier at Lake Monoun on 15 August 1984. This was a smaller event, but it still killed 37 people. Both events were in August, the time of minimum stability in Cameroon lake waters. Is this a coincidence, or is this a normal overturning of lake water during the rainy season?

Could this event happen again? Definitely. CO_2 is constantly being fed through the bottom of Lake Nyos. Since 2001, however, a system of degassing pipes has been installed to allow high-pressure gas to shoot out of the lake as a fountain of gassy water (Figures 6.40 and 6.41). This prevents the CO_2 concentrations from building up to dangerous levels.

As this hazard has become better understood, other similar lakes have been recognized. For example, the giant Lake Kivu that straddles the border between Rwanda and Congo holds 1000 times as much CO_2 as Lake Nyos.

Figure 6.39
The water of Lake Nyos is muddy after a huge volume of gas escaped in 1986.
Source: J. P. Lockwood/USGS.

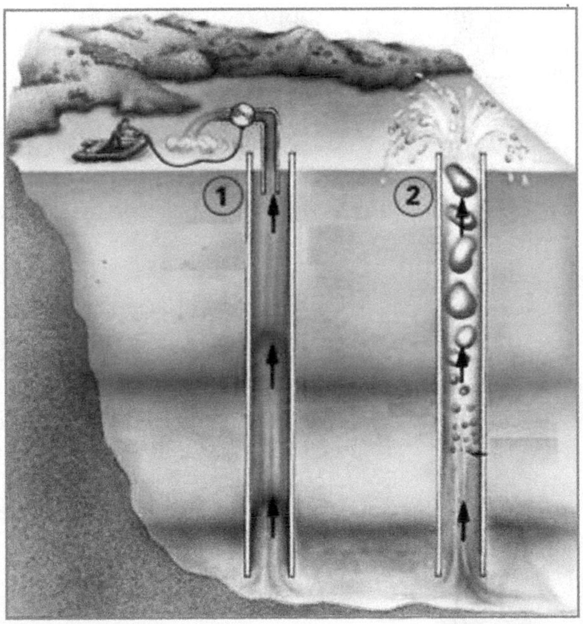

Figure 6.40
The degassing principle is ingenious in its simplicity. (1) A pump raises water in the pipe to a level where it becomes saturated with gas. (2) Degassing lightens the water column and pushes it upward. The system is self-powered as long as dissolved gas is available. This effect is similar to the formation of a buoyant plume during a volcanic eruption (Figure 5.12).
Source: Project "Degassing Nyos".

Figure 6.41
Plume of water spewing out from the degassing pipe at Lake Nyos.
Source: Reprinted by permission from Macmillan Publishers Ltd: NATURE, Battle to degas deadly lakes continues. Photo of a plume of gassy water spewing from Lake Nyos Nature, M. Halbwachs (2010) Nature p. 466:1033, copyright (2010). Used with permission via Rightslink.

LAVA FLOWS

Lava flows are common and impressive, but are they big killers? No (Table 6.2). Why don't lava flows kill more people? Usually they move too slowly, but not always.

Nyiragongo, Democratic Republic of the Congo, 1977, 2002

As East Africa slowly rifts away from the African continent, magma rises to build stratovolcanoes such as Mounts Kilimanjaro and Nyiragongo in the East African Rift system (Figure 2.24b). Mount Nyiragongo has a long-lived lava lake in its summit crater. In 1977, Nyiragongo lava flows had exceptionally low SiO_2 content, about 42% (compare this value to those listed in Table 5.3). The low-viscosity lava flowed down the volcano slopes at about 60 km/h, killing an estimated 300 people. A similar episode occurred on 17 January 2002. Lava flowed rapidly down the slopes of the volcano, killing more than 45 people living on the mountain. Upon reaching flatter ground, the lava flows slowed but moved relentlessly toward Lake Kivu. The city of Goma lay in the path of the oncoming lava: 500 000 residents plus uncounted thousands of civil war refugees from Rwanda lived there. Lava reached the lake, but it first flowed through the heart of Goma, destroying about 25% of the buildings, and the refugees were forced to flee again.

WEATHER EFFECTS

Volcanoes affect humans not only directly, but also indirectly by changing the atmosphere and weather, and by harming the plants and animals they depend upon.

Some volcanic eruptions create their own "weather" on a local scale (Figure 6.42). Benjamin Franklin recognized in 1784 that volcanism can also affect the weather globally. He suggested that the haze and cold weather in Europe during 1783–84 were due to the massive outpourings of lava and gas at Laki, Iceland. Large, explosive Plinian eruptions can blast fine ash and gas high enough to be above the normal zone of weather. Free from the cleansing effects of rainfall, the volcanic products can float about in the stratosphere and interfere with incoming sunlight (Figure 6.43). The finest volcanic ash (diameter ~0.001 mm) can stay suspended for years. Most gases blown into the stratosphere disappear into space, but sulphur dioxide (SO_2) picks up oxygen and water to form an aerosol of sulphuric acid (H_2SO_4) that may also stay aloft for several years. The combined ash and sulphuric acid produce **haze,** reducing the amount of sunshine that reaches the troposphere and the ground surface; thus, cooling results. Conversely, an excess of carbon dioxide in the atmosphere creates a greenhouse effect, which causes warming. In both cases, agricultural production might be adversely affected, which in turn can lead to famine, disease, and death.

The main variables that must come into play for volcanism to affect weather include

1. The size and rate of eruptions.
2. The heights of eruption columns.
3. The types of gases and the atmospheric level they reach.
4. The latitude: low-latitude eruptions spread atmospheric debris across more of the world and have greater global effects than high-latitude eruptions.

Figure 6.42
Lightning illuminates the ash cloud from the Puyehue-Cordón Caulle volcanic eruption, which disrupted air traffic in Chile in June 2011. Rock fragments, ash, and ice particles collide to inseminate the cloud with static electricity charges, later released in lightning.
Source: REUTERS/Carlos Gutierrez

Laki Fissure Eruption, Iceland, 1783

After a week of earthquakes, on the morning of 8 June 1783, a 25 km long fissure opened near Laki, Iceland, and basaltic lavas gushed for 50 days. The Laki event was a textbook fissure eruption, where the magma typically flowed at 5000 m^3/s. To better appreciate this volume of magma, consider that North America's mightiest river, the Mississippi, empties into the Gulf of Mexico at about three times this volume. When the eruption ended, an area of 565 km^2 was buried beneath 13 km^3 of basaltic lavas. The volume of ash and larger airborne fragments totalled another 0.3 km^3.

The 50 days of eruption were accompanied by the release of an enormous volume of gases that enshrouded Iceland and much of northern Europe in a "dry fog" or blue haze. This haze was rich in SO_2 (one of the visible components of today's urban smog) and an unusually large amount of fluorine. The gases slowed the growth of grasses and increased their fluorine content. An Icelandic farmer named Jon Stein-Grimmson wrote

> The hairy sand-fall and sulfurous rain caused such unwholesomeness in the air and in the earth that the grass became yellow and pink and withered down to the roots. The animals that wandered around the fields got yellow-covered feet with open wounds, and yellow dots were seen on the skin of the newly shorn sheep, which had died.

The volcanic gases helped kill 75% of Iceland's horses and sheep, and 50% of the cattle. The resulting famine weakened the Icelandic people, and about 20% of the population (10 000 people) died. In today's world of instant communication and rapid air transport, these deaths would have been avoided.

Tambora, Indonesia, 1815

In the early 1800s, Mount Tambora, on the island of Sumbawa in Indonesia, stood 4000 m tall. After the explosive eruptions of 10–11 April 1815, Tambora was only 2650 m tall and had a caldera 7 km wide and 650 m deep. About 150 km^3 of rock and magma were blasted out during the eruption, producing 175 km^3 of ash and other pyroclastic debris. The eruption has been called the greatest in historical times, killing about 10 000 people outright by pyroclastic flows and another 117 000 indirectly through famine and disease. It destroyed the feudal kingdoms of Sanggar and Tambora, leading to the death of the Tambora language, the easternmost Austro-Asiatic language.

The volcanic ash and aerosols blown into the stratosphere, especially those associated with sulphur dioxide (SO_2), blocked enough sunshine to make 1816 still remembered as "the year without a summer," the "Poverty Year," or "Eighteen hundred and froze to death [sic]." Agricultural production was down throughout the world as global temperatures were lowered by a further 0.3°C during an already cold series of years. In eastern North America, snow or frost occurred in every month of the following year. Over 30 cm of snow fell in southern Quebec in June. In July and August, lake and river ice was observed as far south as Pennsylvania. Dramatic temperature swings were common, sometimes plummeting from normal or above normal temperatures of 35°C to near freezing in hours. It has been suggested that the Tambora-cooled weather induced the famine in India that year, and weakened the population enough to trigger a cholera epidemic. The disease then slowly migrated around the world, killing people who lived under the harshest, least sanitary conditions.

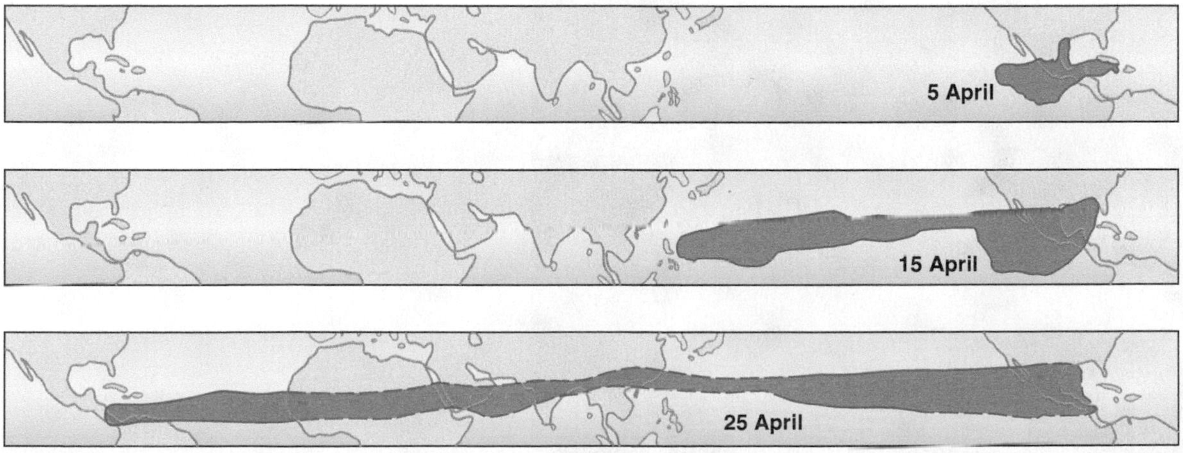

Figure 6.43

The gaseous cloud from El Chichón (Mexico) moving west in the stratosphere in 1982. The cloud took 23 days to circle the globe.

Source: Adapted from Robock, Alan, and Matson, "Circumglobal transport of the El Chichón volcanic dust cloud" in *Science*, 221 (1983):195–97.

LO4 Volcano Monitoring and Warning

Can we monitor the activity of a volcano and provide advance warning before a large eruption (Figure 6.44)? Unfortunately, there is no such thing as an "eruptometer," as pointed out amusingly by Dr. Peter Cervelli, geophysicist in Yellowstone National Park. The most important tools for forecasting volcanic activity are seismometers, global positioning system (GPS) stations, sensors that record changes in gas characteristics, and, last but not least, the judgment of experienced volcanologists.

SIGNS OF IMPENDING ERUPTIONS

Seismic Waves

As magma rises toward Earth's surface, it causes rocks to snap and break, sending off short-period seismic waves with periods of 0.02 to 0.06 seconds. Magma on the move through an opened conduit generates longer-period seismic waves with periods of 0.2 to 2 seconds. Eruption is then imminent!

Very sensitive, special seismometers are used to capture the faint seismicity related to magma movement. In 1991, during the two weeks before Mount Pinatubo erupted, there were about 400 long-period seismic events a day coming from about 10 km deep. These long-period events were related to the arrival of new magma loading the volcano for eruption.

Ground Deformation

Magma moving into a volcano changes the volcano's shape. In recent years, satellite radars and global GPS stations have been used to measure movements of the ground over time (Figure 6.45). The more the ground inflates, the more likely it is that some magma will break through to the surface and erupt.

In addition to overall movements of the ground, change in shape of the ground surface can be measured by anchoring tiltmeters at two points and measuring the slope between them. When the volcano fills up with magma, its flanks become steeper and the slope angle measured by tiltmeters increases (Figure 6.45).

Figure 6.44
Following an order to leave the immediate area surrounding a volcano, clearly marked routes are critical to an orderly evacuation. This example is from Cajón del Maipo near the San José volcano at the border between Chile and Argentina. The dormant San José volcano last erupted in 1960.
Source: © Claire Samson.

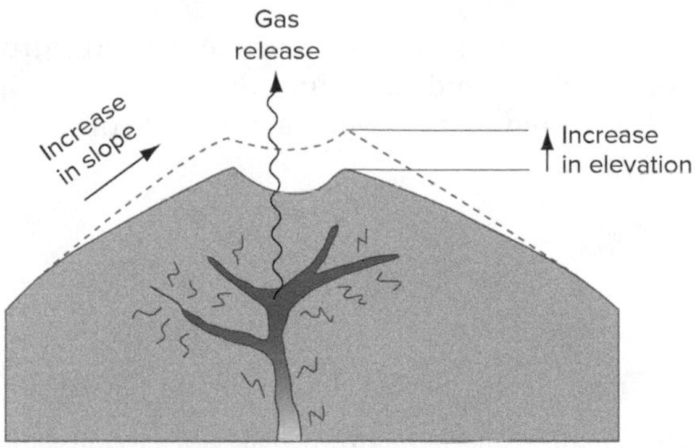

Figure 6.45
Sketch (not to scale) illustrating how magma moving into a volcanic edifice fractures rocks, changes the shape of the volcano (initial shape in solid line; inflated shape in dotted line), and releases gases.

Gas Measurements

As magma rises toward the surface, the pressure on it drops and dissolved gases escape. In that respect, magma degassing can signal an impending eruption (Figure 6.45). However, this interpretation can be misleading. In 1993, at Galeras Volcano in Colombia, a decrease in gas emissions was interpreted as meaning an eruption was less likely. But, in fact, it meant that the volcano had become plugged by its sticky magma and gas pressure was building toward the eruption that killed six volcanologists. So, both increases and decreases in gas emissions can be bad. More research needs to be done in this area.

Lava Samples

Once a volcano starts erupting, sampling lava helps to determine the residence time of the magma in the magma chamber. If chemical composition indicates that the magma is derived directly from mantle, fresh magma is fuelling the eruption. In this case, the eruption is likely to be sustained for an extended length of time.

Mount Pinatubo, Philippines, 1991

A volcano-warning success story occurred in the Philippines in 1991 before the climactic eruption of Mount Pinatubo on 15 June 1991. The volcanic eruption was the largest to occur near a heavily populated area in the twentieth century. Nearly one million people lived in the danger zone.

In March 1991, Mount Pinatubo awoke from a 500-year-long slumber as magma moved upward from a depth of 32 km, causing thousands of small earthquakes, creating three small steam-blast craters, and emitting thousands of tonnes of sulfur dioxide–rich gas. Volcanologists and seismologists began an intense monitoring program to anticipate the size and date of a major eruption. On 7 June, magma reached the surface but had lost most of its gas (like a stale glass of sparkling water), so the magma simply oozed out to form a lava dome. Then on 12 June (Philippine Independence Day), millions of cubic metres of gas-charged magma reached the surface, causing large explosive eruptions. The message to speed the evacuation was spread quickly and loudly. Virtually everyone, and every movable thing, left hurriedly. On 15 June, the cataclysmic eruption began. It blew more than 5 km^3 of magma and rock up to 35 km into the atmosphere, forming an ash cloud with a diameter of 480 km. The airborne ash blocked incoming sunlight. Pyroclastic flows of hot ash, pumice, and gas rolled down the volcano flanks and filled valleys up to 200 m deep. Then, as luck would have it, a typhoon arrived and washed tremendous volumes of volcanic debris downslope as lahars.

How successful was the advance warning? Although almost 300 people died, it is estimated that up to 20 000 people might have died without the forceful warnings. The monitoring program from March to June 1991 cost about $1.5 million and saved 20 000 lives and $500 million in evacuated property, including airplanes. What a dramatic and cost-effective success!

SUMMARY

- Spreading centres sit on top of the asthenosphere, which yields basaltic magma that rises to fill fractures between diverging plates. Eruptions are usually peaceful and basaltic volcanoes may be successfully colonized.
- Subduction-zone eruptions involve basaltic magma contaminated by crustal rock to yield water-rich, highly viscous magma containing trapped gases. Their explosive eruptions pose the greatest risk to humans.
- Hot-spot volcanism can exhibit a range of explosiveness depending on the amount of crustal rock incorporated in magma.
- In the last 500 years, the most devastating direct volcanic causes of deaths have been pyroclastic flows, tsunamis, and lahars. Volcanoes also kill indirectly via famine.
  - Gas-powered, scorching-hot pyroclastic flows move at speeds up to 250 km/h, for distances up to tens of kilometres.

- Pyroclastic debris and water can combine and flow downslope as lahars.

- Volcanism has major effects on weather. When ash and sulphur dioxide (SO_2) are blasted into the stratosphere, they block some incoming solar radiation, leading to cooling.
- It is possible to monitor seismic activity, ground deformation, and gas and lava releases at a volcano and give advance warning of a major eruption.

Terms to Remember

haze
jokulhlaup
nuée ardente
pyroclastic flow
tuya
volcanic belt

Questions for Review

1. Why is it relatively safe to watch the eruption of a Hawaiian volcano but dangerous to watch the eruption of a Cascade Range volcano?
2. How does a jokulhlaup form? Explain using a cross-section.
3. What is the origin of the Cascade Range volcanoes? Draw a tectonic map to support your explanation.
4. What volcanic processes have killed the most people in the last 500 years?
5. Are strong earthquakes associated with volcanic activity?
6. Why do pyroclastic flows travel so quickly? How do they kill?
7. How do lahars form, move, and kill?
8. What hazard does Mount Baker present to Vancouver?
9. How do events unfold at an African killer lake, such as Nyos? Explain using a cross-section.
10. Can an eruption with a low VEI rating kill thousands of people? If so, how?
11. How do the ages vary along a chain of subduction-zone volcanoes versus along a chain of hot-spot volcanoes?

Questions for Further Thought

1. Is it likely that there will be a volcanic eruption in Canada in your lifetime? Are more volcanoes expected in Canada in the future?
2. A volcano can have effects beyond the borders of the country where it is located. How can neighbouring nations collaborate to mitigate volcanic hazards?
3. What action can governments take to discourage people from living in areas where lahars and pyroclastic flows are a hazard?
4. How could a major volcanic eruption anywhere in the world affect Canadian weather?
5. If major volcanic eruptions occurred nearly every year for a century, what might happen to the global climate?

Interesting Websites

- Cascades Volcano Observatory, United States Geological Survey
  http://volcanoes.usgs.gov/observatories/cvo/

- International Airways Volcano Watch Operations Group, International Civil Aviation Organization
  http://www.icao.int/safety/meteorology/iavwopsg/Pages/default.aspx

CHAPTER SEVEN

7

Tsunamis

INTERNAL ENERGY

GRAVITY

IMPACTS

Devastation over the port of Sendai, Japan, a day after the 2011 Tohoku earthquake and tsunami. Black smoke is coming from the damaged Sendai oil refinery. Source: U.S. Navy.

"There is nowhere in the world that is better prepared."

—David Brodie, a Vancouver-based consultant who has worked in Japan to help Canadian and British embassies prepare for earthquakes (quoted in *The Globe and Mail*, 12 March 2011)

Outline

- 2011 Tohoku, Japan, Earthquake and Tsunami
- Waves in Water and on the Coastline
- Wind-Caused Waves versus Tsunami Waves
- Causes of Tsunamis
- Earthquake-Caused Tsunamis
- Volcano-Caused Tsunamis
- Landslide-Caused Tsunamis
- Seiches
- Surviving a Tsunami
- Summary

LO1 Distinguish between waves caused by wind and tsunamis.

LO2 Explain four different origins for tsunamis.

LO3 Describe the causes and impact of tsunamis along the Pacific and Atlantic coasts of Canada.

LO4 Take action to survive a tsunami.

LO5 Describe mitigation strategies against tsunamis.

The biggest, most feared waves can pass mostly unnoticed across the open sea and then rear up and strike the shoreline with devastating blows. The 2011 Tohoku tsunami reminds us that the country with the most detailed history of these killer waves is Japan, and the waves are known by the Japanese word *tsunami* (*tsu* = harbour; *nami* = wave). The reference to harbour waves emphasizes the greater heights that a tsunami can reach in inlets and harbours because the narrowed topography focuses the wave into a smaller space. For example, a wave 8 m high on the open coast may be forced to heights of 30 m as it crowds into a narrow harbour.

Major tsunamis occur about once per decade. Historical data reveal that more than half of them have occurred around the Pacific Ocean (Figure 7.1 and Table 7.1). For Canadians, tsunamis may seem to be a very foreign hazard, bringing destruction to faraway lands. In fact, the Arctic, Atlantic, and Pacific coasts of Canada are all at risk from tsunamis (Figure 7.2).

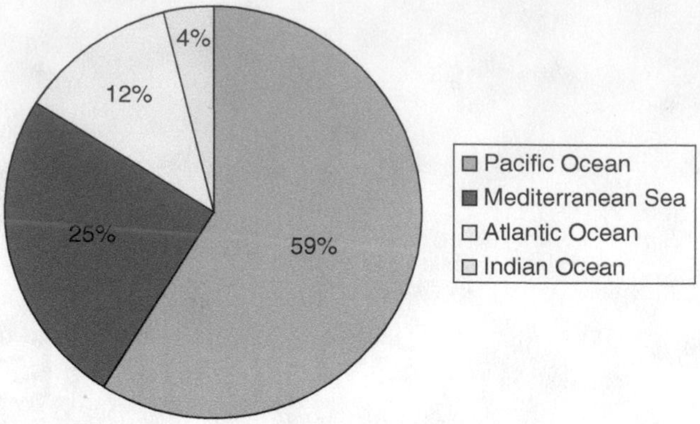

Figure 7.1
Geographical occurrence of tsunamis.
Source: Based on data from Pacific Tsunami Warning Center/NOAA.

2011 Tohoku, Japan, Earthquake and Tsunami

The Tohoku earthquake—the fourth greatest earthquake in the world since modern recordings began (Table 2.4)—occurred at 2:46:23 local time on 11 March 2011, offshore northeastern Japan. At first glance, the plate tectonics of eastern Japan seem fairly simple. The Pacific plate moves northwest 8.3 cm per year and dives under Japan (Figure 2.37). The subducting plate is slowed by friction, and stress builds until there is enough to rupture individual segments of the megathrust fault, resulting in earthquakes of magnitudes 7 to 8. This has been the pattern of the

TABLE 7.1

Notable Tsunamis in Recent Times

Date		Cause	Height	Site	Deaths
1 November	1755	Earthquakes	10 m	Portugal (Lisbon)	>30 000
21 May	1792	Volcano avalanche	10 m	Japan (Unzen)	>14 000
11 April	1815	Volcano eruption	10 m	Indonesia (Tambora)	>10 000
27 August	1883	Volcano eruption	35 m	Indonesia (Krakatau)	36 000
15 June	1896	Earthquake	29 m	Japan	27 000
11 October	1918	Underwater mass movement	6 m	Puerto Rico	116
2 March	1933	Earthquake	20 m	Japan	3 000
1 April	1946	Earthquake	15 m	Alaska	175
22 May	1960	Earthquake	10 m	Chile	>1 250
27 March	1964	Earthquake	6 m	Alaska	125
1 September	1992	Earthquake	10 m	Nicaragua	170
12 December	1992	Earthquake	26 m	Indonesia	>1 000
12 July	1993	Earthquake	31 m	Japan	239
2 June	1994	Earthquake	14 m	Indonesia	238
17 July	1998	Underwater mass movement	15 m	Papua New Guinea	>2 200
26 December	2004	Earthquake	10 m	Indonesia, Sri Lanka, India	>245 000
17 July	2006	Earthquake	7 m	Indonesia	>600
25 October	2010	Earthquake	3 m	Indonesia (Mentawai Islands)	545
11 March	2011	Earthquake	13 m	Japan	15 505

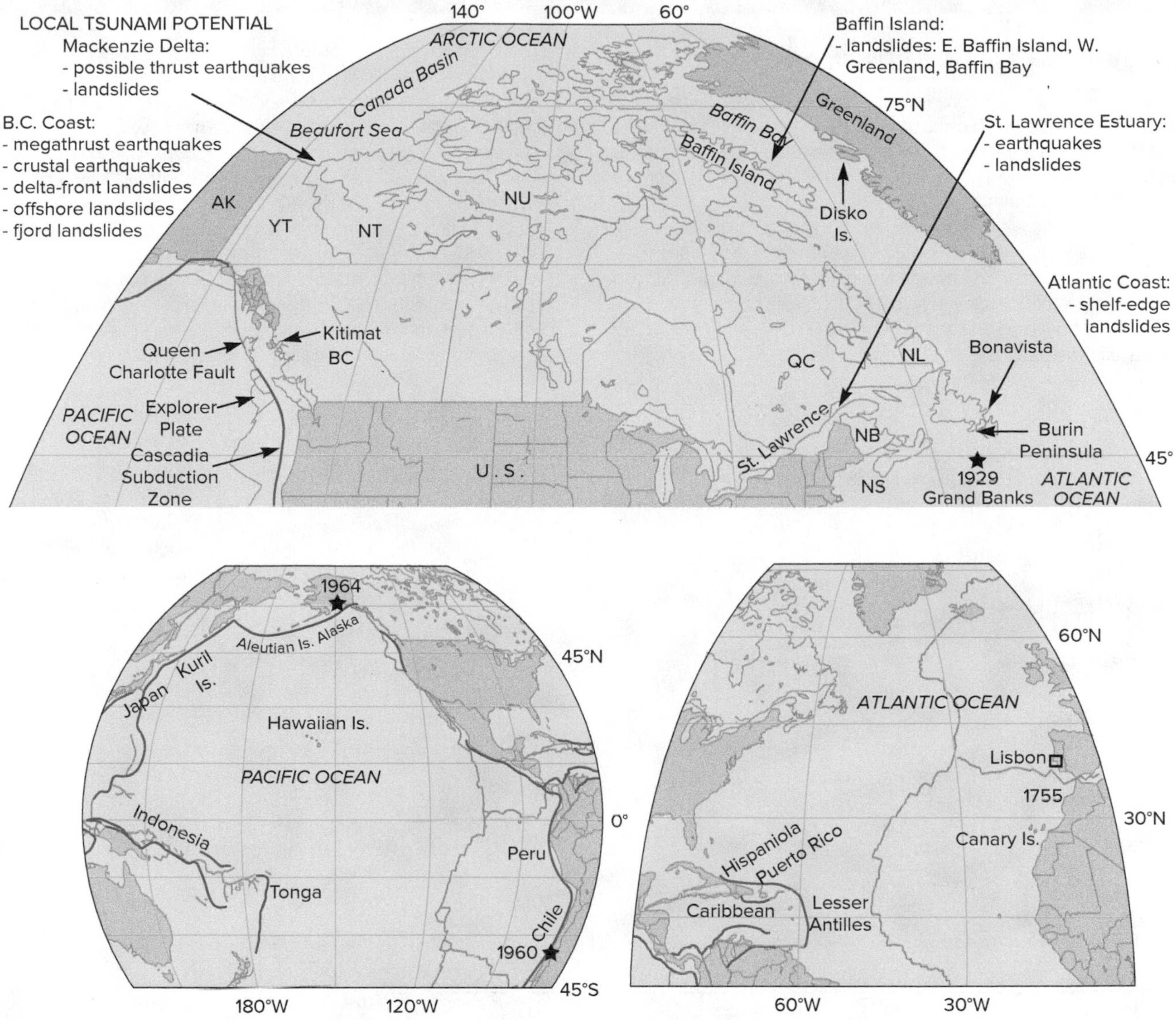

Figure 7.2
Tsunami hazard map of Canada. Canada's coasts are exposed to tsunamis from local (top) and distant (bottom) sources. Megathrust plate boundaries are shown in red.
Source: Geological Survey of Canada, Open File 6552.

past several centuries. This time, however, five adjacent segments of the fault ruptured together along a length of more than 600 km. Two central segments had enormous slips up to 50 m, which helped produce the 9.0M_w seism. Before the earthquake, 15 years of global positioning system (GPS) data showed that the eastern edge of Japan was being dragged downward. Apparently the down-going Pacific plate was stuck to the overlying plate, causing it to warp downward. The strain of this warping accumulated for many centuries. When the stuck zone ruptured, the overlying plate carrying Japan sprang upward and released elastic strain.

The country had an exemplary level of preparedness. Ten seconds after the initial jolt, the Japanese Meteorological Agency (JMA) issued an earthquake warning. A tsunami warning followed three minutes later, while JMA headquarters in Tokyo were still shaking!

Did the warnings save lives? Without doubt. Millions of people reacted promptly and took cover during the earthquake. Many of them were at work, in modern, well-designed building that resisted the vibrations well. The sight of the downtown Tokyo skyscrapers swaying in response to ground shaking was remarkable.

IN GREATER DEPTH

Fukushima Daiichi Nuclear Incident

A triple disaster occurred in Japan on 11 March 2011. First, a magnitude 9 earthquake broke loose. Second, tsunami waves were sent racing toward the coastline. Third, these events cascaded into one of the most serious nuclear incidents in history, reaching Level 7, the maximum value on the International Nuclear Event Scale.

Nuclear reactors are cooled with water to keep the nuclear reaction under control and at an optimal level to produce steam, which drives turbines to generate electricity. After the earthquake, the cooling systems regulating the operating nuclear reactors at Fukushima Daiichi power plant malfunctioned. Forty-one minutes later, a tsunami burst through the plant's defenses and damaged the emergency back-up generators, leaving the plant without power to run the cooling systems. The facility had not been designed to withstand such a powerful tsunami. Meanwhile, the ongoing decay of radioactive isotopes continued to heat the reactor cores. The nuclear fuel melted the core and inner containment vessels in three out of four reactors. During the next several days, released hydrogen gas exploded through the reactor buildings, allowing the release of radioactive iodine-131, xenon-133, and cesium-137 into the atmosphere and ocean (Figure 7.3).

By 18 March, trace amounts of the gas xenon-133, pushed by the westerly winds, had reached the west coast of Canada. Canada was prompt to respond and mobilized an aircraft to measure concentrations. Fortunately, the levels of radioactivity measured were much lower than those due to natural phenomena (Figure 7.4). The data helped to better understand the processes that disperse radioactivity in the atmosphere.

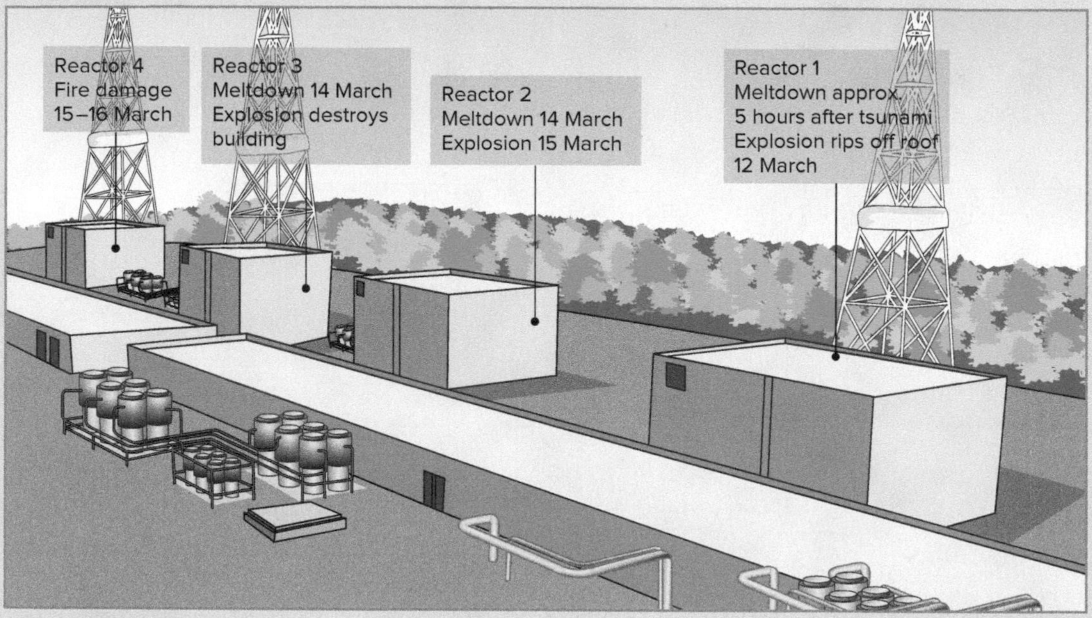

Figure 7.3
A series of malfunctions affected the reactors of the Fukushima Daiichi nuclear power plant following the Tohoku earthquake.

Source: British Broadcasting Corporation.

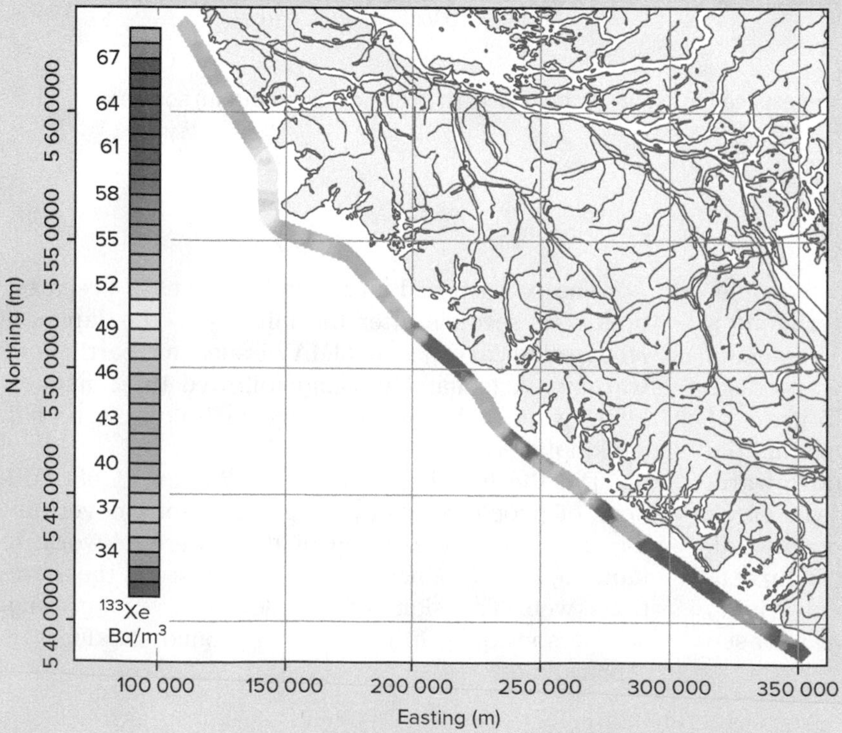

Figure 7.4
Measured radioactivity from xenon-133 leaking from the Fukushima nuclear reactors on the west coast of Vancouver Island in March 2011.

Source: Reproduced with the permission of Natural Resources Canada 2014.

The response to the tsunami was more chaotic. Structural countermeasures (Figure 7.33) were in place but the tsunami waves were larger than expected. At least 101 designated tsunami evacuation sites, and the evacuees who took shelter there, were overrun. Tsunami waves overwhelmed coastal barriers and flowed inland as overpowering masses of seawater and debris that destroyed almost everything in their path (Figure 7.5). Several people took shelter in buildings that were perceived to be strong but that did not withstand the force of the waves. Others tried to escape to high ground by car, got stuck in traffic jams, and died trapped in their vehicles.

The tsunami also exposed another weakness. Japan's complex industrial infrastructure proved to be vulnerable. Fire erupted in a major refinery, and it took 10 days for firefighters to extinguish the blaze (see chapter opener photo). The nuclear incident at the Fukushima Daiichi reactor revived concerns about the safety of nuclear energy all around the world (see In Greater Depth box: Fukushima Daiichi Nuclear Incident).

The tsunami waves also "exported" destruction across the Pacific Ocean within a few hours (Figure 7.6) causing damage in Hawaii, California, Chile, and even in Antarctica where they broke a 125 km^2 area of the Sulzberg Ice Shelf into 80 m thick icebergs. In the longer term, tsunami debris drifting in the Pacific is a hazard to navigation and marine ecosystems (Figure 7.7).

Figure 7.5
Tsunami roars into Natori, Japan on 11 March 2011.
Source: Kyodo via AP Images.

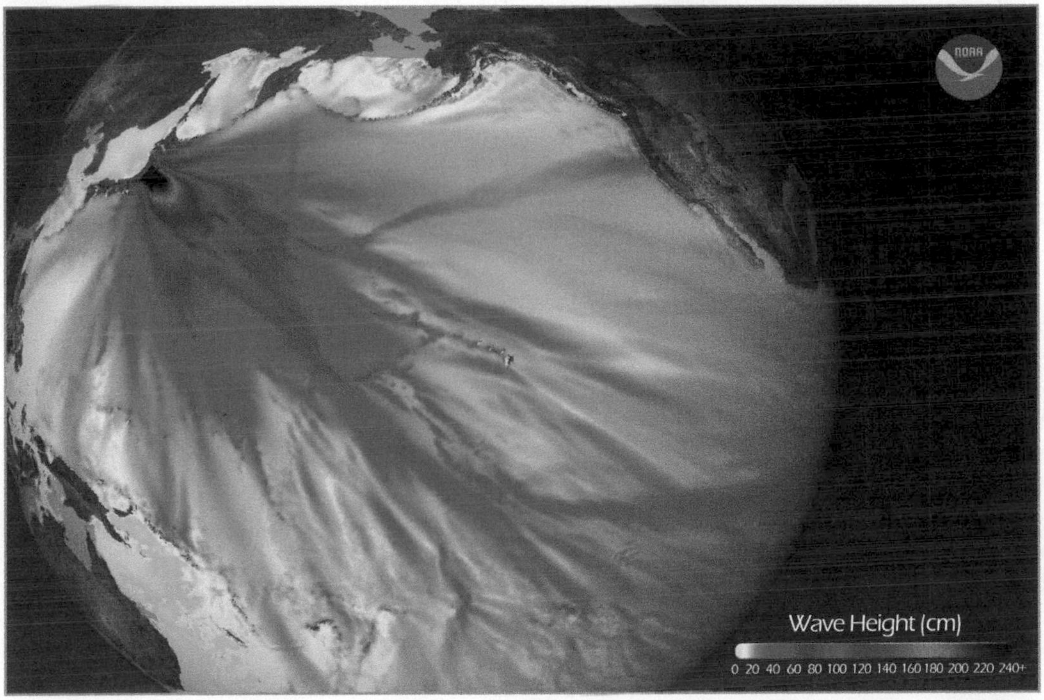

Figure 7.6
Wave heights of the 2011 Tohoku tsunami across the Pacific Ocean.
Source: NOAA.

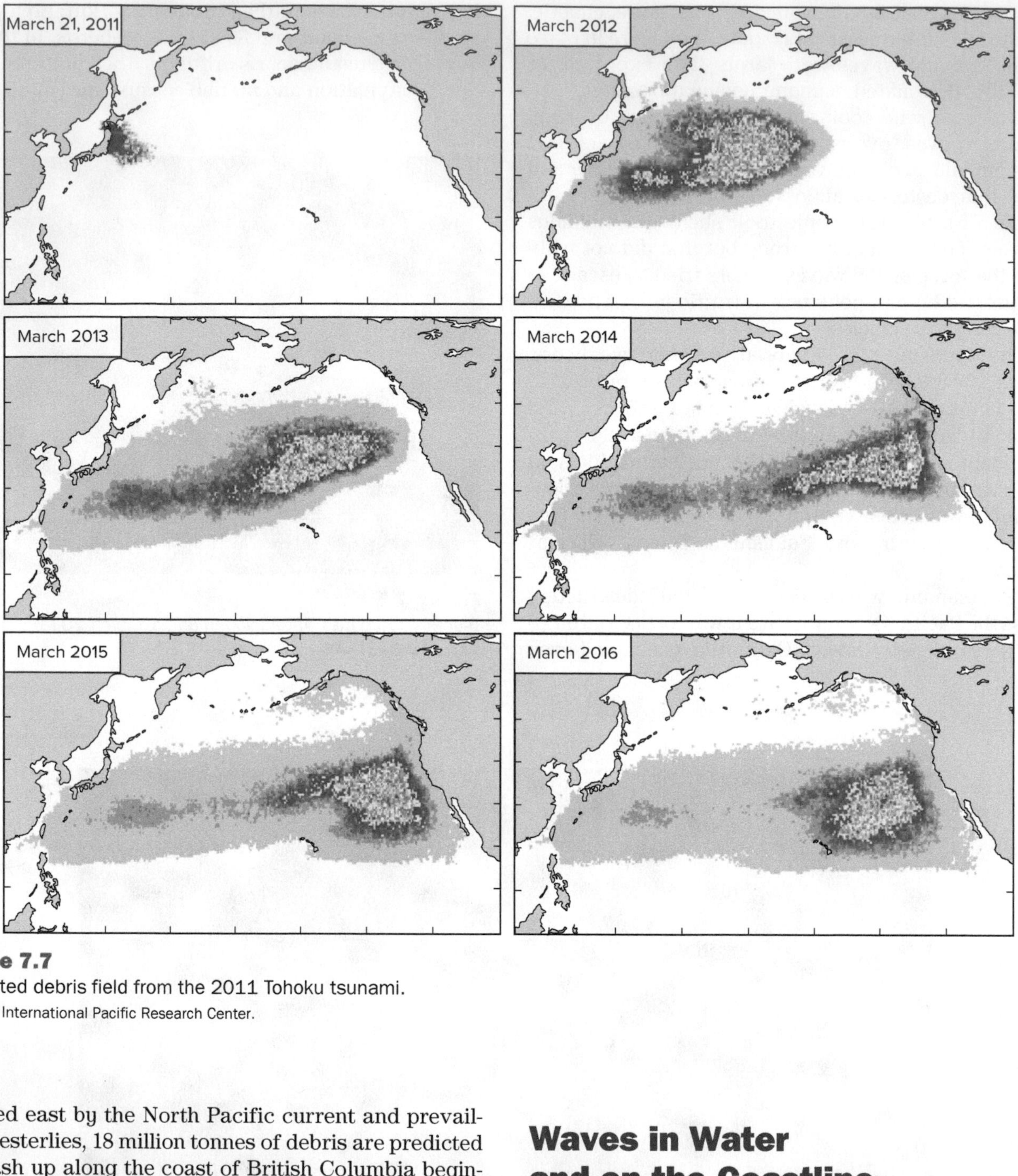

Figure 7.7
Predicted debris field from the 2011 Tohoku tsunami.
Source: International Pacific Research Center.

Pushed east by the North Pacific current and prevailing westerlies, 18 million tonnes of debris are predicted to wash up along the coast of British Columbia beginning in 2014. Japan will assume part of the clean-up costs. Protocols are also in place to return items of sentimental or cultural significance to Japan.

A concern now is that the March 2011 earthquake transferred stress southward, closer to Tokyo, which was hit hard in 1923 by a 7.9 magnitude earthquake. An official Japan earthquake assessment committee forecast a 30% chance of a magnitude 9 event closer to Tokyo in the next 30 years. The fault there is closer to shore, meaning more intense shaking for buildings and less time before tsunamis come ashore.

Waves in Water and on the Coastline

All water waves are pulses of energy that move through a water mass, causing water particles to rotate in place, similar to the passage of Rayleigh seismic waves (Figure 3.10c and Figure 3.10d). You can feel the orbital motion within waves by standing chest-deep in the ocean. An incoming wave will pick you up and carry you shoreward and then drop you downward and back as it passes. At the water surface, the water particles move in an orbit with a diameter equal to the wave height. The diameters of the water particle orbits decrease rapidly

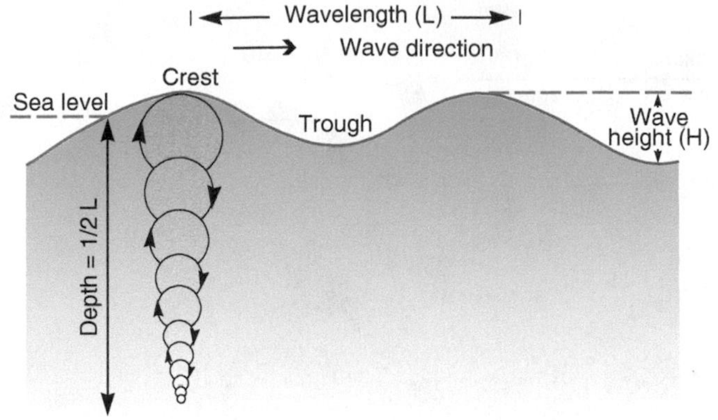

Figure 7.8
Waves are energy fronts passing through water, causing water particles to rotate in place. Rotational movement becomes insignificant at depths greater than one-half the wavelength.

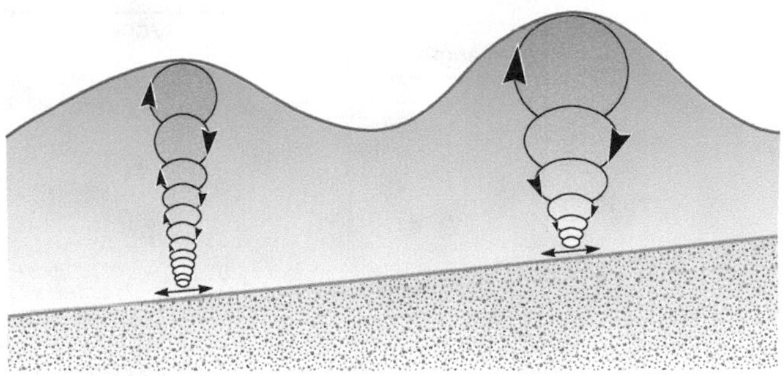

Figure 7.9
As a wave moves into shallower water, it rises higher. Rotating water touches bottom, gradually causing a flattening into ellipses, and a back-and-forth motion.

with depth. The orbital motion ceases at a depth equal to about one-half the wavelength (Figure 7.8).

Waves undergo changes when they move into shallow water—at depths less than one-half their wavelength. Friction on the floor of the shallow ocean flattens the water orbits into ellipses and, ultimately, back-and-forth movements, and waves begin slowing. As waves slow, their wavelengths decrease, thus concentrating water and energy, resulting in waves growing higher, a phenomenon known as **shoaling** (Figures 7.9 and 7.10).

LO1 Wind-Caused Waves versus Tsunami Waves

PERIODS AND WAVELENGTHS

Waves caused by wind are created by the friction between wind and the ocean surface. Controlling factors include the velocity, duration, and consistency of the wind, together with the length of the body of water across which the wind blows. Although the periods and wavelengths of wind-caused waves vary by storm and season, they are distinctly different from those of tsunami waves (Table 7.2).

The familiar wind-caused waves rise up as they near the beach, roll forward, run up the beach for several seconds, and then withdraw (Figure 7.11a). Not only do wind-caused waves come and go quickly, but the water **run-up** and retreat is confined to the beach (Figure 7.11b). Even huge wind-blown waves are different from tsunamis. For example, at Waimea on the north shore of Oahu Island in Hawaii, the world-famous surfing waves may reach 15 m in height, but each wave is a solitary unit. These huge waves have short wavelengths and brief periods, meaning that each wave is an entity unto itself; there is no additional water mass behind the wave front. These waves are spectacular to view or ride, but what you see is what you get; the wave is the entire water mass.

When the wave height-to-wavelength ratio (H:L) reaches about 1:7, the wavefront has grown too steep, and it topples forward as a breaker (Figures 7.10 and 7.11a). Note that the 1:7 ratio is reached by changes in both wave height and wavelength; wave height is increasing at the same time that wavelength is decreasing. The depth of water beneath a breaker is roughly 1.3 times the wave height as measured from the still-water level. At this depth, the velocity of water-particle motion in the wave crest is greater than the wave velocity, thus the faster-moving wave crest outraces its bottom and falls forward as a turbulent mass.

Tsunamis are different. Tsunamis arrive as the leading edge of an elevated mass of water that rapidly runs up and *over* the beach and then floods inland for many minutes (Figure 7.11c and Figure 7.11d). Tsunamis are dangerous because their tremendous momentum carries water and debris far inland. They may be no taller than the wind-blown waves we see at the beach everyday, but they are much more powerful. Even a knee-high tsunami can kill you; the power of the fast-moving water can knock you down, then beat your body and head with debris, and drown you.

The long wavelengths and periods of tsunami waves allow them to bend around many islands and hit all shores with high waves. Tsunami wavelengths are typically longer than the dimensions of an island. During the 2004 Indian Ocean tsunami, waves encircled the island nation of Sri Lanka, which was hit by waves from 4 to 7 m high at sites on all shores (Figure 7.12 and Figure 7.13). The tsunamis were originally directed at

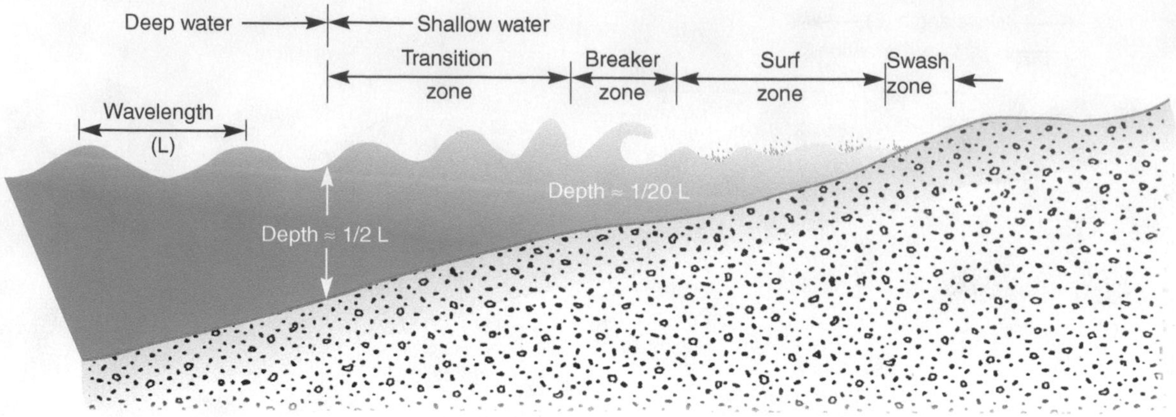

Figure 7.10
Schematic cross-section of deep-water waves entering shallow water. Wavelengths decrease and wave heights increase, leading to pitching forward as breakers.

the east shore, where more than 14 000 people were killed, but more than 10 000 were killed on the south shore and more than 6000 were killed on the north shore. Nearly 100 people were killed in the capital city of Colombo on the "protected" west shore.

VELOCITIES

The differences in velocities between wind-caused waves and tsunamis are also great. In deep water, the velocities of waves caused by wind are about 8 m/s for a 5-second wave and about 31 m/s for a 20-second wave (Table 7.2). The velocity of tsunamis can be calculated using the formula

$$v = \sqrt{gD}$$

where v equals wave velocity, g equals acceleration due to gravity (9.81 m/s^2), and D equals depth of ocean water. The Pacific Ocean has an average depth of 5500 m. Calculating the square root of g times D yields a tsunami velocity of 232 m/s.

The calculated velocities of tsunamis are faster than those typically measured. The energy pulse that creates the wave also puts the water into a forward rotating motion to depths of about one-half the wavelength (Figure 7.8). Tsunami wavelengths can be as great as 840 km (Table 7.2), meaning that ocean water would be disturbed to depths of 420 km. But the ocean's average depth is only 3.7 km and the deepest trenches just exceed 11 km. Therefore, the energy pulse of a tsunami moves the entire water column it passes through. Tsunamis have such long wavelengths that they are always dragging across the ocean bottom, no matter how deep the water. The topography of the ocean bottom is varied enough to slow most tsunamis to a speed of approximately 185–215 m/s. Still, this figure is equivalent to 725 km/h, the speed of a jet!

A tsunami 1 m height in the deep ocean may be moving at nearly 200 m/s. As the tsunami enters shallower water, the increasing friction with the seafloor and internal turbulence of water slow its rush, but it still may be moving at highway speeds. Shoaling then compresses the wave and increases its amplitude. Water behind it begins to build up. The visible tsunami wave is only the leading edge of a tabular sheet of water that will flow on land for several minutes.

TABLE 7.2

Representative Periods and Wavelengths

	Period (second)		Wavelength (metre)	Velocity (metre/second)
	Short:	5	39	8
Wind-caused waves	Medium:	10	156	16
	Long:	20	624	31
Tsunamis	**Very long:**	**3600**	**837 000**	**≈ 200**

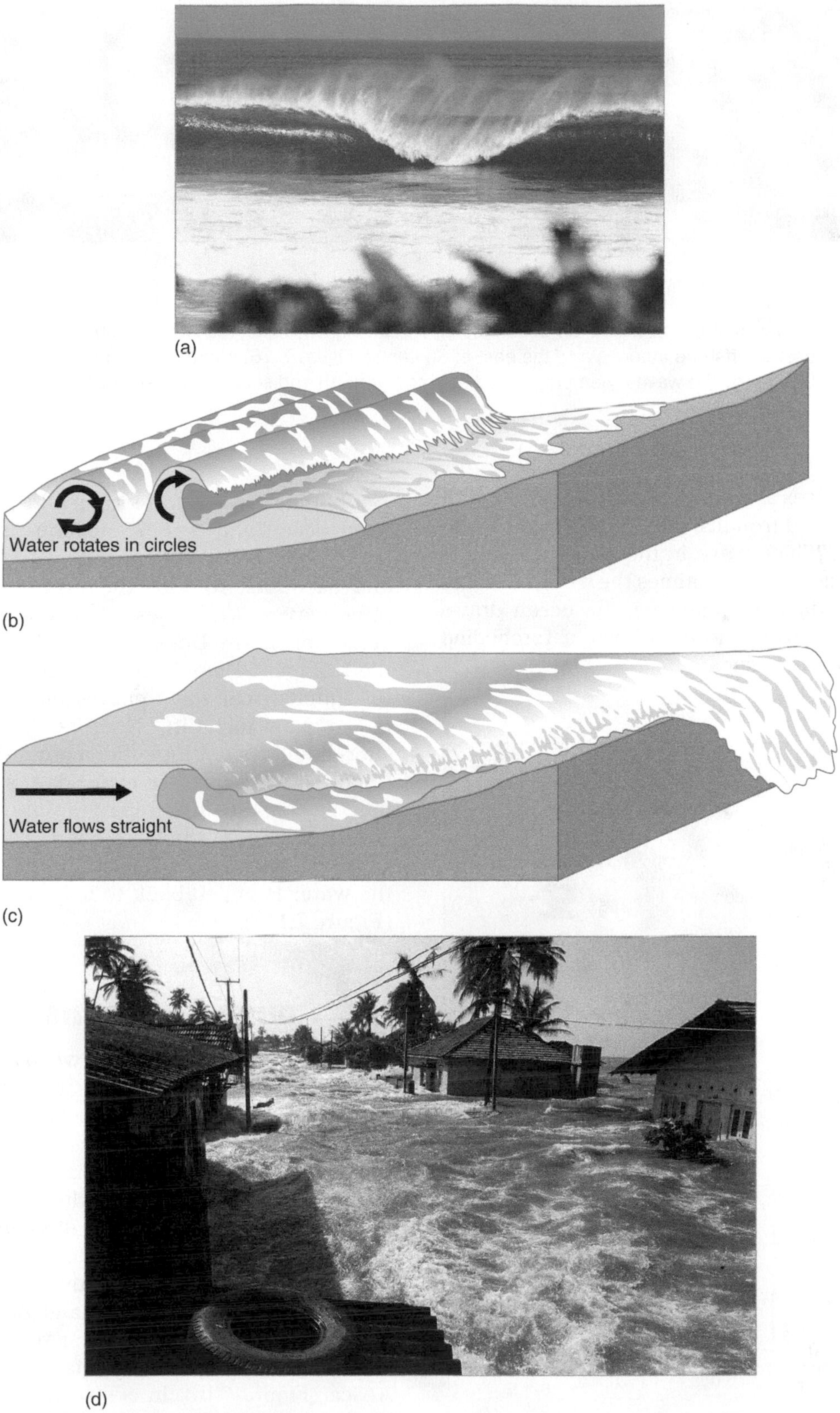

Figure 7.11

Ocean waves. (a) A wind-blown wave rolls onto the beach in Natal, South Africa. (b) Daily wind-blown waves break on the beach and do not flood higher areas. (c) Tsunamis pour across the beach and flood inland for many minutes. (d) A tsunami flows as a long-lasting sheet of water through Maddampegama, Sri Lanka, on 26 December 2004.

Source (a): © Digital Vision/PunchStock. (d) © Gemunu Amarasinghe/AP Photos.

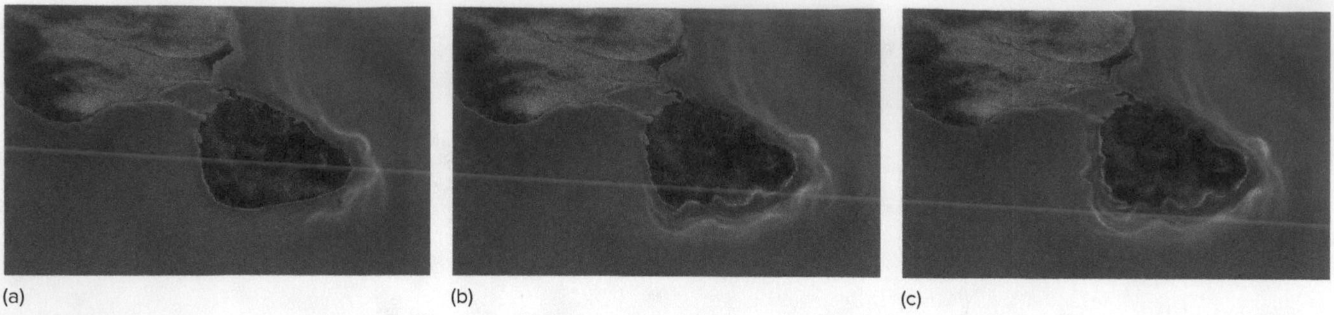

Figure 7.12
Simulation showing the waves of the 2014 Indian Ocean tsunami gradually encircling the island of Sri Lanka. (a) The epicenter of the earthquake was located offshore Indonesia to the east of Sri Lanka (Figure 7.16) and therefore tsunami waves first reached the east coast of Sri Lanka. (b) The waves then progressed both to the north and south of the island. (c) Finally, the entire coastline was affected.
Source: Baird Engineering.

A tsunami arrives as a series of several waves, with successive peaks and troughs, and periods in the 10- to 60-minute range. Which wave in the series will be the biggest is unpredictable. Sometimes the trough reaches the coast first. When this happens, the ocean draws down water away from the coastlines, a foreboding sign of an approaching tsunami.

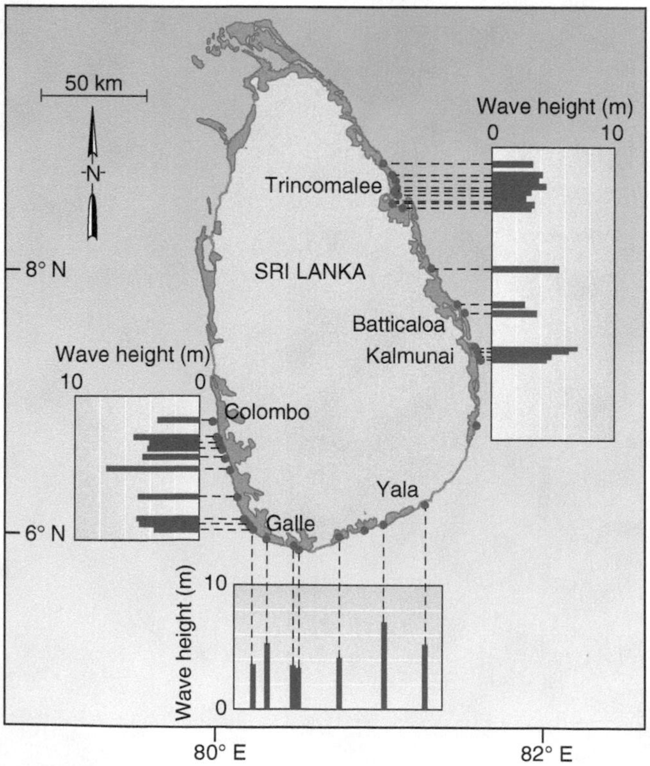

Figure 7.13
Tsunami waves from 4 to 7 m high were common all around Sri Lanka.
Source: © Science, v. 308 (2005).

Tsunami waves are typically 1 m high in the open ocean and 6 to 15 m high on reaching shallow water, except where topography, such as bays and harbours, focuses the energy to create much taller waves. What does a tsunami look like when it comes onshore? Does it resemble the animation in the Hollywood movie *Deep Impact,* where a beautiful symmetrical wave curves high above the buildings of New York City? No. A tsunami arriving at the shoreline does not look like a gigantic version of the breaking waves we see every day. A typical tsunami hits the coastline like a very rapidly rising tide, but it does not stop on the beach; it keeps rushing inland, causing destruction for about 30 minutes before the water is pulled back to help form the next wave (Figure 7.11c).

LO2 Causes of Tsunamis

Powerful tsunamis are caused when a water mass is hit with a massive jolt of energy. Common causes include earthquakes, volcanoes, mass movements, and very rarely, impacts.

In earthquake-caused tsunamis, movement is initiated along an active fault on the seafloor. The energy released tends to move in a direction perpendicular to this linear source, with little attenuation. The 2004 Indian Ocean tsunami, for example, was generated by a north-south oriented fault and propagated mainly in an east-west direction across the ocean basin with enough power to strike the faraway shores of east Africa (Figure 7.16). In contrast, volcano-caused and landslide-caused tsunamis originate from point sources—similar to a stone dropped into a pond. Their energy flows away radially from the source point, and as it does so, the energy "spreads out" along the wavefront, which gets longer as the wave moves. This increased loss of energy results in attenuation over shorter distances. Waves from volcano-caused and landslide-caused tsunamis might start out higher than those generated by earthquake-caused tsunamis. However, they do not carry energy as far. The biggest tsunamis are caused by the impact of high-velocity asteroids and comets. Consider the amount of energy injected into the ocean when an asteroid 10 km in diameter hits the ocean at 13 000 m/s. These events will be discussed in Chapter 14.

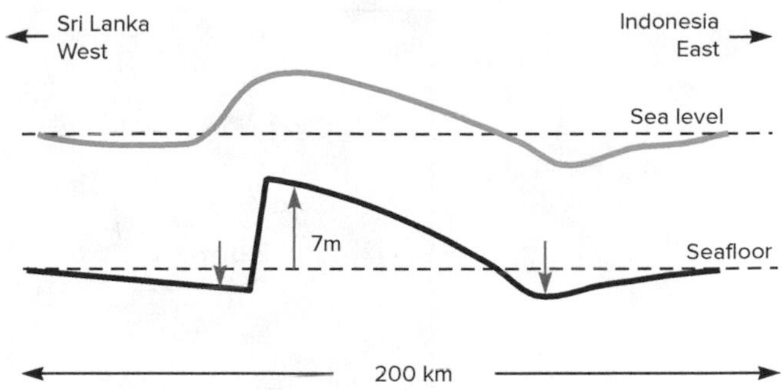

Figure 7.14
Schematic cross-section showing movements of the seafloor and the tsunami they generated, 26 December 2004.

Earthquake-Caused Tsunamis

Tsunamis are most commonly created at subduction zones by earthquakes with shallow hypocentres, more specifically by fault movements with pronounced vertical offsets of the seafloor that disturb the deep ocean-water mass. In general, the fault movements need to uplift or down-drop the seafloor in an earthquake with a magnitude of at least $7M_w$ in order to produce a tsunami (Table 7.3). Not being compressible, water acts like a piston (Figure 7.14 and Figure 7.15). The water column cannot easily absorb the fault-movement energy; therefore, it transmits the energy throughout the ocean in the waves we call tsunamis.

INDIAN OCEAN TSUNAMI, 26 DECEMBER 2004

On 26 December 2004, a killer tsunami swept through the Indian Ocean and crossed Asian and African shorelines, causing death and destruction in 13 countries. Countries hit especially hard were Indonesia (about 198 000 dead), Sri Lanka (about 30 000 dead), India (about 11 000 dead), and Thailand (about 6000 dead). Five Canadians are confirmed to have died in the event; 146 are missing.

TABLE 7.3

Fault Displacements of Seafloors

Earthquake Magnitude (M_w)	Fault Slip (metre)	Rupture Duration (second)	Vertical Movement of Seafloor (metre)
7	0.6	23	0.2
8	2.7	70	0.7
9	9.0	200	2.3
9.5	27.0	330	7.0

Source: © *Science*, v. 78 (1997).

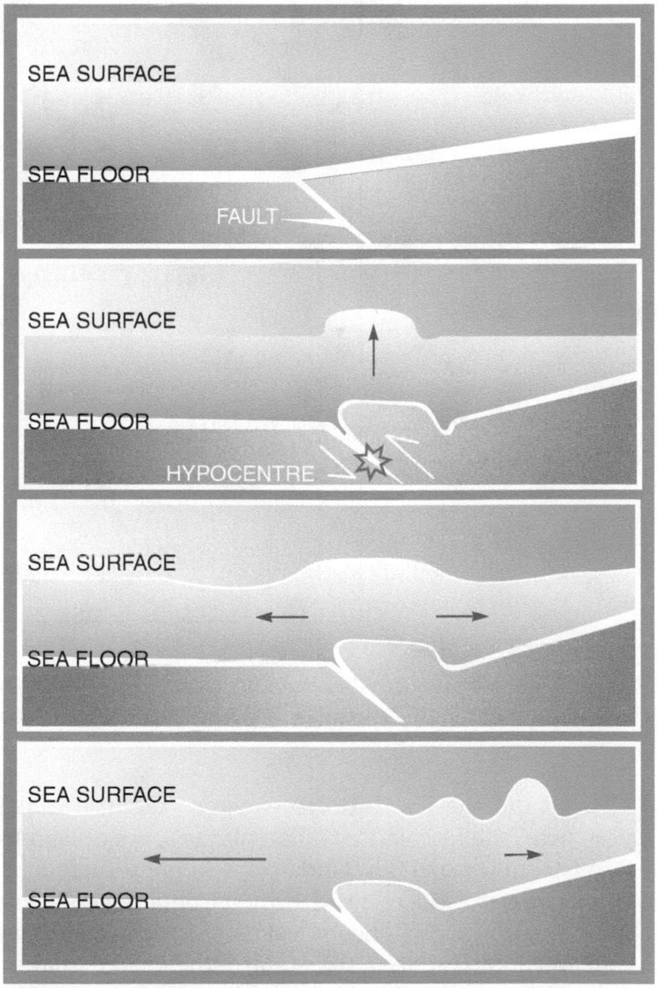

Figure 7.15
Vertical seafloor movements act like a piston to give an initial impulsion to the water column.
Source: Based on UNESCO http://neamtic.ioc-unesco.org/what-to-know/the-causes-of-tsunamis

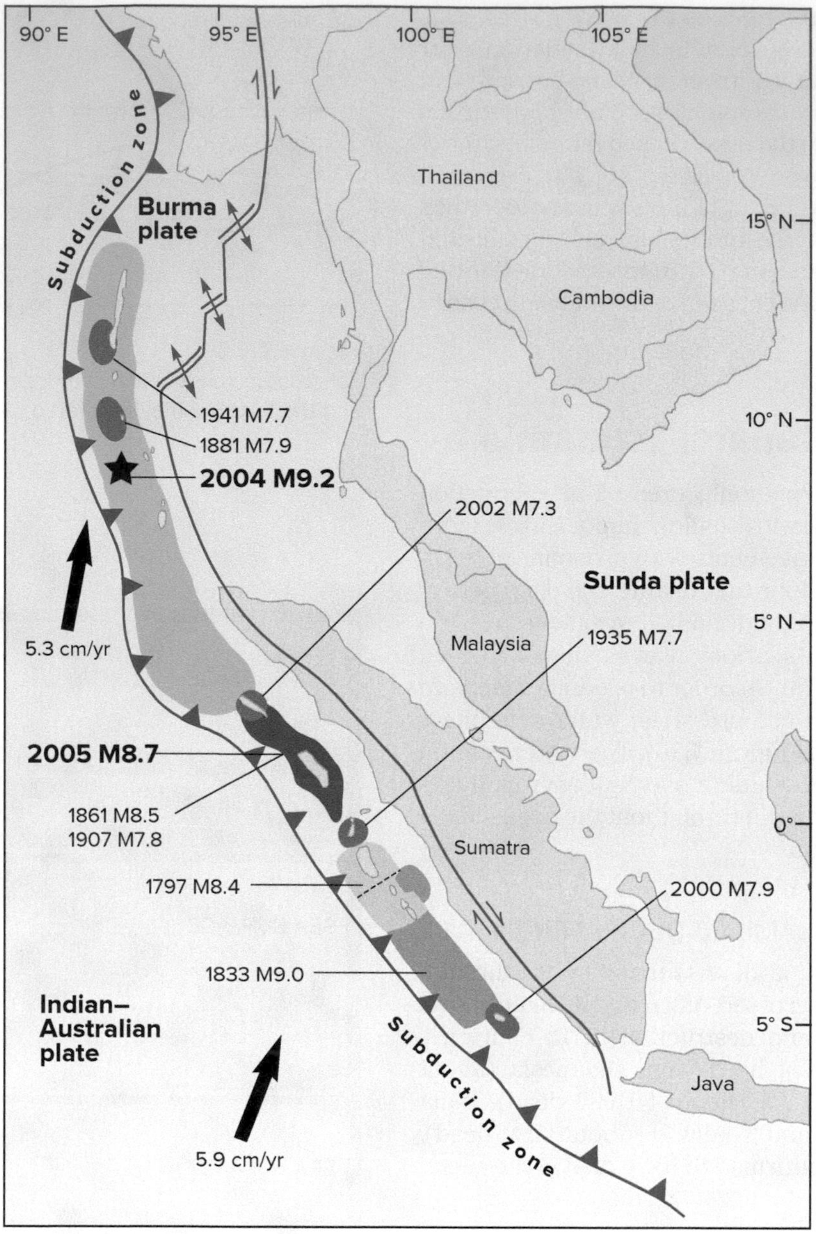

Figure 7.16

Subduction of Indian-Australian plate beneath Indonesia. The region has a long history of large earthquakes, and more will occur. The epicenter of the 26 December 2004 earthquake is indicated by a black star.

What did the Earth do to cause so many deaths? Every year, the Indian-Australian plate moves obliquely 5.3 to 5.9 cm toward the Sunda plate (a microplate part of the Eurasian plate). This enormous, ongoing collision results in subduction-caused earthquakes that are frequent and huge (Figure 7.16). Many of these earthquakes send off tsunamis. On 26 December 2004, a 100 km long portion of the north-south-oriented plate-tectonic boundary ruptured and slipped for a minute, The rupture then moved northward at 3 km/s for four minutes, then slowed to 2.5 km/s during the next six minutes, resulting in a 1200 km long fault rupture. The rupture began 30 km below the seafloor and caused movements up to 20 m that shifted the positions of some Indonesian islands and tilted others. It abruptly raised the seafloor by 7 m, thus charging the water column with energy (Figure 7.14). Waves rapidly moved outward in an east-west direction, perpendicular to the fault. The huge earthquake must have collapsed many nearby buildings that fell and killed many thousands of people, but the evidence of earthquake damage was largely erased by the powerful tsunami that swept across the land minutes later (Figure 7.17). An overwhelming event such as this far-reaching tsunami results in many dramatic stories.

Before

After

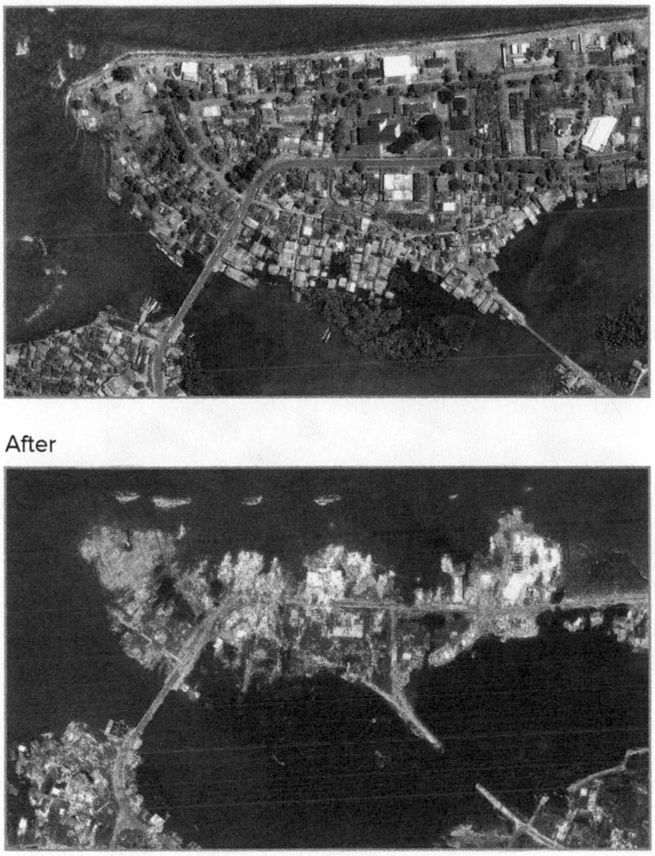

Figure 7.17
Satellite image of the town of Banda Aceh, Indonesia, before and after the 2004 Indian Ocean tsunami.
Photos: DigitalGlobe/Getty Images.

A common heart-wrenching scene occurred when parents fought to withstand the tsunami and hold onto their children. Too many times, the children were pulled from their grasp and killed. In Sri Lanka, about 40% of the dead were children.

Immediately following this great natural disaster, people and countries around the world mobilized to bring aid to the survivors. Canadians were deeply moved by the live television images of this tragedy, which contrasted so strongly with the festive themes of end-of-year celebrations. They responded generously. Governments contributed $343 million to the relief effort, and non-governmental organizations another $75 million. Ten forensic analysts from the Royal Canadian Mounted Police worked alongside international teams of experts in the gruesome task of identifying corpses.

CHILE, 22 MAY 1960

The most powerful earthquake ever measured occurred in Chile on 22 May 1960 (Table 2.4). Tsunamis generated by this magnitude 9.5 subduction movement killed people throughout the Pacific Ocean basin. In Chile, the main seism broke loose at 3:11 p.m. on Sunday. Chileans are familiar with earthquakes, so many people headed for high ground in anticipation of a tsunami. About 15 minutes after the seism, the sea rose like a rapidly rising tide, reaching 4.5 m above sea level. Then the water retreated with speed and an incredible hissing and gurgling noise, dragging broken houses and boats out into the ocean. Some people took the "smooth wave" as a sign that these tsunami waves could be ridden out at sea, thus remaining on their boats. About 4:20 p.m., the second tsunami arrived as a wave 8 m high travelling at 55 m/s. The wave crushed boats and their terrified passengers, and wrecked coastal buildings. But *the third wave was the largest;* it rose 11 m high, but it travelled at only half the speed of the second wave. Over 1000 Chileans died in these tsunami waves.

The Chilean tsunami was predicted to travel 14 hours across the Pacific and arrive in Hawaii at 9:57 a.m.; it arrived at 9:58 a.m. (Figure 7.18). Since 1960, Hawaiians have been given warnings before tsunamis arrive. But 61 people drowned anyway, including sightseers attracted to the shore to watch the tsunami roll in. The tsunami raced on to Japan, where it killed another 185 people, 22.5 hours after the earthquake. The energy in this set of tsunamis was so great that it was recorded on Pacific Ocean tide gauges for a week as the energy pulses bounced back and forth across the entire ocean basin.

ALASKA, 27 MARCH 1964

In the Bible, Saint Matthew's account of the first Good Friday included the description "And, behold the earth did quake, and the rocks rent." His words applied again, over 1900 years later, on Good Friday, 27 March 1964. At 5:36 p.m., in the wilderness at the head of Prince William Sound, a major subduction movement created a gigantic earthquake. This was followed in sequence by other downward thrusts 9, 19, 28, 29, 44, and 72 seconds later as a slab nearly 1000 km long and 400 km wide lurched its way deeper into the mantle. Hypocentre depths were from 20 to 50 km. The earthquake magnitude was 9.2 M_w. The duration of strong ground shaking was lengthy—more than four minutes; it induced many avalanches, landslides, ground settlements, and tsunamis. Of the 131 lives lost, 122 were due to tsunamis.

The tsunamis reached Port Alberni on Vancouver Island three hours after the earthquake (Figure 7.18). Residents had received warnings and retreated to high ground, and no one was killed. They returned home, however, to a scene of destruction (Figure 7.19). A tsunami over 6 m high (Figure 7.20) had destroyed

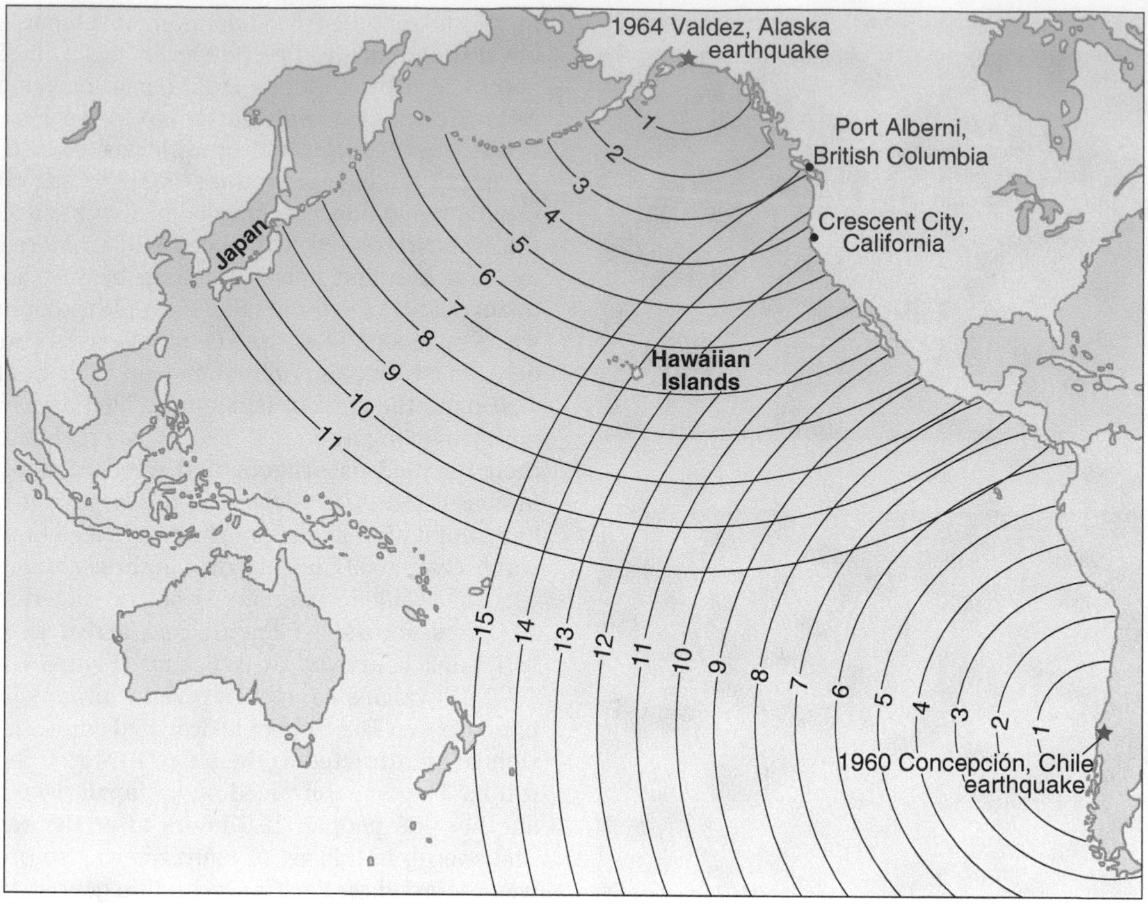

Figure 7.18

Tsunami travel times in hours.

Source: data © Kious, W.J. and Tilling, R.I., *The Dynamic Earth*, p. 77, United States Geological Survey.

Figure 7.19

Tsunami damage in Port Alberni, British Columbia, in March 1964.

Source: © Alberni Valley Museum (PN19023).

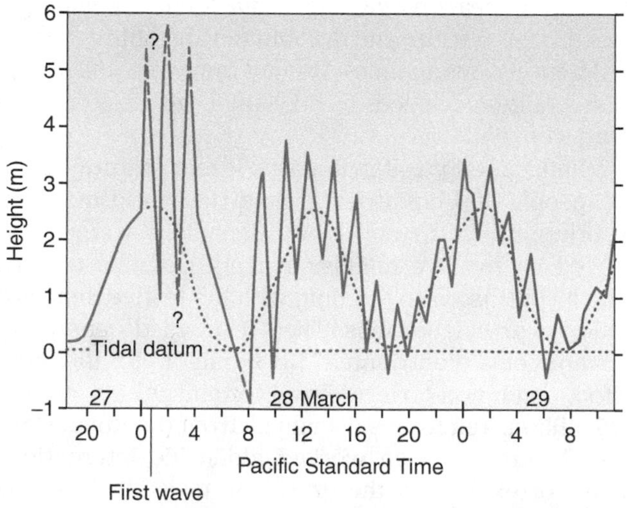

Figure 7.20

Tidal records for Port Alberni, British Columbia, 27–29 March 1964. The three main waves of the Alaska tsunami arrived between 12:20 a.m. and 3:30 a.m. on 28 March, forcing the tide gauge off the scale. Normal tidal heights are shown by a dotted line.

Source: Reproduced with the permission of Natural Resources Canada 2014. courtesy of the Geological Survey of Canada (GSC Bulletin 548).

58 buildings in the small town and damaged 320 others. Thanks to advance warning, the Crescent City, California, waterfront area was also evacuated, and residents waited upslope while tsunamis arrived and did their damage. After watching four tsunamis and seeing their sizes, many people could no longer stand the suspense of not knowing the condition of their properties. Some people went down to check—a big mistake. At that location, *the fifth wave* in the tsunami series was the biggest; it was 6.3 m high, and it killed 12 of the curious people.

LO3 TSUNAMI HAZARDS IN COASTAL BRITISH COLUMBIA

Nowhere in Canada are tsunami hazards greater than along the coast of British Columbia (Figure 7.2). Three types of tsunami threaten coastal British Columbia. Five zones have been developed for planning purposes, depending on wave heights, run-up distances, and subsidence expected (Figure 7.21). Basin-wide tsunamis are energetic enough to travel across the Pacific Ocean. The 1960 Chile tsunami is an example (Figure 7.18).

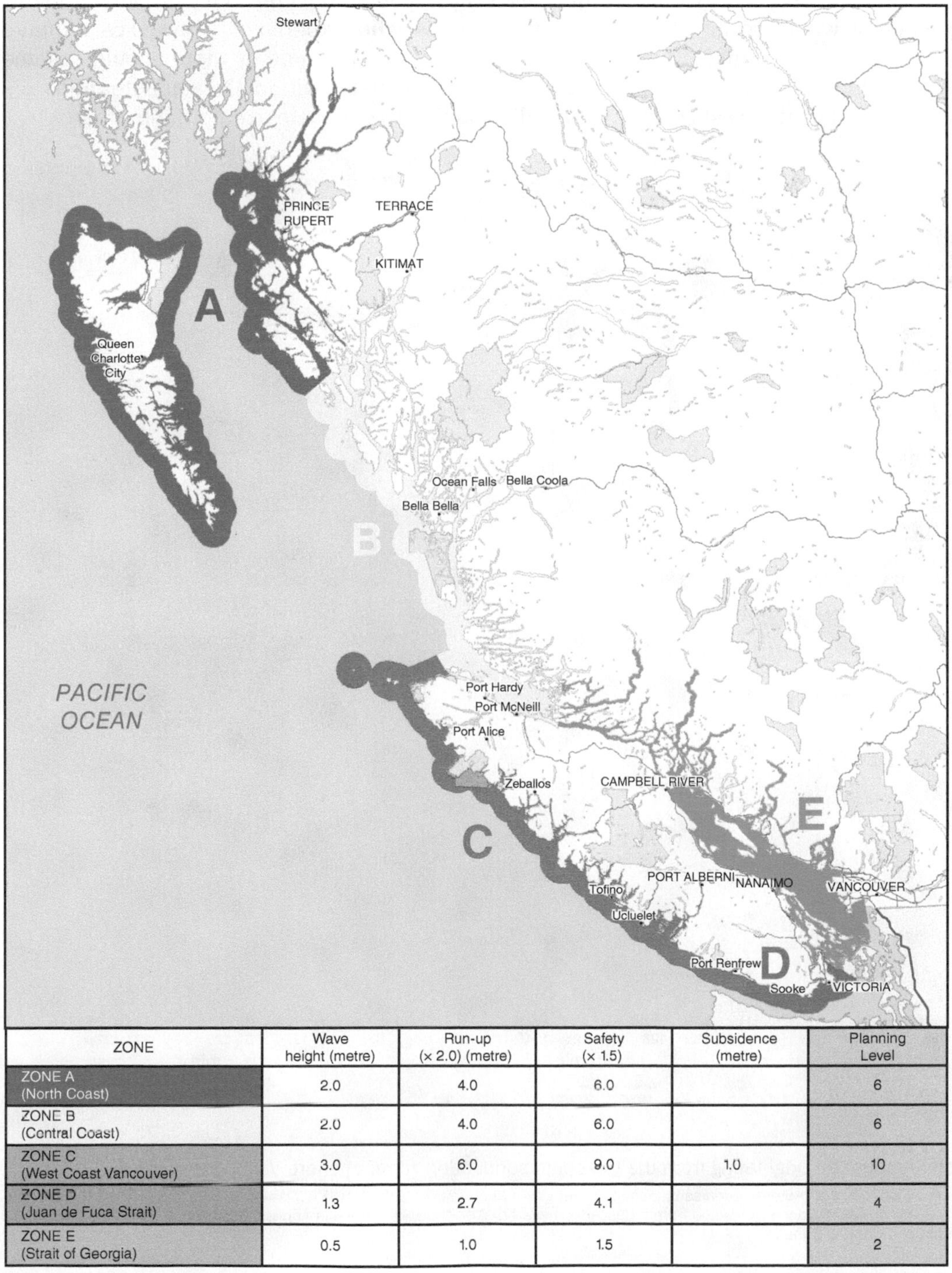

ZONE	Wave height (metre)	Run-up (× 2.0) (metre)	Safety (× 1.5)	Subsidence (metre)	Planning Level
ZONE A (North Coast)	2.0	4.0	6.0		6
ZONE B (Contral Coast)	2.0	4.0	6.0		6
ZONE C (West Coast Vancouver)	3.0	6.0	9.0	1.0	10
ZONE D (Juan de Fuca Strait)	1.3	2.7	4.1		4
ZONE E (Strait of Georgia)	0.5	1.0	1.5		2

Figure 7.21
British Columbia tsunami notification zones. Planning level is highest for the west coast of Vancouver Island (Zone C), where a tsunami could strike only a few minutes after a megathrust earthquake.
Source: Provincial Emergency Program, British Columbia.

Depending on the point of origin of the tsunami, British Columbia residents have between 5.5 and 18 hours to take safety precautions. Regional tsunamis originate from the active tectonic zones of western North America (Figure 4.14). Because of the size and frequency of its earthquakes, and the flow direction of ocean currents, Alaska is the most frequent source. Regional tsunamis can strike anytime between 0.5 and 5 hours after a large earthquake, as in the case of the Alaska tsunami that ravaged Port Alberni in 1964. Finally, local tsunamis may be triggered by earthquakes occurring offshore British Columbia or in the inner waters separating Vancouver Island from the mainland.

The most devastating tsunami would result from a megathrust earthquake in the Cascadia Subduction Zone, similar to the event of 1700 (Figure 4.17b). In such a case, the areas most affected would be the west coast of Vancouver Island, which is facing the open ocean, where wave heights up to 9 m are predicted as soon as 15 minutes after the earthquake (Figure 7.22). The long-wavelength tsunami waves would circle around Vancouver Island and also hit its eastern shores and the continental coast. Fortunately, the cities of Victoria and Vancouver are in sheltered waters. Wave heights of only one metre are expected in these areas.

In the event of a Cascadia megathrust earthquake triggering a local tsunami, there might not be enough time for formal warnings due to the proximity between the epicentre and the shore. In such a case, authorities give one simple, potentially life-saving advice: "Persons in coastal areas who experience a large earthquake with shaking lasting a minute or more should assume that a tsunami will arrive within a few minutes and take immediate action to evacuate to safer high ground."

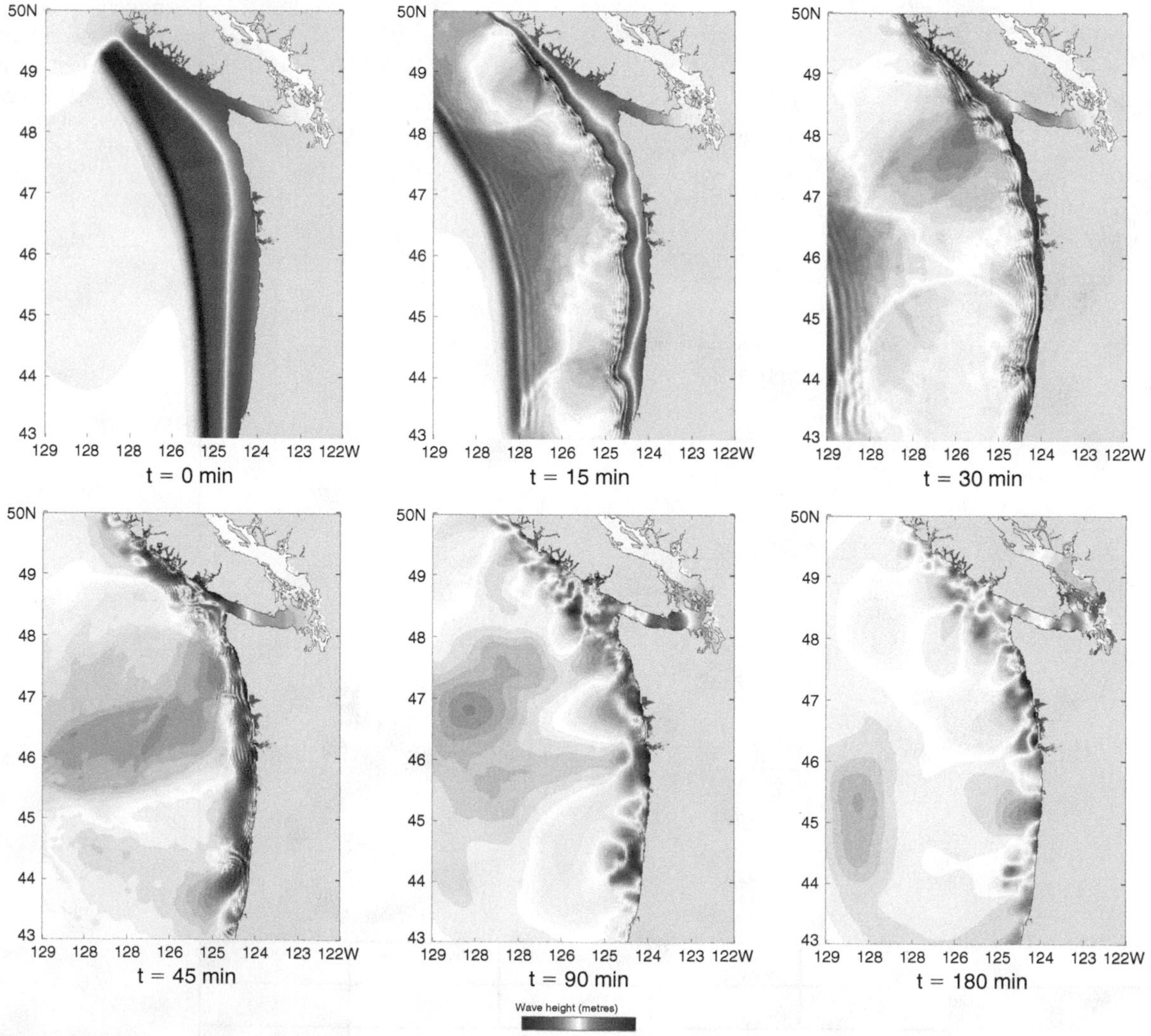

Figure 7.22

Modelled snapshots of an incoming tsunami originating from the Cascadia subduction zone, offshore Vancouver Island.

Source: http://www.pac.dfo-mpo.gc.ca/science/oceans/tsunamis/coarse-tsunami-faible-eng.htm Cherniawsky, J.Y., Titov, V.V., Wang, K. and J.-Y. Li. 2007. Numerical simulations of tsunami waves and currents for southern Vancouver Island from a Cascadia megathrust earthquake. Pure and Applied Geophysics. 164(2–3):465–492. © 2014 Used with permission of Fisheries and Oceans Canada.

Volcano-Caused Tsunamis

Volcanic action can create killer tsunamis (Table 6.2). Volcanoes can put jolts of energy into a water body in several ways: they can explode, they can collapse, and they can send avalanches of debris into the water. It seems likely that tsunamis were generated by all three mechanisms during the eruption of Krakatau in 1883.

KRAKATAU, INDONESIA, 26–27 AUGUST 1883

Krakatau sits in the sea between the major Indonesian islands of Sumatra and Java (Figure 7.23). It is part of the grand arc of volcanoes built above the subducting Indian-Australian plate. Krakatau is a big stratovolcano that builds up out of the ocean and then collapses.

From the ruins of an earlier collapse, magmatic activity built Krakatau upward through the seventeenth century. After two centuries of quiescence, volcanic activity resumed on 20 May 1883. By August 1883, moderate-size Vulcanian eruptions were occurring from about a dozen vents. On Sunday afternoon, 26 August, volcanic eruptions and explosions increased in frequency and strength. At 2 p.m., a large blast shot volcanic ash and pumice 28 km high as one of the cones collapsed into the sea, setting off huge tsunamis. In the evening, eruptions were so noisy that sleep was not possible in western Java, including the capital city of Djakarta (then called Batavia). Some of the eruptions blasted large volumes of gas-charged rocky debris downslope into the sea. These volcanic masses flowed rapidly downslope, across the shoreline, and collided with the sea, putting energy into the water that radiated outward as tsunamis, ravaging villages on the shoreline. The highly irregular coastline in this region affected tsunami height and run-up in the various harbours, inlets, and peninsulas (Figure 7.23).

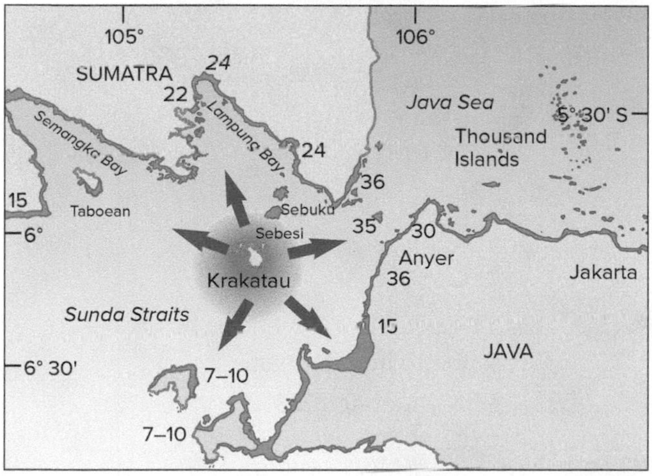

Figure 7.23
Many killer tsunamis were sent off by the eruptive behaviours of Krakatau in Indonesia on 26–27 August 1883. Tsunami run-up heights are shown in metres. Tsunami flooded areas are coloured pink.

On Monday morning, gigantic explosions occurred around 5:30, 6:45, and 8:20. These explosions sent tsunamis with their maximum energy focused in different directions, wiping out several villages. These explosions may have been due to seawater coming in contact with the magma body and rapidly converting the thermal energy of the magma into the mechanical energy of tsunamis. The eruption sequence culminated about 10 a.m. with an overwhelming explosion when the volcano mountain collapsed into the void formed by its partly emptied magma chamber. Tsunamis pushed into harbours and ran up and over some coastal hills up to 40 m high. The volcanic eruptions killed less than 10% of the people directly; over 90% of fatalities were due to volcano-caused tsunamis. The tsunamis during this 20-hour period destroyed 165 villages and killed more than 36 000 people. This tsunami death total was not exceeded until 26 December 2004, again in Indonesia. The world population of humans in 1883 was about 1.6 billion, but it had grown to 6.4 billion people in 2004. The dramatic growth of the human population during those 121 years contributed to the huge death toll in the 2004 tsunami.

The Krakatau final blast was heard distinctly 5000 km away but, in the figurative sense, the event resonated far beyond that distance. Only 13 years earlier, a submarine telegraph cable had been laid to connect the island of Java to the international telegraph network. Via telegraph, the Krakatau eruption was the first great natural disaster to be broadcast to the "global village," a fact captured in the title of a recent book by Simon Winchester: *Krakatoa—The Day the World Exploded: August 27, 1883.*

In 1927, Krakatau began rebuilding a new volcanic cone called Anak Krakatau—"child of Krakatau"; it is still growing. We will hear more from Krakatau.

Landslide-Caused Tsunamis

Gravity pulls rock and sediment masses into and beneath the seas. Energy from these mass movements is transferred to the water, locally causing higher and larger run-ups of water than caused by earthquake-caused tsunamis.

EARTHQUAKE-TRIGGERED MASS MOVEMENTS

Not only do earthquakes generate tsunamis directly, but also their energy can trigger the movement of large masses of rock or sand whose kinetic energy causes tsunamis.

Grand Banks Earthquake and Tsunami, 18 November 1929

At 5:02 p.m. on 18 November 1929, an earthquake of magnitude 7.2 M_w occurred offshore Canada's Maritime Provinces (Figure 7.24). In fact, the "Grand Banks" earthquake is somewhat of a misnomer since its epicentre was located south of the Grand Banks, 18 km away from the continental slope, where the water is 2 km deep. The earthquake triggered the submarine movement of a sediment mass with an estimated volume of 200 km^3, which ruptured 12 transatlantic telegraph cables in its path. In an elegant analysis, Bruze Heezen and Maurice Ewing used the times at which the cables stopped functioning to estimate the speed of the material. At the onset of the event, when the material was moving down the steepest part of the slope, the speed exceeded 90 km/h. Some 12 hours later, when the last cable broke, the speed has decreased to 20 km/h. Finally, the sediment came to rest on the flat abyssal plain.

This was the first earthquake ever felt by the inhabitants of the Burin Peninsula of Newfoundland. Quoted by Janet Looker, who wrote a description of the event, merchant George Bartlett of the village of Burin commented, "People gathered in little knots and discussed the occurrence, and went home to their tea. That night the moon rose with its silvery light and it died out calm, not a ripple on the water." People were unaware that the kinetic energy of the sediment mass moving downslope had set off tsunamis. The tsunamis began arriving about 2.5 hours later (Figure 7.25); the waves came in three major pulses during a 30-minute interval. The long, narrow bays caused tsunamis 1 m high to build to 3 m in many inlets and to 7 m in Taylor's Bay. When waves reached the heads of inlets and bays, they had so much energy and momentum that their run-up onto land reached 13 m elevation in some areas.

The tsunamis ripped boats from their moorings and lifted houses from their foundations, dragging everything out to sea (Figures 7.26 and 7.27). People scrambled for survival. One story tells of a man swept out to sea. He swam toward a house, its upper windows bobbing just

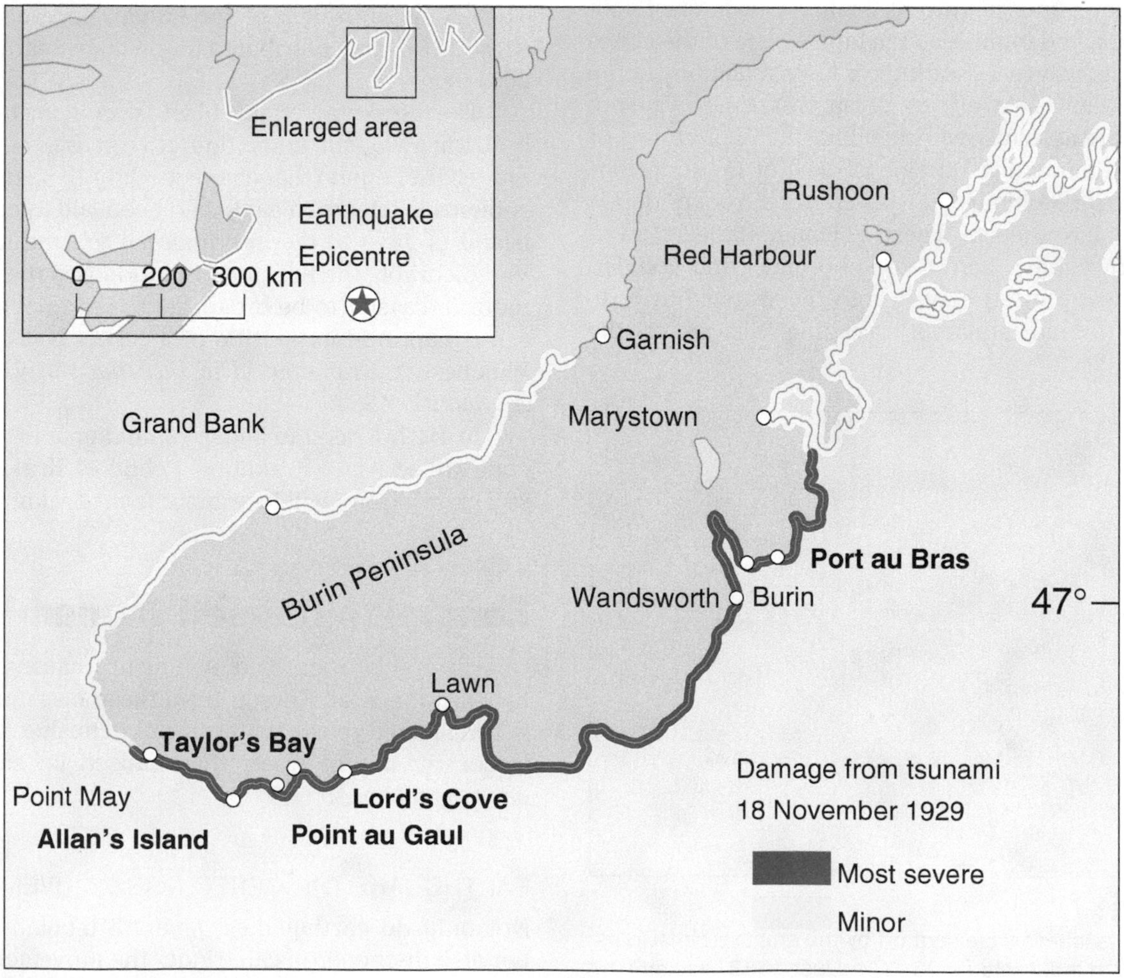

Figure 7.24
The irregular coastline of the Burin Peninsula in Newfoundland focuses the energy of tsunamis. Deaths occurred in the bold-lettered villages.

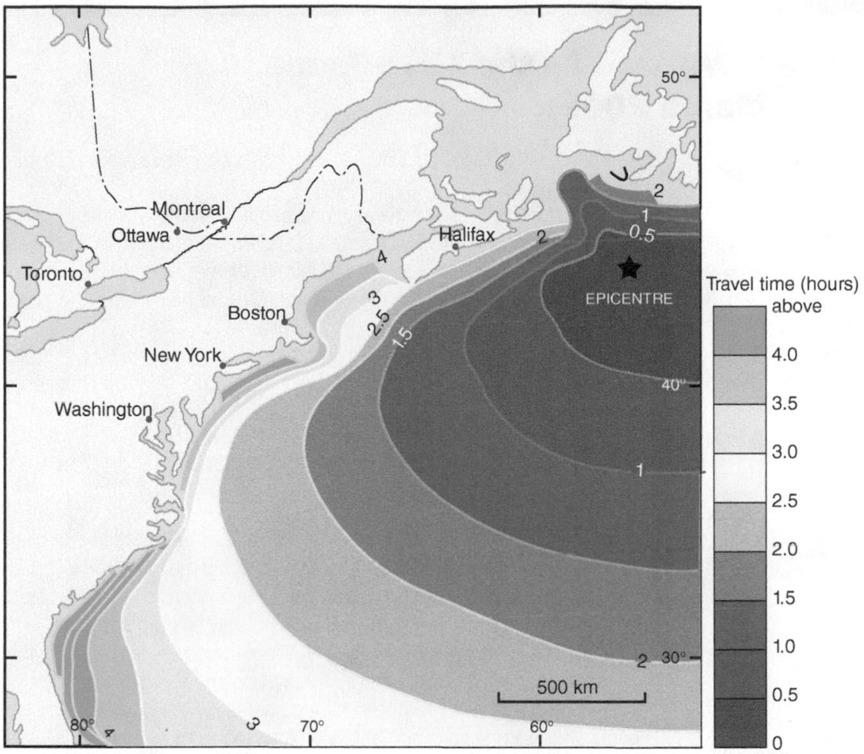

Figure 7.25
Travel times for the 1929 Grand Banks tsunami. Contour interval is half an hour. Note how the tsunami waves travel slower in the Grand Banks plateau than in the open ocean because of seafloor friction.

Source: Reproduced with the permission of Natural Resources Canada 2014, courtesy of the Geological Survey of Canada (GSC Bulletin 548).

above the waves. Breaking through a window, he climbed inside, only to discover he was in his own home.

Help was slow to arrive. Because the telegraph cables were severed, villagers were cut off from the outside world and unable to send an SOS signal. At first, they could count on only themselves to organize relief. Their fate was discovered two days after the tsunami when a coastal steamer made a scheduled stop.

In total, about 40 villages were affected by the tsunami, where 500 buildings, 100 fishing boats, and 26 schooners were damaged. Twenty-eight people died in what is Canada's most devastating earthquake-related loss of life recorded in written documents. The tsunami also disturbed the seabed ecosystem, resulting in poor fish catches in the following years. It dealt a crippling blow to the local fishing industry and almost drove Newfoundland to bankruptcy.

The Newfoundland tsunami is not an isolated event. Beneath the Atlantic Ocean off the east coast of North America, new images of the seafloor show significant scars where big submarine landslides have occurred. Similar landslides in the future will generate tsunamis.

Figure 7.26
Remnants of a destroyed dwelling, Port au Bras, Newfoundland.

Source: The Rooms Provincial Archives, A2-146/S.H.Parsons & Sons.

Figure 7.27
The home of Steven Henry Isaacs of Port au Bras, Newfoundland, which was swept out to sea by the tsunami. The house was anchored to a fishing schooner and towed back to shore.

Source: The Rooms Provincial Archives, A2-146/S.H. Parsons & Sons.

HUMAN FOCUS

An Interview with Joseph Mitchell, Witness to the 1929 Tsunami in Wandsworth, Burin Peninsula (March 2008).

Can you describe Wandsworth at the time of the tsunami?

Wandsworth was a small fishing community on the east coast of the Burin Peninsula. The name Wandsworth was borrowed from a town in England and was chosen by English settlers who came there many years before. It was the community where my family lived for five generations before it was closed down by the government in the 1960s.

In the 1920s, there were about 120 people living in 30 households in Wandsworth. Each family had its own wharf, colloquially known as a "stage." The houses were built fairly close to each other and there was a main road and footpath connecting the houses to each other.

Fishing was the mainstay of the community. In addition, most families harvested a few crops such as potatoes, carrots, and turnips to support themselves. They grew fruit such as apples and plums in order to make preserves for use in the winter months.

Did you feel the earthquake?

At the time of the tsunami I was nine years old. I felt the earthquake while I was walking home from a neighbour's house with my mother and older sister. The earth shook violently, enough to cause damage to a few homes. During the tremor I was initially very frightened and confused about what was happening. Most everyone else felt the same way—including my family and our neighbours. Nothing like this had ever happened before. Some thought that a large airplane had passed overhead while others believed that the world was coming to an end. This all took place around 5:00 p.m. while many families were sitting down to their suppers.

What happened when the tsunami struck?

Wandsworth was a sheltered harbour, protected by various points and islands, which prevented the massive wave from fully reaching the community. The water level did rise about 3 m higher than usual, causing some slight damage to stages but not to the homes, since they were built farther up on the hillside.

The tsunami was completely unexpected by the people and the community was in turmoil as it struck. Children were crying, women were screaming, and everyone began to scramble to reach higher ground. The whole situation was chaotic. This was about three hours after the earthquake, around 8:00 p.m.

A few people did make the connection between the earthquake and the tsunami; however, most were confused about what had happened to them.

What happened in the aftermath of the tsunami?

There was virtually no communication at the time, even between communities that were close together. The only method of transportation was by boat, and the next day people began travelling around to other places to see the extent of the damage. News spread mainly by word of mouth.

Help was mainly organized for the affected communities when word of the disaster reached St. John's. Food, supplies, and clothing were all distributed to those who had been hit the hardest by the disaster. Although people who were spared any damage were too poor to help those less fortunate, they tried to do anything they could to help, such as helping to clean up.

Although it took quite a while to repair the damage, most people stayed in their communities and rebuilt their lives. A few did leave, as the government relocated them since they had lost their homes and possessions.

Most people who are still alive that survived the tsunami disaster remember the event vividly, since it was so unexpected and frightening. Children such as my grandson have done research projects about the disaster for school, which also helps keep the memories alive.

C. Samson would like to express her sincere condolences to the family of Mr. Mitchell; he passed away in 2009.

VOLCANO COLLAPSES

Volcanic islands are huge and impressive features. As oceanic volcanoes grow, they tend to develop internal weaknesses and sides that are too steep, and thus, they collapse in gigantic events. Worldwide, approximately one **flank collapse** occurs every 10 000 years.

Hawaiian Islands in the Pacific Ocean

The largest submarine mass movements were recognized first on the seafloor along the Hawaiian Islands volcanic chain. Slump and debris-avalanche deposits there cover more than five times the land area of the islands (Figure 7.28). Some individual debris avalanches are over 200 km long with volumes greater than 5000 km^3, making them among the largest on Earth. The events that caused these were not just loose debris sliding down the side of the volcano; they were catastrophic flank collapses, in which the whole side of an oceanic volcano breaks off and falls into the sea. There have been at least 70 flank collapses from the Hawaiian Islands in the last 20 million years.

Pause and think about this for a moment: each Hawaiian Island has major structural weaknesses that lead to massive failures. The not-so-solid earth here betrays us; it can fail rapidly and massively. For example, the island of Molokai has no volcano. Where did it go? Apparently, the northern part of the island fell into the ocean (Figure 7.28), leaving steep cliffs behind.

What happens to the ocean when a gigantic chunk of island drops into it and flows rapidly underwater? Huge tsunamis are created. For example, prehistoric giant waves washed coral, marine shells, and volcanic rocks inland, where they are found today as gravel layers on Lanai lying 365 m above sea level and on Molokai over 2 km inland and more than 60 m above sea level. Tsunamis of this size would not only ravage Hawaii but also cause death and destruction throughout the Pacific Ocean basin.

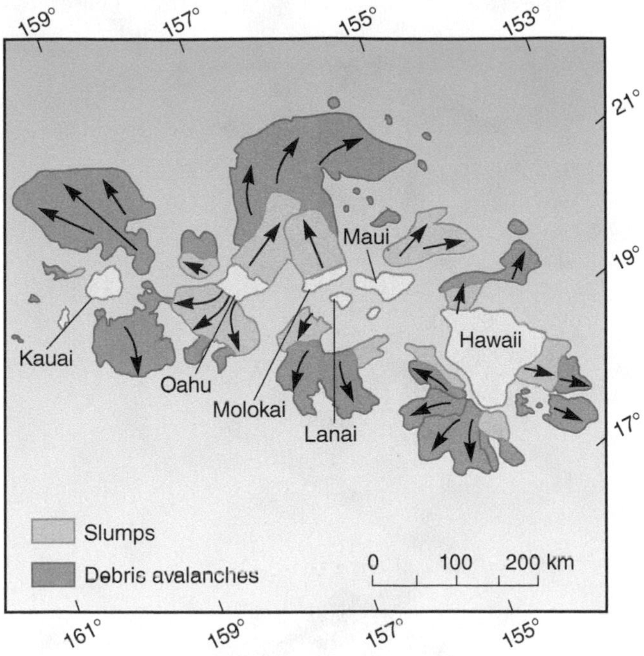

Figure 7.28
The Hawaiian Islands cover less surface area than the slumps and debris avalanches that have fallen from them.

TSUNAMIS IN BAYS AND LAKES

Tsunamis may be also created by smaller faults that cause unstable sand and rock masses to slip and slide under water. The constricted topography of bays and lakes allows some landslides to create huge local tsunamis.

Kitimat, British Columbia, 27 April 1975

The small town of Kitimat, British Columbia, sits some 70 km away from the Pacific coast at the end of a long and narrow fjord. At 10:05 a.m. on 27 April 1975, a large-scale underwater slope failure, triggered by construction work in the area, set an enormous volume of marine debris in motion. The ensuing tsunami damaged a wharf and carried away shore installations at the First Nations settlement of Kitamaat across the fjord. The maximum wave amplitude reached 8.2 m, based on observations of water marks on pilings. Fortunately, no one was injured.

Andrey Skvortsov and Brian Borhnold carried out a detailed simulation of the event (Figure 7.29). Their models show that the slide mass first detached from the fjord wall near the wharf. It reached a maximum velocity of 22.5 m/s at 19 seconds, after which the material slowed down in an area of lower seafloor slope until it stopped approximately 4 minutes and 30 seconds after the start of the failure. A tongue of sediment stretching 4.5 km was deposited on the seafloor. Water turbulence during the first few seconds generated a crest in front of the slide and a trough in the generation region. The main tsunami wave propagated across the fjord where it struck Kitamaat at a height of 10.9 m after 72 seconds. The wave reflected back to the terminal area after 180 seconds and came back to Kitamaat after 250 seconds. The waves gradually died down after multiple reflections on the coastline.

The Kitimat disaster illustrates the potentially dangerous cocktail formed by mixing rough topography and water, a topic that will be discussed in Chapter 13. With unstable slopes hidden beneath the sea surface, underwater mass movements are especially challenging to predict and mitigate.

Seiches

Seiches are oscillating waves that slosh back and forth within an enclosed body of water such as a sea, bay, lake, or swimming pool. The process was observed and named in Lake Geneva, Switzerland, in 1890. The word "seiche" (pronounced "SAY-sh") comes from a Swiss-French word that means to sway back and forth.

The energy to cause a seiche can come from a variety of sources. Winds blowing across a lake can cause the water body to oscillate at some natural frequency. Seiches are common in the Great Lakes of Canada and the United States, where they may be called sloshes. For example, with its elongated shape and relatively shallow water, Lake Erie can experience seiches up to five metres high, alternating from one end of the lake to the other, when strong winds blow.

People living in seismically active areas commonly see seiches when the water in swimming pools sloshes back and forth and overflows the sides during an earthquake.

HEBGEN LAKE, MONTANA, 17 AUGUST 1959

Shortly before midnight on 17 August 1959 two faults running beneath the northern end of Hebgen Lake moved in magnitude 6.3 and 7.5 earthquakes. These two normal faults had their southwestern sides drop 7 and 7.8 m, also dropping the northern end of Hebgen Lake. The foreman at the Hebgen Lake Dam was awakened by the earthquake, dressed, and went outside for a look. He became eyewitness to a spectacular seiche where lake water sloshed back and forth for 11.5 hours. In foreman Hungerford's own words:

> The dust was so intense you could hardly see. You could hardly breathe, or anything. It obscured the moon. We went to the river gauge . . . Just as we got to it, we heard a roar and we saw this wall of water coming down the river . . . We thought the dam had broken . . . Then we went up to the dam. When we got

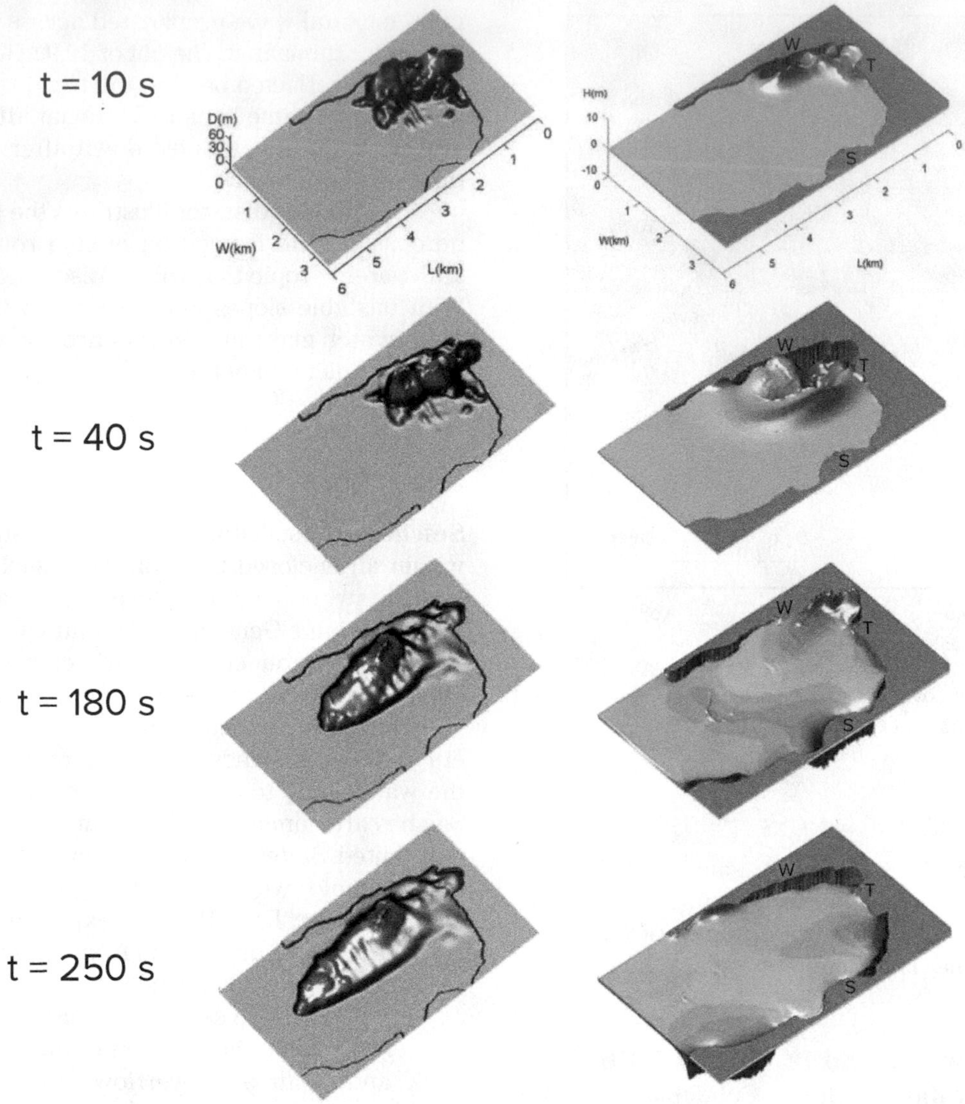

Figure 7.29

Modelled sequence of events during the 1975 Kitimat underwater mass movement and tsunami. Left: sliding mass. Right: tsunami waves (crests in pink, troughs in dark blue). S: Kitamaat Haisla First Nations settlement; T: Eurocan Terminal; W: Northlands Navigation Wharf.

Source: Skvortsov, A. and Bornhold, B. 2007, Journal of Geophysical Research.

there we couldn't see much, but I walked over to the edge of the dam and all we could see was blackness. There was no water. No water above the dam at all, and I couldn't imagine what had become of it. By that time the dust had started to clear, and the moon had come out a little. And then here came the water. It had all been up at the other end of the lake. . . . We rushed back when we heard the water coming. We could hear it before we could see it. When it came over the dam, it was a wall of water about three to four feet [0.9–1.2 m] high completely across that dam, and it flowed like that for what seemed to me to be 20 minutes, but possibly it could have been 5 or 10. I have no idea of time. It flowed for a while, and then it started to subside. Then it all cleared away, and no water again. The lake was completely dry as far as we could see. All we could see down the dam was darkness again. It seemed like a period of maybe 10 to 15 minutes, and the water came back, and then it repeated the same thing over again.

LO4 Surviving a Tsunami

IF YOU FEEL THE EARTHQUAKE

When confronted with a tsunami, the best strategy is avoidance. Recent tsunami tragedies show how important it is to broadcast this simple message widely to populations living in coastal areas (Figure 7.30).

(a)

(b)

Figure 7.30
Warning signs clearly identify (a) tsunami hazard zones and (b) evacuation routes.
Source: (a) © Judith Patterson. (b) Claire Samson.

If you are near the coast and feel an earthquake, then think about the possibility of a tsunami. The earliest warning of a local tsunami is often strong shaking of the ground, and people near the shoreline should evacuate immediately without waiting for an official warning. Other clues can alert you to the possibility of powerful tsunami. Before the first big wave of a tsunami, the sea may either withdraw significantly far from shore, or suddenly rise. Sometimes the ocean water changes character or makes different sounds. Watch for these changes in ocean behaviour.

If you think a tsunami might be coming, seek high ground immediately. If no high ground is available, then go upstairs in a well-built building or climb a tree—the so-called vertical evacuation (Table 7.4). It doesn't matter how strong a swimmer you are; it is not only the water that can hurt you but also the debris it carries.

LO5 TSUNAMI WARNING SYSTEMS

Nagging questions arose about the lack of warning about the approaching 2004 Indian Ocean tsunami. For example, the first tsunami arrived in Sri Lanka two hours after the earthquake. Couldn't warnings have been spread to alert people in time to save thousands of lives?

The circum-Pacific nations were first to coordinate efforts toward an integrated warning system, leading to the creation in 1949 of the Pacific Tsunami Warning Center (PTWC). The PTWC receives data from seismograph stations deployed around the globe and screens earthquakes as they occur. An earthquake with the following characteristics could potentially generate a tsunami: (1) Richter magnitude of 7.0 or greater, (2) epicentre on the ocean floor, and

TABLE 7.4

Surviving a Tsunami

Abandon your belongings.
Many lives are lost while trying to save possessions.

Head for high ground—and stay there.
If there is no high ground nearby, then

Climb to an upper floor or roof of a strong building.
If there is no sturdy building, then

Climb a tree.
If there are no climbable trees, then

Grab onto something that floats.
Look for something to use as a raft.

(3) hypocentre shallower than 100 km. When an earthquake meeting these criteria is identified, computers calculate the travel times to coastal communities and a regional "tsunami watch" is issued. A "tsunami watch" is an advance alert to areas that could be impacted by destructive tsunami waves, based on seismic information alone, without confirmation that a tsunami is underway. When sea-level data from buoys and tidal gauges detect tsunami waves, the threat is confirmed and a "tsunami warning" is broadcast across the entire Pacific Ocean basin. National authorities are responsible to take appropriate actions, which could include the evacuation of low-lying coastal areas and ordering ships out of harbour to deep water.

An extra component was added to the warning system when the first seafloor pressure sensors were activated in October 2003 by the U.S. National Oceanographic and Atmospheric Administration (NOAA). The sensors exploit a fundamental feature of tsunami waves—the fact that they disturb the entire water column down to the ocean floor as opposed to waves caused by wind, which create turbulence only a few tens of metres below the water surface. Each instrument consists of a bottom pressure recorder and a surface buoy (Figure 7.31). The recorder is anchored securely on the seafloor. Its pressure sensor is sensitive to the passage of tsunami waves. When anomalous pressure variations are detected in this otherwise very quiet environment, the recorder sends a signal to the surface buoy, which relays it to the PTWC via a satellite link.

On 16 November 2003, a magnitude 7.5 earthquake rocked the seafloor in the Aleutian Islands of Alaska. In 25 minutes, a seafloor sensor triggered a tsunami warning for U.S. coastal areas. But in another 40 minutes, computer analysis predicted that the tsunami would be only 19 cm high at Hilo, Hawaii. The tsunami warning was cancelled in Hawaii, saving $68 million, the economic impact of a statewide coastal evacuation—an impressive start for a new warning system.

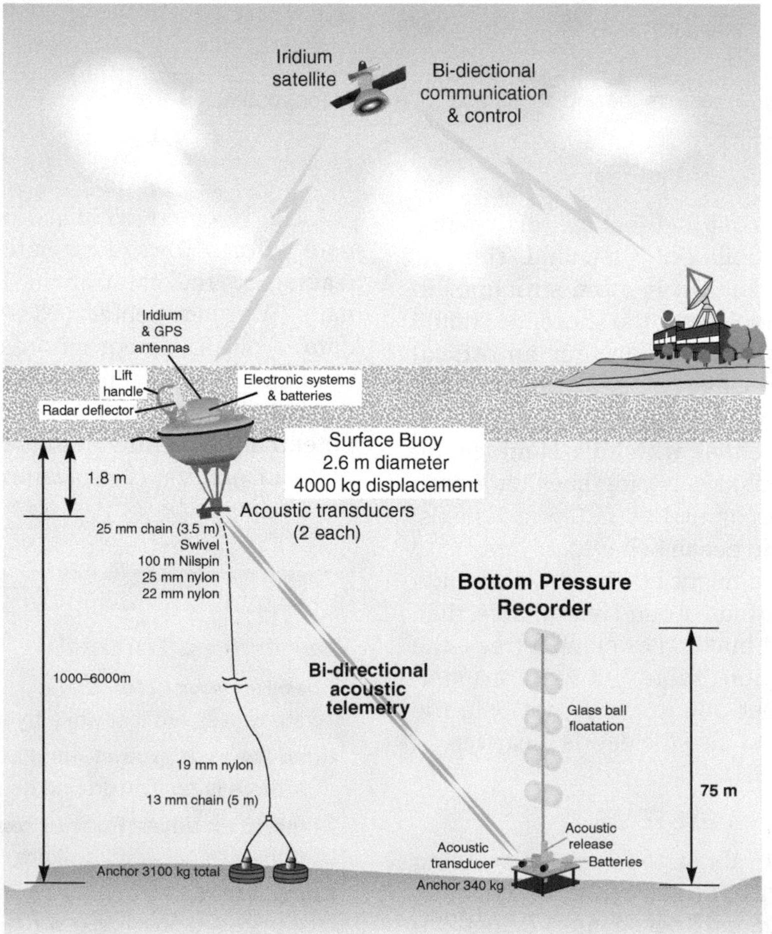

Figure 7.31

DART™ (Deep-ocean Assessment and Reporting of Tsunami) tsunami warning system.

Source: DART tsunami warning system http://nctr.pmel.noaa.gov/Dart/Jpg/DART-II_05x.swf.

Before the 2004 Indian Ocean tsunami, NOAA operated a six-buoy warning system in the northern Pacific Ocean. After the 2004 disaster, funding was provided to install a more extensive network. There are now almost 60 seafloor sensors currently in operation worldwide, most deployed near the subduction zones around the Pacific Ocean (Figure 7.32). Warning systems have been installed in the Indian Ocean and Caribbean Sea where the shorter travel times between the earthquake epicentres and coastal areas present a particular challenge. With the 1929 Grand Banks tsunami in mind, the Canadian federal government is upgrading several Atlantic sea-level gauges and seismic-data transmission links. The goal is to provide real-time warnings before tsunamis hit the shorelines of Atlantic Canada.

STRUCTURAL COUNTERMEASURES

Four strategies can be applied to reduce tsunami risk (Figure 7.33). (1) Hazards can be avoided by placing infrastructure on berms or natural high grounds and erecting towers and elevated platforms for people to take refuge. (2) Building breakwaters, underwater berms or rubble mounds increase friction, dissipate wave energy and can slow down the waves. (3) Constructing angled walls and ditches can help steer waves away from vulnerable infrastructure. (4) Seawalls and water gates can block incoming waves.

COASTAL MAPS

In the long term, a sensible mitigation strategy against tsunamis includes identifying and managing vulnerable coastal areas. Centrally located in the earthquake-prone Pacific Ocean, Hawaii has experienced tsunamis generated in all parts of the Pacific. The broad-scale threats to homeowners and businesses are presented in a tsunami hazard map for the Big Island of Hawaii (Figure 7.34). The map predicts the effect of local topography on the heights and run-ups of tsunami waves at the shoreline. Notice how the large bay of Hilo is particularly vulnerable. Following the 1960 tsunami, the citizens of Hilo have rebuilt their city centre several blocks inland from the shoreline. The waterfront area of Hilo is now recreational parkland.

Mapping of coastlines in Indonesia, India, and Sri Lanka following the killer tsunami of 2004 showed how human activities increased damages and deaths in some areas. The coastal areas where forests had been removed suffered more extensive damages than neighbouring areas with the natural vegetation intact. Trees and shrubs tend to reduce the amplitude and energy

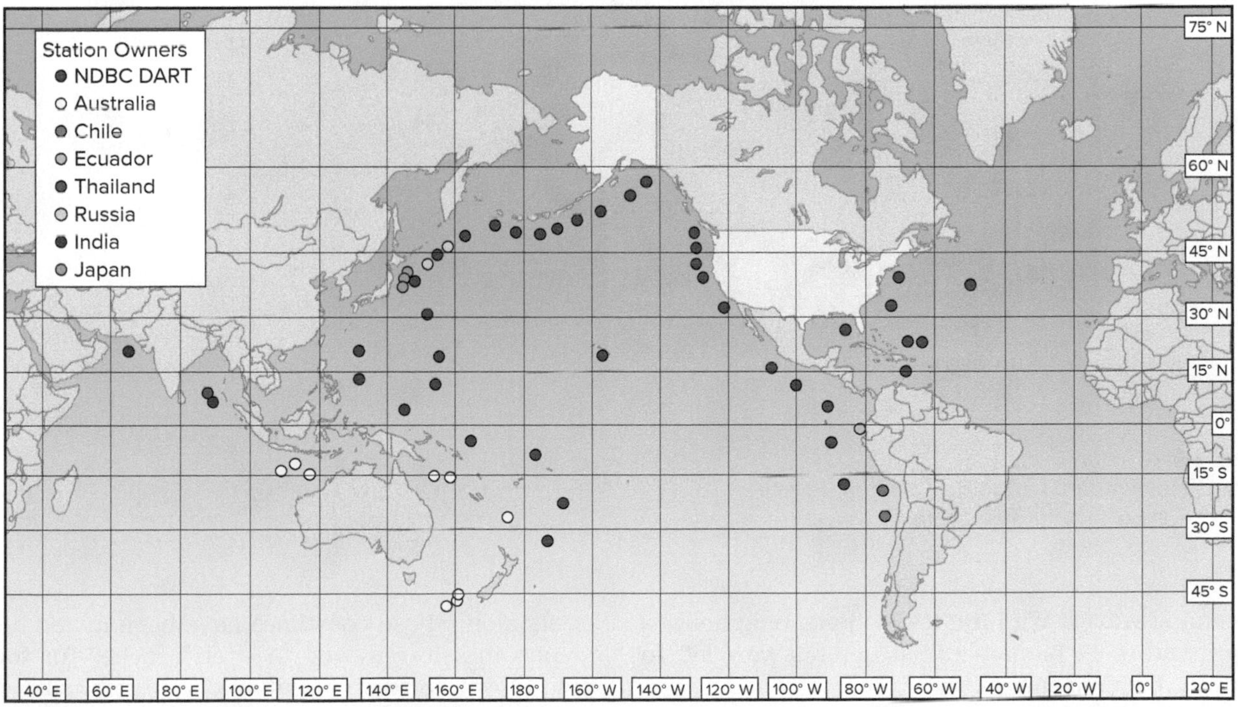

Figure 7.32

Geographical distribution of DART™ tsunami warning systems as of 2014.

Source: Geographical distribution of DART http://nctr.pmel.noaa.gov/Dart/.

(a) (b) (c)

Figure 7.33

Examples of countermeasures against tsunamis in Japan: (a) evacuation tower in Mie Prefecture; (b) tetrapods and seawall in Beppu Bay, Oita Prefecture; (c) flood gate in Tokyo. Several such engineering works were overwhelmed by the 2011 tsunami. They were designed to specifications that had underestimated the potential height of tsunami waves.

Source: (a) International Tsunami Information Center/UNSECO/NOAA. (b) Tylerbell.net. (c) Claire Samson.

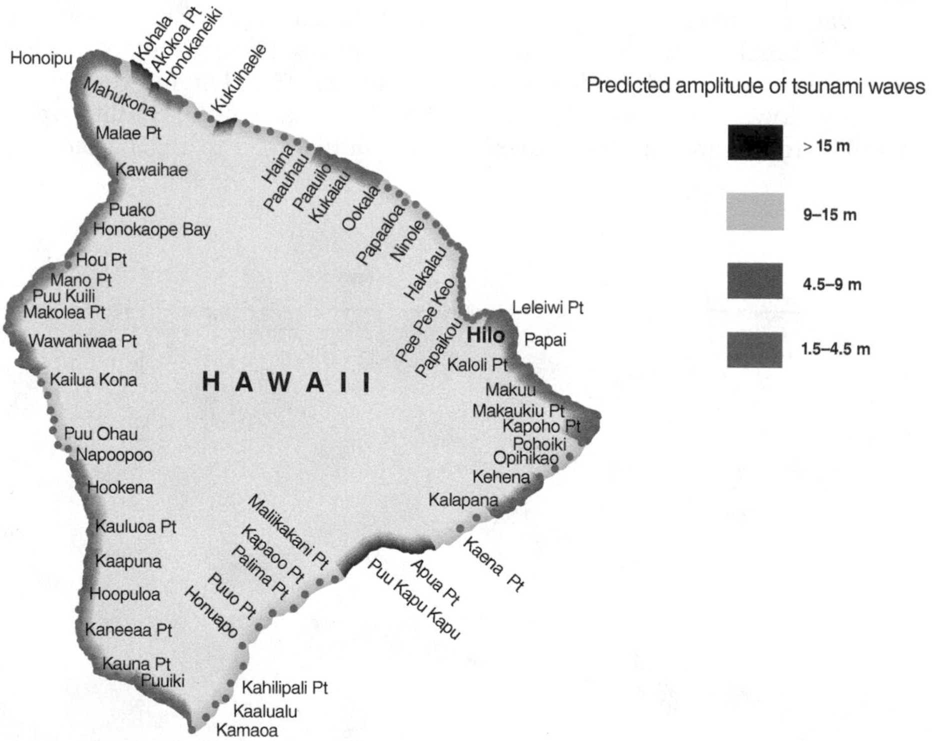

Figure 7.34

Map of tsunami hazard for the Big Island of Hawaii.

Source: United States Geological Survey Professional Paper 1240B.

of incoming waves. With the forest gone, only houses, bridges, and other human-built structures were left to absorb the tsunami energy.

In Sri Lanka, many of the hardest-hit coastlines were ones where coral reefs had been removed. Coral reefs along those coastlines have been mined for souvenirs to sell, removed to open beaches for tourists, and blown up to stun and catch the fish inside them. With coral barrier reefs removed, tsunamis were able to charge farther inland with greater energy.

IN GREATER DEPTH

Project NEPTUNE: Revolutionizing Ocean Science

Project NEPTUNE (North-East Pacific Time-series Undersea Networked Experiments) was launched in 2003 as a collaborative effort between 12 Canadian universities, government laboratories, and international institutions. It aims to address fundamental questions in ocean science with high-tech instruments reminiscent of space exploration. The NEPTUNE "tool box" includes seafloor rovers, robots, high-definition cameras, seismometers, and different sensors to monitor the movements of sea creatures (Figure 7.35).

Figure 7.35
Project NEPTUNE will monitor seafloor processes on the northern portion of the Juan de Fuca plate with high-tech equipment: (1) sonar imager, (2) high-definition camera, (3) rover, (4) seismometer, (5) microbial incubators, (6) optical cable, (7) control system, (8) self-propelled gas collection system, (9) cable sensor, (10) service robot.
Source: *Wired.*

What could be a better natural laboratory for the project than the Juan the Fuca plate (Figure 6.8). The plate, one of the smallest in the world, features a large variety of tectonic environments in a relatively small geographical area and an active underwater volcano, the Axial seamount. The innovative concept of Project NEPTUNE is to equip the plate with an array of sensors linked by a large optical cable loop connected to a shore station in Port Alberni on Vancouver Island (Figure 7.36). These sensors are interactive: via the Internet, scientists can control their configuration to adapt to changing conditions such as storms, earthquakes, plan on blooms, and fish migration.

There are currently 125 sensors connected to the loop at 5 seafloor nodes, transmitting live data to a vibrant user community of 6300 people from 98 countries. All data are free. All nodes are instrumented with seismometers and seafloor pressure sensors. A practical goal is to give advance warning of a megathrust earthquake quickly enough to allow utility companies to turn off gas and electricity in time to limit the spread of fire. Although the NEPTUNE network has not been designed as a tsunami warning system, the data recorded by the seafloor pressure sensors are vital for that application (Figure 7.37). An agreement is in place to share these data in real time with first responders.

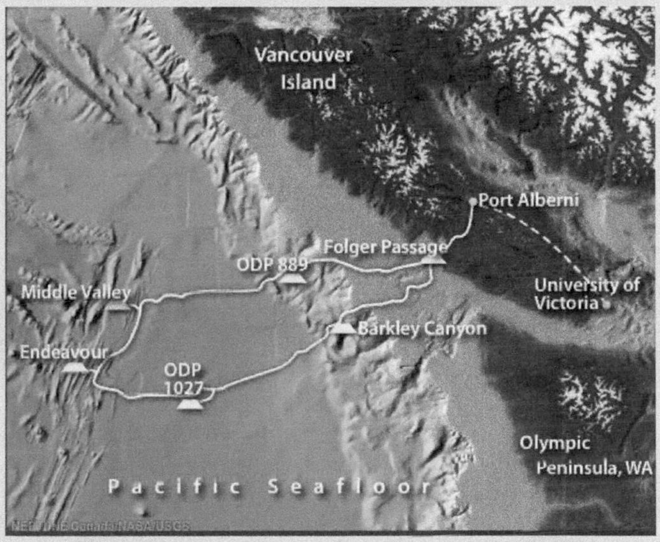

Figure 7.36
Five active nodes (in yellow) of the NEPTUNE network. Node ODP889 is strategically located to study earthquakes of the Cascadia Subduction Zone, and node ODP1027 to investigate tsunami propagation.
Source: NEPTUNE Canada.

continued

IN GREATER DEPTH *continued*

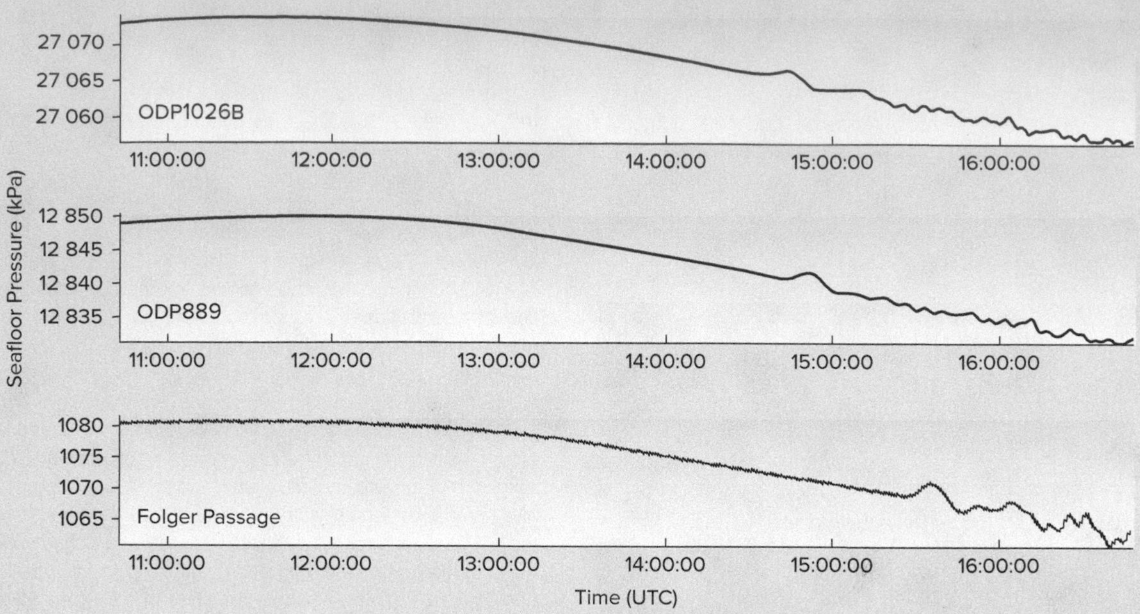

Figure 7.37
The first wave of the Tohoku tsunami as recorded by three seafloor pressure recorders of the NEPTUNE network on 11 March 2011.
Source: NEPTUNE Canada.

SUMMARY

- Wind-caused waves are induced by the friction between wind and the water surface. They typically have periods of a few seconds and wavelengths ranging between a few tens to several hundreds of metres. Wind-caused waves are solitary waves that curl over at the shore, run partway up the beach, and then pull back to the sea.
- Tsunami waves are created when the entire water column of the ocean is disturbed. They commonly travel at 200 m/s in the open ocean and may be spaced as much as 60 minutes apart. Tsunami waves are the leading edge of a tabular mass of water that may keep running onshore for 5, 10, or even 30 minutes before being pulled back to the sea. Their long period and momentum make tsunami waves dangerous.
- Tsunamis are most often triggered by large earthquakes. Other causes include volcanic eruptions, terrestrial and underwater mass movements, and asteroid impacts.
- Earthquakes that could potentially generate tsunamis have the following characteristics: (1) large magnitudes, (2) epicentres on the ocean floor, and (3) shallow hypocentres. They are especially dangerous if associated with large vertical displacement of the ocean floor.
- Seiches are oscillating waves that slosh back and forth within an enclosed body of water such as a bay or a lake. The energy for a seiche commonly comes from strong winds, seismic waves, or ground movements.
- If a tsumani is coming: Abandon your belongings. Head for high ground and stay there. If there is no high ground, climb to an upper floor of a strong building. If no building is nearby, climb a tree. If there are no trees, grab something that floats.

Terms to Remember

flank collapse
run-up
seiches
shoaling

Questions for Review

1. What is the energy source of (a) everyday waves at the beach? (b) tsunamis?
2. What are four major causes of tsunamis? Complete these statements to rank the four causes: Tsunamis are most frequently caused by _____. Tsunami are largest when caused by _____.
3. How fast can tsunamis travel (a) in the deep ocean? (b) in shallow water? What are typical tsunami wavelengths and periods?
4. How many waves are typically generated in a tsunami event?
5. Which wave is the biggest in a tsunami event?
6. How does a tsunami behave as it approaches land? Are tsunamis more dangerous along a straight coastline or in a V-shaped harbour or inlet?
7. How do tsunamis differ from seiches?
8. Do all oceans have tsunamis?

Questions for Further Thought

1. Is there any way to prevent a tsunami?
2. What are the additional challenges of designing a tsunami warning system for the smaller Indian Ocean as opposed to the larger Pacific Ocean?
3. What features should tsunami-resistant houses have?
4. If you are at the beach and feel an earthquake lasting 30 seconds or more, what should you do?

Interesting Websites

- Tsunami Society International
  http://www.tsunamisociety.org
- 1929 Grand Banks Tsunami, Earthquakes Canada, Natural Resources Canada
  http://earthquakescanada.nrcan.gc.ca/historic-historique/events/19291118-eng.php
- Animations of Tsunami Generated by Cascadia Subduction Zone Earthquakes, Fisheries and Oceans Canada
  http://www.pac.dfo-mpo.gc.ca/science/oceans/tsunamis/modele-tsunami-model-eng.html
- Project NEPTUNE Canada
  http://www.oceannetworks.ca
- Pacific Tsunami Warning Center, National Oceanic and Atmospheric Administration, United States
  http://ptwc.weather.gov
- West Coast and Alaska Tsunami Warning Center, National Oceanic and Atmospheric Administration, United States
  http://wcatwc.arh.noaa.gov

CHAPTER EIGHT

8

The Ever Changing Climate

SOLAR ENERGY

"All across the world, in every kind of environment and region known to man, increasingly dangerous weather patterns and devastating storms are abruptly putting an end to the long-running debate over whether or not climate change is real. Not only is it real, it's here, and its effects are giving rise to a frighteningly new global phenomenon: the man-made natural disaster."

—Senator Barack Obama, 3 April 2006

Outline

- A Global Energy Budget
- Global Warming
- Climate Observations and Predictions
- Summary

LO1 Distinguish between climate and weather.

LO2 Describe what happens to solar radiation that reaches Earth.

LO3 Explain the greenhouse effect.

LO4 Summarize the different processes of the hydrologic cycle.

LO5 Give examples of several observations of climate change.

During the summer, the Canadian Coast Guard icebreaker Amundsen is dedicated to scientific research in the Arctic, including the study of the impact of climate change on the northern environment.

Source: Lee Thomas/Alamy Images/GetStock.com

The news media bring us tales of killer heat waves, tornadoes, hurricanes, and floods. These extreme weather events occur as the contemporary climate is changing faster now than it has in a very long time. **Weather** covers short-term processes, whereas **climate** refers to long-term conditions. We experience the hour-to-hour, day-to-day, and season-to-season changes in atmospheric conditions known as weather. When weather is viewed over longer time spans such as decades, centuries, and millions of years, it is called climate. Mark Twain wrote in his short story, *English as She is Taught,* "Climate lasts all the time and weather only a few days." Or, as Robert Heinlein puts it more bluntly, "Climate is what you expect, weather is what you get." Because weather and climate are connected, climate cannot change without changing the weather.

The one certainty about climate change is that the climate is indeed changing. Sometimes the change is abrupt; other times the climate appears stable with little apparent change. Since weather is highly variable, it is difficult to recognize and identify climate trends over years or decades. For this reason the World Meteorological Organization has determined that it takes 30 years of weather observations to define a climate. When you hear a meteorologist on television give the average temperature for a particular date, he or she is quoting the 30-year average. This 30-year running average shifts over time though, allowing observations of climate change to be made.

Are we seeing more weather extremes because there are more to see—which would be consistent with the predictions of climate change—or are we just getting better at seeing them? Observational evidence of severe weather trends is sketchy—scientists cannot say with full certainty that extremes of weather are on the rise, or that severe weather is more intense or is lasting longer than in the past. Wild weather is generally rare, localized, and short lived, which makes the detection of meaningful trends difficult. You cannot blame a single storm, a dump of snow, or a week's heavy rain on climate change. The young science of climate change study, however, is making rapid progress and more and more studies are unraveling causal relationships between long-term variations in temperature and precipitations, and natural hazards such as extreme weather events, floods, and forest fires.

LO1 A Global Energy Budget

The Earth's climate is powered primarily by heat energy emitted by the Sun. Energy flowing from the Earth's interior to the surface accomplishes impressive geological work (Chapter 2), yet the total amount of this energy is miniscule compared to the energy the Earth receives from the Sun. Only a minute percentage of the radiant energy of the Sun reaches the Earth, yet that amount is about 4000 times greater than the energy that flows from the Earth's interior.

Let's look at a global energy budget for the top of the atmosphere and the surface of the Earth (Figure 8.1). There is a balance between gains (incoming energy) and losses (outgoing energy). On this grand world scale, the planet is approximately in equilibrium and the average annual temperature at and near the surface is relatively stable.

LO2 SOLAR RADIATION RECEIVED BY THE EARTH

All objects radiate energy. The energy radiated from the Sun covers a broad spectrum of wavelengths ranging from radio waves with wavelengths of tens of kilometres to gamma rays with wavelengths smaller than one-billionth of a centimetre but is mostly concentrated in the spectrum of light that is visible or nearly visible (infrared and ultraviolet) to humans (Figure 8.2). Hotter objects radiate more energy and a greater proportion of energy at shorter wavelengths. The Sun radiates hundreds of thousands of times more energy than does the Earth, mostly at shorter wavelengths. Solar radiation is commonly called "short wavelength," and radiation from the Earth is called "long wavelength." If we consider the planet as a whole, about 70% of the Sun's energy reaching the Earth is involved in creating activity in and among the Earth's systems (Figure 8.1). About 30% is reflected back to space as short-wavelength radiation and is known as **albedo**.

The Sun's energy heats the Earth unevenly; the Earth receives different amounts of solar energy at different latitudes. Solar radiation is absorbed in massive amounts in the equatorial belt between about 38°N and 38°S latitudes (Figure 8.3). The equatorial zone faces the Sun directly, thus incoming sunlight strikes the surface at steep angles, allowing a high percentage of the energy to be absorbed, especially in seawater.

Polar latitudes receive far less of the Sun's energy because the incoming solar radiation arrives at a low angle, causing much of it to be reflected. Incoming solar energy is also spread over a large area. In fact, the high latitudes show a net cooling because the heat reradiated back to space is greater than the amount locally gained from the Sun. There is an interesting climatic feedback cycle in the polar zones. They receive less solar energy and are colder, thus helping snow and ice to form. The presence of highly reflective snow and ice raises albedos from the 5 to 35% range for water, soil, and vegetation up to 60 to 90%. Increasing the albedo makes the cold polar climate even colder.

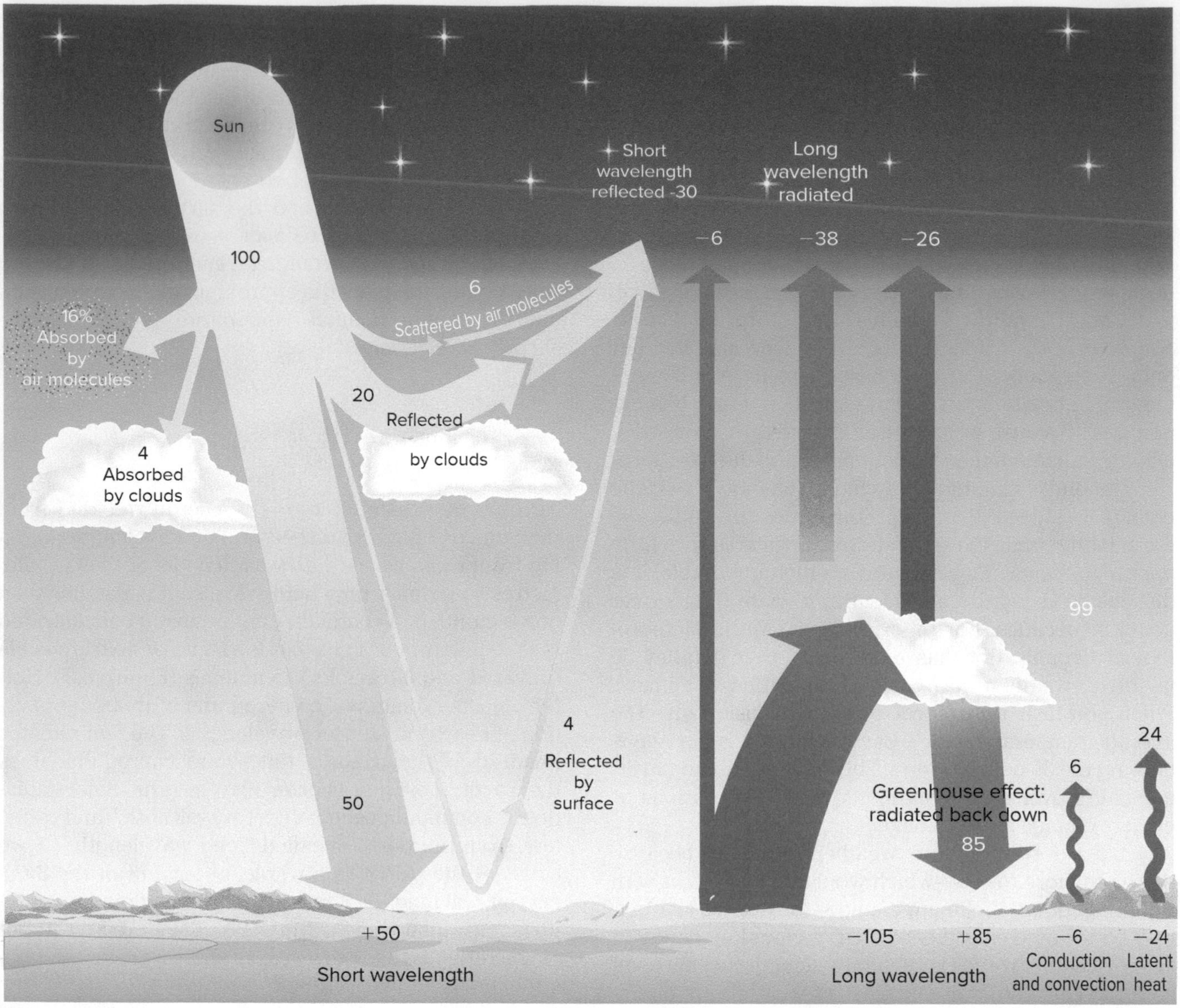

Figure 8.1

A global energy budget. Solar radiation reaching the Earth's atmosphere is 30% reflected and 70% absorbed into the Earth's systems (yellow arrows). The energy absorbed is radiated at long wavelengths (red arrows). The amounts of incoming and outgoing energy balance at the top of the atmosphere (100 − 30 − 6 − 38 − 26 = 0) and on the ground surface (50 − 105 + 85 − 6 − 24 = 0).

Source: Modified from Peixoto and Oort (1992).

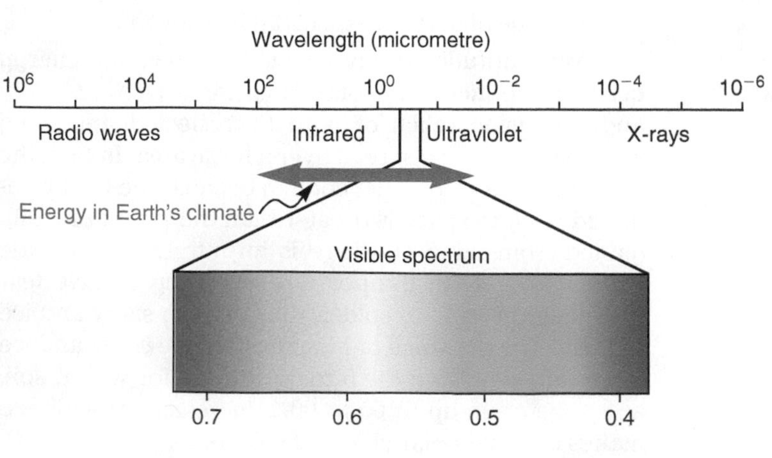

Figure 8.2

The electromagnetic spectrum (one micrometre = one-thousandth of a millimetre). Visible light represents approximately 43% of the solar radiation received on the Earth.

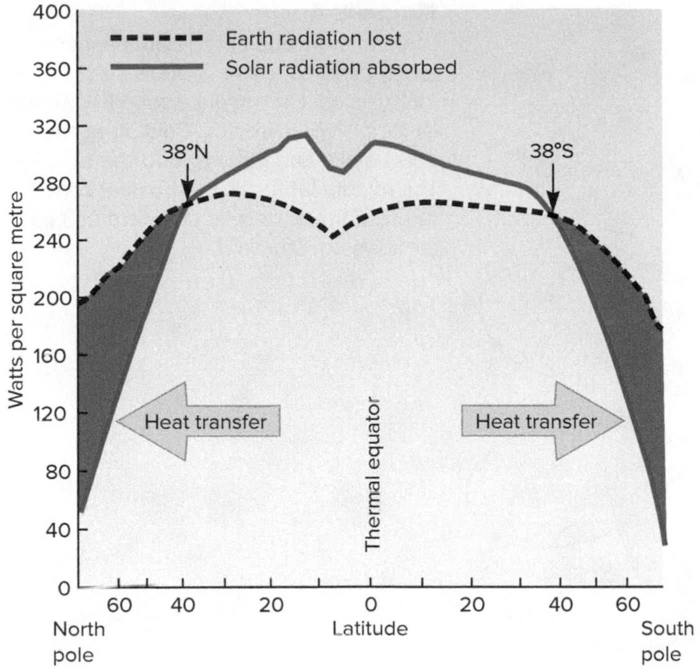

Figure 8.3
Energy radiated from the Earth's surface and energy absorbed from solar radiation are plotted against latitude. Poleward from latitudes 38°N and 38°S, the energy deficit increases. Heat is transported poleward from tropics via ocean and atmosphere, tending toward energy equilibrium.
Source: NOAA Meteorological Satellite Laboratory, Washington, DC.

The Earth's spin helps set the heat-carrying oceans and atmosphere in motion. Gravity then works to even out the unequal distribution of heat by pulling more forcefully on the colder, denser air and water masses. The mid-latitudes are zones of energy transfer. Circulation of the relatively rapidly moving atmosphere and slowly flowing oceans is a major determinant of climate and weather all around the Earth.

LO3 OUTGOING TERRESTRIAL RADIATION AND THE GREENHOUSE EFFECT

Although the Earth receives solar radiation every day, year after year, all this heat is not retained. A significant amount of heat is reradiated back from the Earth to space in the longer wavelengths of the infrared portion of the electromagnetic spectrum. But the energy is not returned to space simply as it arrived. The average calculated surface temperature of the Earth is about 15°C. This temperature seems reasonable from our day-to-day life experience. However, temperature measurements from satellites tell us that the Earth is sending heat to space as if its average temperature were −16° C. Why this discrepancy? Because of the **greenhouse effect**. Gases in the lower atmosphere such as water vapour—by far the most abundant, carbon dioxide, and methane absorb much of the outbound long-wavelength energy and then reradiate it downward to the Earth's surface, where it raises the Earth's average temperature to about 15°C.

ENERGY TRANSFER IN THE ATMOSPHERE

The general circulation of the Earth's atmosphere transports heat from the low latitudes around the equator to the high latitudes of the poles. In simplest form, this redistribution of energy could be accomplished by one large convection cell flowing between the equator and the pole in each hemisphere. Heated equatorial air would rise and flow toward the poles at upper levels, becoming progressively cooler until reaching the poles, where it would sink and flow as cold air over the surface, becoming progressively warmer on its return to the equator. But the rapid rotation of the Earth complicates the process; it reduces the size of the convection cells and increases their number to three in each hemisphere, in the low (0°–30°), middle (30°–60°) and high (60°–90°) latitudes (Figure 8.4).

LO4 ENERGY TRANSFER IN THE OCEANS

About 24% of the solar radiation received by the Earth is used to evaporate water and begin the hydrologic cycle. The hydrologic cycle is a continuously operating distilling-and-pumping system (Figure 8.5). The heat from the Sun evaporates water, while plants transpire into the atmosphere (give off water vapour through stomata in their leaves). Moisture in the atmosphere condenses and precipitates as snow and rain. The water then flows under the pull of gravity as glaciers, streams, and groundwater, returning to the seas. This system is over four billion years old and the same water, for the most part, has run through the same cycle, time and time again.

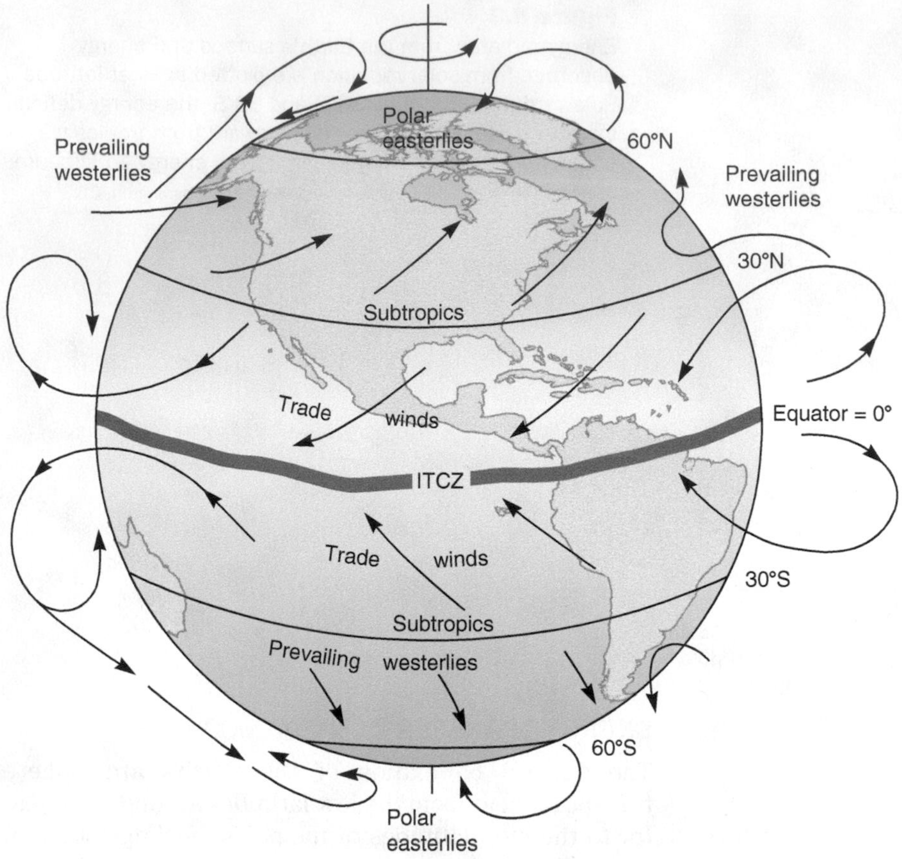

Figure 8.4
General circulation of the atmosphere. Warm air rises at the equator at the intertropical convergence zone (ITCZ) and sinks in the subtropics. Cold air at the poles sinks and flows toward the equator. The middle latitudes are transfer zones where warm air moves poleward and cold air flows equatorward.

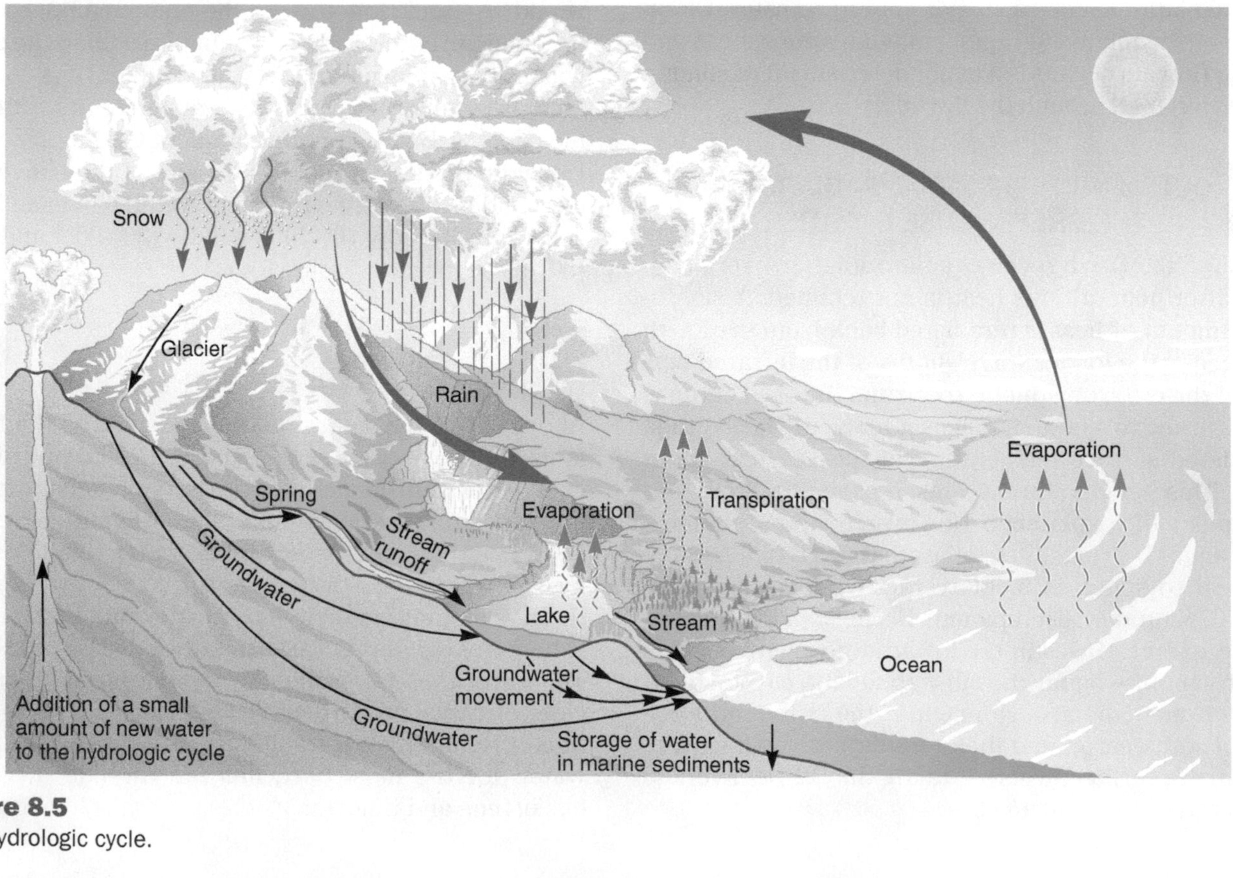

Figure 8.5
The hydrologic cycle.

Where is the water on the Earth held? The oceans hold the greatest share: 97.2% of the Earth's water, covering 71% of the Earth's surface. Three-quarters of the remaining 2.8% of all water is locked up in glaciers (Table 8.1).

Water is uniquely qualified to absorb and release solar energy (see In Greater Depth box: Water—The Most Peculiar Substance on the Earth?). The circulation of surface and deep waters distributes heat throughout the oceans and affects climate around the world. The surface circulation of water through the ocean basins is mostly driven by winds (Figure 8.6). Blowing winds drag on the sea surface and push against swells to move water. When the top layer of water moves, it drags on the underlying water layer, causing it to move, and so forth; this process moves water down to a depth of about 100 m. The flow directions of surface water are modified by the **Coriolis effect** (see In Greater Depth box: Coriolis Effect) and by deflection off continents. For example, look at the North Atlantic Ocean in Figure 8.6. Warm surface water is blown westward from Africa into the Caribbean Sea and Gulf of Mexico, where its westward path is blocked by land, forcing the seawater to escape northward along the eastern side of North America and over to Europe. The heat in this oceanic current, known as the Gulf Stream, adds significant warmth to the winter climate of Atlantic Canada and northwestern Europe. The Gulf Stream was first recognized by Benjamin Franklin who wondered why ships sailed faster from North America to Europe than on their return journeys.

TABLE 8.1

Where Is the World's Water?

Oceans	97.2%
Glaciers	2.15
Groundwater	0.60
Lakes (fresh and saline)	0.017
Soil moisture	0.005
Atmosphere	0.001
Rivers	0.0001

The oceans are layered bodies of water with less-dense water layers floating on top of progressively denser water layers. The density of water is increased by (1) lowering its temperature or (2) increasing its content of dissolved salts. Deep-ocean waters flow in an overturning circulation called thermohaline flow (Figure 8.7) (*thermo:* heat; *haline:* halite, the name for rock salt). Seawater density is increased (1) at high latitudes, where water temperature is lowered, (2) in the Arctic and Antarctic, where seawater is made saltier by salts excluded from sea ice, and (3) in warm climates, where evaporation leaves the

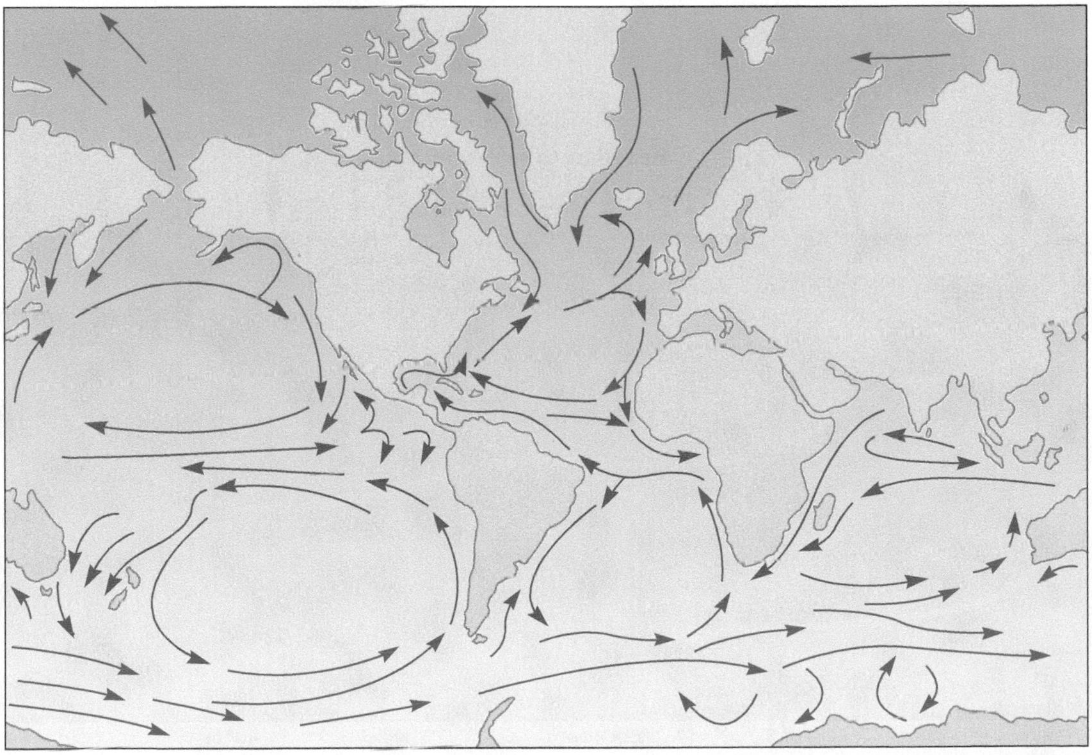

Figure 8.6
Circulation of the surface waters of the oceans (water depth < 500 m). Notice how the equatorial waters are deflected both northward and southward by the continents, thus sending warmer waters toward the poles. Also note that the only latitude not blocked by continents (60°S) has a latitudinal flow; this is the Southern Ocean and it encircles Antarctica. Red and blue arrows indicate warm and cold water, respectively.

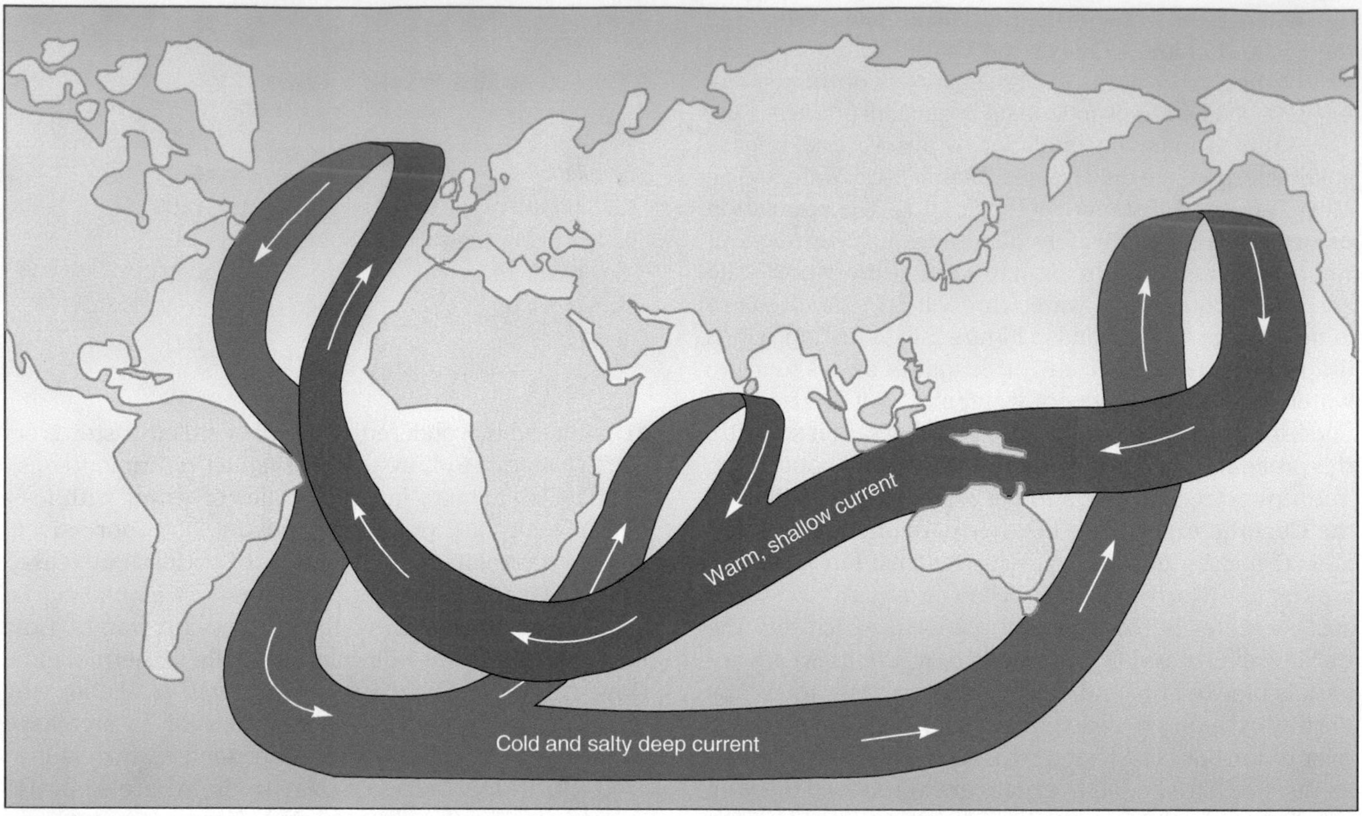

Figure 8.7
Circulation of deep oceanic currents (water depth > 500 m). This ocean flow system is the equivalent of 100 Amazon Rivers.

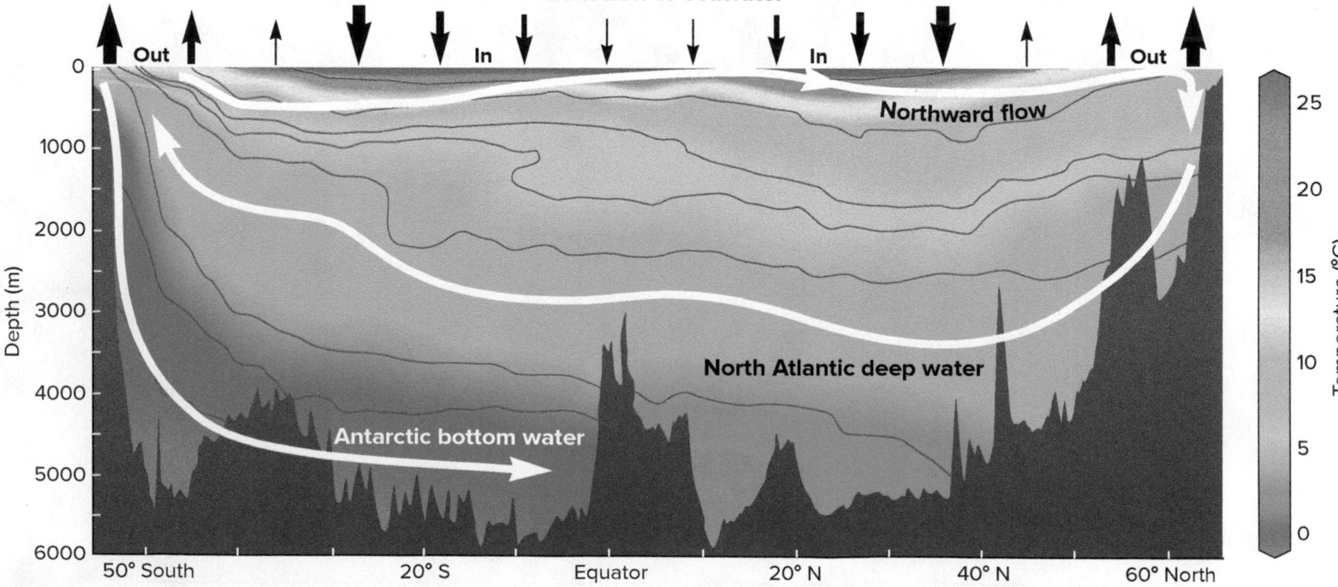

Figure 8.8
Water flow in Atlantic Ocean. Warm equatorial surface water flows north to the Arctic and releases heat to the atmosphere. As water density increases northward, water sinks and flows at depth to Antarctica.

Source: Adapted from G.Hegerl and N. Bindoff, *Science*.

IN GREATER DEPTH

Water—The Most Peculiar Substance on the Earth?

It is an understandable human trait to consider things that are common and abundant as being ordinary and those that are uncommon and rare as being extraordinary. The most common substance at the surface of the Earth is water. It is so much a part of our daily lives that it is all too easy to regard water as being ordinary. Nevertheless, water is a truly extraordinary chemical compound. Were it not such an odd substance, everything on the Earth, from weather to life, would be radically different.

1. Water is the only substance on the Earth that is present in vast quantities in solid, liquid, and gaseous states.
2. Water has a remarkable ability to absorb heat. It has the highest **heat capacity** of all solids and liquids, except liquid ammonia. Solar radiation penetrates through ocean water to depths of several hundred metres. Because water stores so much heat, the circulation of water in the ocean transfers immense quantities of heat.
3. Water has the highest heat conduction of all liquids at normal Earth surface temperatures.
4. Water has the highest **latent heat** of vaporization of all substances (Figure 8.9). At 100°C, it takes 2 260 000 joules (J) to evaporate 1 kg of water. This latent heat is carried by water vapour into the atmosphere and is released when water vapour condenses to liquid rain. Much heat is transported about the atmosphere as air masses circulate.
5. Water has the second highest latent heat of fusion, exceeded only by ammonia (Figure 8.9). When ice melts at 0°C, it absorbs 334 000 J/kg. When water freezes, it releases 334 000 J/kg.
6. Water is a bipolar molecule. The negative oxygen and positive hydrogen atoms bond together, yielding a molecule with a negative and a positive side (Figure 8.10). This bipolarity allows water to readily bond with **ions**.
7. Water has the highest **dielectric constant** of all liquids. This property tends to keep ions apart and prevent their bonding, thus maintaining a solution. This is why water has been called the universal solvent.
8. Water has the highest **surface tension** of all liquids.
9. Water expands by about 9% when it freezes. This is anomalous behaviour. Most substances shrink in volume as they get colder, and become denser. The maximum density for water occurs at about 4°C. Imagine what lakes and oceans would be like if ice were denser than liquid water and sank to the bottom.
10. Water vapour in the atmosphere ranges from near 0 to 4% by volume, and is measured as **humidity**.
11. Water vapour is the Earth's most abundant greenhouse gas.

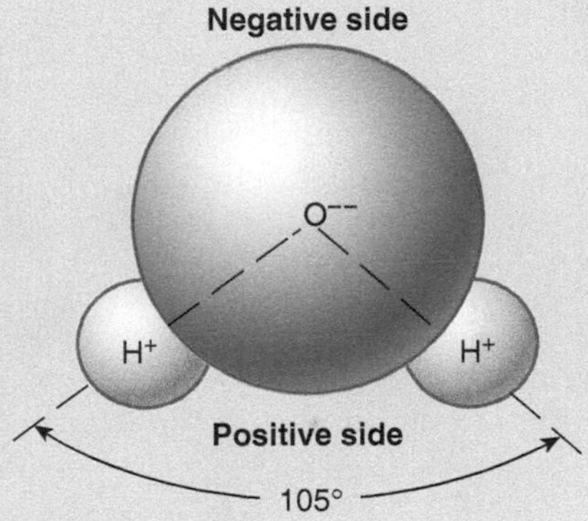

Figure 8.10
Water is a bipolar molecule exhibiting a negative and a positive side. This bipolarity greatly increases the activity of water.
Source: © Meteorological Service of Canada.

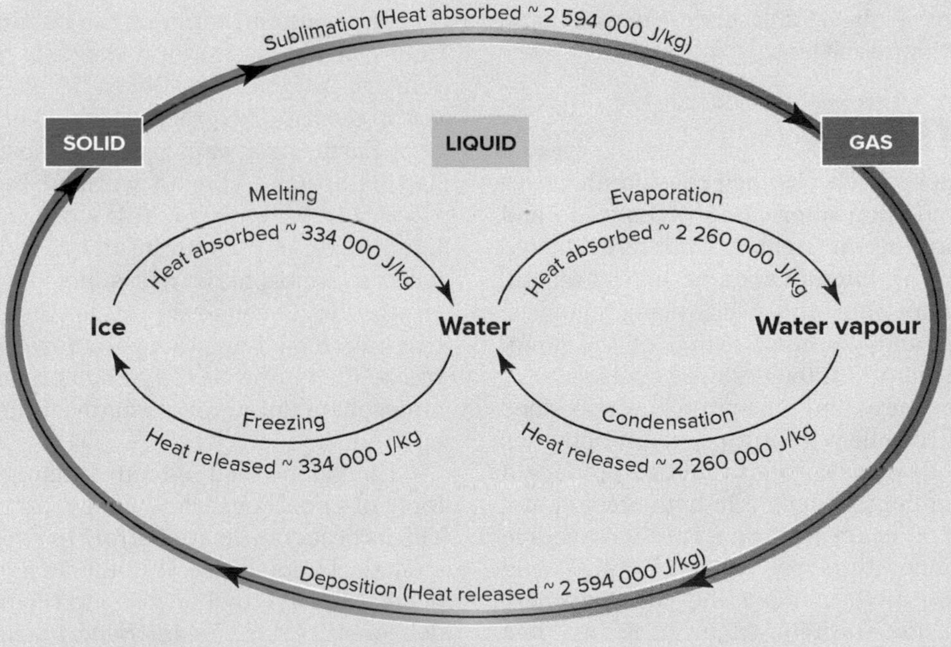

Figure 8.9
Water changing state from solid to liquid to gas absorbs heat. Water changing state from gas to liquid to solid releases heat. The energy transferred during a change of state is referred to as "latent heat."

IN GREATER DEPTH

Coriolis Effect

The Earth rotates rapidly and sets cold and warm air and ocean masses into motion. The velocity of rotation on the Earth's surface varies by latitude from 1600 km/h at the equator to 0 km/h at the poles (Figure 8.11). Because there are different rotation velocities at different latitudes, bodies moving across latitudes will follow curved paths.

An as analogy, think of a vintage vinyl record on a turntable. Looking down at the turntable, imagine taking a piece of chalk and making a mark from the center toward the edge of the record while it is spinning. You will note the chalk line will actually be curved. A force is pushing sideways, otherwise the mark would be a straight line. That force is called the "Coriolis" force.

On the Earth, the same phenomenon occurs. Bodies that travel around the planet experience the Coriolis force because the Earth is spinning. In the northern hemisphere, all moving masses will veer to the right when viewed down the direction of movement; in the southern hemisphere, moving masses will veer toward the left (Figure 8.11). The magnitude of the Coriolis effect increases with the horizontal velocity of the moving body and with latitude; it is zero at the equator.

The Coriolis effect is important in determining the paths of the surface waters of the ocean currents (for example, large wind systems (Figure 8.4), the flow patterns of surface waters in the North and South Pacific Ocean (Figure 8.6), and the primary circulation of air around hurricanes (Figure 10.10)).

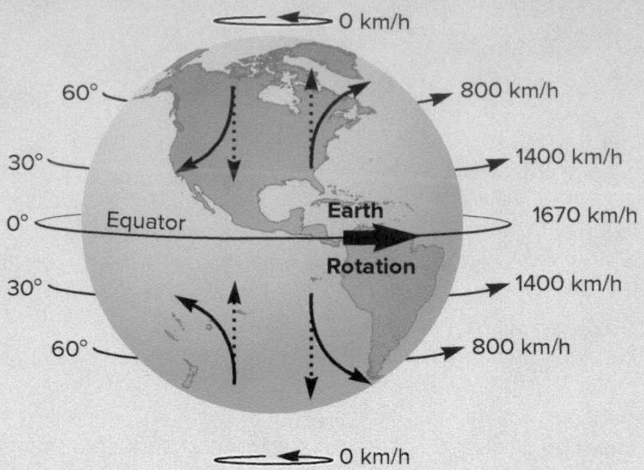

Figure 8.11
The Coriolis effect describes how air and ocean masses tend to follow curving paths because of the Earth's rotation. Looking down the direction of movement (dashed lines), paths veer toward the right (solid line) in the northern hemisphere and toward the left (solid line) in the southern hemisphere.

remaining seawater even saltier. Cooling in the Arctic increases ocean-water density, causing water to sink and flow at depth southward towards Antarctica (Figure 8.8). Most of the coldest and densest ocean water today forms in the high-latitude North-Atlantic Ocean and in the Southern Ocean.

Global Warming

The Earth's atmosphere has changed considerably over geological time, creating alternating greenhouse and icehouse conditions (see In Greater Depth box: Climate History of the Earth). Factors such as solar strength, variations in Earth's spin and orbit, plate tectonics, ocean circulation, and the composition of the atmosphere have been important temperature controls.

Global temperatures have been on the rise since 1700. During the twentieth century, human activities have contributed to this warming trend to produce a period of warming unprecedented in both amount and rate in the last 1100 years (Figure 8.12). The average global surface temperature rose 0.6° C (± 0.2° C). Did it warm continuously throughout the twentieth century? No. Most of the warming occurred in two time intervals: 1910 to 1944 and since 1977 (Figure 8.12). It appears that the early warming was largely due to a hotter Sun and a lack of global volcanism. Natural processes (changes in Earth's orbital patterns and solar activity) caused a net increase in temperature of about 0.2°C. Human activities were probably responsible for the remaining 0.4°C increase. Nowhere have changes been greater than in Canada—warming by twice the global average amount in half the time (Figure 8.13).

The warming trend of the twentieth century continues in the twenty-first century. The decade from January 2000 through December 2009 was the warmest on record. The greenhouse effect is not something new. Earth has always had an atmosphere and always had its surface climate warmed by the greenhouse effect, but the strength of the greenhouse has varied. Life processes play an influential role in the level of various atmospheric gases present (see In Greater Depth box: Greenhouse Gases). For example, during respiration all living things remove O_2 from their environment and release CO_2. Plants remove CO_2 from the atmosphere during photosynthesis and release O_2 as a by-product.

Human-induced climate change has become a topic of great concern to people all around the world. The largest coordinated effort to evaluate the risks of climate change caused by human activity is the Intergovernmental Panel on Climate Change (IPCC), which delivered its *Assessment Report 4* in 2007. The initiative involved more than 3700 authors and reviewers representing more than 130 countries. Their consensus marks a milestone and was judged to be so significant that they shared the 2007 Nobel Peace Prize (Table 8.2).

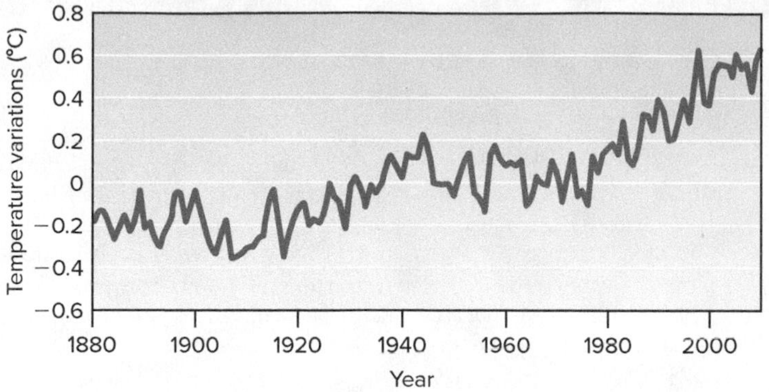

Figure 8.12

Observed changes of average global surface temperatures (1880–2010).

Source: X. Zhang, L.A. Vincent, W. D. Hogg and A. Niitsoo. *Temperature and Precipitation Trends in Canada during the 20th Century. Atmosphere—Ocean*, Vol. 38(3): 395–429. 2000 (updated 2005 and 2010).

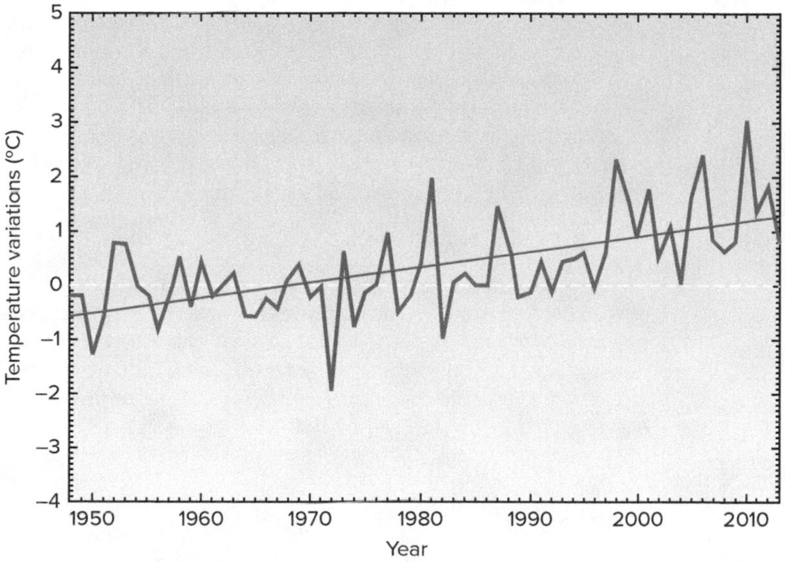

Figure 8.13

Annual Canadian temperature variations from the 1961–1990 average (1948–2013). The blue line shows the long-term trend.

Source: © Her Majesty The Queen in Right of Canada, Environment Canada, 2014. Reproduced with the permission of the Minister of Public Works and Government Services Canada.

TABLE 8.2

Climate Consensus for Twenty-first Century

- Warning of Earth's climate is unequivocal.
- Most of the increases in global temperatures since 1950 are very likely (>90%) due to human greenhouse-gas emissions.
- Atmospheric concentrations of CO_2, CH_4, and N_2O have increased markedly as a result of human activities since 1750 and now far exceed preindustrial values of the past 650 000 years.
- The probability that global warming occurs by natural changes alone is less than 5%.
- World temperatures could rise between 1.1° and 6.4°C during the twenty-first century.
- There is a probability greater than 90% of more frequent warm spells, heat waves, and heavy rainfall.
- There is a probability greater than 66% of increased droughts, tropical cyclones, and extreme high tides.
- Sea level will probably rise 18 to 59 cm.
- Past and future CO_2 emissions will continue to contribute to warming and sea-level rise for more than 1000 years.

Source: IPCC *Assessment Report 4* (2007).

LO5 Climate Observations and Predictions

OBSERVATIONS

Not only have average temperatures in Canada shown a sustained increase since the middle of the twentieth century (Figure 8.13), but the same is true for summer and winter precipitation (Figure 8.18). The hydrologic cycle has become more active. Temperature and precipitation are two basic meteorological variables that, in turn, influence large-scale phenomena such as ice coverage and sea levels.

Arctic sea ice melts back each summer, and reaches its smallest geographical extent in August or September each year. Following most summers, the ice cover grows back, usually reaching its highest extent and thickness in March. For 30 years, until about 2002, the average sea ice extent in late summer was 7.7 million square kilometres, declining about 7% per decade (Figure 8.19). Since then, the rate of ice decay has accelerated dramatically. In 2012, Arctic sea ice reached its lowest extent on record since aircraft reconnaissance of ice cover in the 1950s and the start of satellite measurements in 1979, with a mere 4.10 million

IN GREATER DEPTH

Climate History of the Earth

Throughout Earth's history, climate has swung like an irregular pendulum between cold and warm eras (Figure 8.14). Climatic cycles can be found at any timescale we choose to examine.

Time Scale in Millions of Years: Ice and Torrid Ages

Late Paleozoic Ice Age

One of the major Ice Ages in Earth's history began around 360 million years ago and lasted until 260 million years ago. For a glacial interval to last so long, broad-scale and long-lasting conditions are required. The major factors appear to be changes in the shapes, sizes, and orientations of the continents and oceans.

1. An initial, absolute requirement for an Ice Age is having one or more large continental masses near the poles. A polar landmass is necessary to collect the snowfall that allows the build-up of immense ice sheets that grow to a thickness of three kilometres and bury continents. In Late Paleozoic time, the continents were largely united as the single landmass Pangaea. The southern portion of the Pangaea super-continent is Gondwanaland; it moved across the south-polar region and was progressively covered by major ice sheets.
2. The geological record shows that Ice Ages are favoured when oceanic circulation is more longitudinal (north–south) than latitudinal (east–west). When the continents are aligned in a north-south direction, they allow warm equatorial waters to travel toward the poles, where evaporation can form the clouds that yield the snowfall that builds up on polar landmasses as glaciers. The continents had a north–south alignment during Late Paleozoic times, as they do today in the current Ice Age.

Why did the Late Paleozoic Ice Age end? Possibly because Gondwanaland began to break up and disperse. As the continents moved apart, ocean circulation patterns around the world were changed. Warm waters stayed near the equator, and cold waters encircled the poles, drastically reducing the moisture supplied to polar landmasses. Additionally, when continents move away from the poles, no platform exists for the accumulation of snow and the building of glaciers.

Late Paleocene Torrid Age

There was more heat in the Paleocene oceans and atmosphere 65 to 55 million years ago than at any time since. Most of Canada was covered by either tropical or subtropical climates. Along the coastal zones, subtropical conditions existed above the Arctic Circle, as shown by the fossil crocodiles and palm trees that have been found there. Several factors apparently combined to turn up the heat.

1. The equatorial zones were largely covered by oceans, allowing more absorption of solar heat.
2. As oceans warmed, areas covered by snow and ice decreased, exposing more land. While snow and ice reflect the Sun's rays, land absorbs heat.
3. Enormous outpourings of lava from the opening North Atlantic Ocean are likely to have released large volumes of gases to the atmosphere, which may have increased global warming via the greenhouse effect.
4. The oceans changed their style of density differentiation. The densest waters might have been tropical waters that had become saltier due to evaporation. These warm, salty waters apparently sank, warming up the oceans from surface to bottom.

What was responsible for the final increase in warmth? The warming of ocean bottom waters by about 8°C caused melting of icy **methane hydrates** on the seafloor over a 10 000-year-long interval about 55 million years ago. Over time, the methane oxidized to CO_2. As the CO_2 was withdrawn and used by living organisms, global temperatures finally began to decrease. Beginning from the temperature peak at 55 million years ago, the Earth began the long-term cooling trend that has carried us into our current Ice Age.

Time Scale in Hundreds of Thousands of Years: Glacial Advance and Retreat

The emerging story for the last one million years is of worldwide glacial advances that last about 100 000 years followed by retreats termed "interglacials" that take place more rapidly—over periods of a few thousand years.

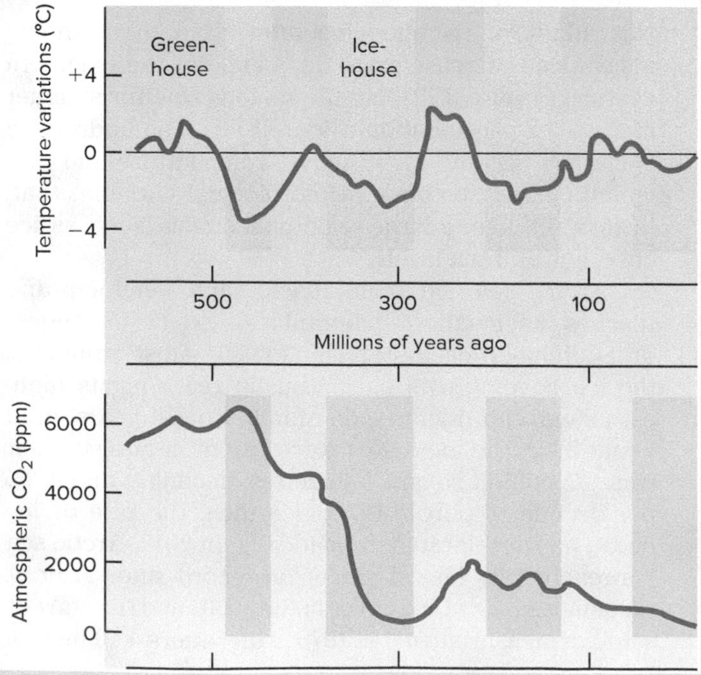

Figure 8.14
Five hundred million years of climate change and atmospheric CO_2 concentrations. The Earth's climate alternates between greenhouse and icehouse conditions that are controlled by a variety of factors. The horizontal reference line in the top graph is the current global average temperature.
Source: Veizer, J. (2005). Celestial climate driver: a perspective from four billion years of the carbon cycle. *Geoscience Canada*, 32, 13–28.

continued

The cause of these cycles lies in the peculiarities of the Earth's spin and its orbit around the Sun, first described by Serbian astronomer Milutin Milankovitch in the 1920s and 1930s. **Milankovitch theory** explains that glaciers advance and retreat due to variations in solar radiation received at high latitudes during summer and that these variations are due to changes in Earth's eccentricity, tilt, and wobble. At present, the eccentricity and tilt (23.5°) both contribute to cooling while the wobble works to warm the climate.

Time Scale in Thousands of Years: Variations Since the Last Glaciation

Even during the heart of the latest Ice Age glacial advance, there have been spikes of warmer temperatures. Look at the temperature conditions over the past 20 000 years (Figure 8.15): (1) conditions began to warm, (2) the warming was interrupted by the Older Dryas cold stage, (3) the cold interval was suddenly replaced by the elevated temperatures of the Bølling period, (4) the higher temperatures deteriorated through the Allerød interval, (5) then temperatures plunged back into the depths of the Ice Age during the Younger Dryas stage from 12 900 to 11 600 years ago, and (6) the current interglacial period.

About 7000 years ago, average global temperatures were warmer and rainfall totals had risen. At this time, known as the "climatic optimum," even North Africa had enough rainfall to support civilizations. Since then, there has been a 7000-year-long lowering of global average temperature totalling about 2°C. However, the cooling trend has had several smaller cycles of glacial expansion and contraction superimposed on it.

Looking at Figure 8.16 reveals a warm period from about 1000 to 1300 CE referred to as the **Medieval Maximum**. During this time, the coastal plains of Greenland were settled by Europeans who farmed the land. In England, wine grapes were grown and harvested. But this did not last.

The **Little Ice Age** affected Europe from about 1400 to 1900 CE. Late in the Little Ice Age, part of northeastern Canada had accumulated permanent snowfields and the beginning of an ice sheet. Cold winters in Europe led to shorter growing seasons, with reduced crop yields leading to local famine. Climatic conditions during the Little Ice Age were far from constant as smaller-scale warmings and coolings occurred. One colder interval between 1645 and 1715 CE is known as the **Maunder Minimum**. During this time, minimal sunspot activity was noted by astronomers and it is estimated that the Sun may have been 0.25% weaker (Figure 14.43).

Our current Ice Age is not over. We live during one of the coldest intervals in Earth history, despite the current glacial retreat. About 10% of the continents today remain buried beneath about 25 million cubic kilometres of ice, primarily on Antarctica and Greenland. Based on the previous records of glacial cycles, it can be predicted that our "warm" interglacial period will come to an end within the next few millennia at most. Canada as we know it will cease to exist as it becomes buried under kilometres of ice, spanning thousands of square kilometres.

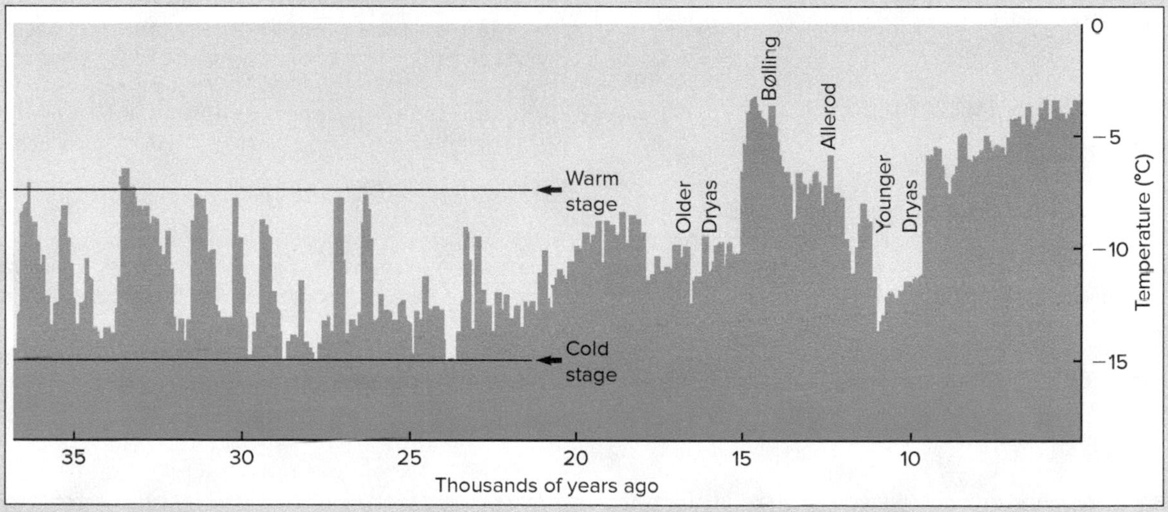

Figure 8.15
Air temperature over the Greenland continental glacier over the last 35 000 years.

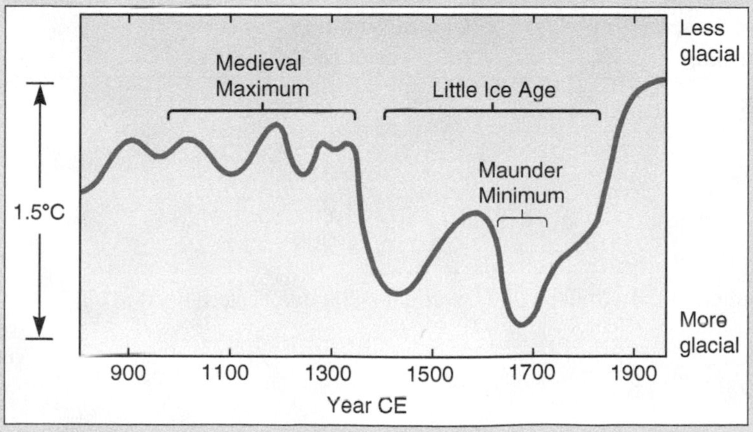

Figure 8.16
Climate of the last 1000 years, based on European winters.

Source: Data from J. Imbrie, and K. P. Imbrie, *Ice Ages*, 1979; Harvard University Press, Cambridge.

IN GREATER DEPTH

Greenhouse Gases

What greenhouse gases are we adding to the atmosphere now? Carbon dioxide, methane, nitrous oxide, ozone, and several industrially produced gases including the chlorine- and fluorine-bearing chlorofluorocarbons. Table 8.3 lists these greenhouse gases, ranks how responsible each has been for greenhouse warming, and assesses the relative ability of each gas to trap heat via the **global warming potential (GWP)** of the gas compared to carbon dioxide.

Water Vapour

Water vapour is a vast, natural control on temperature and climate. As the atmosphere warms, more water vapour can be absorbed into the warmer air in a positive feedback cycle that leads to ever greater warmth. The warmer the air, the greater the percentage of water vapour it can hold, and this includes the warmer air resulting from the CO_2 and CH_4 put into the atmosphere by human activities.

Carbon Dioxide (CO_2)

Since the late 1940s humans have been changing the CO_2 concentration in the atmosphere by burning tremendous volumes of plants, both living (trees and shrubs) and dead (coal, oil, and natural gas). About 8 gigatonnes (1 gigatonne equals 10^9 tonnes) of carbon are returned to the atmosphere each year by these processes. The human contribution is small compared to the natural fluxes between the atmosphere and ocean, and between the atmosphere and continents, each of which exchanges in excess of 300 gigatonnes annually (Figure 8.17). They may be enough, however, to trigger climate shifts that cause major problems.

Methane (CH_4)

The global warming potential of **methane** is 21 times greater than that of carbon dioxide. Air trapped in glacial ice tells us that methane concentrations in the year 1750 were about 700 parts per billion (ppb), but they have risen more than 150% since then. The increase in atmospheric methane was slow in the nineteenth century and rapid in the twentieth century. About 30% of methane release occurs by natural decomposition, mostly in wetlands and secondarily via termites. About 70% of methane is given off by human activities, listed in order of decreasing importance: burning fossil fuels, growing rice, and maintaining livestock. Lesser amounts originate from landfills, burning wood, and rotting of animal waste and human sewage.

Remember that the hottest climate in the last 65 million years occurred when deep-ocean water warmed enough to melt icy methane hydrates on the seafloor, thus releasing a huge volume of methane gas into the atmosphere. If the warming of the deep oceans occurring today continues for enough decades to melt methane hydrates, then a warm climate could become a torrid climate.

Nitrous Oxide (N_2O)

Nitrous oxide is produced naturally by bacteria removing nitrogen from organic matter, especially within soils. Humans cause the release of nitrous oxide via agricultural activities, including the use of chemical fertilizers. The second important way humans release N_2O is by combustion of fuels in car and truck engines.

Ozone (O_3)

Ozone is a gaseous molecule composed of three atoms of oxygen rather than the usual two-atom molecule (O_2). Ozone in the stratosphere acts as a greenhouse gas, helping to warm the stratosphere. It is this heat that places the "lid" on the troposphere (Figure 9.3). Ozone is effective at absorbing ultraviolet (UV) radiation emitted by the Sun, thus partially shielding life from dangerous rays. The UV rays that do pass through the atmosphere and make it to the ground surface cause sunburn and skin cancer.

Ozone is also a principal component of the smog that chokes urban atmospheres. Our automobiles and industries emit gases, some of which react with sunlight to produce the ozone that makes our eyes water and lungs ache. Ozone in the stratosphere shields us from killing UV rays, but ozone in the air we breathe weakens us and shortens our lives.

Chlorofluorocarbons (CFCs)

Chlorofluorocarbons do not occur naturally. They are examples of gases produced solely by humans. CFCs are used as coolants in refrigerators and air conditioners, foam insulation in buildings, solvents, and other applications. Chlorofluorocarbons are not only greenhouse gases, but also contribute to the destruction of the protective ozone layer in the stratosphere. CFCs may remain in the atmosphere for a century, causing so many problems that international treaties have been signed restricting their use.

TABLE 8.3

Greenhouse Gases

Gas	Relative Percentage Responsible for Greenhouse Warming	Global Warming Potential (compared to $CO_2 = 1$)
Carbon dioxide (CO_2)	60	1
Methane (CH_4)	16	21
Nitrous oxide (N_2O)	5	310
Ozone (O_3)	8	2 000
Chlorofluorocarbons (CFCs)	11	~ 12 000

Note: Water vapour is not included because its concentration in the atmosphere is ever changing due to variations in air temperature.

continued

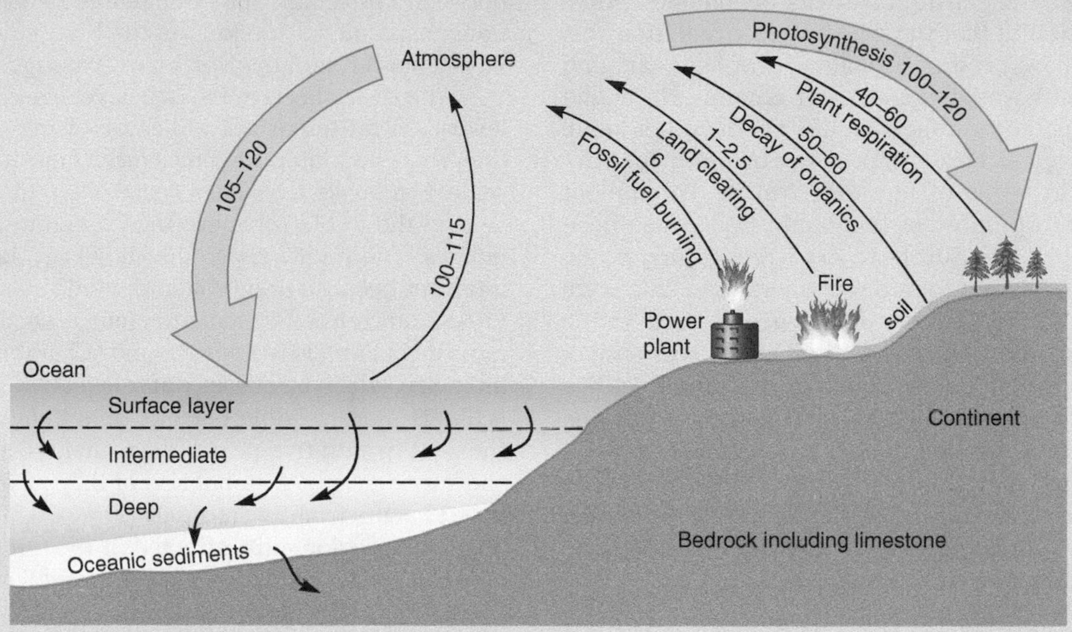

Figure 8.17

Annual cycle of carbon exchange measured in gigatonnes. Plants take in CO_2 from the atmosphere during photosynthesis. CO_2 is returned during plant respiration, during decay after death, and by burning of forests and fossil fuels. Near equilibrium exists between CO_2 in ocean surface water and the atmosphere. The ocean "pumps" some CO_2 into deep-water storage. Organisms remove dissolved CO_2 to build shells, which end up in sediments.

square kilometres. It is not only area covered by ice that is important but also sea-ice thickness and age, and both are decreasing. Thinner ice melts away faster, and younger ice melts more easily than older ice. In 1987, 57% of Arctic sea ice was five or more years old, and 14% was nine or more years old. By 2007, only 7% of Arctic sea ice was five or more years old, and none was nine or more years old. With heat going into the ocean, it is becoming more difficult for the ice to grow back.

Now the Arctic Ocean has growing areas of ice-free, dark seawater absorbing solar energy and warming rapidly. The global deep-water circulation is driven

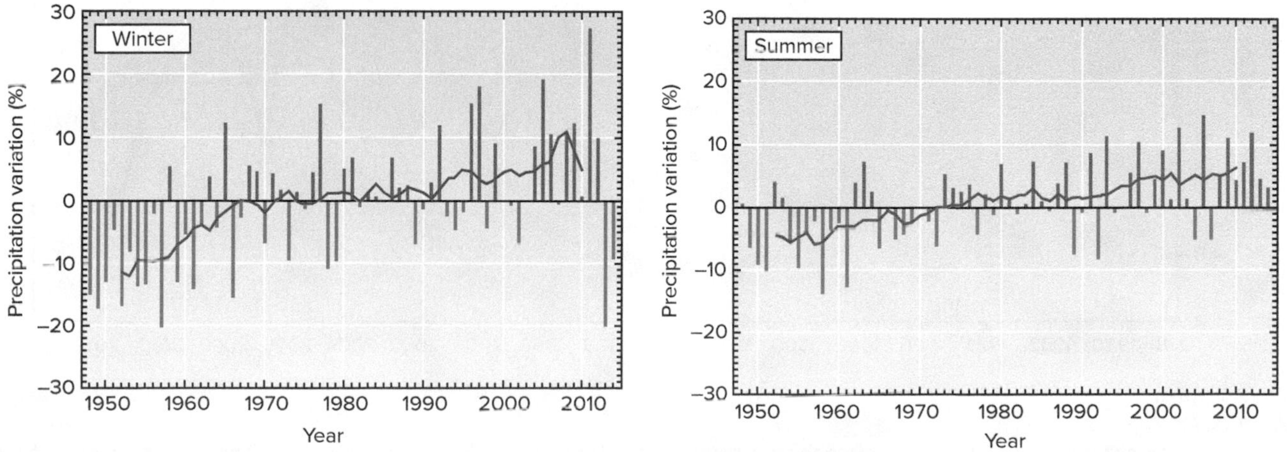

Figure 8.18

Winter and summer precipitation variations from the 1961–1990 average. The purple line shows the 9-year running average.

Source: C Her Majesty The Queen in Right of Canada, Environment Canada, 2014. Reproduced with the permission of the Minister of Public Works and Government Services Canada.

by density contrasts in seawater (Figure 8.8). As the oceans warm, the density contrasts become less, raising the possibility that the deep-water circulation system could slow or stop. Changing the heat-carrying ocean currents would cause major climatic shifts and far ranging ecologic effects on life. On the other hand, this might represent a business opportunity for Arctic Canada in terms of maritime traffic. Throughout recorded history, most of the Arctic Ocean has been covered by sea ice. European explorers sailing in the Arctic Ocean looking for a direct passage to Asia were blocked by sea ice for about 500 years, even in the warmest summer months. But the barrier was temporarily lifted in September 2007 when enough sea ice had melted to open the long-sought Northwest Passage (Figure 8.20), a meandering set of channels between Arctic islands. In 2009, two German ships made the first commercial trips through the Arctic carrying cargo from South Korea to the Netherlands. In summer 2010, the use of the Arctic Ocean as an intercontinental trade route grew as huge ships from Norway, Denmark, and other countries carried cargo through the Arctic. In summer 2011 shipping involved more nations, as both the Northwest Passage along Canada and the Northeast Passage along Russia were open. The numbers speak for themselves. The sea distance between Rotterdam and Shanghai is 25 588 km via the Panama canal, 19 550 km via the Suez canal, but only 16 100 km through the Northwest Passage.

When ice sheets melt, sea levels rise. Global sea levels are an important indicator of climate because they represent integrated measurements at a planetary scale. Sea levels have been recorded in major ports all around the world for more than a century using tidal gauges. The tidal gauge data, however, is difficult to interpret because it is "contaminated" by several local effects not related to climate change such as tectonic movements and isostatic rebound (Chapter 2). Satellite altimetry, which measures water levels at a much larger scale, is more reliable but has only been available in the past twenty-five years. Nevertheless, satellite data show evidence of a global rise of 3.2 ± 0.5 mm/year in only 17 years from 1993 to 2009 (Figure 8.21). Southeast Asia is the region most affected. If the trend continues, consequences will be dire as only a small rise can have devastating effects on the densely-populated coasts of nations such as the Philippines and Indonesia.

On the global map of Figure 8.21, Canada's Pacific and Atlantic coasts show no increase or decrease in sea levels over the time period surveyed. The situation,

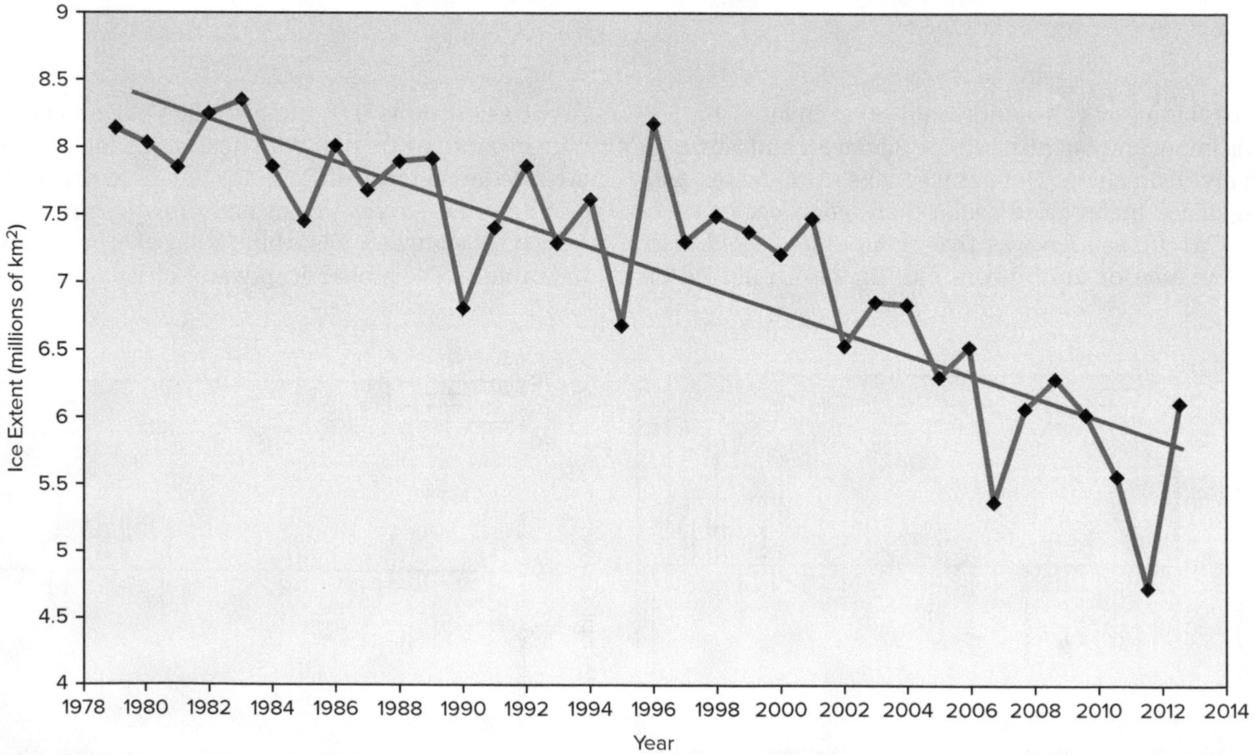

Figure 8.19

Arctic sea ice extent, measured in August of each year between 1979 and 2013 by satellite imagery. Scientists predict that the summer ice cover will likely continue to decrease until the ice disappears sometime in the twenty-first century, marking the first time in a million years the Arctic Ocean is ice free.

Source: National Snow and Ice Data Center.

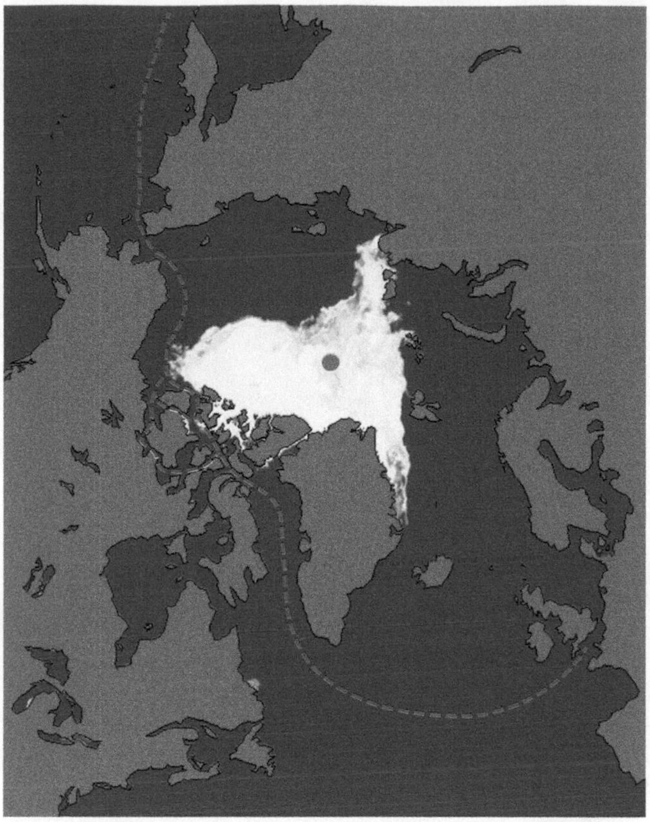

Figure 8.20
Sea ice on the Arctic Ocean, 16 September 2007. The channels of the Northwest Passage are in red.
Source: Modified from National Snow and Ice Data Center.

however, is more complicated in Atlantic Canada where tectonic movements contribute to a sea level increase of approximately 32 cm per century (Figure 8.22). This effect increases the region's vulnerability to erosion and flooding from strong waves and storm surges.

PREDICTIONS

What changes will occur to the climate in Canada (Figure 8.23) and worldwide in the twenty-first century? This question is addressed by constructing climate models. These complex computer simulations attempt to predict the behaviour of many variables through time, such as greenhouse gas and aerosol contents of the atmosphere, temperatures around the Earth, ocean warmth and circulation patterns, wind strengths and positions, cloud cover, and more. Since CO_2 is under much scrutiny, models are run with emission levels decreasing, increasing, and remaining stable. Added complications arise because a change in one variable may cause other variables to change. All the computer-model scenarios of the twenty-first century climate are provisional. As real measurements of climate continue to be made, and the amounts of data and time covered increase, the computer models will increase in accuracy.

All computer models forecast increasing Earth-surface temperatures. The greatest warming will occur in polar regions; this means that there will be less area

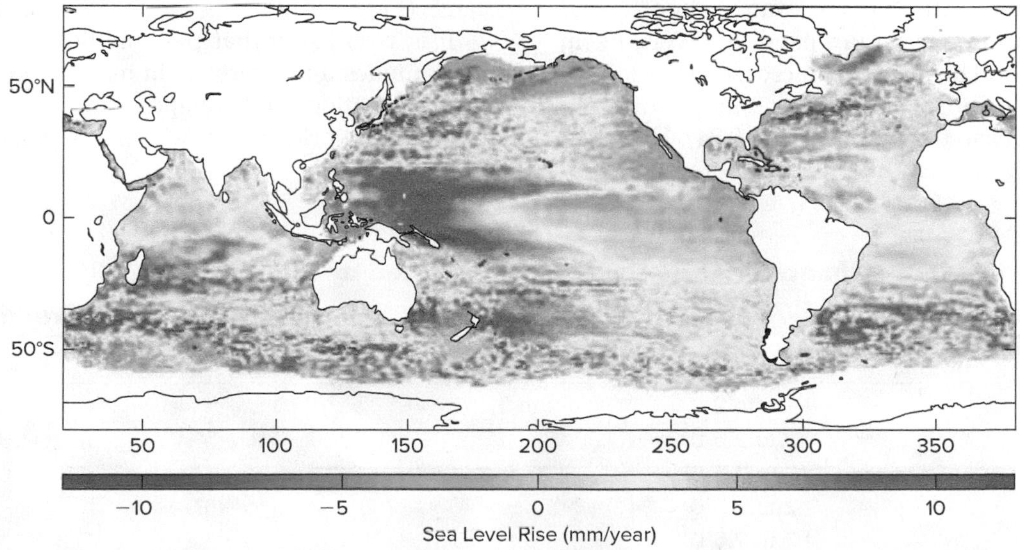

Figure 8.21
Change in sea level (1993–2009) from radar altimeter data from several satellites.
Source: Willis, J.K., D.P. Chambers, C.-Y. Kuo, and C.K. Shum. 2010. Global sea level rise: Recent progress and challenges for the decade to come. Oceanography 23(4):26–35, doi:10.5670/oceanog.2010.03.

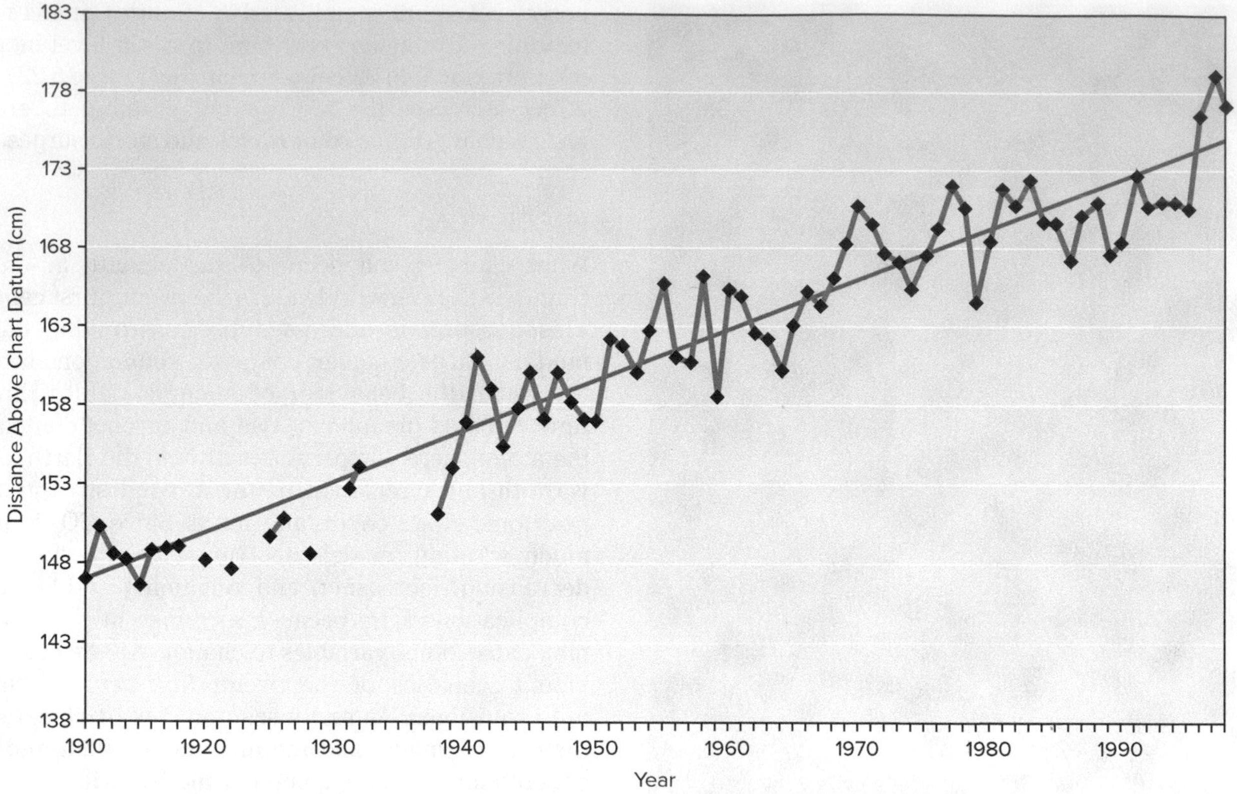

Figure 8.22

Annual mean water levels at Charlottetown, Prince Edward Island (1911–1998) in centimetres above a fixed reference plane. Similar rates of sea-level rise are reported for Halifax, Nova Scotia, New Brunswick's southeastern coast, and St. John's and Channel-Port aux Basques, Newfoundland.

covered by snow and ice, decreased sea ice, increased thawing of permafrost, disappearance of more mountain glaciers and late-summer water runoff, and increased evaporation from farmland. It is very likely that heat waves and drought will increase in the middle and low latitudes. In Canada, winter temperatures are predicted to increase the most (Figure 8.24). However, a major public health challenge will be to protect the population against extreme summer heat in urban islands (Figure 9.19).

It is very likely that precipitation will increase in high latitudes and decrease in most subtropical lands. As precipitation and temperature patterns change around the world, there will be regions of winners

TABLE 8.4

Summary of Regional Climate Change Scenarios Expected by 2050 (1971–2000 Baseline)

Major Regional Cities	Temperature Trend		Precipitation Trend	
	Summer	Winter	Summer	Winter
St. John's	+1.5 to 2°C	+2 to 2.5°C	0 to +5%	+5 to 10%
Montreal	+2 to 2.5°C	3.5 to 4°C	0 to +5%	+10 to 15%
Toronto	+2 to 2.5°C	2.5 to 3°C	0 to +5%	+10 to 15%
Winnipeg	+2 to 2.5°C	3.5 to 4°C	0 to +5%	+15 to 20%
Calgary	+2 to 2.5°C	2.5 to 3°C	0 to +5%	+10 to 15%
Vancouver	+1.5 to 2°C	+2 to 2.5°C	−15 to −20%	+5 to 10%

Source: Observations from ensemble climate models developed by CCCSN 2010.

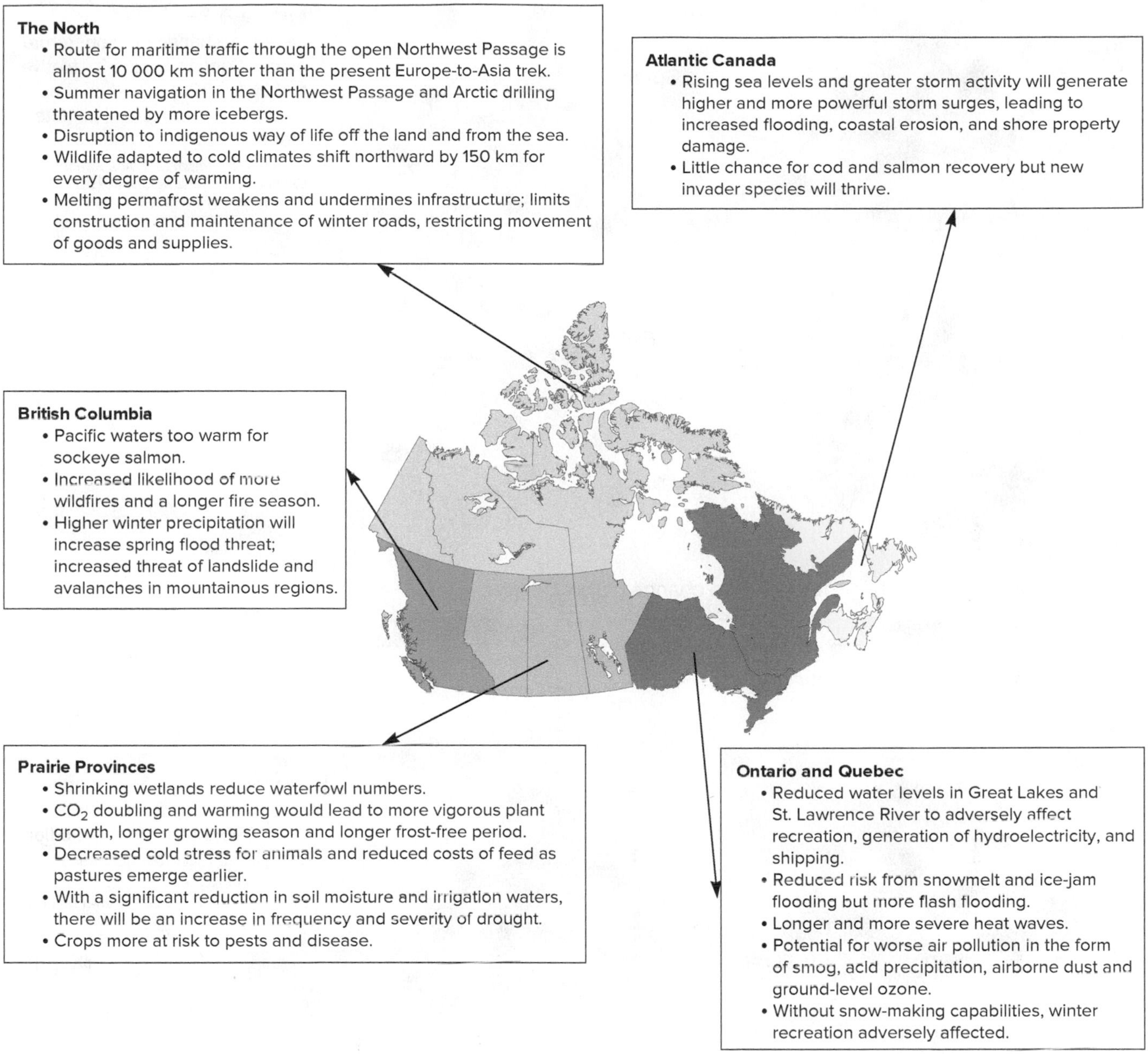

Figure 8.23
Potential effects of a warmer world on Canada.

and regions of losers. And a winner in one decade may become a loser in following decades as temperatures continue to rise and precipitation decreases, increases, or shifts location. In regions where temperature rises and precipitation falls, drought and famine might become problems. In Canada, models predict a more vigorous hydrologic cycle throughout the whole year in all regions except southern British Columbia (Figure 8.25).

Table 8.4 summarizes the results of recent simulations for several Canadian cities. Much has been said about Canada's aging municipal infrastructure, in particular about the water management systems that help to channel excess water in urban areas. Not only is this infrastructure in need of maintenance and repairs in many cities but it was originally designed for precipitation levels below what we are currently experiencing, let alone what the future has in store for us.

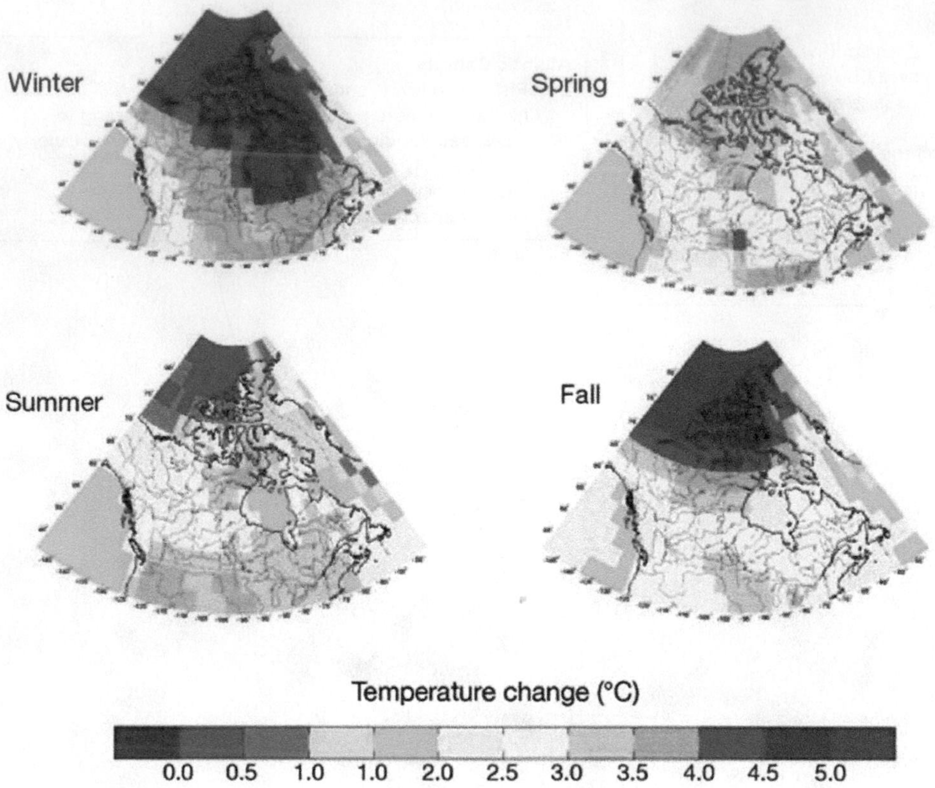

Figure 8.24

Seasonal change in temperature across Canada by 2050 (relative to 1961–1990) based on the median of seven global climate models.

Source: *From Impacts to Adaptation: Canada in a Changing Climate 2007*, Government of Canada (2007).

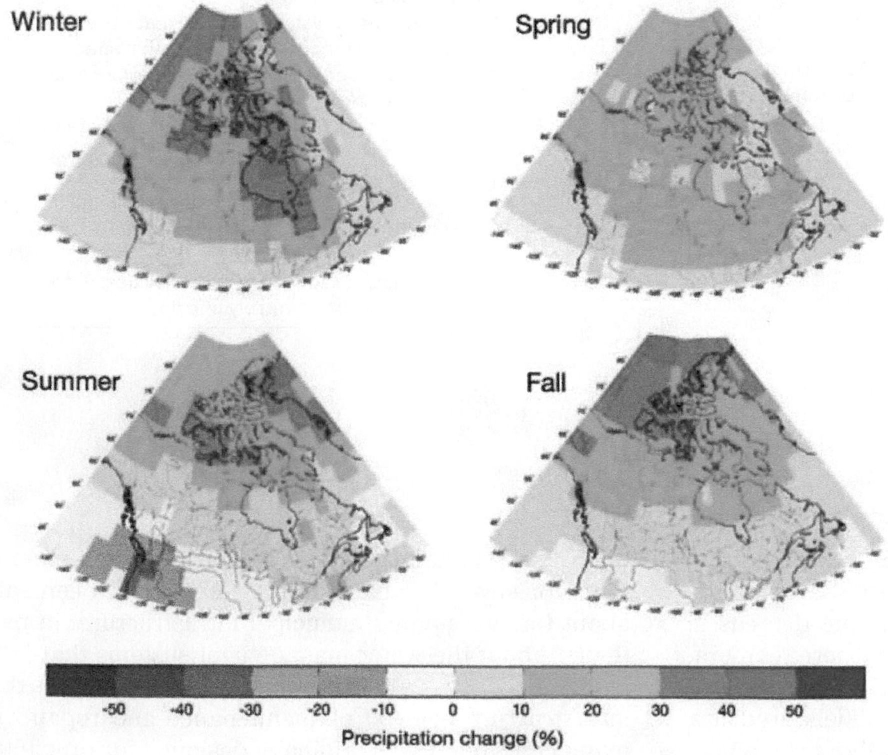

Figure 8.25

Seasonal change in precipitation across Canada by 2050 (relative to 1961–1990) based on the median of seven global climate models

Source: *From Impacts to Adaptation: Canada in a Changing Climate 2007*, Government of Canada (2007).

SUMMARY

- Long-term changes in atmospheric conditions are known as climate, while short-term changes are referred to as weather.
- The Sun is the largest contributor of energy to the Earth. The energy of the Sun and its interaction with Earth's atmosphere and oceans is responsible for climate and weather.
- Nearly one-quarter of the Sun's energy that reaches the Earth is used to evaporate water to begin the hydrologic cycle. Under the pull of gravity, snow and rain fall back to the land and then run downslope as glaciers, streams, and groundwater until the water is returned to the ocean to complete the cycle. While in motion, ice, water, and wind act as agents of erosion that wear down the land and deposit the debris into the ocean basins.
- The amount of solar energy received by the Earth varies over time and with latitude. The circulation of deep-ocean currents is the most important process in the global redistribution of solar energy on Earth.
- Many processes have affected climate throughout Earth's history, each with its own operating principles and time scale.
  - Torrid Ages are times when tropical and subtropical conditions cover much of the Earth. They commonly involve buildup of greenhouse gases and extensive shallow seas that absorb solar energy.
  - Ice Ages require large continents at the poles to support thick glaciers and continents aligned to deflect warm ocean water toward the poles, where it can evaporate and then fall as snow on land to build glaciers.
  - Advances and retreats of glaciers during an Ice Age occur on a timescale of thousands of years. These changes are largely due to variations in the orbit and rotation of Earth, affecting the amount of solar energy received.
- In the last thousand years, Earth's average surface temperature has fluctuated by about 1.5°C. During the twentieth century, humans increased global warming via the greenhouse effect as they poured carbon dioxide (CO_2), methane (CH_4), nitrous oxide (N_2O), ozone (O_3), and chlorofluorocarbons into the atmosphere. The twenty-first century will most likely bring much more warming.
- Canada's climate is changing. In addition to warmer temperatures, the hydrologic cycle is becoming more active and precipitation is increasing. Models predict that these trends will continue well into the twenty-first century.

Terms to Remember

albedo
climate
Coriolis effect
dielectric constant
global warming potential (GWP)
greenhouse effect
heat capacity
humidity
ions
latent heat
Little Ice Age
Maunder Minimum
Medieval Maximum
methane
methane hydrates
Milankovitch theory
ozone
surface tension
weather

Questions for Review

1. How does the amount of energy flowing from the interior of the Earth compare to the energy received from the Sun?
2. What are the differences between climate and weather?
3. Climate is related to amount of solar radiation received on Earth. How is incoming solar radiation affected by continental ice sheets? Elevated levels of atmospheric CO_2?
4. Explain how the hydrologic cycle operates. What are the roles of the Sun and gravity?
5. What properties make water so peculiar?
6. What causes glacial advances and retreats during an Ice Age?
7. Name six greenhouse gases. How do they cause Earth's average surface temperature to rise?
8. How much did global surface temperature rise in the twentieth century? How much is temperature projected to rise in the twenty-first century?

Questions for Further Thought

1. How does the Earth compare with other rocky planets in its energy balance?
2. How does the lack of atmosphere or oceans affect the surfaces of other rocky planets?
3. What are the consequences of changing the chemical composition of the lower atmosphere due to pollution or the greenhouse effect?
4. What changes in the natural environment are likely to happen in the next 40 years? How might your life change because of them?

5. Humans are causing global warming by burning wood, coal, natural gas, and oil and thus returning CO_2 to the atmosphere. What global changes may result?
6. What would be the global effect of melting the Greenland ice sheet? What would happen to coastal cities in Atlantic Canada?
7. What natural hazards are exacerbated by increasing temperatures? Increasing precipitation?
8. Will there be economic advantages to a warmer Canada in the future?

Interesting Websites

- Canada's Action on Climate Change, Environment Canada
  http://www.climatechange.gc.ca/
- Climate Change Adaptation Project (Canada)
  http://adaptnowcanada.ca/
- *From Impacts to Adaptation: Canada in a Changing Climate 2007*, Government of Canada (2007)
  http://www.nrcan.gc.ca/sites/www.nrcan.gc.ca/files/earthsciences/pdf/assess/2007/pdf/full-complet_e.pdf
- Climate Monitoring, National Oceanic and Atmospheric Administration, United States
  http://www.ncdc.noaa.gov/climate-monitoring
- United Nations Framework Convention on Climate Change
  http://unfccc.int/

9

Severe Weather

The Elie, Manitoba, tornado of 22 June 2007, the strongest in Canadian history.
Source: Wikipedia Commons, GNUFD.

"We were walking home last night and the four houses that are gone, they're gone. It's totally flat and the bush, the trees that were all around them are broken off halfway up and stripped clean of branches."

—Henry Hudek, resident of Elie, Manitoba, inspecting damages after the passage of the 22 June 2007 tornado

Outline

LO1 Summarize the weather conditions that produce heat waves, storms and tornadoes.

LO2 Explain how a thunderstorm starts, matures, and dissipates.

LO3 Describe how a supercell thunderstorm can generate tornadoes, rain, lightning, and hail, all at the same time.

LO4 Describe how different air masses interact to form tornadoes.

The Rising Cost of Severe Weather

Weather kills. People die during heat waves or cold snaps, are struck down by random bolts of lightning, and are chased by tornadoes.

Based on an analysis of the worldwide frequency and distribution of natural disasters from 1988 to 1997, Munich Reinsurance Company concluded that almost two-thirds of the 6000 events recorded were storm- or flood-related. A similar analysis from the World Meteorological Organization in Geneva for the decade 1991–2000 revealed that the number of people affected by weather-related disasters averaged 211 million per year, seven times those affected by conflict, with 98% of the people affected living in developing countries.

Severe weather is expensive and getting costlier. And that trend is accelerating (Figure 9.1). According to insurers, 2005 was the costliest year ever, with record losses from weather-related disasters around the world totalling $200 billion. In Canada, weather-related natural disasters increased from 2 to 4 per year in Canada in the first half of the twentieth century to about 15 per year between 1990 and 2010 (Figure 1.8). Costs are also increasing, as seen in the many recent entries in Table 1.4.

LO1

Meteorology 101

THE LAYERING OF THE LOWER ATMOSPHERE

Gravity pulls on the atmosphere. Nearing the Earth's surface, air is increasingly compressed under the cumulative weight of the air layers above, and becomes progressively denser. About 75% of the atmosphere lies within its bottom ten kilometres.

The atmosphere of the Earth is separated into layers of different density. Most of "weather" occurs in the lowest layer of the atmosphere, the **troposphere** (Figure 9.3). The troposphere ranges from about 8 km thick at the poles to 18 km at the equator. The troposphere is warmer at its base and colder above, thus creating a basic instability as lower-level warm air rises and upper-level cold and dense air sinks. The density contrasts set off a constant mixing of tropospheric air that is part of our changing weather patterns.

The top of the troposphere, the **tropopause**, is a significant boundary where the cooling-upward trend reverses and the air begins to warm upward through the **stratosphere** (Figure 9.3). The temperature inversion acts as a barrier that confines weather to the troposphere. The stratosphere, which draws its name from its stratified condition where warmer air sits on top of cooler air, is a stable configuration. The stratosphere is home to cold, dry, and ever sunny conditions.

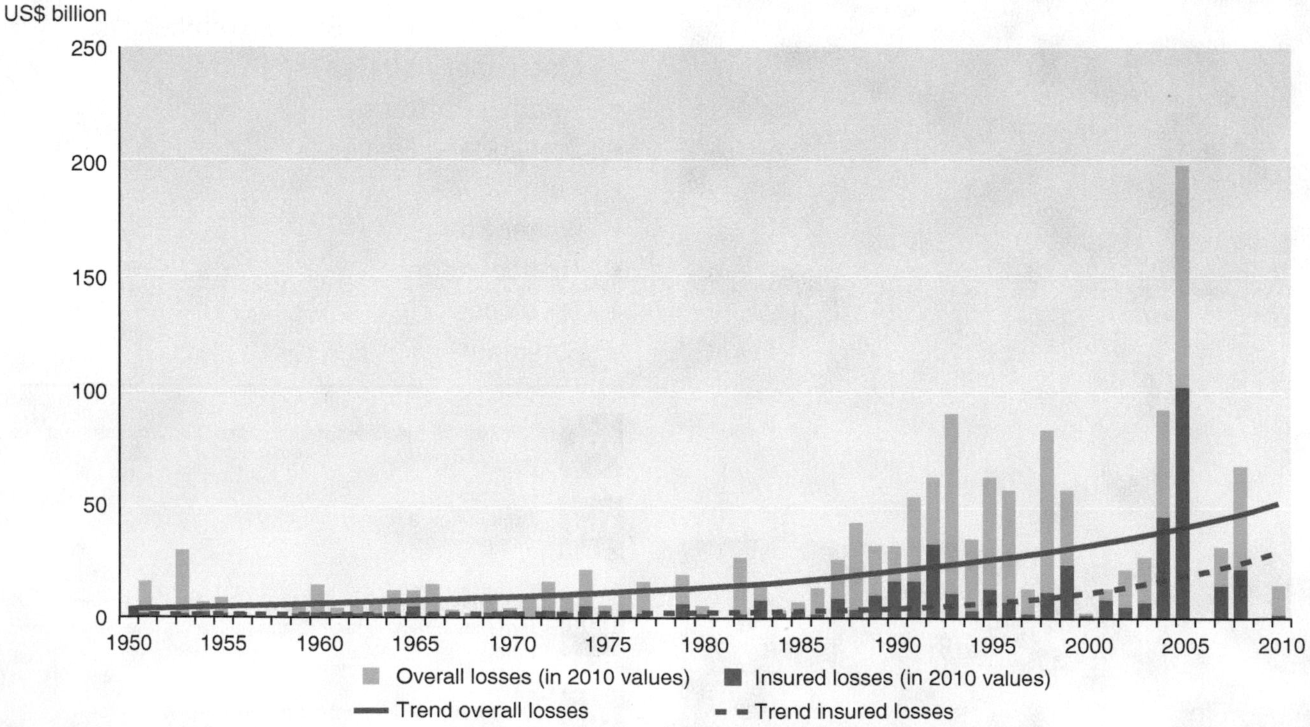

Figure 9.1
Dollar losses from weather-related disasters, 1950–2010. The 2005 peak coincides with Hurricane Katrina in the United States.
Source: Munich Reinsurance Company.

HUMAN FOCUS

David Phillips, Senior Climatologist, Environment Canada

I have been studying Canadian weather for more than 45 years! It is my passion. I was originally trained as a geographer and my ambition was to become a high school teacher. After my undergraduate degree at the University of Windsor, however, I joined the Meteorological Service of Canada following the recommendation of one of my professors. I continued to study towards my Masters' degree part-time at the University of Toronto. My research focus was the climate of the Great Lakes Basin, and I had the opportunity to go onboard ships to collect data and make observations. The work expanded to include marine waters across Canada collaborating with others in different government departments on such practical topics as siting deep water terminals. I felt I was making a contribution.

Over time I became more and more of a generalist, and started to make public presentations on the significance of weather and climate to Canada and Canadians. I started to realize how fascinated Canadians are with weather. Canada sure has a lot of weather and people are emotionally attached to it, not just because it is something to talk about but because it directly affects our lives and livelihood. In the early 1980s, the Treasury Board asked me where the most severe weather in Canada was. I studied data from 150 locations across the country, defined 17 subjective elements related to challenging weather conditions, such as "deep snow" and "freezing rain", and interviewed dozens of my colleagues who had spent time in various postings across the country. I came up with a climate severity index. My report got shelved. A journalist, however, presented my results as a battle between cities and wrote "Vancouver has the most depressing weather in Canada". That headline got the attention of the public, and I was interviewed on radio and television. Since then, science outreach has been an important activity of mine. I give approximately 50 talks per year to diverse groups. In a way, my classroom includes 35 million Canadians and my lifelong dream of being an educator has been fulfilled.

We do not feel climate because its changes are too slow. Instead we feel and see the weather. Severe weather is riveting; people are in awe of the power of nature. Observations show that climate is warming faster now than it has in a long time, and that weather is likely becoming more extreme. Severe weather events are becoming more intense, longer lasting, and affecting larger areas than in the past. It is not only climate, however, that has changed in the last 30–50 years, we as a society have changed. They are more of us, more wealth, and more technology-dependent people in the way of severe weather. That has increased the vulnerability of communities.

When I took my first course in climatology, the basic premise was that climate was stable. Oh it changed—every 100 000 years there was an Ice Age. It was said that the past was the guide to the future. We now realize climate has been changing at an unprecedented pace in the last few decades. In making operational decisions like planting crops we would probably be wiser to use the last 6 years instead of the last 60 years. We cannot prevent severe weather coming our way. Cleaning up after a disaster and returning to the status quo is not an option anymore because the future is not going to look like the past. What can we do? We need to build safer neighbourhoods taking into account our changing climate. All the disasters I have seen have a human signature. We should not be fatalistic. On the contrary, I believe this should motivate us to prepare proactively for the changes to come.

Figure 9.2
David Phillips
Source: Photo courtesy of David Phillips

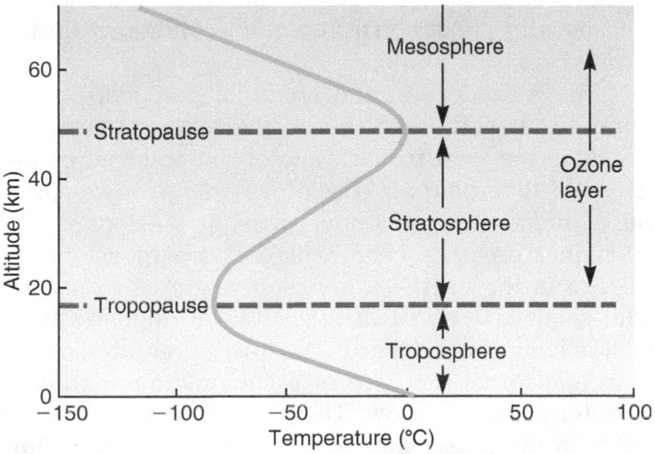

Figure 9.3
Cross-section through Earth's lower atmosphere. Ozone captures solar energy. The temperature inversion at the tropopause acts as a lid holding moisture and "weather" in the troposphere below.

HORIZONTAL AND VERTICAL MOVEMENTS OF AIR

Pressure within the atmosphere varies both horizontally and vertically. Air flows from areas of higher pressure toward areas of lower pressure, seeking an equilibrium condition. We call the horizontal flow of air wind.

The vertical movement of air is small compared to its horizontal motion. Vertically, air tends to flow from the higher pressures at the Earth's surface up through the progressively lower pressures high in the atmosphere. This tendency to flow upward from high to low pressure must overcome the opposing pull of gravity. How can air near the surface overcome the pull of gravity and rise? The most common way is through **adiabatic processes**. As heated air rises, it encounters progressively lower pressures, causing the air to expand and become less dense. The expanding mass of air has to do work to increase its volume and must use its own internal energy. The process of expanding causes adiabatic cooling, in which temperature decreases without the transfer of heat. Conversely, when cool air from aloft sinks into altitudes of greater pressure, the air is compressed and energy is converted to heat, causing the air temperatures to increase adiabatically. Adiabatic temperature changes produce cooling when air rises and expands in volume, and warming when air descends and compresses into a smaller volume.

Adiabatic cooling of rising air is a dominant cause of cloud formation. As rising air moves upward through ever-decreasing pressure, it expands and cools adiabatically about 10°C per kilometre of rise. As the air cools, it has less ability to hold water vapour; thus, its relative humidity increases. When the rising air reaches 100% humidity, excess water vapour condenses and forms clouds. When water vapour condenses, it releases the latent heat it absorbed when it evaporated. The released latent heat slows the rate of upward cooling to about 5°C per kilometre of rise.

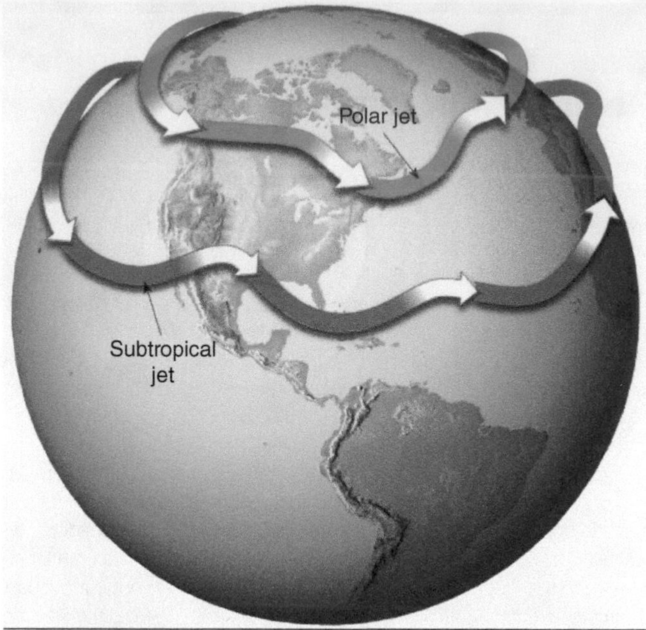

Figure 9.4
The subtropical (in red) and polar (in blue) jet streams of the northern hemisphere flow in meandering paths from west to east.

Source: Lutgens, Frederick K, Tarbuck, Edward J., *The Atmosphere: An Introduction to Meteorology*, 8th © 2001. Printed and electronically reproduced by permission of Pearson Education, Inc., Upper Saddle River, New Jersey.

Jet Streams

Jet streams are relatively narrow bands of high-velocity winds that flow at high altitudes from west to east, under the influence of the Earth's rotation. There are two main jet streams in each hemisphere, a polar jet and a subtropical jet (Figure 9.4). The most powerful and variable is the polar jet, which races from west to east at an average latitude of 55° and elevations of 10 to 14 km. During each hemisphere's winter, the atmospheric temperature contrasts between pole and equator are greatest, and each polar jet races its fastest. When polar jets reach speeds around 200 km/h, they have significant effects in moving heat and air masses, as well as in provoking storms.

A polar jet is a belt of winds about 1000 km wide and a few kilometres thick, flowing as quickly as 600 km/h in its central "core." Its path is ever changing, like that of a meandering river. In the northern hemisphere, the polar jet flows over Canada during the summer, when the warm air volume is greatest; during the winter, it migrates over the United States as the volume of cold air increases to its maximum.

ROTATING AIR BODIES

Rising warm air in the northern hemisphere creates a low-pressure zone, called a **cyclone**, that is fed a surface inflow of air that moves counter-clockwise (Figure 9.5). These winds blow counter-clockwise as the pressure gradient causes air to flow inward and the Coriolis effect deflects the airflow to the right (see In Greater Depth box: Coriolis Effect, in Chapter 8). The surface inflow of winds toward the low-pressure core feeds a large updraft of rising air that cools, forming clouds and possibly producing rainy weather, along with an upper-level outflow of air moving counter-clockwise.

Descending air in the northern hemisphere forms a high-pressure zone, called an **anticyclone**, accompanied by clockwise-blowing winds (Figure 9.5). The air flowing outward at the ground surface is replaced by sinking air from above. The descending air warms and usually creates dry and calm conditions on the ground.

The meanders in the polar jet can help create rotating air bodies. In the northern hemisphere, the bends in the west-to-east flow of the polar jet create areas of diverging air east of *troughs* of lower pressure, and regions of converging air west of *ridges* of higher pressure (Figure 9.6). A trough in the jet stream in the northern hemisphere refers to a bend that is concave northward, whereas a ridge is a bend that is convex northward. The lower-pressure zone at a trough forms the core of a cyclonic circulation, a counter-clockwise flow. The process is reversed at a ridge in the jet stream. Here, the upper-level airflow imparts a clockwise rotation about a high-pressure zone (Figure 9.6). Commonly, low pressure indicates clouds and rain, and high pressure indicates clear weather (Figure 9.7).

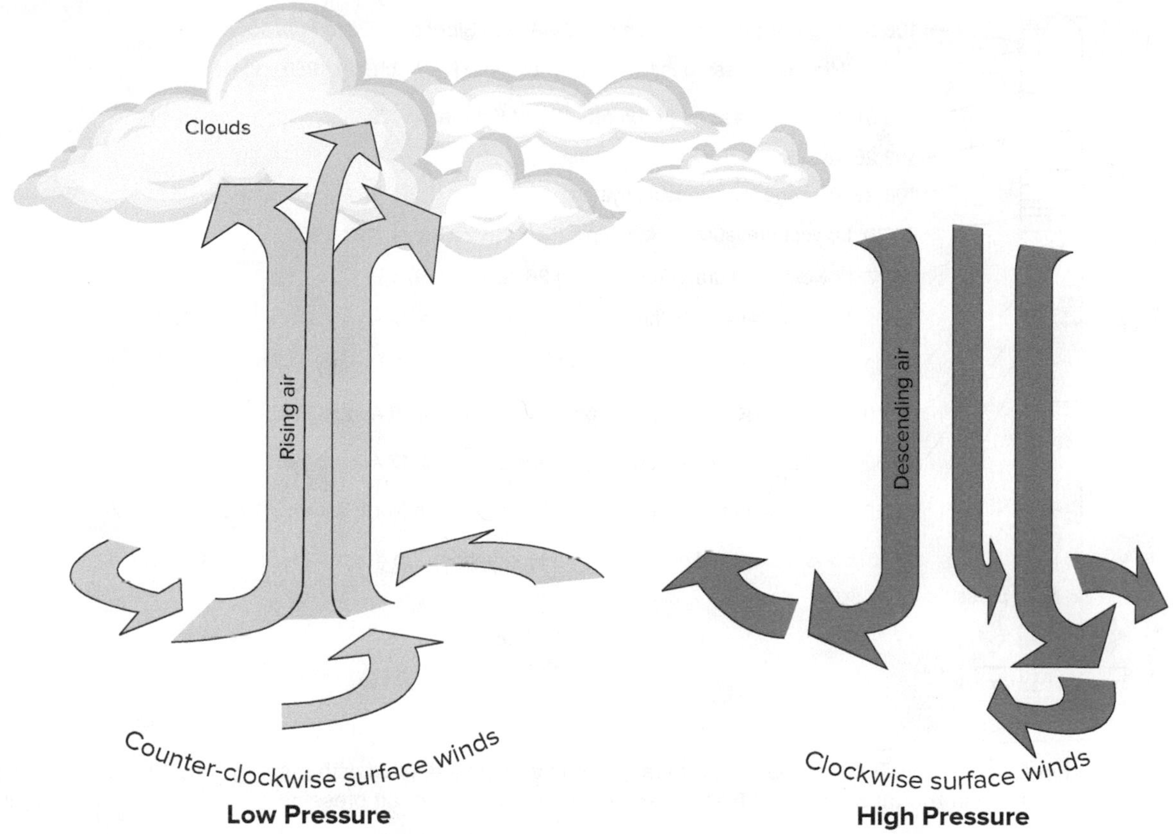

Figure 9.5
Air flowing counter-clockwise rises at a low-pressure zone in the northern hemisphere. Descending air at a high-pressure zone flows over the ground surface as clockwise winds.

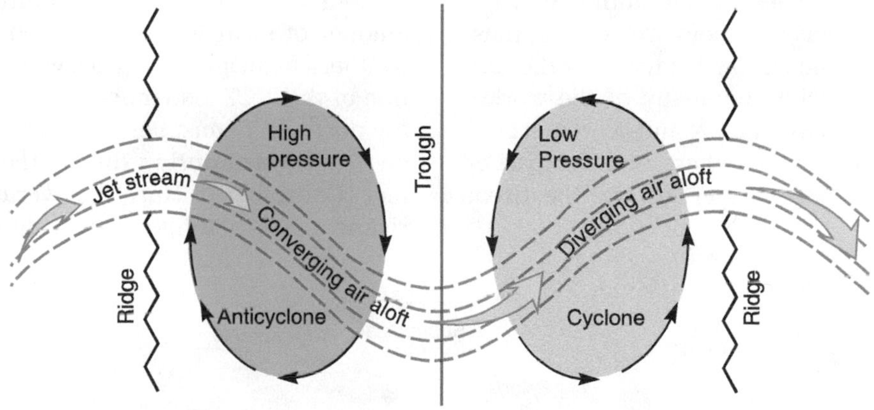

Figure 9.6
Influence of the polar jet in creating clockwise anticyclonic winds around a high-pressure zone and counter-clockwise cyclonic winds around a low-pressure zone.

Weather Patterns

PATTERNS ACROSS LATITUDES

The intense sunshine received in the equatorial belt powers huge air circulation patterns known as **Hadley cells** (Figure 9.8). Warm, moist equatorial air rises in giant columns to high altitudes, where it cools and drops its condensed moisture as abundant rain on the tropics.

After dropping rain on the tropics, the upper-elevation air is then cooler and drier; it spreads both north and south. Around 30°N and 30°S latitudes, the now-denser air sinks at the Subtropical High Pressure Zone, warming adiabatically as it descends and returns

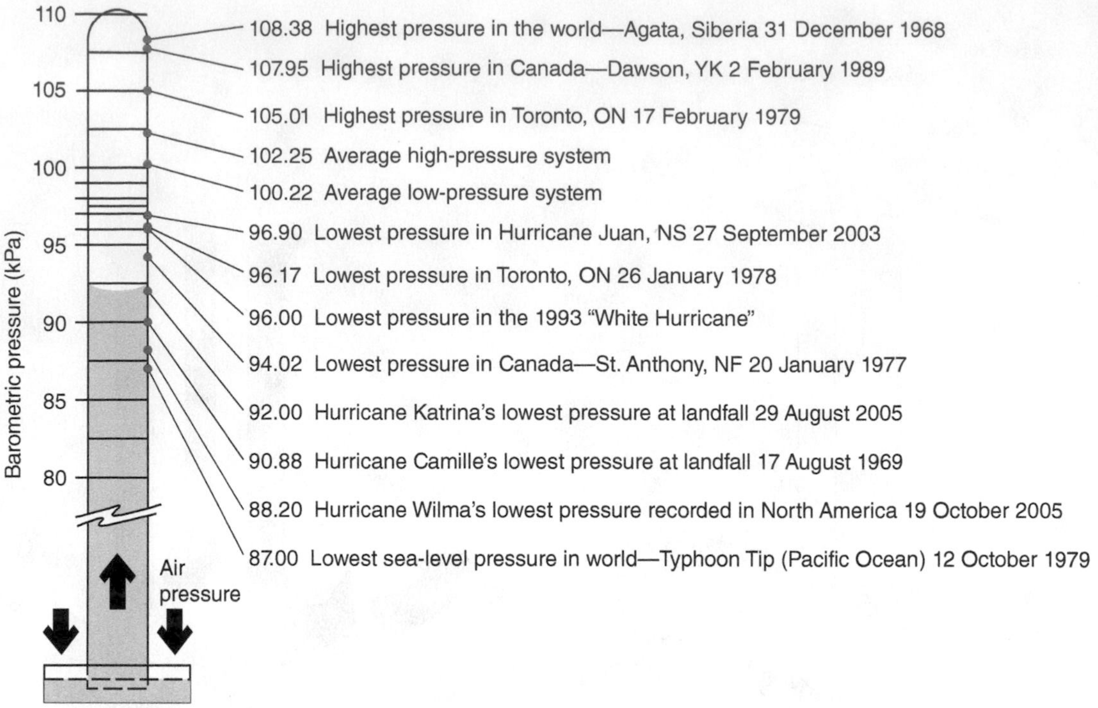

Figure 9.7

Air pressures recorded in a barometer. The barometer is a tube with one end closed, filled with mercury, and turned upside down in a dish of mercury. The mercury in the tube rises and falls depending on the amount of air pressure.

to the surface as a warm and dry air mass. Some of the descending air flows poleward as westerly winds (westerlies), and some flows equatorward as the trade winds (Figure 8.4). The warm air descending in the Subtropical High Pressure Zone has low moisture content; thus, precipitation is scarce. The warm, dry winds of the subtropical belts are responsible for many of the world's great deserts, located between 20°N and 30°N and 20°S and 30°S latitudes, such as the Sahara and Kalahari of Africa, the Sonora of North America, and the Great Australian Desert.

The Hadley cell circulation is completed where the trade winds from the northern and southern hemispheres meet in the tropics at the **Intertropical Convergence Zone (ITCZ)** (Figure 8.4). Because the amount of solar energy received in the northern and southern hemispheres varies with the seasons, the location of the ITCZ also moves; it shifts northward during the northern hemisphere summer (June to September) and southward during the southern hemisphere summer (December to March). Several North Atlantic hurricanes start their lives as thunderstorms in the ITCZ.

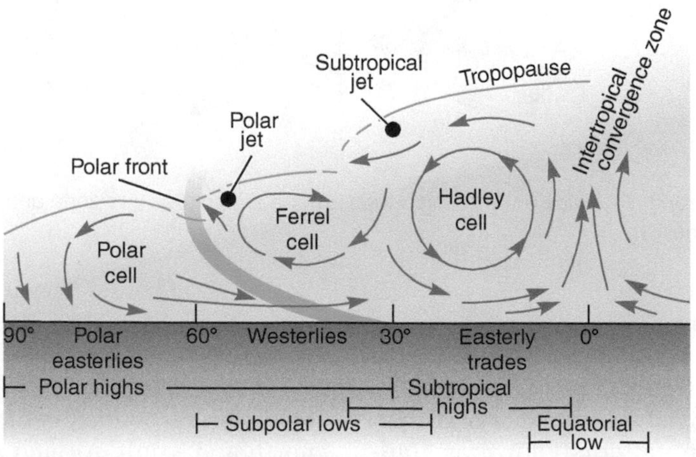

Figure 9.8

Cross-section of the air circulation between the equator and a pole.

Cold, dense air in the polar region flows along the Earth's surface toward lower latitudes in both hemispheres. When this airflow nears 60°N or 60°S latitude, the air has picked up enough warmth and moisture to rise via convection and help drive a thermal loop, the Polar cell, somewhat analogous to a Hadley cell (Figure 9.8).

The Hadley cell and the Polar cell are both thermally driven loops. The middle latitudes have neither a strong heat source nor a strong cold sink to drive an air-circulation loop. The middle latitudes feature a secondary air circulation, called the Ferrel cell, which exists between the Hadley and Polar cells and is driven by those adjoining cells (Figure 9.8). The middle latitudes are a turbulent zone where competing tropical and polar air masses transfer their energies back and forth as the seasons vary, commonly creating severe weather conditions.

Air Masses and Fronts

The **air masses** that move across North America come mainly from several large source areas (Figure 9.9). Polar air masses are cool to cold, while tropical air masses are warm to hot. Air masses that gather over land are dry, whereas those that form over water are moist. The dominant wind direction is from west to east under the influence of the Earth's rotation. Thus, air masses that build over the northern Pacific Ocean have a much greater chance of affecting North America than those that form over the North Atlantic Ocean.

The boundaries between different air masses are called **fronts**. (The term *front* came out of World War I, from the battlefronts where armies clashed.) A front is a sloping surface separating air masses that differ in temperature and moisture content (Figure 9.10). The advance of a cold front acts like a wedge, lifting warm air up to higher altitudes (Figure 9.10a). When rising warm air is moist and unstable, it often forms tall clouds that may grow into thunderstorms. A warm front flows up and over a cooler air mass along a gentle slope (Figure 9.10b). The warm air cools as it rises along the broad and gentle front, commonly producing widespread clouds and drizzle. The largest frontal system in the northern hemisphere separates cold polar air from warm tropical air along the polar front (Figure 9.8).

ANNUAL WEATHER PATTERNS

Air pressure and wind patterns on Earth show some consistency by hemisphere and season over a one-year cycle (Figure 9.11). The southern hemisphere is dominated by water with its great capacity for heat storage, so seasonal changes are not as great. The northern

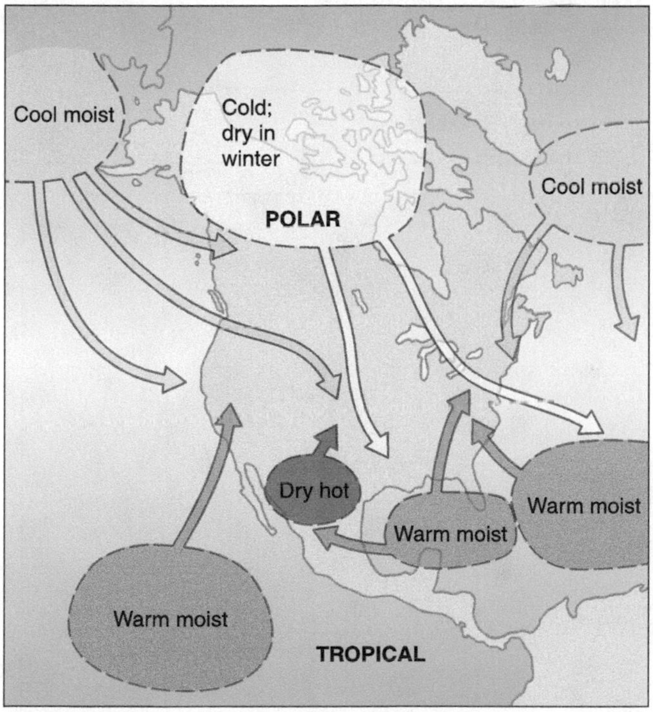

Figure 9.9
Map showing areas where large air masses acquire their temperature and moisture characteristics before moving about North America.

Source: Adapted from J. Eagleman, *Severe and Unusual Weather*, 1983; Van Nostrand Reinhold, New York.

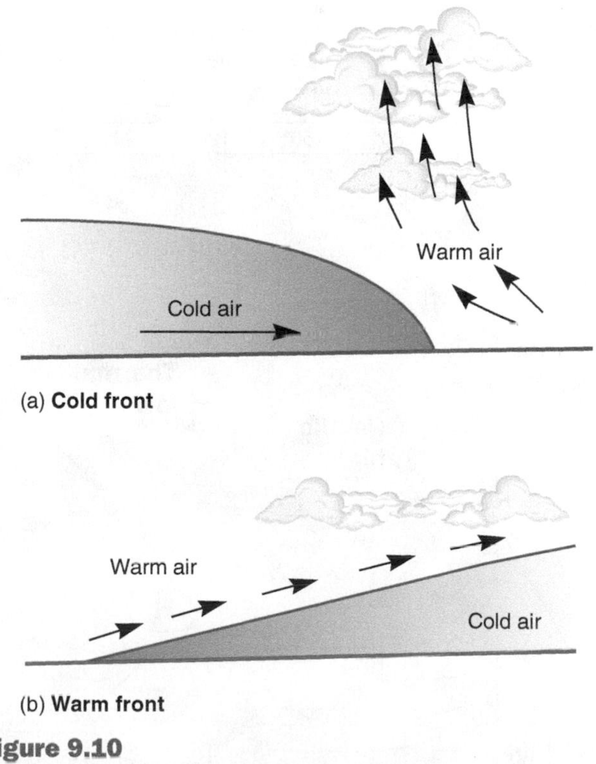

Figure 9.10
Schematic cross-sections of fronts and air masses. (a) A cold front wedges under warm air, forcing it upward. (b) A warm front runs up and on top of a cold air mass.

hemisphere is dominated by land, with its smaller heat capacity leading to significant variations in wind patterns. As the seasons change, the directions of winds and heat flows change.

In January, in the northern hemisphere winter, a strong high-pressure air mass of cold air known as the *Siberian high* influences Eurasian weather; there is an analogous but smaller high-pressure system over wintry North America (Figure 9.11a). Cold air flows off the continents as increasing volumes of air rise in subpolar low-pressure zones known as the *Aleutian* and *Icelandic lows.*

In July, in the northern hemisphere summer, the Eurasian and North American continents have warmed and hot air rises in thermal lows (Figure 9.11b). This aids the strength of the high-pressure systems over the oceans known as the *Pacific* and *Bermuda highs.* The onshore flow of moist air brings monsoonal rains and tropical cyclones onto the land, especially in South Asia.

The seasonal shifts of the Pacific and Bermuda highs and the Aleutian and Icelandic lows are major determinants of the paths of jet streams and hurricanes.

More locally, annual weather patterns can be affected by differential heating of land and water. Land

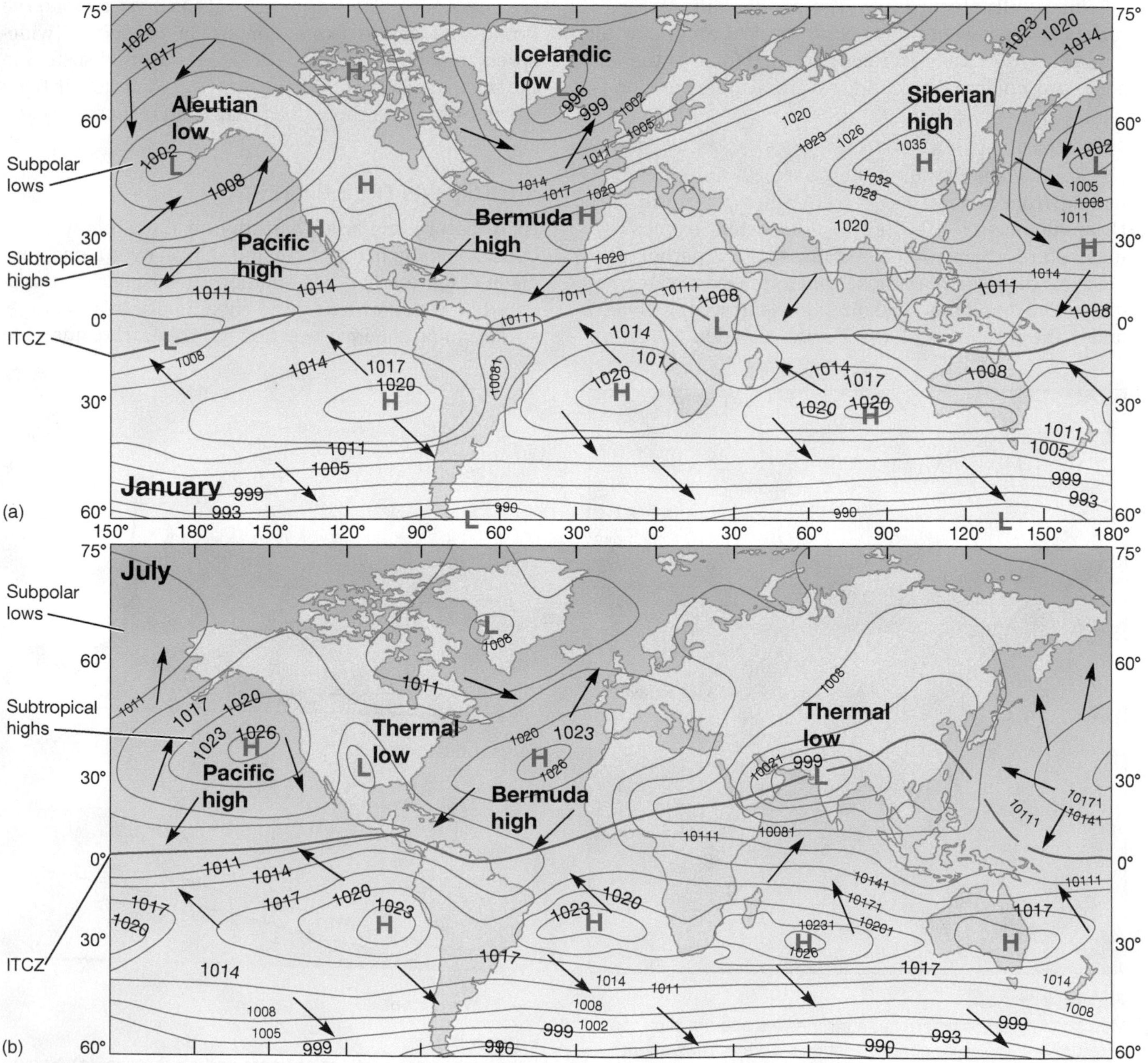

Figure 9.11
Average surface pressure (in hectopascals) and global wind patterns for January (top) and July (bottom).

heats up quickly, but the low heat capacity of rock causes it to cool down quickly, as well. Water warms up more slowly, but its high heat capacity allows it to retain heat and cool slowly.

As temperatures drop in the winter, the land cools quickly but the ocean retains its warmth, causing warm, moist air to rise (Figure 9.12a). Cool air over the land sinks toward the surface, forming a region of high-pressure air over the land. This cold, dry air flows out over the ocean.

As temperatures rise in the summer, the land heats up quickly while the ocean warms up much more slowly. Hot, dry air forms over the land and rises, producing low pressure air over the land (Figure 9.12b). Cooler moist air above the ocean is drawn in to replace the rising warm air. The moist air from above the oceans warms as it moves over the hot land, and then it rises and reaches colder levels of the atmosphere, where its water vapour condenses and falls as rain. This process creates the summer **monsoon** rains that are especially important to agriculture in India and Bangladesh. On the darker side, monsoonal air helps bring tropical cyclones ashore.

DECADAL WEATHER PATTERNS

The boundary between weather and climate becomes less distinct when considering durations of a few decades. Over this time scale, several ocean–atmosphere coupling phenomena provide background trends over which everyday weather unfolds.

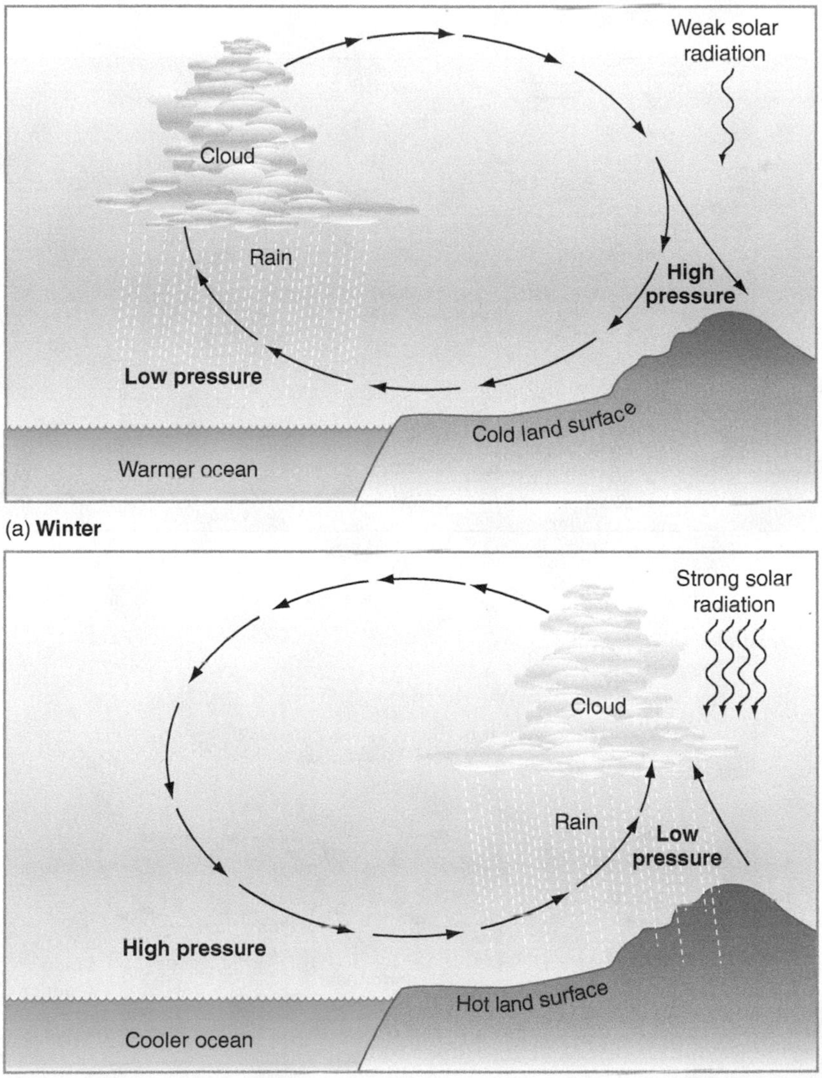

(a) **Winter**

(b) **Summer**

Figure 9.12
(a) Winter. Rapid cooling of the land causes cool air that flows offshore to replace the air rising above the warmer ocean; this airflow produces rain on the ocean. (b) Summer. Rapid heating of the land causes warm air to rise; it is replaced by moist air drawn in from above the cooler ocean; this airflow brings rain to the land.

El Niño

An example of ocean–atmosphere coupling is the phenomenon commonly marked in South America by the arrival of warm ocean water to Peru and Ecuador near Christmas, where it is known as **El Niño** (Spanish for "the child").

Typical conditions in the central Pacific Ocean find high atmospheric pressure in the east, resulting in trade winds that blow toward the equator from the northeast and southeast. The trade winds push Pacific Ocean surface waters to the west within the equatorial zone, where they absorb solar energy (Figure 9.13). The winds push so hard that sea level is not flat; it is about 50 cm higher on the western side of the ocean. Every two to seven years, the typical ocean–atmosphere pattern breaks down for about 6 to 18 months. The trade winds weaken, the atmospheric low pressure over Indonesia moves out over the central Pacific Ocean, and winds blow into the Pacific basin from the west (Figure 9.14). The warm surface waters then flow "downhill" toward South and Central America. Some surface currents are reversed as some winds from the west blow surface water to the east. The reversal places a huge mass of warm water against the Americas, which evaporates more readily and produces heavier rains than the coastal deserts can handle. This phenomenon is what we now term "El Niño."

The El Niño of 1997–1998 was the strongest weather event of the 20th century. The subsequent moderate El Niño years of 2002–2003 and 2009–2010 look pale in comparison. Early effects of the 1997–1998 El Niño included drought and high temperatures, which

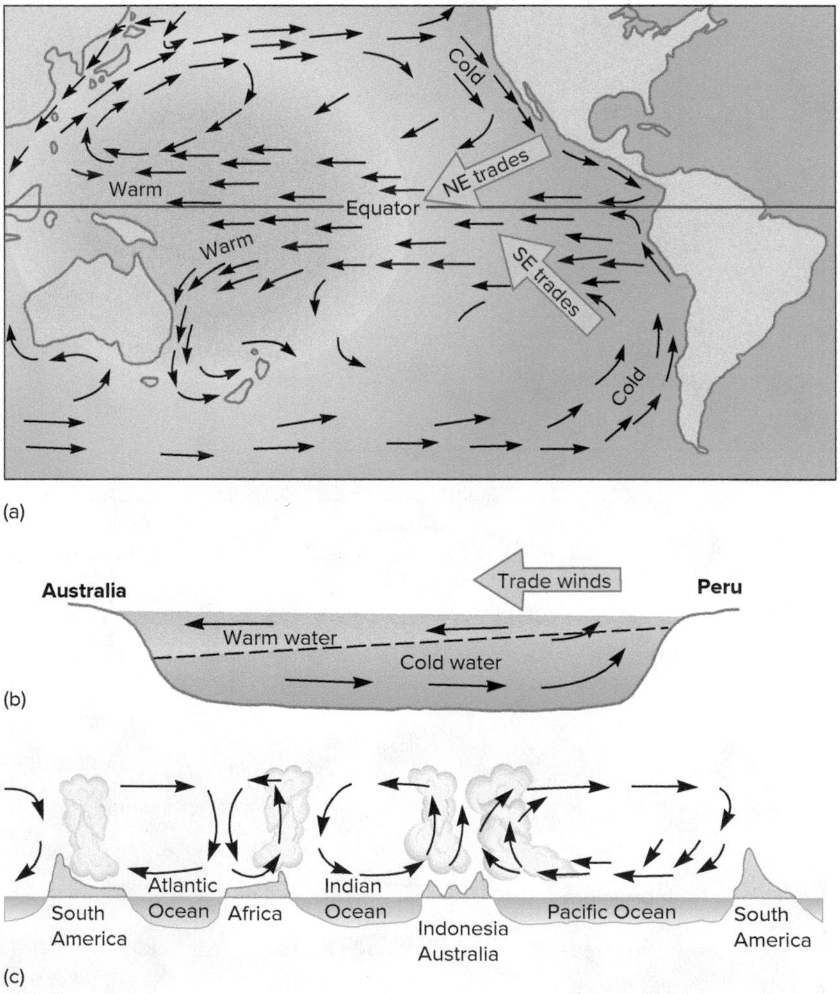

Figure 9.13

Pacific Ocean typical circulation. (a) Map. The northeast and southeast trade winds combine to push warm surface water westward across the ocean in the equatorial belt. After circling near the poles, the water returning along the North and South American coasts is cold. (b) Schematic cross-section. Strong trade winds stack up a thicker layer of warm surface water on the western side of the Pacific Ocean. (c) Schematic cross-section. Moist air rises, condenses, and falls as rain on eastern South America, eastern Africa, Indonesia, and Australia.

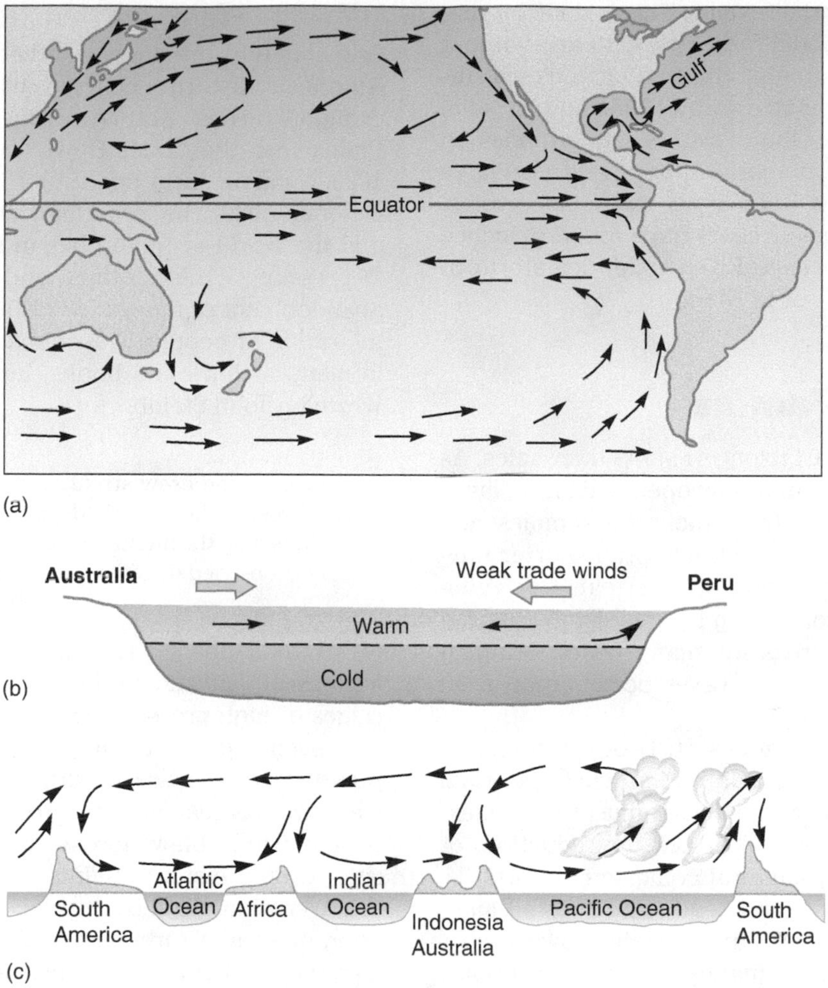

Figure 9.14

Pacific Ocean circulation during El Niño. (a) Map: Equatorial winds blow toward the centre of the ocean from both sides. Schematic cross sections: (b) Weakened trade winds plus winds from the west cause a greater than usual accumulation of warm water along the equatorial Americas. (c) Eastern Africa, Indonesia, and Australia do not get their customary rain, while western South America receives heavy rainfall.

triggered fires in Australia in the fall of 1997. Hurricanes also pounded the Mexican Pacific coast through this interval. In the southern United States, extensive flooding paralyzed communities in North Carolina and Tennessee. Further north, the stream of warm air from the Gulf of Mexico fooled cherry trees into blooming in Washington D.C. On the positive side, the El Niño may have been responsible for an unusually thick blanket of snow, which saved the lives of all 42 passengers on Air Canada Flight 646 that crashed when landing in poor visibility in Fredericton, New Brunswick, on 16 December. High-level atmospheric winds also are affected by reversal of flow direction during an El Niño. In 1997–1998, the winds helped break apart Atlantic and Caribbean storms, resulting in fewer hurricanes along the Atlantic coast.

La Niña

El Niño has a sister called **La Niña** ("the girl") and she has a different personality. La Niña occurs when cooler water moves into the equatorial Pacific Ocean.

During a La Niña, trade winds are stronger and other wind systems change their paths, bringing different weather patterns across North America. A typical La Niña winter brings cold air with high rainfall precipitation to the northwestern United States and western Canada but causes below-average precipitation elsewhere in North America.

One of the most difficult, and most common, questions meteorologists receive is "was that storm caused by El Niño or La Niña?" To identify the impact of these phenomena, researchers perform modelling experiments aimed at identifying how El Niño and La Niña affect forecasts of weather events. This is done by running an ensemble of model forecasts, with and without boundary conditions containing the anomalous sea surface temperatures associated with El Niño and La Niña. The difference between the two forecasts provides an indication of how a particular weather event may have been influenced by the anomalous sea temperatures. Using this approach, researchers have found evidence that the great St. Lawrence River Valley ice storm of 1998 was a direct result of El Niño.

Drought and Famine

Dry weather may occur on long or short timescales. As continents drift and ocean basins open and close, large regions may be cut off from moisture supplies and kept in long-term desert conditions. On a shorter time scale, changes in the position of jet streams or atmospheric convergence zones may keep moisture-bearing air away from large areas for many years, bringing on drought conditions. Heat waves occur on an even shorter timescale.

Drought does not equal desert. Drought describes times of abnormal dryness in a region when the usual rains do not appear and all life must adjust to the unexpected shortage of water. The lack, or reduction, of moisture can cause agricultural collapse or shortfalls, bringing famine, disease, and death, and causing mass migrations to wetter areas. Famine is the slowest moving of all disasters. Earthquakes, volcanic eruptions, tornadoes, and the like all hit suddenly and with great force and quickly pass through an area. But famine is slow. First, the expected rains do not arrive, and then vegetation begins to wither, food supplies shrink, and, finally, famine sets in.

Unlike other natural disasters, drought tends to drive people apart rather than bring them closer together. The shortages of food and water lead to conflict as people, communities, and governments battle each other for the means to survive. After an earthquake or flood, people are commonly at their best as they aid their neighbours and strangers in need; during a drought, people are typically at their worst as they fight for survival.

In the *early stage* of a famine, food is still available, but there is not enough. Healthy people can lose up to 10% of their body weight and still remain mentally alert and physically vigorous. In the *advanced stage,* body weight decreases by around 20%, and the body reacts to preserve life itself. Body cells lower their activity levels, reducing the energy needed to keep vital functions going. People sink into apathy. In the *near-death stage,* when 30% or more of body weight has been lost, people become indifferent to their surroundings and to the sufferings of others, and death approaches.

THE 1930S DUST BOWL

One of the greatest weather disasters in North American history occurred when several years of drought turned grain-growing areas in the Great Plains into the "Dust Bowl." The drought began in 1930, a particularly bad time. Only months before, in October 1929, the American stock market crashed, and the world economy began sinking into the Great Depression. Failed crops and malnutrition caused abandonment of thousands of farms and a broad-scale migration of people. This human drama was captured in many articles and books, including *The Grapes of Wrath* by John Steinbeck:

> Now the wind grew strong and hard, it worked at the rain crust in the corn fields. Little by little the sky was darkened by the mixing dust, and the wind felt over the earth, loosened the dust and carried it away.

What happened to cause the drought? Recurrent large scale meanders in the upper airflow created ridges of high pressure with clockwise flows resulting in descending air (Figure 9.15). The upper-level high-pressure air was already dry, but as it sank, it became warmer, thus reaching the ground hot, dry, and thirsty. As the winds blew across the ground surface, they sucked up moisture, killing plants and exposing bare soil to erosion. Wind-blown clouds of dust built into towering masses of turbulent air. When they rolled across an area, the Sun was darkened, and dust invaded every possible opening on a human body and came through every crack in a home.

The effects of drought in Canada are felt mostly in the Prairies, especially in the arid portion of southern Saskatchewan and Alberta known as Palliser's Triangle. During the "Dirty Thirties," a quarter million people abandoned the West, which led to major policy changes in agriculture and land management. Between 1933 and 1937, the Prairies received about 40% less rainfall than normal for that area. Thousands of head of livestock were lost or killed by ranchers with no water to offer them. Crops were withered and stunted.

Since the 1930s, other serious droughts have plagued North America (Figure 9.16). The hottest summers are generally drought years, so when the rains fail, crops wither rapidly in the torrid heat. On the Prairies, 9 of the 10 driest years since 1948 were also warmer than normal, including 1961, which featured both the driest (49% less precipitation than average) and the hottest (+2.6°C) summer in 60 years of record (1948 to 2007).

Rivalling the 1930s in terms of drought frequency, intensity, and duration were the 1980s. In many areas, 1988 was the hottest summer on record. Growing-season

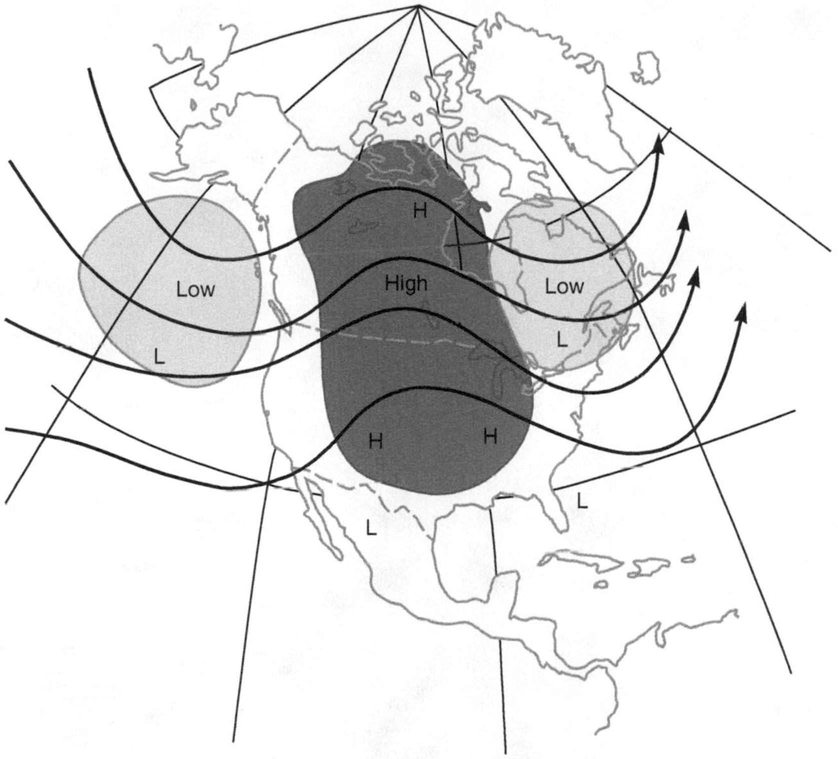

Figure 9.15
Dry conditions in Canada and the central United States are commonly caused by a long-lasting, high-pressure ridge in the upper troposphere. The ridge causes anticyclones where warm air descends, warming further and lowering its humidity, and then sucking up moisture from the land below. The mid-continent high-pressure ridge also blocks the northward flow of moist Gulf of Mexico air.

rainfalls across the southern Prairies averaged only 50% to 80% of normal. The dry period really began in September 1987 and continued through the relatively snow-free winter and record dry spring. The effects of the 1988 drought were disastrous for nearly all segments of the Canadian economy, although agriculture was particularly hard hit. Grain production was down by an average 31% from 1987, and export losses were estimated at $4 billion. Ranchers were forced to thin their herds or move their cattle long distances to find adequate grazing land. As a result of their economic difficulties, about 10% of farmers and farm workers left agriculture in 1988.

Recent droughts on the Prairies have also been quite severe. For some areas, the years 2001 and 2002 were drier than the driest years of the 1930s. While past growing seasons might have been drier, recent winters have been a third drier than winters 70 years ago. Recent droughts are year-round.

Researchers at the University of Regina have used tree rings and mud from Prairie lake bottoms to conclude that twentieth-century droughts were characterized by moderate severity and single drought years or, at worst, back-to-back drought years. Prior to the twentieth century, prolonged droughts of more than a decade in duration had been common. If anything, the past 100 years have been relatively benign—wet and humid. The absolute worst-case scenario occurred 1500 years ago, when a 70-year drought prevailed in central Saskatchewan. In the modern era, one of the worst periods of drought was immediately before the Prairies were settled by Europeans, from the 1850s until about 1890. Droughts also occur in eastern Canada, although there they are usually short lived, localized, less frequent, and less severe than in the Prairies. Drought is one of the hazards likely to worsen as a result of climate change.

HABOOBS

In arid regions around the world, overwhelming dust storms are becoming more common. Such a storm is known as a **haboob,** which means "strong wind" in Arabic. Haboobs form when thunderstorm downbursts or collapses cause air to rush down to the ground and flow outward, pushing out a gust that carries dust, silt, and sand. Haboobs range up to 100 km wide and several kilometres high, move at 35–100 km/h, may arrive with little warning, and last up to three hours. For example, Tehran was overrun by a dramatic haboob in June 2014, plunging the Iranian capital into darkness, killing five people, and causing massive disruption (Figure 9.17).

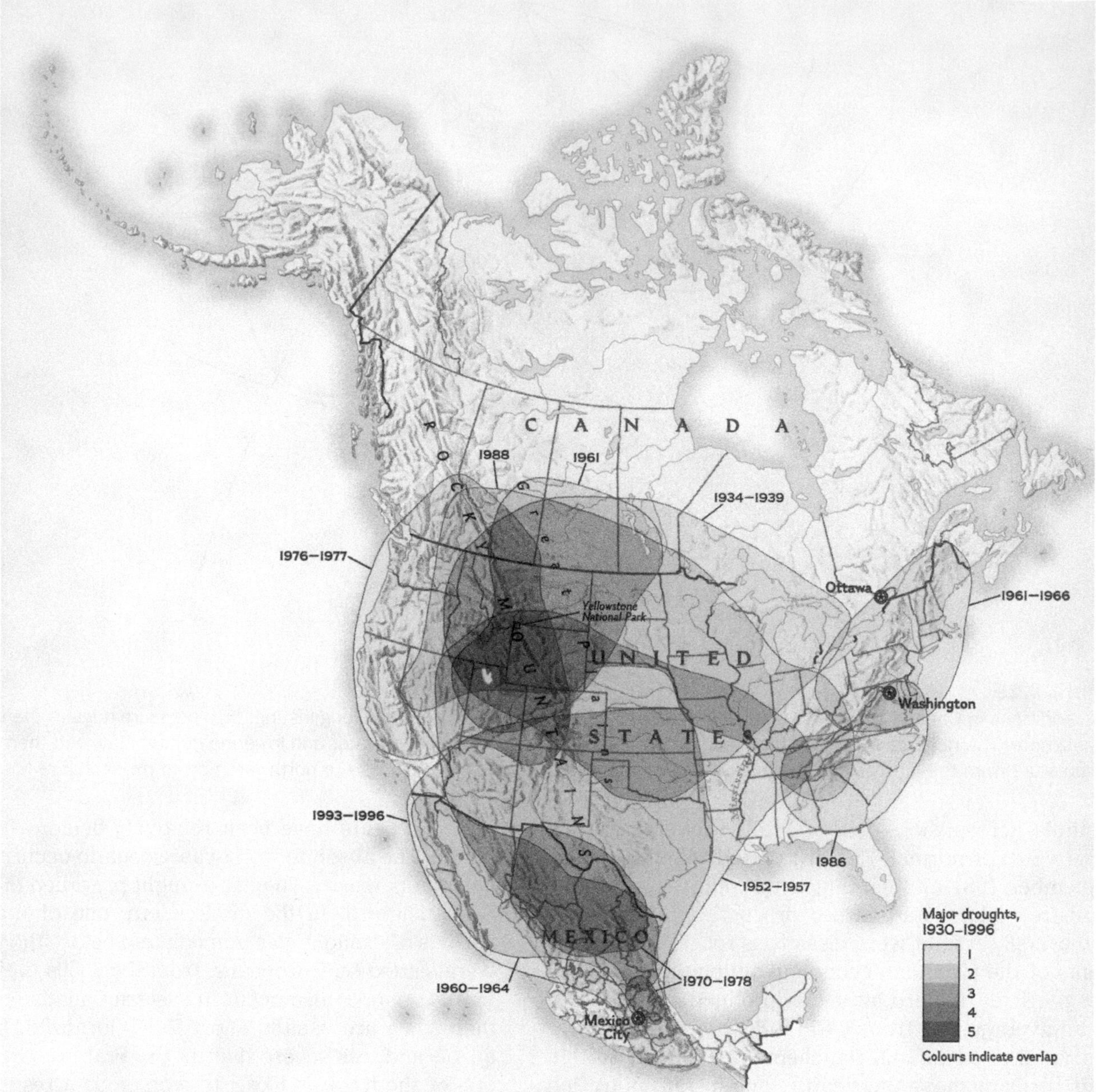

Figure 9.16
Major droughts in North America 1930–1996.
Source: NG Maps/ National Geographic Stock

Figure 9.17
Haboob engulfing Tehran, Iran, on June 2 2014.
Source: Alireza Nasen, Livescience.

Heat Waves

The days of high temperatures during a heat wave may be one of the least appreciated of the weather-related disasters. The heat wave is an invisible, silent danger and it can kill in large numbers. To describe the hazard, in 1965 Canadian meteorologists devised an index, the humidex, which combines temperature and relative humidity into a measure of perceived temperature that more accurately describes what we feel on hot, humid days (Figure 9.18).

Air temperature (°C) \ Relative humidity (%)	100	95	90	85	80	75	70	65	60	55	50	45	40	35	30	25	20
21	29	29	28	27	27	26	26	24	24	23	23	22					
22	31	29	29	28	28	27	26	26	24	24	23	23					
23	33	32	32	31	30	29	28	27	27	26	25	24	23				
24	35	34	33	33	32	31	30	29	28	28	27	26	26	25			
25	37	36	35	34	33	33	32	31	30	29	28	27	27	26			
26	39	38	37	36	35	34	33	32	31	31	29	28	28	27			
27	41	40	39	38	37	36	35	34	33	32	31	30	29	28	28		
28	43	42	41	41	39	38	37	36	35	34	33	32	31	29	28		
29	46	45	44	43	42	41	39	38	37	36	34	33	32	31	30		
30	48	47	46	44	43	42	41	40	38	37	36	35	34	33	31	31	
31	50	49	48	46	45	44	43	41	40	39	38	36	35	34	33	31	
32	52	51	50	49	47	46	45	43	42	41	39	38	37	36	34	33	
33	55	54	52	51	50	48	47	46	44	43	42	40	38	37	36	34	
34	58	57	55	53	52	51	49	48	47	45	43	42	41	39	37	36	
35		58	57	56	54	52	51	49	48	47	45	43	42	41	38	37	
36			58	57	56	54	53	51	50	48	47	45	43	42	40	38	
37					58	57	55	53	51	50	49	47	45	43	42	40	
38							57	56	54	52	51	49	47	46	43	42	40
39									56	54	53	51	49	47	45	43	41
40										57	54	52	51	49	47	44	43
41											56	54	52	50	48	46	44
42												56	54	52	50	48	46
43													56	54	51	49	47

Humidex (°C)	Degree of comfort
20–29	No discomfort
30–39	Some discomfort
40–45	Great discomfort; avoid exertion
46 and over	Dangerous; probable heat stroke

Figure 9.18
The humidex, a table combining temperature and relative humidity to yield the temperatures perceived by humans.
Source: © Meteorological Service of Canada.

Somewhat surprising for Canada, being the second coldest country in the world, is that the greatest cause of death from a natural disaster in the last 100 years was not cold or snow but a lengthy hot spell in 1936 when 1180 people died (Table 1.3 and Figure 1.10). In late June and July that year, hot air from the American southwest drifted northward into Canada, causing a huge heat wave over much of the continent. Shade temperatures reached 44°C in Manitoba, and 42°C in Ontario—temperature records that still stand. As with most heat waves, it was the high nighttime minima that took the greatest toll because they were too elevated to offer any respite to people already stressed by heat exposure during the day. The daily minimum temperature in Toronto on 11 July was 26.6°C; and for four nights the temperature did not dip below 25°C. Only twice before in 100 years had the nighttime minimum temperature stayed above 25°C, in 1911 and 1917; and only seven times since 1936. The extreme heat buckled highways, warped bridge girders, and twisted heavy steel rail lines. Brick sidewalks and roadways heaved, and sidewalks cracked under the intense heat. Surface temperatures on tarred roads exceeded 65°C. In some instances, the softened asphalt melted and flowed freely into ditches. Road crews sanded streets in order to reduce skidding. But mostly it was a killer heat wave.

Most people who die in heat waves are elderly, young, or ill, and most deaths occur in cities. City areas are *urban heat islands* where buildings and streets absorb solar heat all day and then release stored heat at night, thus robbing residents of the relief that cool nights bring (Figure 9.19). Nighttime temperatures in the city may be 5.5°C warmer than in the nearby countryside. City dwellers' body temperatures stay higher, so their bodies are under greater stress.

Heat does not kill many Canadians nowadays due to the availability of air conditioning and greater health awareness. Seventy years ago an average of 50 Canadians died each year from extreme heat or too much

Figure 9.19
Surface temperature on 15 July 2003 in the Greater Montreal area. The highest temperatures (in red and purple) are found on the densely urbanized island of Montreal, and in the cities of Longueuil and Laval. The lowest temperatures are found in the suburban belt where there is more vegetation.

Source: Camilio Pérez Arrau, Urban Heat Islands.

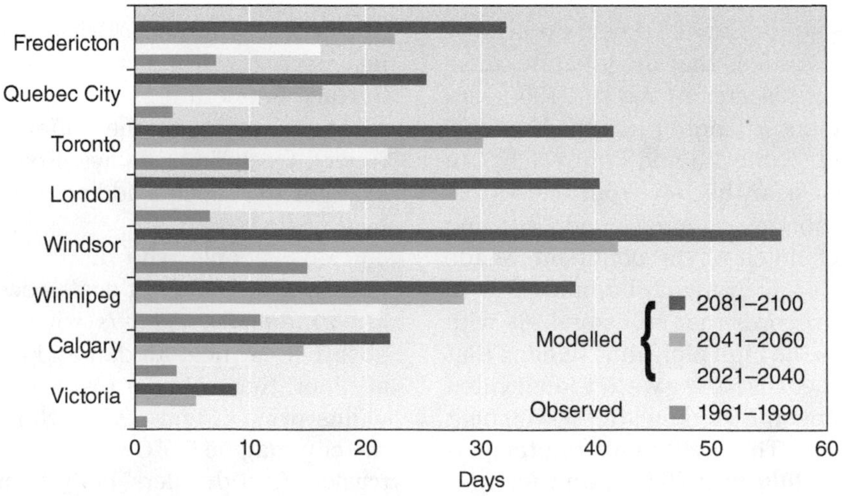

Figure 9.20
Number of days with temperatures exceeding 30°C, observed for 1961–1990 (blue) and predicted for 2021–2040 (yellow), 2041–2060 (green), and 2081–2100 (red), for several Canadian cities.

Source: © Environment Canada, Figure provided by Slava Kharin, Climate Research Division, 2014. Reproduced with permission.

sun. Heat mortality figures dropped to 7 a year in the 1970s. Today, a single death from heat stroke usually makes the national news. Warming scenarios, however, suggest that hot spells in Canada will become more frequent and intense. By 2050, for example, hot days are likely to become three or four times more frequent than today in southern Canada (Figure 9.20). For Toronto, the yearly number of hot days is projected to double by 2030, triple by 2050, and more than quadruple by 2090.

Because climate is likely to continue to warm through the twenty-first century, more and more heat waves will occur at the same time as the world population grows rapidly and huge numbers of people migrate into cities. Sometime in 2006, the world's population crossed over from being mostly rural to being mostly urban. In summer 2010, as a result of a strong La Niña event, the deadliest heat wave ever affected the northern hemisphere. Russia was hardest hit, with 56 000 fatalities. We need to learn more about how to survive heat waves in an urban environment.

Winter Storms

Much of the severe weather in the mid-latitudes of the northern hemisphere occurs via cyclones: air masses rotating counter-clockwise about a low-pressure core. Some of the largest-scale cyclones are linked to jet-stream troughs (Figure 9.6).

NOR'EASTERS

In Atlantic Canada and the northeastern United States, large-scale cyclones can create potent storms known as **nor'easters**. When a low-pressure system moves up the eastern United States–Canada coastline, its counter-clockwise circulation brings different air masses into contact. Its eastern or seaward side picks up warmer moist air from the Atlantic Ocean, which is fed into the cyclone by northeast winds. One of the most important factors in a nor'easter's potential destructiveness is the presence of a strong, stable high-pressure system positioned over eastern Canada. The high blocks a developing nor'easter from tracking swiftly up the east coast, thus lengthening its duration near the water. On its western or landward side, the trough of the jet stream draws cold air down from the north, keeping temperatures along the Atlantic coast well below freezing. The collision of the cold Arctic air and the warmer oceanic air can create nor'easters that are disastrous.

Nor'easters are far more frequent than hurricanes. During the height of their season (December through March), an average of 30 nor'easters track up eastern North America, often with gale-force or stronger winds and towering waves that batter the coast, causing serious beach erosion, property damage, and even loss of life. Most of the major snowstorms along North America's Atlantic Coast arise from nor'easters.

A very explosive form of nor'easter is a "weather bomb," a powerful, rapidly intensifying maritime storm that seems to pop out of nowhere, making it tough to forecast. The key to weather bombs' identity is the rate at which these storms intensify. Central pressures must drop at least 2.4 kilopascals in 24 hours. Some of the more explosive weather bombs drop at twice that rate. The lower the pressure, the stronger the winds. Weather bombs tend to occur after the hurricane season between late fall and early spring but can be just as powerful and destructive as a hurricane.

Such a storm occurred on 7 November 2001, when the remnants of two hurricanes and a powerful mid-latitude storm from New England converged and then intensified over the Gulf of St. Lawrence. The storm blew out car windows, swamped wharves and fragile sand dunes, and caused blackouts for more than 100 000 electricity customers in Atlantic Canada. Prince Edward Island and Cape Breton Island received the brunt of the storm—sustaining high winds combined with high tides to produce a storm surge of one metre or more, and waves of nine metres. Rocks as heavy as 14 kg were thrown hundreds of metres inland, some landing on golf greens. The Confederation Bridge between New Brunswick and Prince Edward Island was closed to all traffic for the first time ever when winds were clocked at 123 km/h gusting to 155 km/h, the strongest ever measured. The storm also tore out chunks of the Canso Causeway connecting Cape Breton Island to mainland Nova Scotia.

Another type of powerful mid-latitude cyclone that shares similarities with nor'easters is a "witches of November" storm over the Great Lakes. November is one of the windiest and stormiest months on the Great Lakes. It accounts for about 10% of the annual traffic on the Great Lakes, but 40% of the shipwrecks. The location of the lakes in the interior of North America, between the source regions of contrasting Arctic and tropical air masses, often brings the region rapidly changing and explosive weather systems. Along the overriding jet stream, developing cyclones track eastward into the Great Lakes where they get an extra shot of energy from the relatively warm lake waters. Lows are often stronger than at other times of the year. At their greatest intensity, these storms reach very low pressures, sometimes rivalling Atlantic hurricanes, and creating tremendous winds and monster waves as high as 12 m.

BLIZZARDS

A **blizzard** is the most violent winter storm, combining strong winds with cold temperatures (Figure 9.21). It differs from other winter storms by the strength of its winds. Whiteouts, drifting, and blowing snow with

Figure 9.21
Proudly flying a Canadian flag under blizzard conditions!
Source: THE CANADIAN PRESS/Dave Chidley.

heavy snow depositions cause many hardships. A blizzard, however, can occur without new snow; strong winds can pick up and blow snow dropped by earlier storms. In February 1978, the southern side of Regina, Saskatchewan, was buried for four days by a blizzard. Snow drifts reached rooftops yet the storm left only a trace of new snow at the airport.

Environment Canada uses different criteria for defining blizzards in different regions. Officially, to be classified as a blizzard, the following conditions must be fulfilled:

- Wind speed of 40 km/h or greater.
- A temperature of less than 0°C (more often below –10°C) or wind chill of –25°C or lower.
- Visibility of less than one kilometre.
- Duration of these conditions for at least three to six hours.

Blizzards are often winter's deadliest storms. Fatalities occur (1) from heart attacks while shovelling snow and pushing stuck cars, (2) when automobiles slide and collide, (3) when people slip on ice and fall, or (4) when people get disoriented or lost, and freeze.

Blizzards in Canada are most frequent in the open prairie but less frequent in the prairie parkland and forests where the force of the wind is broken (Table 9.1). Blizzards in southern Ontario are more frequent downwind of the Great Lakes during bursts of lake-effect snow off open lake waters. Perhaps surprisingly, blizzards are rare in the Western Arctic and Yukon where winds are very light and the snow amount is scant.

Legendary tales are told of pioneer farmers who perished midway between house and barn or of Arctic explorers who died after straying only a metre or two from their campsites. Even today, not a winter goes by without tragic news being heard about travellers succumbing to a blizzard.

TABLE 9.1

Average Number of Hours of Blizzard in a Year for Selected Canadian Cities

Whitehorse	1
Vancouver	0
Yellowknife	4
Edmonton	3
Regina	36
Winnipeg	18
Toronto	2
Ottawa	5
Montreal	11
Quebec City	20
Fredericton	4
Moncton	30
Charlottetown	40
Halifax	9
St. John's	46

The 2004 White Juan, Halifax

They dubbed it White Juan—a hurricane disguised as a blizzard. Late on 17 February 2004, an ordinary winter storm centred over Cape Hatteras, North Carolina, suddenly intensified over the Gulf Stream before striking the Maritimes. Its central pressure plunged 5.7 kilopascals in 42 hours, making it one of the most explosive storms ever—even more powerful than its namesake, Hurricane Juan, which had struck the same area five months earlier.

Huge, lumbering White Juan packed quite a weather wallop—heavy snows, fierce winds gusting to 124 km/h, and zero visibility. Snow fell at a phenomenal rate of 5 cm/h for 12 straight hours. Blowing snow and high winds maintained blizzard conditions for a day or more and created drifts as tall as three metres. Halifax, Yarmouth, and Charlottetown broke all-time 24-hour snowfall records, receiving almost a metre of snow. For Halifax, the snowfall almost doubled the city's previous record for a single day. With over 300 000 people, Halifax is the largest city in the world to ever receive such a dump of snow in one day.

Lake-Effect Snow

The southern and eastern shores of the Great Lakes in Canada and the United States are world-famous sites for lake-effect snow. These snows fall after cold, dry air moves long distances over the warmer waters of the lakes and then crosses the downwind shoreline (Figure 9.22). Lake-water temperatures may be only 0°C, but an Arctic air mass blowing across the water may be –18°C. The warmer surface waters of the lakes add heat and water vapour to the colder air mass. Note on Figure 9.22 that the cold air moves across the lake for a long distance before becoming saturated with the water vapour that condenses to form clouds. When the clouds reach the downwind shore, they encounter colder earth with rough land surfaces that increase friction, causing the air to slow, cool, and drop huge volumes of snow.

Lake-effect snow is common within 40 km of shorelines. For example, the southern shores of Lake Erie commonly receive thick blankets of lake-effect snow in late fall or early winter when lake-water temperatures are warmer. When Lake Erie, the shallowest of the Great Lakes, freezes over, lake-effect snows are no longer possible.

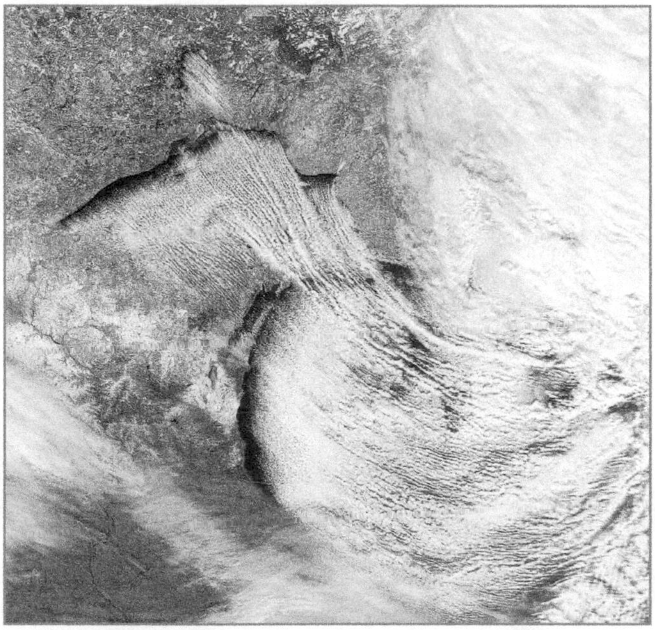

Figure 9.22
Cold dry air from the northwest (upper left) blows over the warmer Great Lakes, picks up water vapour, and forms clouds that drop lake-effect snow on the downwind sides of the lakes, 5 December 2000.
Source: NASA.

ICE STORMS

Forecasting the occurrence and amount of **freezing rain** is tricky, yet this form of precipitation affects Canadian cities several times a year, most often in the east (Table 9.2). When it is cold, clouds may drop precipitation as snowflakes or ice particles (Figure 9.23). Falling snow and ice commonly pass downward though air warm enough to melt the snow or ice and turn it into rain. If the falling rain then enters a below-freezing air layer near the ground, the rain may refreeze into tiny (1.6 mm) ice particles called **sleet**. If falling rain is not in subfreezing air long enough to freeze to ice, it may turn into a supercooled liquid (water droplets at a temperature below 0°C) and become freezing rain. Upon striking a colder object, such as pavement, hydro wires, tree branches, building walls or cars, the supercooled raindrops spread out and freeze almost immediately, forming a smooth thin veneer of slick ice.

The 1998 St. Lawrence River Valley Ice Storm

The 1998 ice storm in the St. Lawrence River Valley left a profound impression on people who experienced it. This great natural disaster highlights the vulnerability of

TABLE 9.2

Average Number of Hours of Freezing Rain in a Year for Selected Canadian Cities

Whitehorse	4
Victoria	2
Vancouver	4
Yellowknife	35
Edmonton	21
Regina	35
Winnipeg	31
Toronto	35
Ottawa	64
Montreal	48
Quebec City	54
Fredericton	47
Charlottetown	53
Halifax	33
St. John's	148

Source: Based on *The Day Niagara Falls Ran Dry!* Key Porter Books 1993.

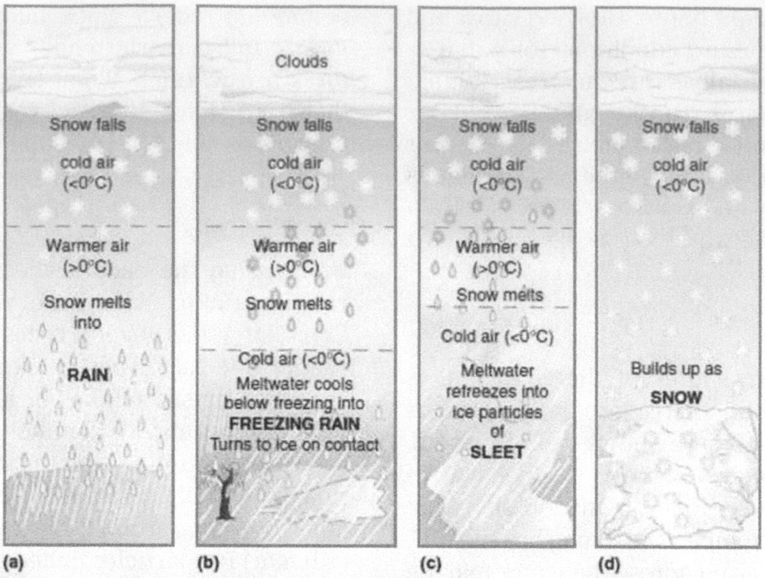

Figure 9.23
Snowflakes fall and then: (a) melt into RAIN, (b) melt and then cool below freezing, becoming FREEZING RAIN, (c) melt and refreeze as SLEET, or (d) stay as SNOW.

Canadian society to extreme weather conditions, and its dependency on electricity. As straightforwardly stated by Mark Abley, "storm survivor" and author of two books on the topic: "... the evacuees didn't pray for a return of fine weather. They prayed for a return of power."

People in Eastern Canada are used to freezing rain, which typically happens 12–17 days per year, resulting in an average of 45–65 hours of freezing rain precipitation annually (Table 9.2). The ice storm of 1998 was anomalous because of the stability of the weather conditions. As a mass of cold Arctic air and a warm and moist low-pressure system from the Gulf of Mexico remained static over the St. Lawrence River Valley, freezing rain fell for 80 hours over 5 days, from 5 to 9 January. In Montreal, the thickness of ice accumulated on trees and infrastructure reached 20 mm on day 1, 55 mm on day 3 and in excess of 100 mm on day 5. An ice thickness of more than 25 mm causes major damage to trees (Figure 9.24).

Figure 9.24
Coniferous tree bending under a thick ice cover. Damage is likely to be irreversible.
Source: Michael Stawicki.

As freezing rain kept falling, heavy branches broke off and fell to the ground, cutting power lines and blocking streets in countless locations. The electrical pylon is often described as "the official tree of Quebec" since the province has an extensive electrical network and many Quebeckers rely on this energy source to heat their homes. The pylons, designed to withstand an ice thickness of 15 mm, started to collapse, interrupting the regional delivery of electricity (Figure 9.25). Sporadic blackouts became widespread and, by 9 January, four of the five main power lines feeding Montreal were out of commission. A staggering 3.5 million people were without electricity in mid-winter temperatures. The treacherous driving conditions made it impossible for people to leave their homes.

In the countryside, the situation was equally dramatic. Farmers struggled to protect animals and keep dairy operations running using generators. Maple

Figure 9.25
Major power transmission line collapsed under the weight of ice.
Source: Hydro-Quebec.

producers were hit hard: 22% of all sugar maple taps in Canada were subjected to the weight of over 40 mm of ice. It will take decades for production to recover, as a small maple must grow for 40 years before it is large enough to be tapped.

On 7 January, the provinces of New Brunswick, Ontario, and Quebec requested aid from the federal government and "Operation Recuperation," led by the Canadian Armed Forces, began the following day. It was the largest domestic deployment of troops in response to a natural disaster in Canadian history, involving more than 15 000 army, navy, and air force personnel. Canadian Forces members sheltered and fed about 100 000 people evacuated from their homes, and maintained law and order. Military engineers and technicians worked with hydro and telephone crews to repair and replace downed pylons and utility poles. At the peak of the outage, nearly 10 000 people were working to restore power.

Finally, on 9 January, the weather pattern changed, signalling a gradual return to normal conditions. On that day, however, both water filtration plants providing drinking water to the Montreal metropolitan area shut down simultaneously after pumping stations lost power, an example of cascading effects of systems failure. The situation was resolved quickly but could have had disastrous consequences on public health if it had persisted. In total, the ice storm crisis claimed 28 lives in Canada and 17 lives in the neighbouring U.S. states. People died from hypothermia, ice falls, and carbon monoxide poisoning and fire while using unsafe alternative heating sources.

In the words of a senior executive from Hydro-Québec, the public electricity company in Quebec: "The crisis was a great teacher for us, a real-life classroom where we painfully learned more about building a robust network." Since the 1998 ice storm, Hydro-Québec has taken several concrete actions to reinforce its network. Efforts have focused on diversifying the sources of supply so that major urban centres are now serviced from many different power lines. Anti-cascading towers, aimed at preventing the collapse of adjacent pylons, are used systemically along new lines: one tower is built every ten pylons. New pylons are built of stronger and thicker steel elements. Finally, on critical corridors, a new de-icing technology uses direct current flowing along power lines to prevent ice buildups.

The 2013 Toronto Ice Storm

The ice storm that paralyzed Canada's largest city from 20 to 22 December 2013 is a bit like the "Grinch who stole Christmas". . . Ice accumulation was greatest in the city of Toronto, where many residents spent Christmas in the cold and dark (see cover photo). So much for Christmas lights and turkey dinner. The area affected, however, covered an extensive corridor from the American Midwest to Cape Breton Island, Nova Scotia (Figure 9.26). The scale of the event took meteorologists by surprise, and fueled speculation that climate change might not only bring more frequent ice storms but also cause a new class of "mega" ice storms in the future.

This was truly an urban disaster, exposing both the fragility of the electrical infrastructure at the neighbourhood scale and a dysfunctional municipal response. In most Toronto neighbourhoods, electricity is transported on small aerial lines to individual houses surrounded with mature trees. When electrical lines were damaged by falling branches, responders needed to "mend" them block by block, street by street, and house by house. Progress was very slow (Figure 9.27). After critical facilities such as hospitals and community centres, who should be reconnected next: residential high rises where hundreds of families live or single family homes? There was a lack of planning in this regard

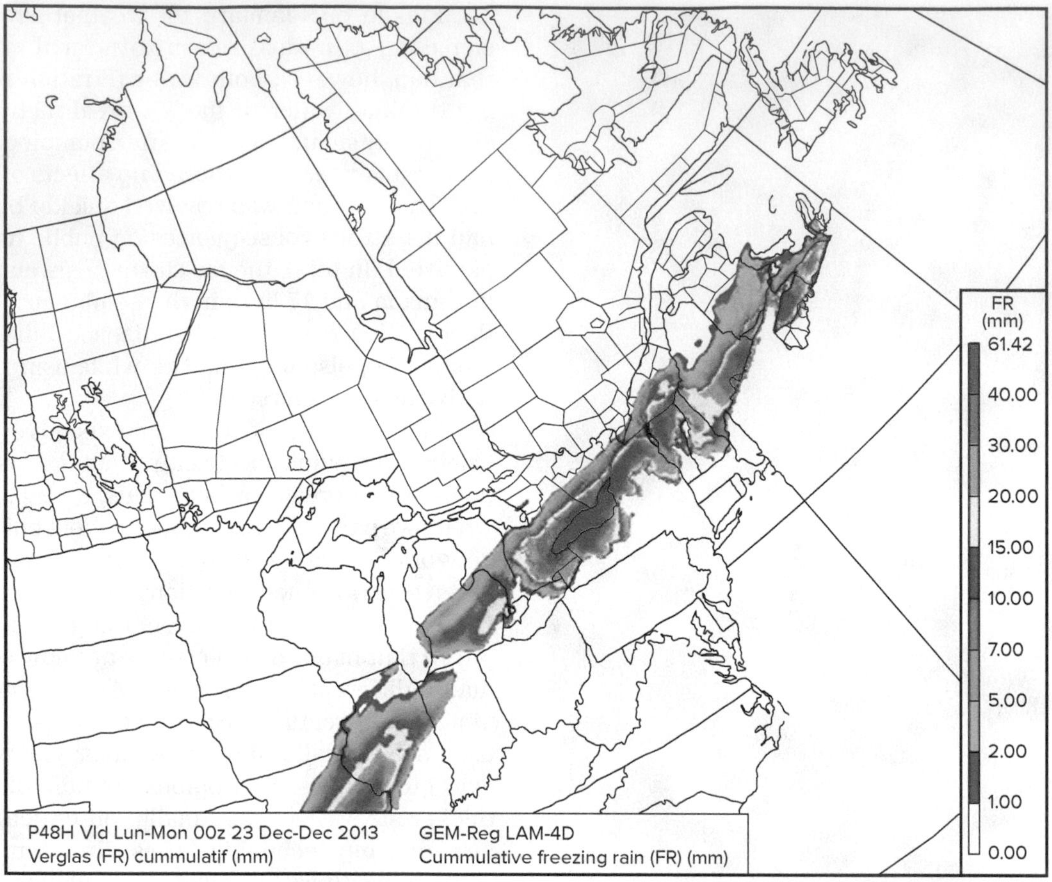

Figure 9.26
Total ice accumulation for the 2013 Toronto ice storm.
Source: Environment Canada.

Figure 9.27
Upon falling, this branch blocked access to a house and tore down a power line. It did not sever the electrical connection, which would have added an electrocution hazard to the fray. The undeterred resident is shown doing the yoga-inspired "tree pose." A sense of humour often triumphs in the worse situations.
Source: Anne Mehta.

leaving many vulnerable people captive in apartment buildings for up to two weeks. Many disenchanted citizens voiced their concerns at the lack of leadership from municipal leaders.

LO2

Thunderstorms

Thunderstorms are born from tall, buoyant cumulus clouds of raising moist air (Figure 9.28a). They generate lightning and thunder, rain, gusty winds, and sometimes hail.

HOW A THUNDERSTORM WORKS

Air temperature normally decreases upward from the ground surface through the troposphere at an average rate of about 6°C/km. At this rate, the troposphere is stable. On those days when the rate of cooling with height is greater than 6° to 10°C/km, the atmosphere is unstable. The degree of atmospheric instability increases as the temperature differences increase between warm bottom air and overlying cool air. Warm, low-altitude air is less dense and it tends to rise by convection. Once convective upwelling begins, the warm air mass continues to rise as long as it is less dense than the surrounding air.

If heat builds up in dry air near the surface, the warm air rises and cools adiabatically at a rate of 10°C/km after a moderate ascent, and no thunderstorms form. However, if the air near the ground is both warm and moist, the warm air may rise high enough to pass through the **lifting condensation level**, allowing condensation of water vapour to begin and cumulus clouds to build. Once condensation begins, the rising cloud also is fuelled by a large and important energy source—release of the latent heat of condensation. This latent heat provides fuel to help form thunderstorms, tornadoes, hurricanes, and other severe weather.

Single-Cell Thunderstorms

Most individual, single-cell thunderstorms form on sunny days in the late afternoon or early evening, when temperatures of the ground surface and lower troposphere are the highest. A thundercloud begins with an initial updraft of warm, moist air, maybe aided by wind pushing up a hill slope, surface-wind convergence, or frontal lifting. The early stage of thunderstorm development requires a continuous supply of rising, warm, moist air to keep the updraft and cloud mass growing (Figure 9.29a).

When the amount of ice crystals and water drops formed from the condensation of rising water vapour becomes too heavy for the updrafts to support, some upper-level precipitation begins. Falling rain causes downward drag, developing downdrafts and pulling in cooler, dryer air surrounding the tall cloud mass. In the thunderstorm's mature stage, the cloud-mass top commonly spreads out as an icy cap (Figure 9.29b). Updrafts and downdrafts operate side by side as warm, moist air is rising high at the same time that cool, dry air is descending rapidly. This is the most violent stage of the thunderstorm, with gusty winds and rain.

The dissipating stage is reached when downdrafts drag in so much cool, dry air that it chokes off the updrafts of warm, moist air necessary to fuel the thunderstorm (Figure 9.29c). Without new moisture, the tall thundercloud mass evaporates in the surrounding dry air.

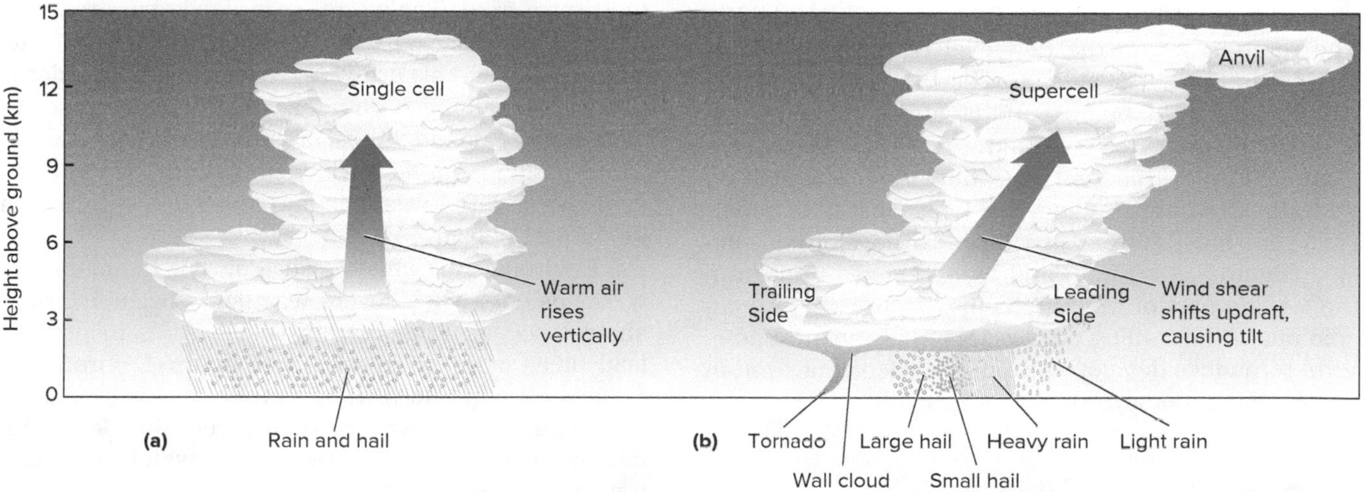

Figure 9.28
Types of thunderstorms. (a) *Single-cell thunderstorm:* Warm, moist air rises vertically, forming rain that falls down through the cloud, cooling it down. (b) *Supercell thunderstorm:* Tilted cloud has rain and hail on leading side with tornadoes on trailing side.

IN GREATER DEPTH

Downbursts: An Airplane's Enemy

In the mature stage of a thunderstorm, violent downdrafts of air may occur (Figure 9.29b). These sudden, strong downrushes of wind are known as **downbursts**; they can hit the ground and spread outward in all directions with straight-line wind speeds up to 240 km/h. Downbursts may be referred to as microbursts if they affect an area with a diameter less than four kilometres; downbursts that affect larger areas are called macrobursts.

Downbursts may be dry or wet. A thunderstorm with abundant rainfall concentrated in shafts may drop a wet macroburst because of its heavy load of water and hail. Alternatively, some air parcels surrounding a thundercloud may become trapped within the cloud where the water droplets and ice crystals in the trapped air readily evaporate, cooling the cloud further, increasing its density, and thus triggering a downburst. When a wet macroburst hits the ground, it does so with enough violence to leave a splattered pattern of damage.

Airplane safety is also challenged during downbursts by a radical change in horizontal wind direction. As a plane moves into a downburst, the winds shift from head winds, which maintain the lift of the airplane, to tail winds as the plane exits the downward-rushing wind area.

A crude analogy can be made to dropping a water-filled balloon from the roof of a house and watching it splatter with force on the ground. What if the "water balloon" is a heavy ball of wind with rainwater descending at about 270 km/h? The danger to airplanes is obvious. Downbursts are especially hazardous to airplanes during takeoff and landing. The airplane is so close to the ground that the unexpected downdraft can push it into the ground before the pilot has a chance to react.

On 2 August 2005, an Air France flight from Paris landed in a driving rainstorm at Toronto Pearson International Airport. The jet overran the runway, slammed into a ditch, and burst into flames. Miraculously, the more than 300 people aboard survived. By the time the Air France pilot lined up to land, shifting and shearing winds with strong gusts, an intense downpour that reduced visibility, and frequent lightning flashes filled the air at and near the airport. Speculation was that a microburst flowing from a nearby thunderstorm could have either increased the wind ground speed or reduced the airspeed of the plane in the seconds immediately preceding touchdown, forcing the jet to careen off the runway into a gully.

Many airports in microburst-prone regions now use Doppler radar to detect microburst conditions in time to warn pilots. Training is given to pilots on how to fly an aircraft out of microbursts.

LO3

Supercell Thunderstorms

Severe thunderstorms commonly form where weather-system fronts collide, sending up numerous large thunderclouds along a zone 10 to 1000 km long. The large areas covered by severe thunderstorms allow updrafts and downdrafts of air to occur simultaneously and to reinforce each other.

Supercell thunderstorms are a particularly violent type of severe thunderstorm that forms from a huge updraft of air. A supercell can cover an area with a diameter of 20 to 50 km and may move in a large-scale rotation lasting two to four hours (Figure 9.30). The rotation within the mid-level of the supercell is known as the mesocyclone. This large-scale rotation occurs around the updraft and creates a spiralling column of air, or vortex, rotating around a vertical axis. Complexities within the huge thunderstorm, such as updrafts, downdrafts, and wind shear, can tilt the supercell, allowing different processes to develop side-by-side (Figure 9.28b) Rain and hail commonly fall from the leading part of the supercell, while tornadoes may spin out of the trailing portion. Many of the most powerful tornadoes develop from the mesocyclones within supercell thunderstorms.

Thunderstorms in Canada

Thunderstorms develop both in isolation and as parts of larger weather systems. The distribution of lightning activity in Canada shows a non-uniform pattern (Figure 9.31). Southern Ontario has the most thunderstorms; the Arctic and the east and west coasts the fewest. Windsor, Ontario, averages 33 days of thunderstorms per year. Canada's most southern city is the most humid place and has one of the warmest summers—prime ingredients for initiating thunderstorm activity. Further, it is away from the stabilizing effects of the Great Lakes.

Occasionally, a winter thunderstorm arrives when advancing warm air from the south rides above retreating cold air at Earth's surface, as might occur ahead of a warm front. The warm air is slowly but gradually forced aloft. In being lifted, it becomes destabilized. The air is cooled, clouds grow, and occasionally thunder is heard. Generally, you do not see lightning because the widespread low cloud obscures the towering thunderclouds rising from it. A winter thunderstorm or "thundersnow" is rare in Canada and much less severe than its summer cousin.

Environment Canada issues severe thunderstorm warnings only when severe weather is occurring or is about to occur. The weather service tries to provide lead times of 15 minutes to two hours. Environment Canada usually issues watches first, then warnings. In some situations, however, when severe thunderstorms develop quickly, forecasters skip the watch stage and issue warnings directly.

Severe thunderstorms can wreak havoc on people and property with their lethal arsenal—heavy rain, flash floods, hail, lightning, and high-speed winds,

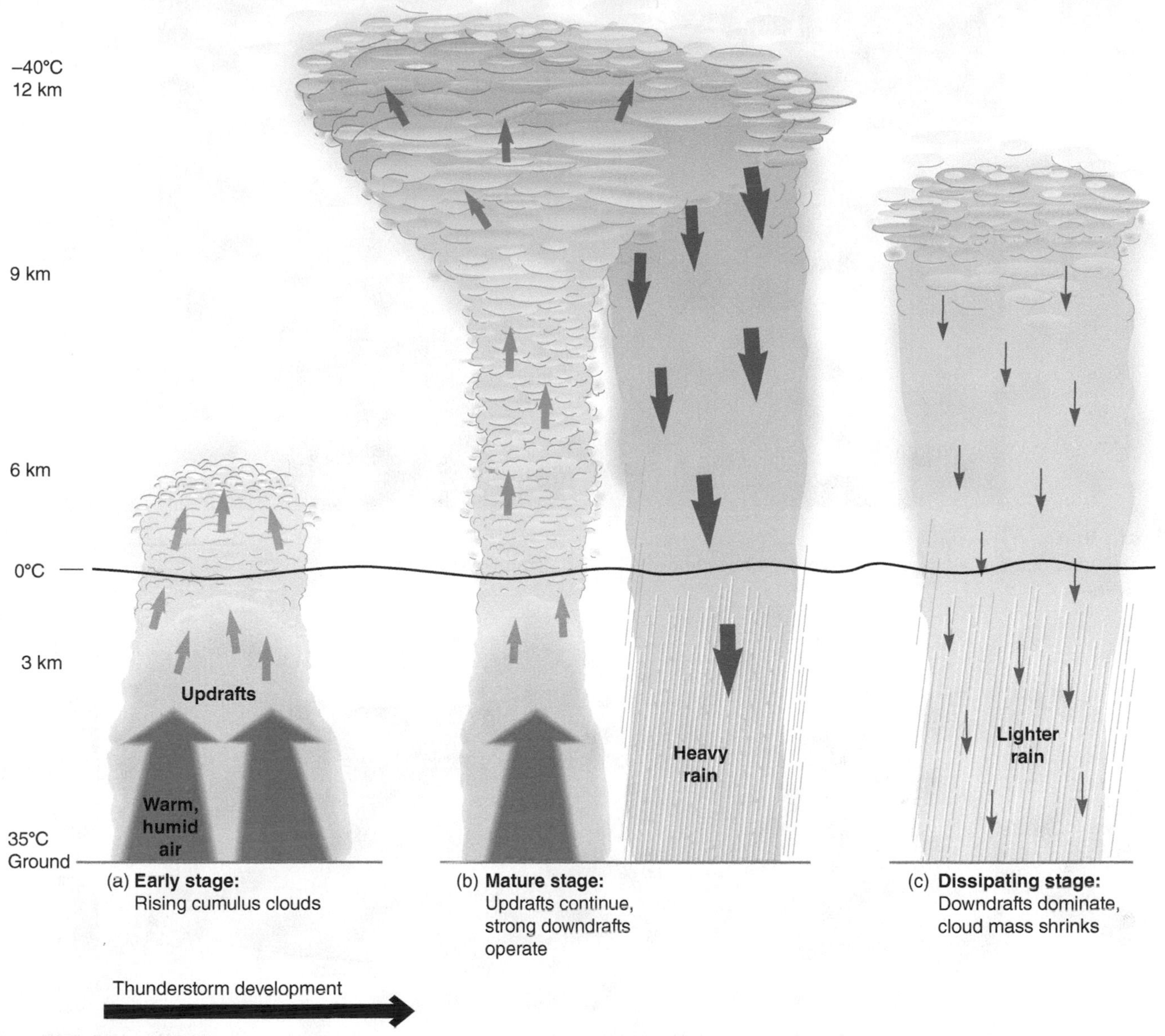

Figure 9.29
Stages in the development of a thunderstorm. (a) *Early stage:* Warm, humid air rises in updrafts, cooling causes condensation to form clouds, air keeps rising as long as it is warmer than surrounding air. (b) *Mature stage:* Ice crystals and large raindrops become too heavy for updrafts to maintain them in suspension; ice and rain fall, forcing air to move in downdrafts, while updrafts still pump warm, moist air into the thunderstorm. (c) *Dissipating stage:* Downdrafts dominate, warm and moist updrafts cease, and rain becomes weaker as clouds begin to evaporate.

which can be either straight-line blasts or rotating tornadoes. A severe thunderstorm warning is issued when one or more of the following is expected to occur:

- Wind gusts of 90 km/h or more.
- Hail two centimetres in diameter or larger.
- Rainfall of 50 mm or more within one hour or 75 mm or more within three hours.

HAIL

Hailstones are layered ice balls most often dropped from severe thunderstorms (Figure 9.32). These stones of varying shapes and sizes crash to the ground at speeds exceeding 150 km/h. There are no records of hail killing anybody in Canada. Wildlife and livestock are less fortunate. Once, hailstones pounded a 270 kg hog to death. On 14 July 1953, a hailstorm in Alberta killed 3000 ducks and thousands of other birds, such as owls and songbirds. Four days later hailstones crushed the skulls of 27 000 ducks in the same area. Hail also takes a tremendous toll on crops, vehicles, and buildings. On 9 August 2007, softball-sized hail struck southern Manitoba, flattening a crop ready to be harvested.

Figure 9.30
Warm, moist, buoyant air rises high, forming a huge supercell thunderstorm over Africa.
Source: NASA.

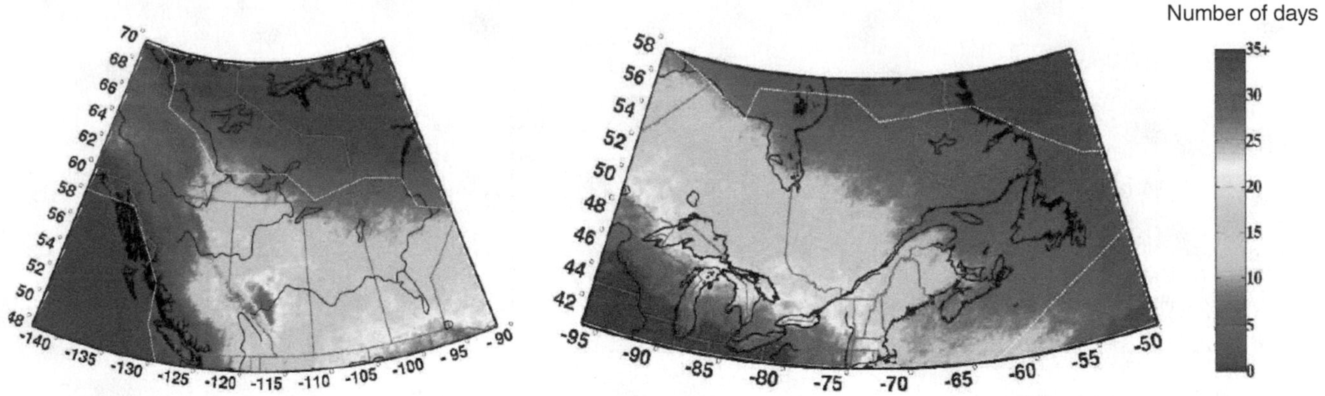

Figure 9.31
Average number of days when at least one cloud-to-ground lightning flash was detected in a 20 km by 20 km area for western (left) and eastern (right) Canada (1999–2009).
Source: A decade of cloud-to-ground lightning in Canada: 1999–2008. Part 1: Flash density and occurrence, William R. Burrows, Bohdan Kochtubajda, Atmosphere-Ocean, 1 September 2010, Canadian Meteorological and Oceanographic Society. Reprinted by permission of the publisher (Taylor & Francis Group, http://www.informaworld.com).

In Dauphin, hardly a car or dwelling's roof was left untouched, with repairs totalling several million dollars.

Important requirements for **hail** are (1) large thunderstorms with buoyant hot air rising from heated ground and (2) upper-level cold air creating maximum temperature contrasts, resulting in (3) the strong updrafts needed to keep hailstones suspended aloft while adding coatings of ice onto ever-growing cores. A cross-section through a hailstone (Figure 9.32) reveals accretionary layers of ice with an onion-like appearance. The layering indicates that the hailstone travelled through parts of the thunderstorm cloud with greater and lesser amounts of supercooled liquid water content (Figure 9.33). A hailstone weighing 290 g was found in Cedoux, Saskatchewan on 27 August 1973, and was estimated to have weighed 450 g at impact. It had a diameter of 114 mm, the largest ever documented in Canada. A much larger hailstone, the biggest ever documented in North America, fell in south-central Nebraska on 22 June 2003. It measured 17.8 cm in diameter—almost as large as a soccer ball. Updrafts must be very powerful to keep hailstones this large suspended in the air.

Thunderstorms that drop large, damaging hailstones are irregularly distributed in Canada. Comparison of lightning activity in Figure 9.31 with hail frequency in Figure 9.34 reveals a marked difference.

Figure 9.32
A broken hailstone shows the layers of its growth.
Source: Weatherstock, Inc.

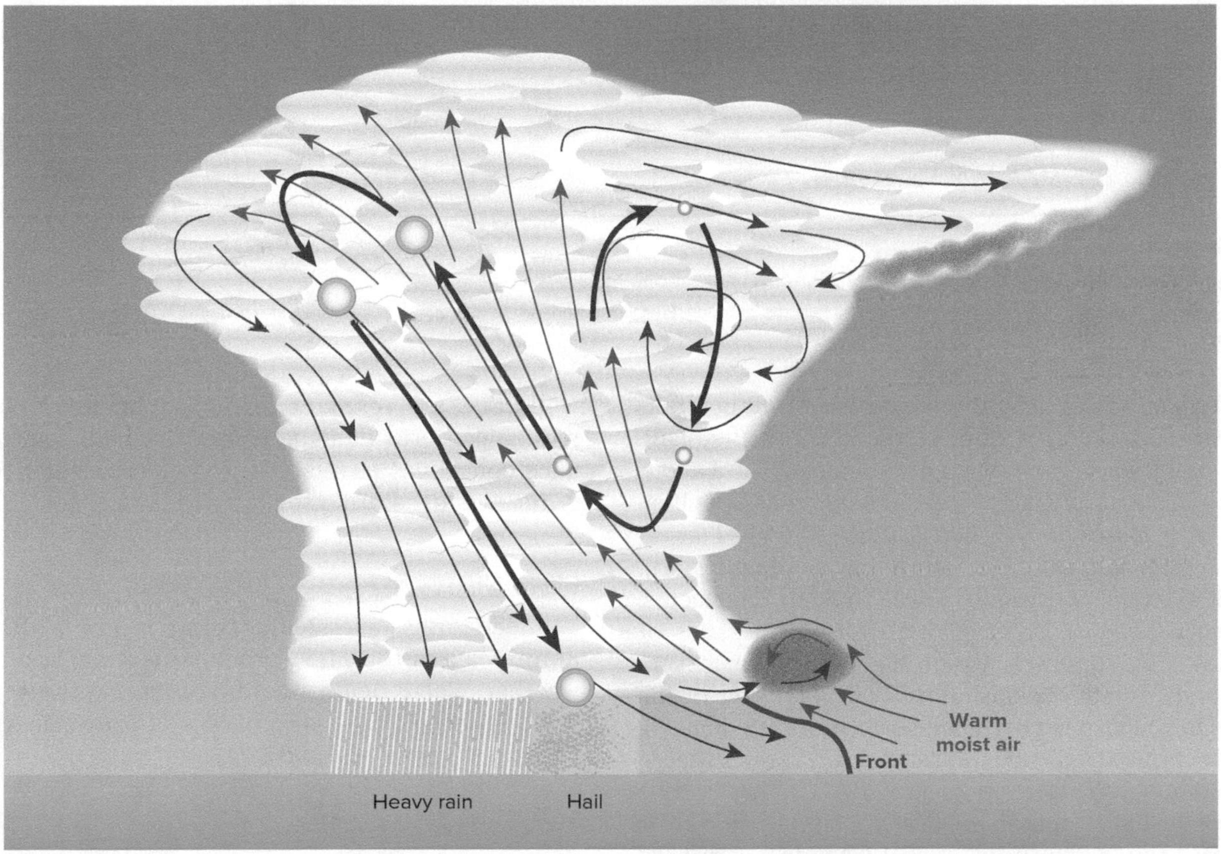

Figure 9.33
Typical hailstone growth path through a thunderstorm cloud. Hailstones add most of their mass during updrafts.
Source: Graphic by Michael Pidwirny.

Thunderstorms are common in Ontario, but the cold air necessary for hail formation is uncommon. Destructive, large hail abounds in the colder Prairies. Some of the most hail-prone geography in the world, central Alberta's hailstorm alley, gets hit on four to six days each year. May to October is the period of maximum hail

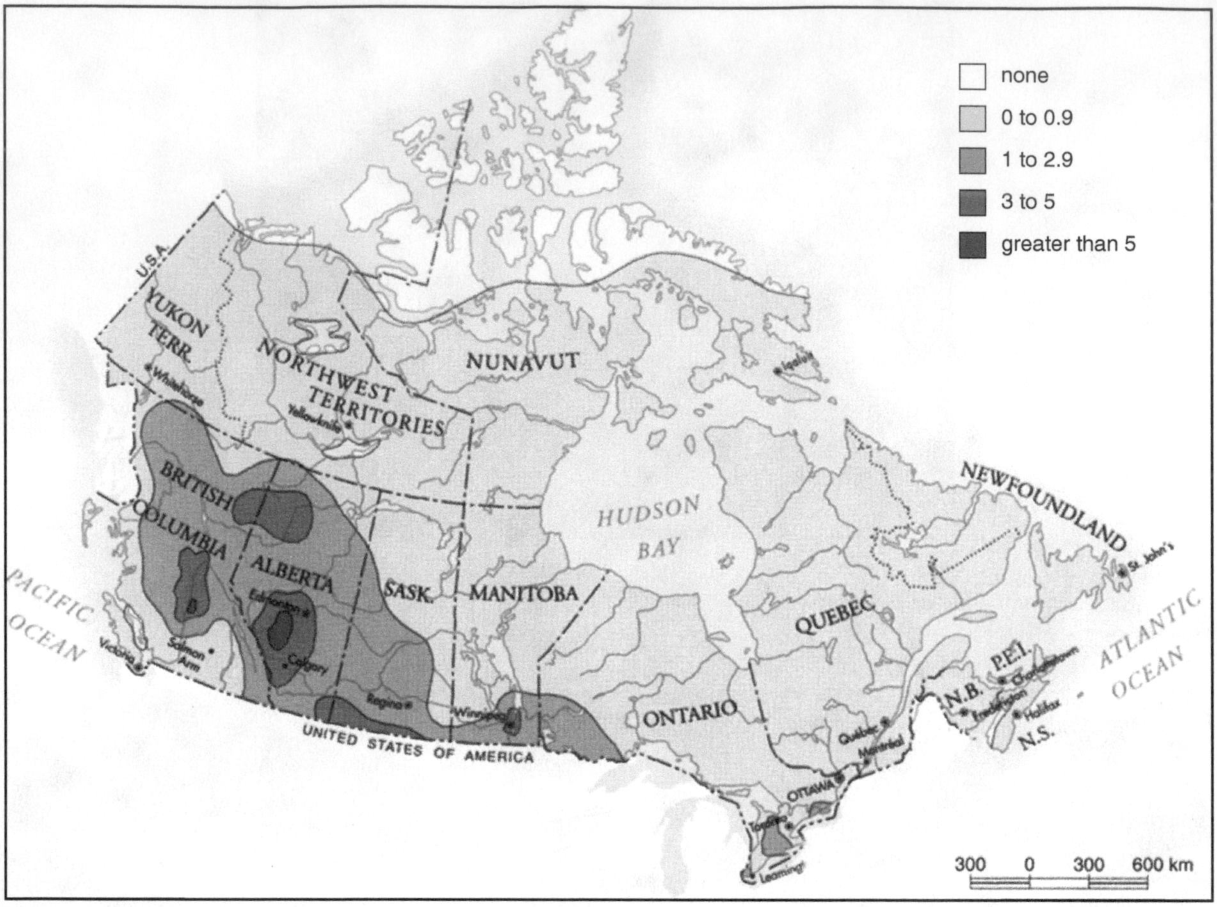

Figure 9.34
Average annual number of days with hail in Canada.
Source: © Environment Canada, Canadian Atmospheric Hazards Network - Prairie and Northern Region 2008. Reproduced with permission.

occurrences, and nearly three-quarters of all hail falls between noon and the dinner hour. The average hailfall usually lasts from six to ten minutes. The Labour Day 1991 storm in Calgary caused up to $412 million in insured losses in 116 000 claims—a record insurance loss for any single hailstorm in Canadian history. The 30-minute storm split trees, flooded basements, broke windows and siding, and dented thousands of vehicles. Raging sewer waters blew off sewer covers and plugged catch basins. More than a quarter of the homes in Calgary experienced some property damage. Many aircraft at Calgary International Airport suffered costly damage. This event was followed by destructive and costly hailstorms in 1999 and 2010, again hitting Calgary—the hailstorm capital of Canada—very hard (Table 1.4). The most recent storm, on 12 July 2010, came with a price tag of $400 million. Unusually hard hailstones pounded the city for 30 minutes, causing extensive damage (Figure 9.35).

To protect property against hail damage, civil engineers and contractors recommend the development of economical building materials for roofs and exterior walls that are resistant to impact by hailstones. To reduce property damage caused by hail, some insurance companies have sponsored cloud seeding, which is aimed at generating small, softer hailstones.

LIGHTNING

Thunderstorms generate **lightning** (Figure 9.36), which in turn causes **thunder**. Lightning is a major cause of weather-related deaths in Canada during the summer. It is also one of the major causes of forest fires in the country (Figures 12.3 and 12.4).

Lightning Hot Spots

At any moment there are 2000 thunderstorms happening worldwide. Lightning strikes at least 100 times a second, nearly nine million times a day, and more than three billion times a year. Lightning is concentrated over land; it is relatively uncommon over the oceans. Land warms up faster and gets hotter than the oceans; more warm, unstable air at the land surface means

Figure 9.35
(a) A few hailstones from the 12 July 2010 storm in Calgary and (b) some of the damage they caused to the rooftop greenhouses at the University of Calgary.
Sources: (a) Bill McMurtry; (b) Derek McBurney.

more convective upwelling to form thunderstorms, and thus more lightning. Lightning is not evenly distributed over the continents. Topography, rainfall, and air temperatures are all controlling factors.

According to Environment Canada, lightning flashes occur in Canada about three million times a year. That corresponds to a rate of one every three seconds during the summer months. Where does

Figure 9.36
A thunderstorm electrifies downtown Montreal.
Source: © Desirable Futures.

lightning occur? Flash density averages approximately 0.5 to 2 flashes per square kilometre per year in much of Canada except southern Ontario, which receives approximately 1.5 to 3.5 flashes per square kilometre per year, and most of British Columbia, Newfoundland, and Labrador, and the northern portions of the country, which receive less than 0.5 flashes per square kilometre per year. While southern Ontario is the lightning "hot spot" in Canada, it receives much less lightning on average than neighbouring areas of the United States, which have warmer climate and more tempestuous weather.

How Lightning Works

You can make your own "lightning." Drag your feet across a carpet and become a negatively charged "thundercloud." Now touch a metal door handle and feel the "lightning" as the negative charges bolt from you to the positive charges on the metal. The lightning of thunderstorms involves a similar flow of electrical current as areas with excess negative charges seek a balance with places having excess positive charges. During the buildup of tall clouds, charged particles separate, creating an abundance of positive charges up high and an excess of negative charges down low (Figure 9.37).

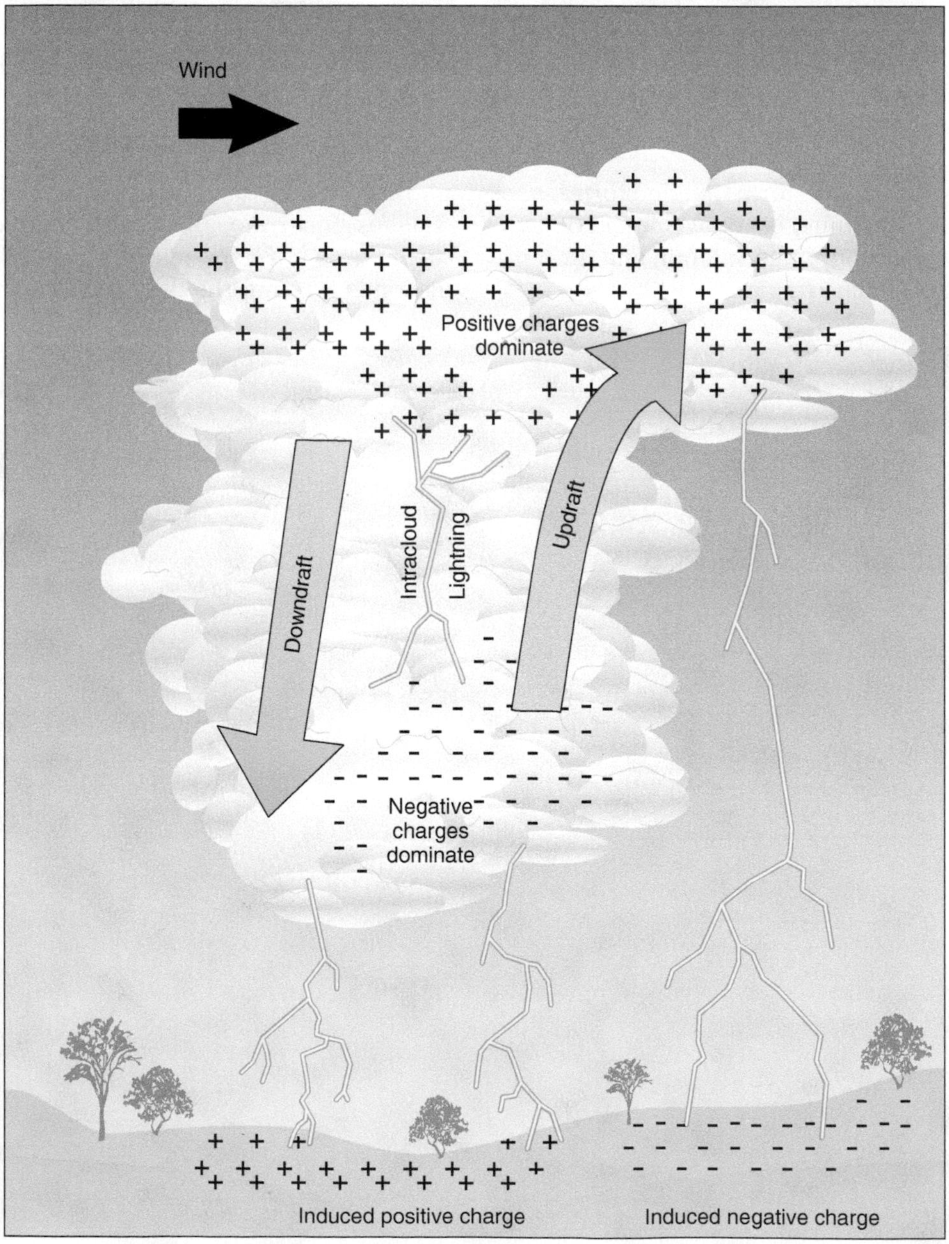

Figure 9.37

Schematic view of charge separation within a thundercloud and the induced charges on the Earth beneath. When electrical potential is great enough, narrow channels of air become ionized, allowing them to conduct the electricity that we see as lightning.

Figure 9.38
Triple lightning modes. On left, cloud-to-ground followed by extra-bright return stroke from ground. In lower right, ground toward cloud seeking to connect. In middle right, cloud-to-cloud.
Source: © NOAA.

The charge imbalance apparently comes about as the freezing and shattering of supercooled water drops initiates charge separations that are distributed by updrafts and downdrafts within the thundercloud. The charge separations occur during the cloud buildup in the early stage of thunderstorm development (Figure 9.29a), and then lightning bolts forth during the mature stage (Figure 9.29b).

A thundercloud interacts electrically with the ground. The abundance of negative charges at the base of the cloud induces a buildup of positive charges on the ground surface, because the opposite charges attract each other. Lightning can move from cloud to earth, earth to cloud, or cloud to cloud (Figure 9.38).

Lightning moves at speeds over 10 000 km/s and typically includes several strokes, all occurring within 0.5 to 2 seconds. Thanks to high-speed photography, it is now possible to explain the basic sequence within a lightning flash. (1) Static electricity builds up within the lower thundercloud and induces opposite charges on the ground. (2) Discharge begins within the cloud and initiates a dimly visible, negatively charged stream of electrons propagating downward (Figure 9.39a). (3) The conductive stream moves earthward in 50 m jumps as a stepped leader (Figure 9.39b). (4) As the stepped leader nears the ground, the electrical field at the surface increases greatly, attracting streamers of positive sparks upward and connecting with the stepped leader about 50 m above ground (Figure 9.39c). (5) The connection closes the electrical circuit and initiates the return stroke, sending positive charges up to the cloud with a brilliant flash (Figure 9.39d). (6) More lightning strokes occur as charges flow between the cloud and the earth.

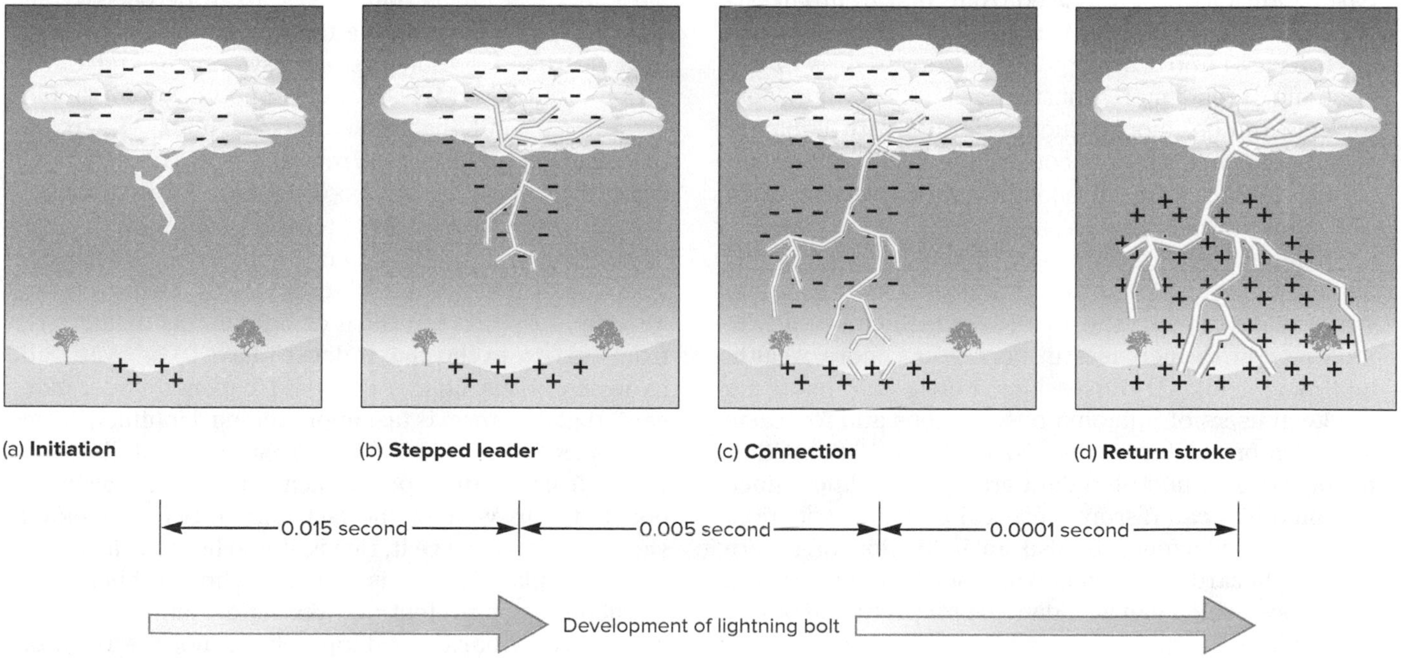

Figure 9.39
Steps in creating a lightning bolt. (a) *Initiation:* Charge separation in cloud builds up static electricity. (b) *Stepped leader:* Negative charges move in dimly visible stream downward in intermittent steps. (c) *Connection:* When leader nears ground, a positive discharge leaps up, completing the attachment. (d) *Return stroke:* The connected path flashes bright as charges exchange between cloud and ground in several events, totalling about 0.5 seconds.
Source: © NOAA.

Several different strokes all occur within the one- or two-second event we call a lightning bolt. If you have seen a lightning bolt that appears to flicker, you have witnessed the several different up-and-down strokes that constitute a given "bolt." The electrical discharge of lightning can briefly create temperatures as high as 30 000°C. The high temperatures of lightning flashes heat the surrounding air, causing it to expand explosively; this expansion of air produces the sound waves we call thunder.

Lightning Deaths

Lightning is one of the most consistent and underrated causes of weather-related deaths or injury in North America. Lightning isn't good at killing people, though. Given that just one lightning bolt contains 100 million volts of electricity, while only 120 volts can kill a person; and that more than 30 million lightning bolts strike North America each year, it's surprising that fewer than 100 people are struck dead each year. That number, however, represents more deaths than all other weather forces combined, including hurricanes, tornadoes, and floods.

In Canada, lightning kills an average of 10 people annually and seriously injures about 125 people. That represents a one in 240 000 chance of being hit, greater than the odds of winning most high-prize lotteries. Lightning mortality has declined significantly over the past century as people moved from rural to urban settings. Falling death rates can also be attributed to better forecasts and warnings, greater awareness of the lightning threat, more substantial buildings available for safe refuge, more structures fitted with lightning rods and conductors to convey the lightning energy to the earth, improved medical care, and more rapid communications.

Whereas the number of lightning deaths has decreased over the years, damages from lightning strikes have been on the increase, which can be attributed mostly to increases in population, more wealth, and more personal possessions. Forest fire managers are keen users of lightning observations and forecasts as indicators of forest fire risks (Figure 12.23). Other major users of lightning data are hydro utilities, since lightning hits can disrupt electrical power distribution. Lightning occurrence is also an indication of severe weather hazards such as downbursts, heavy rains, and tornadoes, which can also damage property and power distribution.

Three-quarters of all lightning casualties occur between May and September (with July the most lightning-prone month) and nearly four-fifths occur between 10:00 a.m. and 7:00 p.m. (Figure 9.40). Each year, about 400 children and adults in the United States and Canada are struck by lightning while working and

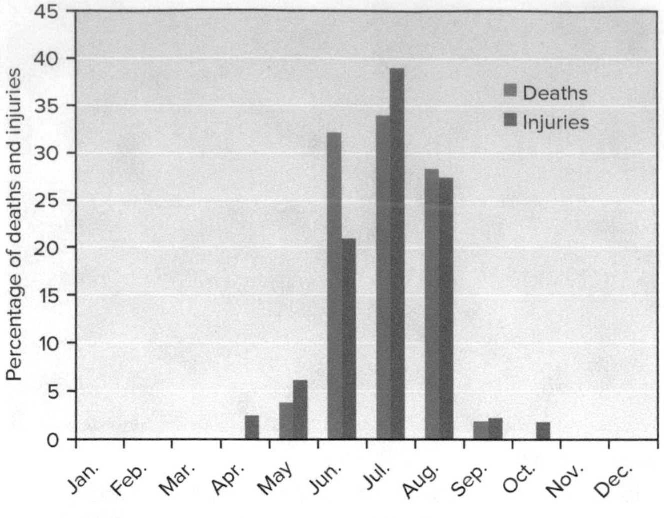

Figure 9.40
Monthly distribution of lightning-related deaths and injuries in Canada (1986–2005).

Source: © Her Majesty The Queen in Right of Canada, Environment Canada, 2014. Reproduced with permission.

playing at outdoor sports events, or while attending concerts or assemblies. Wide-open fields and parks are often cited as the most dangerous places to be during a thunderstorm. Sports fields offer a lot of targets for lightning such as poles, wire fences, dugouts, and metal bleachers. The fields themselves are wide open; players and spectators become the tallest objects around. In and around a thunderstorm, swimming and other water-based activities are very dangerous and should be stopped until the threat is over. Water is a good conductor of electrical current and if lightning should strike the water even at a good distance from the swimmer, he or she could still get a serious shock.

Lightning tragedies can be avoided. Generally speaking, if you see lightning or hear thunder you are already at risk. Every flash of lightning is dangerous, from the first to the last. It doesn't have to be overhead to be dangerous. Louder or more frequent thunder indicates that the storm is fast approaching. Lightning often strikes as far as 15 km away from any rainfall. Many deaths from lightning occur ahead of the storm because people try to wait to the last minute before seeking shelter. If you can see it, flee it; if you hear it, clear it.

A popular fallacy is that somehow rubber tires or rubber soles protect you during a thunderstorm. It is true that a hard metal-top vehicle, not the back of a pickup truck or convertible (even with its top up), away from the danger of falling trees or hydro poles is one of the safest places to be in a lightning storm. School buses are an excellent lightning shelter that can be utilized by large groups of people. But it is not your all-weather tires that guard you against the risk of

IN GREATER DEPTH

What to Do and Not Do in Case of Lightning

When a thunderstorm is approaching, Environment Canada recommends the 30/30 rule:

- Thirty-second flash-to-bang rule: When lightning is recognized, count the seconds until the bang of its thunder. If the time lapse is 30 seconds or less, you should take appropriate shelter immediately.
- Thirty-minute shelter rule: Once lightning has been recognized, it is recommended to wait 30 minutes or more after the last flash of lightning is witnessed or thunder is heard before leaving the safe location. Any subsequent lightning or thunder after the beginning of the 30-minute count should reset the clock and another count should begin.

DO

- Follow forecasts.
- Get inside the house, but do not touch anything. Lightning can flow through plumbing, electrical wires, or telephone wires. Get off the phone, unless it is a cordless or a cell phone; 2.4% of victims are hit through land-line phones.
- Water is a great electrical conductor. Move away from open water such as swimming pools, lakes, rivers, wet beaches, and piers. If you are in a small boat, go ashore.
- Get in your car, but don't touch anything. Lightning usually travels along the outside metal surface of the vehicle and then jumps to the ground through the air, a wet tire surface, or the tire itself, causing it to blow out.
- If you are caught outside, move to a low place. Avoid tall structures, including trees.
- If you are outside with others, stay five metres apart; a charge can jump.
- Crouch and ball up. Don't lie flat. Don't put your hands down; instead, cover your ears or head.

DON'T

- Take a shower, blow-dry your hair, make a cake, or do the dishes—stay away from water and wires.
- Surf TV or the Internet—don't rely on surge protectors.
- Watch out the window—stay well inside.
- Shelter under a tree, in a phone booth, or near a fence, shed, tractor, or tent with metal poles.
- Walk under power lines, beside highway guard rails, or on railway tracks.

lightning. Vehicles are an excellent source of protection because the all-metal steel cage or frame surrounding the vehicle dissipates the current equally before arcing around the tires to the ground, and therefore there is little likelihood that the current will go to the interior.

WINDS

Winds can arrive with tremendous power; they may be hot or cold, straight line or rotating.

Derechos

Since 1888, the Spanish word **derecho**, meaning "straight ahead," has been applied to widespread, powerful, straight-line winds. Thunderstorms advancing in a line can have their individual energies combine to form a line of ferocious winds. An organized line of storms in a region can generate a derecho lasting 10 to 15 minutes. Derechos commonly extend along a line at least 400 km long with wind gusts of 100 km/h; maximum recorded wind speeds are 240 km/h. In North America, derechos mostly occur in the middle and eastern states and in southern Ontario. Derechos can be as damaging as a small tornado: they kill people; cause extensive damage to mobile homes and lightly constructed buildings; cause tragic incidents with airplanes, trucks, and cars; and mow down huge tracts of trees.

Ontario–Adirondacks Derecho, 15 July 1995

In the evening of 15 July 1995, a huge complex of thunderstorms with embedded tornadoes packing hurricane-force winds and tens of thousands of lightning bolts cut numerous paths of destruction from Upper Michigan across Central Ontario to the Ottawa River Valley. Early the next morning, the storm moved south across the Adirondack Mountains of New York State and off the coast of New England. The 1200 km trek took only 12 hours at an average speed of 110 km/h. Wind gusts in the worst damaged area were in the 150–200 km/h range. In Ontario, the winds scattered one-tonne bales of hay as if they were breakfast cereal, and trailers 13 m long were tossed 250 m. Thousands of trees were blown down, with some blocking roadways, severing electrical lines, and damaging or destroying homes and automobiles.

Power outages along the storm band lasted from several days to a week. In some areas, the power grid had to be rebuilt. In New England, millions more trees came down, killing 5 and injuring 11. Most of the dead were hikers and campers in the Adirondack Mountains. The Ontario–Adirondacks derecho was one of the most costly severe thunderstorm events to occur in eastern North America during the twentieth century, causing almost US$0.5 billion (1995 dollars) in damage.

Severe thunderstorms usually occur during the hottest part of the day, in the late afternoon or early evening. Why was this derecho still active in the early hours of the next morning? In mid-July 1995, a heat wave was in progress. Late-evening temperatures on 14 July were still around 30°C and the humidity was high. The hot and humid air just above the ground supplied energy to the mass of thunderstorms travelling through the night. At low altitudes, record heat and humidity moved in while, at the same time, the upper atmosphere remained dry and cool. This sharp contrast produced the potential for extremely violent thunderstorms. As the cloud mass raced across Michigan, Ontario, and New York State, it drew the hot, humid air upward until it condensed, releasing its contained energy. Derecho winds flowed down from the fast-moving cloud mass, causing extensive damage.

Tornadoes

Tornadoes derive their name from the Spanish verb *tornar*, which means "to turn." A **tornado** is a rapidly rotating column of air usually descending from a large thunderstorm (see photo of chapter opener). Tornadoes have the highest wind speeds of any weather phenomenon. The strongest tornadoes are more intense than the biggest hurricanes, but they affect smaller areas. The most violent tornadoes move at speeds up to 100 km/h, but with rotating wind speeds sometimes in excess of 500 km/h. Only slightly more than 1% of tornadoes have wind speeds in excess of 320 km/h, but they are responsible for over 70% of deaths. The core of the whirling vortex is usually less than one kilometre wide and acts like a giant vacuum cleaner, sucking up air and objects.

Tornadoes may touch ground only briefly, or they may stay in contact for many kilometres, moving along an irregular path with abrupt changes in direction.

The rotating wind speeds of a tornado are highest 100 m or so above the ground. This is most likely because the winds at ground level are slowed by the drag resistance of earth, trees, buildings, cars, and other obstacles.

LO4

HOW TORNADOES FORM

Regional Scale

Several conditions are necessary to turn an ordinary thunderstorm into a tornado-spinning monster. Typically, in North America, the following conditions occur simultaneously: (1) a low-altitude, northerly flow of warm moist air, often from the Gulf of Mexico, with temperatures at the ground in excess of 24°C, (2) a middle-altitude, cold, dry air mass, often from Canada or the Rocky Mountains, moving at speeds in excess of 80 km/h, and (3) high-altitude jet-stream winds racing east at speeds in excess of 250 km/h. These three air masses, all moving in different directions, set up shearing conditions, imparting spin to a thundercloud (Figure 9.41).

The warm, moist air lifts vertically, releasing its latent heat and forming a strong updraft that is sheared and spun at mid-levels by the fast-moving dry air and then twisted in another direction at its upper levels by the jet stream. The corkscrew motion is enhanced by vertical movements of air: warm air rising on the leading side, with cool air descending on the trailing side. The rotation of the winds is achieved without requiring the Coriolis effect.

Supercell Thunderstorm Scale

A single-cell thunderstorm (Figure 9.28a) does not grow large enough, or energetic enough, to create violent tornadoes. Sometimes, however, a huge updraft of air builds a massive thunderstorm that is tilted by wind shear and develops into a *supercell thunderstorm* (Figure 9.28b). The tilt of the supercell allows warm air to continue rising into central portions of the storm, while most of the rain and hail fall on the leading side. On the trailing side, downdrafts of cool, drier air exist, and it is between the updraft and the rear flank downdraft that tornadoes usually form. Only 30% of supercells produce tornadoes. Weather forecasters know the atmospheric conditions that may spawn a tornado but the actual process that causes a tornado to pop out of one cloud and not another is largely still a puzzle.

A **wall cloud** may form as a markedly lower cloud beneath the main mass of the mesocyclone (Figure 9.42). Wall clouds form in a supercell and powerful tornadoes may form within wall clouds. The diameter of the wall cloud is smaller than that of the rotating mesocyclone, and an even small-diameter vortex can develop with greater wind speeds. As a rotating core of air pulls into a tighter spiral, its wind speed increases dramatically as its angular momentum is conserved. This principle is analogous to ice skaters spinning with arms outstretched; they can spin even faster by pulling their arms toward their bodies. The vortex may be stretched in length far enough to touch the ground—and then it can wreak havoc as a tornado.

Vortex Scale

Zooming in at the vortex scale, another scenario for tornado formation involves a three-stage sequence of events (Figure 9.43). The collision of a warm air mass with a cold air mass low in the atmosphere can create a nearly invisible, horizontal vortex rotating parallel to

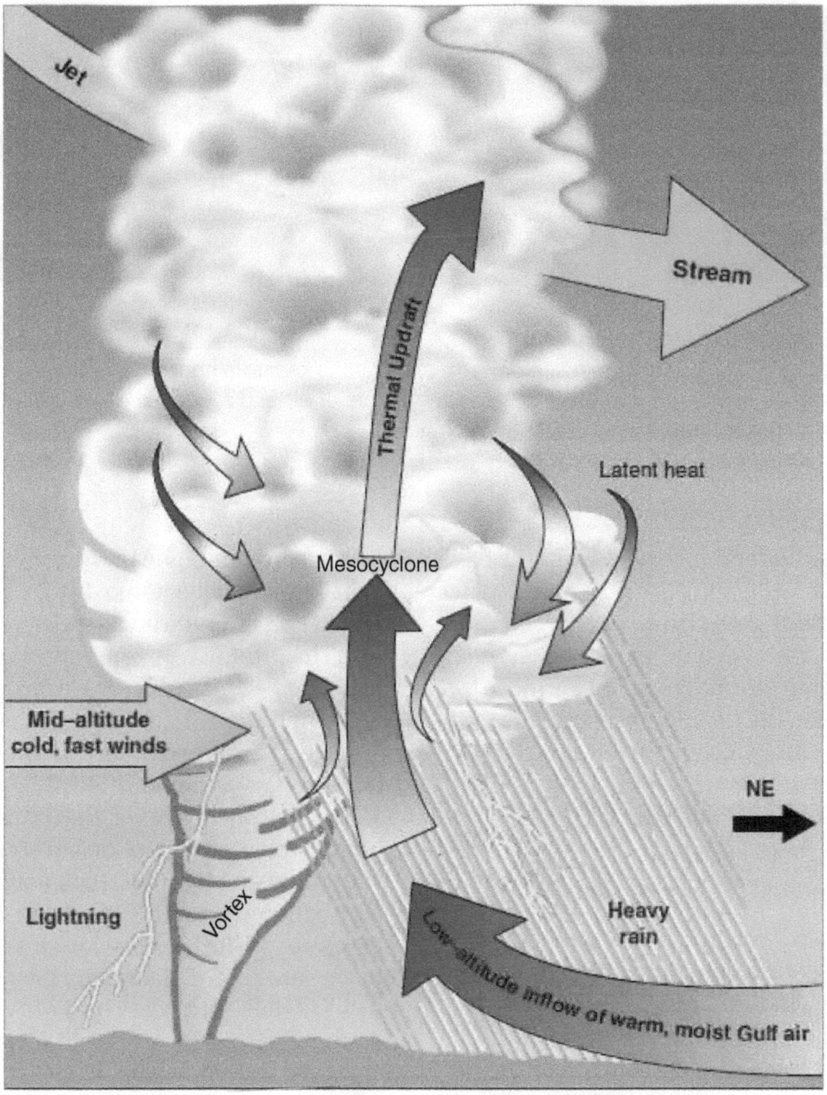

Figure 9.41

Components of a North American tornado. A warm, moist mass of Gulf of Mexico air collides with a fast-moving mass of polar air, causing updrafts that build up into the polar-front jet stream. Three fast-moving air masses, all going in different directions, impart shears, causing rotation. A tornado receives additional energy via lightning and latent heat released by rainfall.

Source: Adapted from J. Eagleman, *Severe and Unusual Weather,* 1983; Van Nostrand Reinhold, New York.

Figure 9.42

Ominous looking wall cloud near Coldwater, Indiana, on 22 July 2010.

Source: Photo courtesy of Samantha Sharpley.

the ground (Figure 9.43a). The warmer air rising above the collision creates an updraft that tilts the rotating tube of air (Figure 9.43b). As the vortex is lifted, it is stretched, thus decreasing its diameter and increasing its velocity to tornado status (Figure 9.43c).

FINAL STAGE OF A TORNADO

When downdrafts of air within the storm begin to interfere with or cut off the energy-supplying updrafts, a tornado enters its final phase. As a tornado weakens, it may be influenced by other winds and deformed into different shapes. A ropelike shape is common for a weakening

(a) (b) (c)

Figure 9.43
Hypothesis of tornado formation: (a) Colliding masses of warm and cold air create a horizontal, spinning tube of air, a vortex, in the lower atmosphere. (b) Rising air within the updraft tilts the rotating tube of air and stretches it upward. (c) As a vortex is lifted and stretched, its spin velocity increases and it develops into a tornado.
Source: NOAA.

tornado, but its smaller-diameter vortex can still have high wind speeds that cause significant damage. After a mesocyclone and tornado form from a supercell thunderstorm and then dissipate, a new mesocyclone may arise near the centre of the storm. Then, one or more tornadoes may develop from the newer mesocyclone.

DEATH AND DESTRUCTION CAUSED BY TORNADOES

Tornadoes cause destruction in several ways:

1. High-speed winds blow away buildings and trees.
2. The winds throw debris that acts like bullets or shrapnel, breaking windows and killing people.
3. When the winds lift and blow away a roof, the exposed walls are easily knocked over and the furniture removed.

Who dies during tornadoes? Tornadoes tend to kill (1) residents in mobile homes and recreational vehicles, (2) occupants of exterior rooms with windows, (3) people with reduced mobility, and (4) those unaware of broadcast tornado alerts. Residents of frame houses can run into interior rooms to gain some protection. But where do mobile-home dwellers run to hide? There are no interior rooms, and who wants to run outside into a severe thunderstorm with heavy rain, lightning, hail, and flying debris? Almost half of those killed by tornadoes die inside their disintegrating mobile homes. Many towns now require that mobile-home communities provide tornado protection with a common basement shelter or an aboveground reinforced concrete building.

Are you safer in a car or a mobile home? Many mobile homes can be tipped over by 130 km/h winds, whereas many modern cars (excluding many SUVs) have low centres of gravity and streamlined shapes that require wind speeds of about 200 km/h to tip over. Also, most new vehicles are equipped with seat restraints and air bags to provide some protection during a rollover or collision. Many mobile-home dwellers facing a tornado threat would do better to run outside and sit inside their cars.

The traditional protection against dying in a tornado has been to go underground, into a cellar. But more and more houses are being built without cellars. What can a homeowner do? A new type of shelter, the "safe room," is being offered by some home builders in tornado-prone areas of the United States. In the interiors of houses, closets or bathrooms are being built as safe rooms with 30 cm thick concrete walls, steel doors, and concrete roofs. These safe rooms are reminiscent of bank vaults. Prices range from about \$1000 for a basic safe room all the way past \$10 000 for larger, custom models with carpet, lights, phones, and Internet connections. Some can hold up to 25 people.

The Fujita Scale: Classifying Tornado Intensity

The Fujita scale (F scale) is a well-known scheme for classifying tornado strength according to the potential damage to homes and other structures (Table 9.3). It is a six-point intensity ranking, designated F0 to F5, in order of increasing wind speed and storm damage. However, over the years, it has become necessary to better define the types and severity of damages done by varying tornado wind speeds. For example, simply stating that house walls were blown down ignores the varying construction styles and ages of houses. Therefore, an extensive study defined more criteria for tornado wind damage and resulted in an Enhanced Fujita scale (EF scale) introduced in the United States in 2007 and in Canada in 2013 (Table 9.3). Now 28 types of structures and trees have been identified, each evaluated based on 9 levels of damage.

There is no such thing as a typical tornado; however, the majority are 75 m across, have winds of about 175 km/h, move at 60 km/h, stay on the ground for

TABLE 9.3

The Fujita and Enhanced Fujita Scales

Fujita Scale	Wind speed (km/h)	Enhanced Fujita Scale	Wind speed (km/h)
F0	64–116	**EF0**	105–137
Little damage		Siding and shingle damage	
F1	117–180	**EF1**	138–178
Roof damage		Uprooted trees and overturned single-wide mobile homes	
F2	181–253	**EF2**	179–218
Roof gone		Permanent houses off foundations	
F3	254–332	**EF3**	219–266
Wall collapse		Severe damage; houses mostly destroyed	
F4	333–418	**EF4**	267–322
House blown down		Devastating; large sections of school buildings destroyed	
F5	419–512	**EF5**	>322
House blown away		Incredible damage; deformation of mid- and high-rise buildings	

15 km or less, and last for minutes. Fortunately, only 6% of all tornadoes are in the category F3-EF3 or higher (Figure 9.46).

TORNADOES IN CANADA AND THE UNITED STATES

The United States is the tornado capital of the world with an average of 1000 to 1200 tornadoes every year. Tornado occurrences are mostly concentrated in an elongated southwest-northeast trending region of the Midwest known as "Tornado Alley." Canada is a distant second with 80 to 100 tornadoes each year (Figure 9.44); southwestern Ontario has the highest incidence of tornadoes because of the presence of warm, moist tropical air capped by cool breezes from the Great Lakes. Canada has nevertheless been the scene of several deadly tornadoes (Table 9.4). In Canada, 63% of tornadoes occur in June and July—when contrasting warm/moist and cool/dry air masses are more prevalent (Figure 9.45). Although the number of tornadoes reported in Canada is increasing—most probably due to a combination of better observations and climatic changes—their intensity distribution according to the Fujita scale has remained stable in the last decades (Figure 9.46). A notable event is the Elie, Manitoba, tornado of 22 June 2007, the first officially documented F5 tornado in Canada (see photo of chapter opener).

TABLE 9.4

Canada's Deadliest Tornadoes (1879–2014)

Date	Location	Fatalities	Intensity
30 Jun 1912	Regina, SK	28	F4
31 Jun 1987	Edmonton, AB	27	F4
17 Jun 1946	Windsor to Tecumseh, ON	17	F4
31 May 1985	Hopeville to Barrie, ON	12	F4
14 Jul 2000	Pine Lake, AB	12	F3
16 Aug 1888	Eastern Ontario to Valleyfield, QC	11	Unknown
3 Apr 1974	Windsor, ON	9	F3
20 Aug 1970	Sudbury, ON	6	F3
14 Jun 1892	Ste-Rose, QC	6	Unknown
6 Aug 1879	Bouctouche, NB	6	Unknown

Source: David Phillips. Climates of Canada. Government of Canada. 1990. 176p.

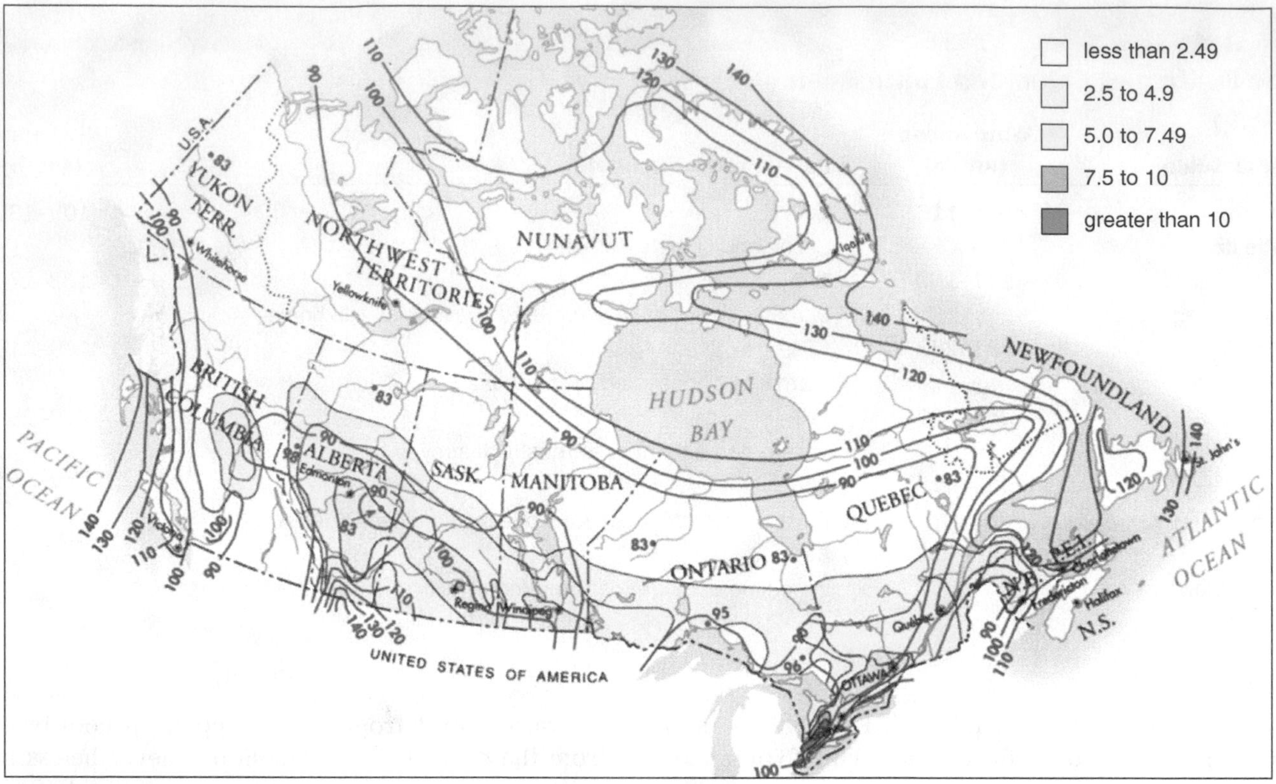

Figure 9.44

Number of tornadoes in Canada per year per 10 000 km². The red contour lines represent the 50-year return period wind speed (km/h).

Source: Reproduced with the permission of Natural Resources Canada 2014, courtesy of the Atlas of Canada.

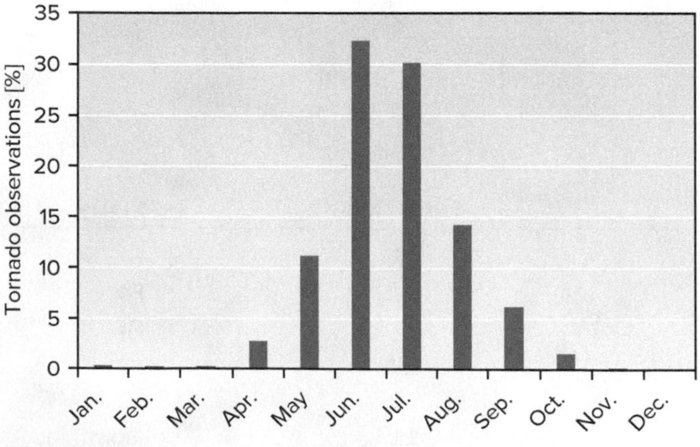

Figure 9.45

Frequency of tornado observations by month in Canada (1980–1997).

Source: Etkin et al. 2001. *International Journal of Climatology.*

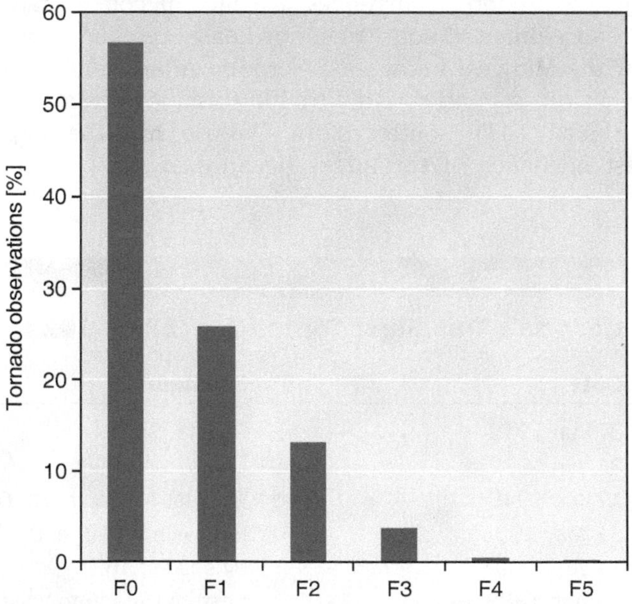

Figure 9.46

Frequency of tornado observations by intensity in Canada (1980–1997).

Source: Etkin et al. 2001. *International Journal of Climatology.*

The 1987 Black Friday, Edmonton Tornado

The deadliest Canadian tornado in recent history occurred on 31 July 1987 in Edmonton, Alberta. That Friday began sunny with warm, moist, southerly winds and a hint of stormy weather in the air. As the day wore on, temperatures and humidity rose. Thunderstorms developed over the Rocky Mountain foothills and moved toward the Alberta capital.

At about 3:00 p.m. the colliding systems triggered a severe thunderstorm that packed baseball-sized hail and torrential rains of 40 to 50 mm. But it was the monster tornado that horrified the community and surprised meteorologists around the world. Never had such a powerful, deadly tornado travelled so far north. The tornado cut a 40 km swath up to 1 km wide and was on the ground for a full terrifying hour. When the horrifying event ended, 27 people were dead, hundreds of others injured, and more than 750 families homeless. Property damage totalled $215 million. The F4 intensity twister packed winds between 330 and 415 km/h. Transmission towers were toppled, cars tossed great distances, trees uprooted, trains derailed, and a giant oil storage tank moved 300 m.

The worst-hit area was the Evergreen Mobile Home Park, in the city's far northeast where 1700 residents lived. There, 15 residents lost their lives. One woman lost four of her family members. More than 200 of the 600 trailers were destroyed or damaged. Some were devastated while those next door were untouched. Officials were thankful the tornado did not strike two hours later when many more people would have been home from work.

The 2011 Joplin, Missouri, Tornado

Joplin, Missouri, lies in the heart of tornado alley and has experienced damaging tornadoes in the past. On Sunday 22 May 2011 at mid-day, the National Weather Service Storm Prediction Center issued a tornado watch for the Joplin area, more than four hours in advance of the tornado touching down. This was followed by a tornado warning with a lead time of 24 minutes at 5:17 p.m. Sirens began to scream. But where do 50 000 people take shelter in such a hurry? They hid in basements, freezers, closets, and bathtubs.

The EF-5 Joplin tornado was a rare type of tornado containing more than one vortex. During its rampage

Figure 9.47
The 2011 Joplin tornado ripped off the roof of this superstore.
Source: CP PHOTO/AP Photo/Charlie Riedel.

Figure 9.48
The aftermath of the 2011 Joplin tornado.
Source: Aaron Fuhrman/Flickr/Getty Images.

through Joplin, it cut a corridor of destruction 10 km long and 800 m wide. Winds reached 325 km/h, carrying debris up to 100 km away. In just a few minutes, a quarter of the city was laid flat (Figures 9.47 and 9.48). The Joplin tornado illustrates the contrast between the short duration of a natural disaster and the long path to recovery. Touring the devastated town a few days after the event, President Obama said, "And then we're just going to have a tough, long slog. But what I've been telling every family I've met here is that we're going to be here long after the cameras leave. We are not going to stop until Joplin is fully back on its feet."

In the days following the tragedy, many residents could be seen alongside cleaning crews rummaging through the wreckage in search of mementos from their destroyed homes. Forensic teams worked promptly to bring closure to families of missing persons by identifying dismembered bodies. Doctors relied not only on dental records to carry on this gruesome task but also—a sign of the times—on tattoos and piercings.

SUMMARY

- Air masses vary in their temperature and water-vapour content. The atmosphere circulates mainly between low and high latitudes pushed by winds, and to a lesser extent vertically due to density differences.
  - Cold polar air is dense and flows toward the equator close to the Earth's surface.
  - Warm equatorial air rises and flows toward the poles at upper levels.
  - Different air masses do not readily mix. They are separated along boundaries called fronts, where most severe weather occurs.
- Intense heat waves kill frail members of society through overexposure to elevated temperatures. On a longer time scale, sustained hot, dry weather over a few-year period causes droughts, which can gradually lead to crop failure and famine.
  - In the central Plains of North America, droughts have resulted from high-pressure ridges in the polar jet stream that foster anticyclonic circulation. An anticyclone rotates clockwise with dry air descending down its core, warming further, and evaporating moisture from the lands below.
  - The deadliest natural disaster in Canadian history was the 1936 heat wave.
- Falling snow may: (1) melt to form rain, (2) melt and then refreeze as sleet, and (3) melt and then be supercooled into freezing rain, or (4) remain as snow.
  - In winter, moist low-pressure systems moving up the Atlantic coast may meet cold arctic air, producing powerful storms called nor'easters.
  - Cold air blowing over the Great Lakes dumps huge volumes of snow on downwind shores.
- Rotating air bodies create some of the most severe weather via thunderstorms and tornadoes.

- In the northern hemisphere, rotation is counter-clockwise as cyclonic circulation. Cyclones have a low-pressure core, so surface winds flow inward toward the core, feeding a large updraft of rising air that cools to form clouds and sometimes rain.
- Many of the largest cyclonic circulations are linked to troughs in the polar jet stream.
- The smaller the radius of a rotating air mass, the faster its wind speeds.

• Intense cyclones a few kilometres across can occur in thunderclouds, commonly producing heavy rain, lightning, thunder, and hail, and sometimes spinning off even smaller-radius rotations—tornadoes. Tornado winds can exceed 500 km/h.

Terms to Remember

adiabatic processes
air masses
anticyclone
blizzard
cyclone
derecho
downbursts
El Niño
freezing rain
fronts
haboob
Hadley cells
hail
Intertropical Convergence Zone (ITCZ)
jet stream
La Niña
lifting condensation level
lightning
monsoon
nor'easters
sleet
stratosphere
supercell thunderstorms
thunder
thunderstorm
tornado
tropopause
troposphere
wall cloud

Questions for Review

1. Draw a cross-section through the atmosphere that defines troposphere, tropopause, and stratosphere.
2. What are the relationships between high- and low-pressure zones and between cyclones and anticyclones?
3. Explain the cause of the polar jet stream. Why does its position vary across Canada and the United States during a year?
4. What is the difference between a drought and a desert?
5. Draw a map showing the polar jet conditions associated with drought in the central Plains of North America.
6. What are the stages of a famine? How do people tend to react during famine compared to during a tornado, flood, or hurricane?
7. Sketch a series of vertical cross-sections showing the stages of development of a late-afternoon thundercloud. Label the processes occurring in the cloud during each stage.
8. What is the relationship between thunder and lightning?
9. How does hail form? Where in Canada does the most large hail fall?
10. Why do higher wind speeds develop in a tornado than in a hurricane?
11. What land and air conditions make the central United States the tornado capital of the world?

Questions for Further Thought

1. What weather events create billion-dollar disasters?
2. You are hiking in the countryside when a lightning bolt flashes, followed quickly by loud thunder. What should you do?
3. What is the impact of tornadoes on large cities?
4. Is it more dangerous to live in earthquake country or tornado country?

Interesting Websites

- Hazardous Weather, Environment Canada
  http://www.ec.gc.ca/meteo-weather/default.asp?lang=En&n=15E59C08-1
- Environment Canada Top Ten Weather Stories Archive
  http://ec.gc.ca/meteo-weather/default.asp?lang=En&n=3318B51C-1
- North American Drought Monitor, National Climatic Data Center, National Oceanic and Atmospheric Administration, United States
  http://www.ncdc.noaa.gov/temp-and-precip/drought/nadm/
- National Severe Storms Laboratory, National Oceanic and Atmospheric Administration, United States
  http://www.nssl.noaa.gov/

CHAPTER TEN

10 Hurricanes

SOLAR ENERGY

This is the disintegrating power of a great wind: it isolates one from one's own kind. An earthquake, a landslip, an avalanche, overtake a man incidentally, as it were—without passion. A furious gale attacks him like a personal enemy, tries to grasp his limbs, fastens upon his mind, seeks to rout his very spirit out of him.

—Joseph Conrad, 1903, Typhoon

Outline

- Hurricane Hazel, Southern Ontario, 1954
- Hurricanes As Energy Conversion Engines
- The Life Cycle of a Hurricane
- Winds and Storm Surges
- How Hurricanes Get Their Names
- Hurricanes in the North Atlantic Ocean
- Tropical Cyclones in the Indian and Pacific Oceans
- Reduction of Hurricane Damages
- Summary

LO1 Describe the life cycle of a hurricane.

LO2 Chart the global distribution of hurricanes, typhoons, and cyclones.

LO3 Summarize what happens to North Atlantic hurricanes when they reach Canada.

LO4 Describe the destructive processes wrought by hurricanes.

LO5 Explain how Cape-Verde-type and Caribbean-type hurricanes form.

LO6 Comment on the mitigation strategies implemented to reduce the impact of hurricanes.

Hurricane Juan severely battered the City of Halifax in September 2003; fallen trees uprooted sidewalks, fences, and road signs.
Source: Chris Fogarty.

Maritimers are **hurricane** hardened, being on the tail end of the North Atlantic hurricane paths. Halifax, for example, has experienced so many weather-driven crises that it is no longer possible for residents to sue the City for fallen trees and storm water damage. The City is committed to becoming more resilient and its long-term mitigation plan includes burying all wires when modernizing neighbourhoods. The rest of Canada, however, seems to be oblivious to hurricane risk. Hurricanes happen only south of the border, don't they? How many Torontonians remember Hurricane Hazel, which, in one terrible night in October 1954, took the lives of 81 people (Table 10.1)? The event seems to have almost vanished from the collective memory.

Hurricane Hazel, Southern Ontario, 1954

Hazel was born offshore West Africa and travelled across the Atlantic Ocean unnoticed. On 5 October 1954, it reached the Caribbean Sea where it was detected by a Hurricane Hunter aircraft. First identified as a tropical storm, Hazel gained strength rapidly and reached hurricane status later that day (Figure 10.1). On October 10, its path veered sharply, heading straight north. Hazel caused nearly 1000 fatalities in Haiti two days later and, on October 15, flattened the resort town of Long Beach in North Carolina where only 5 of the 357 buildings along the shore were left standing. The hurricane caused 95 fatalities in the United States.

TABLE 10.1

Canada's Deadly Hurricanes (1900–2013)

Date	Name	Fatalities	Coast Affected
1900	Galveston hurricane	80–100	Atlantic
1927	"The August Gale"	56	Atlantic
1954	Hazel	81	Atlantic
1959	Unnamed	33	Atlantic
1962	Freda	7	Pacific
1968	Gladys	1	Atlantic
1975	Blanche	1	Atlantic
1984	Ogden	5	Pacific
1989	Gabrielle	1	Atlantic
1990	Bertha	6	Atlantic
1991	Bob	2	Atlantic
2003	Juan	8	Atlantic
2004	Bonnie	1	Atlantic
2010	Earl	1	Atlantic
2010	Igor	1	Atlantic
2011	Irene	2	Atlantic
2012	Sandy	2	Atlantic

Source: (1) Major Hurricanes that Affected Canada, Disaster Database, Emergency Preparedness Canada; (2) Canadian Disaster Database Version 4.4 (see worksheet "Chap10K", cell G12); (3) Reid, J. 2000. The 1900 Galveston Hurricane in Canada. *CMOS Bulletin*, Vol. 28, No. 6, p.167–171.

After its incursion inland, Hazel was expected to lose energy and vanish. On the contrary, on the evening of October 15, Hurricane Hazel (Hazel I) joined another storm coming from the west (Hazel II) and combined forces. The revived weather system now headed directly toward Toronto.

Throughout the day of October 15, meteorologists from the Dominion Weather Office in Malton, Ontario, had been monitoring the situation closely. A special weather bulletin was issued at 9:30 a.m., and an update around noon, both forecasting strong winds. The evening bulletin issued at 9:30 p.m., however, didn't foretell the tragic events that would unravel that night: "The intensity of this storm has decreased to the point where it should no longer be classified as a hurricane. This weakening storm will continue northward, passing east of Toronto before midnight. The main rainfall associated with it should end shortly thereafter, with occasional light rain occurring throughout the night. Winds will increase slightly to 45–50 mph [72–80 km/h] until midnight, then slowly decrease throughout the remainder of the night."

Hazel was before everything else a flooding disaster. The centre of the storm hit Toronto at exactly midnight and dumped 183 mm of rain in the following 24 hours, onto soil already saturated by a very rainy first half of October. Several rivers and creeks swelled, becoming dangerous torrents (Figure 10.2). The rushing waters of the Humber River, in the west end, threatened several streets that lined the river's floodplain. People had to quickly seek refuge on rooftops. On the small residential street of Raymore Drive in Weston, 14 family homes and 35 residents were engulfed in the flow (Figure 10.3). The current was so strong that a few drowning victims were found in New York State, on the south side of Lake Ontario. Boats launched into the raging waters were difficult to manoeuvre, which complicated rescue operations already hampered by darkness. In total, 81 people died in Toronto during the tragic night, including 5 volunteer firefighters who lost their lives while on rescue work. A total of 1896 families were left homeless.

Jim Gifford, author of *Hurricane Hazel: Canada's Storm of the Century*, a book commemorating the fiftieth anniversary of the event, ponders: "Could it happen again? Could a storm like Hazel submerge Toronto?" The most significant mitigation measure taken in the aftermath of Hazel has been the acquisition of floodplain land and the alteration of zoning laws

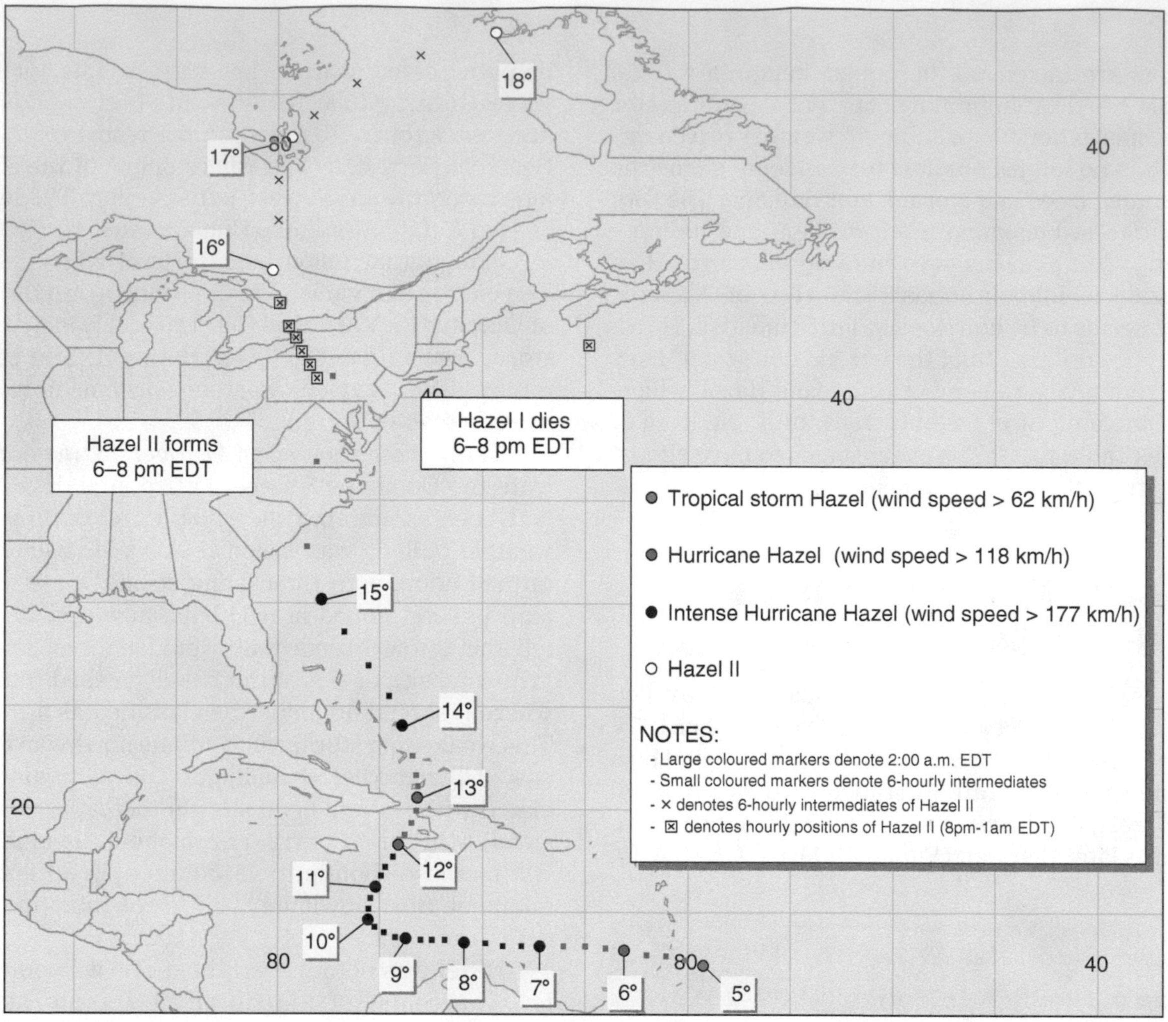

Figure 10.1

Paths of Hurricane Hazel I and storm Hazel II (5–18 October 1954).

Source: © Environment Canada 2008. Paths of Hurricane Hazel and storm Hazel. Source: URL: http://www.ec.gc.ca/ouragans-hurricanes/default.asp?lang=En&n=5C4829A9-1. Reproduced with permission.

Figure 10.2

TTC (Toronto Transit Commission) streetcars carried away by the waters of the Humber River swollen by Hurricane Hazel.

Source: Photography © 2008 Toronto and Region Conservation.

Figure 10.3

The Humber River washed away the lower portion of Raymore Drive where 35 people perished during the passage of Hurricane Hazel over Toronto.

Source: Reprinted with permission from Dundurn Press Ltd. Copyright 2004.

to prevent redevelopment. Today, not only is flooding risk reduced, but also Torontonians enjoy an extensive network of green spaces along the main rivers running through the city. On the other hand, as Jim Gifford points out, the population of the Greater Toronto Area has increased exponentially since 1954. Basements, which are particularly vulnerable to flooding, were traditionally dedicated to storage in the 1950s but many now serve as living space.

Hurricanes As Energy Conversion Engines

Hurricanes can be seen as energy conversion engines exporting excess tropical heat to the mid-latitudes. They are huge **tropical cyclones** that can generate winds over 240 km/h and push massive volumes of seawater onshore as **surges** that temporarily raise sea level over six metres. Their heavy rains can cause dangerous floods, killing people well away from the coastline.

The total energy produced in a typical hurricane is equivalent to 200 times our worldwide capacity to generate electricity. Let's follow the flow of energy through a hurricane (Figure 10.4). First, surface winds converging toward the centre of the storm pick up heat and moisture from the ocean through the process of evaporation. Winds increase their speed inward as the pressure gradient increases and, in turn, more heat is picked up from the ever rougher seas. The heat from the ocean causes the air moving towards the eye to be warmer than the surrounding environment and expand. Upon reaching the eyewall, the air rises rapidly, cools, and releases most of its latent heat through cloud formation and rain. The release of latent heat of condensation is the main fuel source of the hurricane. This exothermic process warms the centre of the storm even further and winds become stronger. Pressure continues to drop, which indicates that the hurricane is intensifying. A small portion of energy is lost through wind generation and long-wavelength radiation at high altitude. The engine will continue working as long as the air flows into the hurricane in the lower levels of the troposphere at a higher temperature than it exits the system in the upper levels of the troposphere. The energy cycle described here is called secondary circulation and involves the hurricane as a whole as opposed to the more local primary circulation, which will be described later (Figure 10.10).

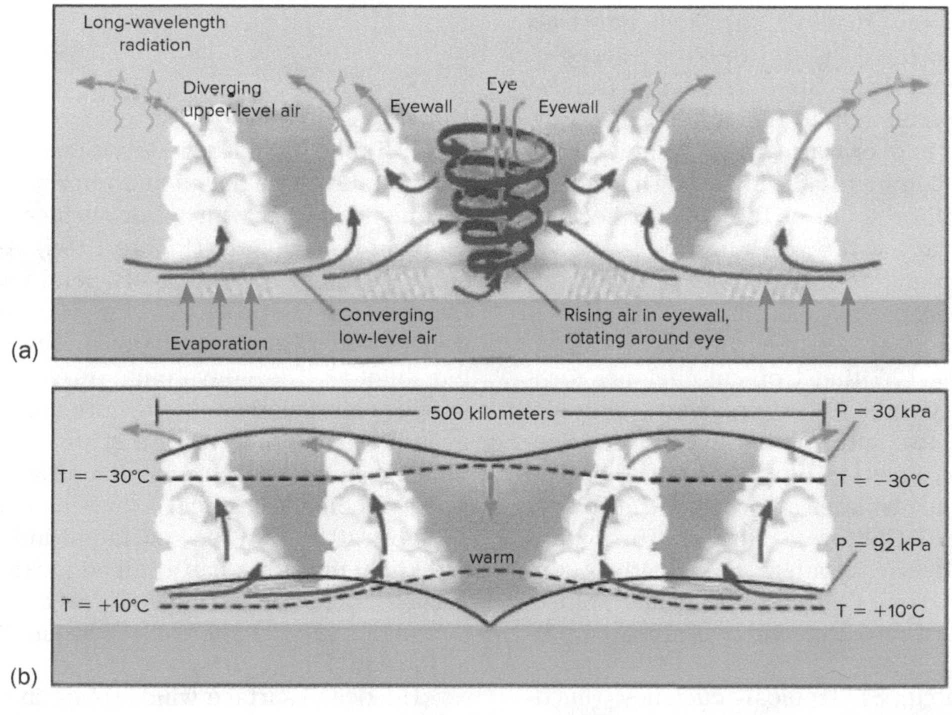

Figure 10.4

Secondary circulation and structure of a hurricane. (a) Low-level air converges toward the storm centre, spirals up the eyewall, and diverges aloft. Energy is supplied to the system by the evaporation of warm water. It is lost through condensation, friction with air (winds) and water (waves), and radiation. (b) Isotherms (dashed lines) and isobars (solid black lines) define the low-pressure warm core of the hurricane, which coincides with the eye.

LO1 The Life Cycle of a Hurricane

BIRTH

Before a hurricane develops, several requirements must be met: (1) seawater must be at least 27°C in the upper 60 m of the ocean (Figure 10.5); (2) air must be warm, humid, and unstable enough to sustain convection; (3) upper-level winds should be weak and preferably blowing in the same direction the developing storm is moving; and (4) the storm must be at least 500 km from the equator so that the Coriolis effect is strong enough to deflect surface winds (see In Greater Depth box: Coriolis Effect, in Chapter 8).

Hurricanes differ significantly from storms formed in higher latitudes. Hurricanes have unique aspects: (1) latent heat released by condensation of water vapour inside a hurricane is its main fuel; (2) hurricanes that move onto land weaken rapidly; (3) hurricanes do not have weather fronts associated with them; (4) the weaker the high-altitude winds, the stronger a hurricane can become; (5) hurricane centres are warmer than their surroundings; (6) hurricane winds weaken with height; and (7) air in the centre of the eye sinks downward.

LO2 A seawater temperature of 27°C is a critical threshold for hurricane development. As the sea-surface temperature increases, the amount of water vapour that air can hold increases exponentially. When the 27°C threshold is exceeded, the amount of latent heat lifted from the tropical ocean becomes large enough to fuel a hurricane. Hurricanes generally form over warm seawater at latitudes between 5° and 20° (Figures 10.6 and 10.7). They do not form within 5° north or south of the equator because the Coriolis effect there is too weak to deflect surface winds. Even an already formed hurricane could not cross the equator because without the Coriolis effect it would lose its rotation.

Notice in Figure 10.7 that tropical cyclones form on the west sides of oceans where warm water is concentrated, with two informative exceptions. Hurricanes form off the Pacific Coast of Mexico because a bend in the coastline isolates a pool of warm coastal water from the cold California current. Hurricanes rarely form off Brazil because the South Atlantic Ocean is too narrow, high altitude winds are too strong, and there are fewer convective precursors to hurricanes.

Each year about 84 tropical cyclones (hurricanes, typhoons, and cyclones) form on Earth. North Americans may think the North Atlantic Ocean–Caribbean Sea–Gulf of Mexico area is where the action is, but on a global scale, it accounts for only about 10 of the 84 events. The typhoons of the northwest Pacific Ocean hit Japan, China, and the Philippines about three times as often, and the storms can be larger (Figure 10.8).

Figure 10.5
Hurricane Katrina grew in strength travelling across unusually warm waters in the Gulf of Mexico. Water temperatures in yellow are 28°C and in red are 32°C and above.
Source : © NOAA.

DEVELOPMENT

Hurricanes go through four distinct stages of development (Table 10.2). Their development begins when a low-pressure zone draws in a poorly organized cluster of thunderstorms with weak surface winds; this is a **tropical disturbance** (Figure 10.9a). As surface winds strengthen and flow more efficiently around and into the centre of the growing storm, it becomes a **tropical depression** (Figure 10.9b) and receives an identifying number. The converging surface winds continue to spiral inward, then up the core along the eyewall at ever-increasing speeds as the system grows in strength. When sustained surface-wind speeds exceed 63 km/h, it has become a **tropical storm** and receives a name (Figure 10.9c). When surface-wind speeds reach 119 km/h, the storm has attained hurricane strength. A classic hurricane typically features a calmer area in the centre of the circulation, 30–60 km in diameter, known as the eye (Figure 10.9d).

Hurricane surface winds rotate in a counter-clockwise (cyclonic) fashion around a central core in the northern hemisphere and in a clockwise fashion in the southern hemisphere. This primary circulation is controlled by four forces (Figure 10.10).

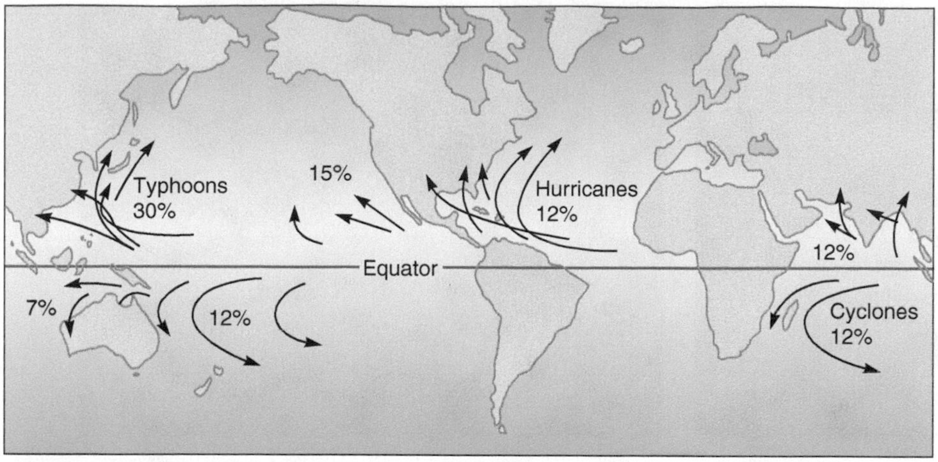

Figure 10.6
Map of areas where hurricanes commonly form, typical paths they travel, and annual percentage of the Earth's large cyclones occurring in each region.

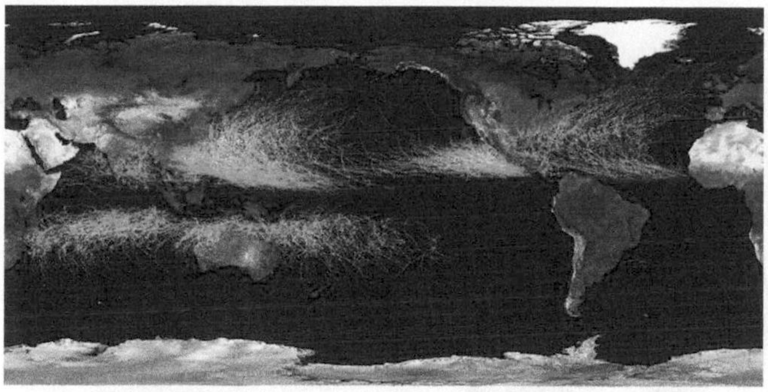

Figure 10.7
Path of all tropical cyclones in the world, 1985–2005. Blue indicates tropical depressions and tropical storms, yellow indicates hurricanes of categories 1 and 2, and orange and red indicate major hurricanes of categories 3 to 5.
Source: Tracks from Nilfanion on NASA image.

Figure 10.8
Typhoons are very much part of the folklore of southeast Asia. In Vietnam, people of the Mekong delta decorate boats with eyes to scare away typhoons, malignant spirits, and crocodiles.
Source: © Claire Samson.

MATURITY

Figure 10.4a shows the structure of a mature hurricane. Rainfall is most intense in spiralling bands of clouds surrounding the eye, and winds strongest along the eyewall. The general wind flow pattern is convergent toward the centre at low levels, rising in convective clouds, and divergent at upper levels. Inside the eye, cool air sinks. As the air descends, it absorbs moisture, leaving the eye clear and cloud free. Sometimes blue sky or stars can be seen through the eye of a hurricane. After the short quiet period associated with the passage of the eye, the winds pick up again, this time in the opposite direction to before (Figure 10.11).

In Figure 10.4b, follow the isotherms, the lines of equal temperature. The T = +10°C isotherm rises up markedly to define the warm core of the hurricane. The warm core is due to the release of huge quantities of latent heat during cloud formation and to adiabatic warming of the sinking air in the eye. At the sea surface, temperatures in the eye may be only 0–2°C warmer than surrounding air, but at altitudes of 10–12 km, the temperatures within the warm core may be 11°C warmer than the surrounding environment. In Figure 10.4b,

TABLE 10.2

Hurricane Development Stages

Development Stage	Wind Speed [km/h]	Designation
Tropical disturbance	36 or less	Not applicable
Tropical depression	37–63	Number
Tropical storm	64–118	Name
Hurricane	119 or more	Name

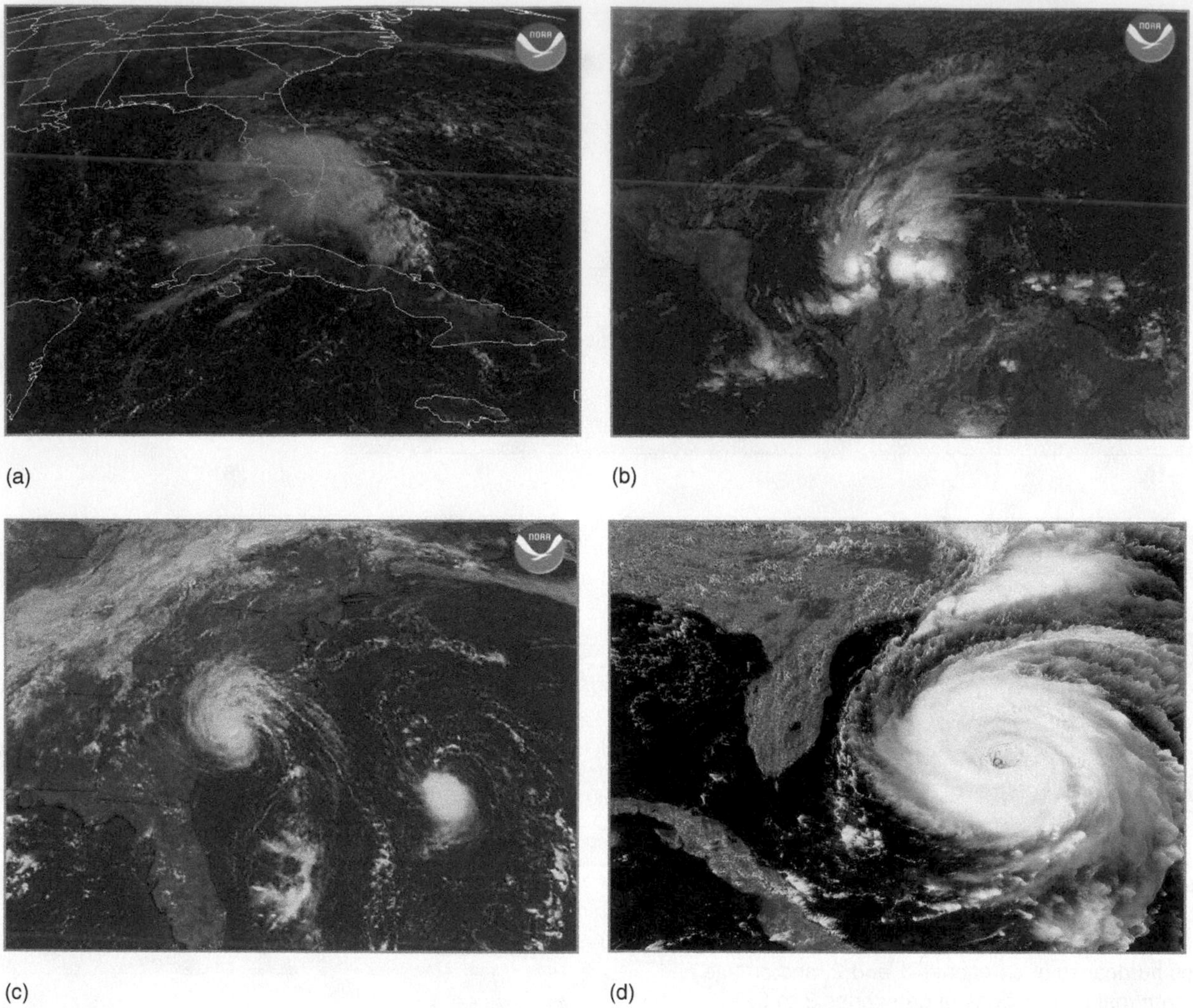

Figure 10.9
Hurricane development stages. (a) Tropical disturbance moving westward over southern Florida; (b) Tropical depression south of Kingston, Jamaica; (c) Tropical storm Gaston making landfall northeast of Charleston, South Carolina, in August 2004; (d) Hurricane Mitch with its well-developed eye, offshore Honduras and Nicaragua in October 1998.

Source: (a), (b), (c) http://www.noaa.gov/ National Oceanic and Atmospheric Administration, 2003 & 2004 Regional Imagery Hurricanes; (d) © Laboratory for Atmospheres; NASA GSFC.

follow the isobars, the lines of equal pressure, and see the big drop in air pressure at the hurricane centre. At low levels around the hurricane centre, the differences in air pressure are sharpest, causing the highest wind speeds to occur there.

DECLINE

Hurricanes decline when they are cut off from their main source of energy: warm water. This occurs abruptly when hurricanes ram onshore. It is not so much friction with the land that causes hurricanes to lose strength, a common misconception, but the fact that they become starved for energy. In the last hours of their lives, however, hurricanes venturing inland often cause their maximum destruction, as they can be accompanied by storm surges, torrential rains, and severe flooding. In developed countries, deaths by hurricanes have dropped dramatically in the last decades. This trend is reflected in Canadian statistics (Table 10.1). Thanks to the advanced warnings that are now broadcast widely before a hurricane makes landfall, most people take cover or evacuate the low-lying areas and save themselves. Although hurricane deaths have decreased, the amount of damage they cause has increased. An ongoing trend is for the wealthy to move to coastlines and build larger and more expensive homes filled with costlier possessions.

Hurricanes can decline gradually as they travel to northern latitudes. When entering Canadian waters in

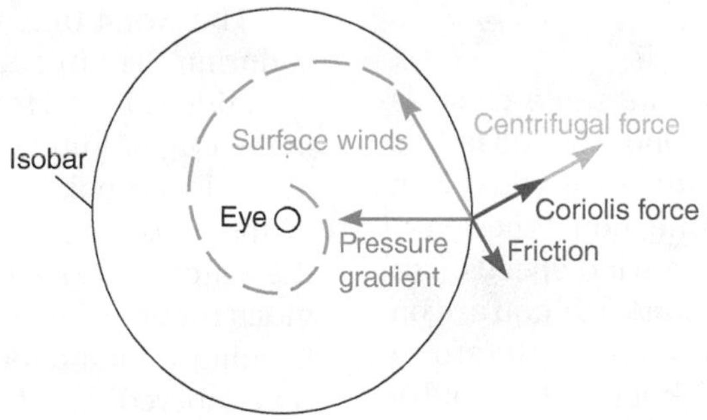

Figure 10.10

Four forces control the primary circulation of hurricane surface winds: the pressure gradient, the Coriolis force, the centrifugal force and friction. The pressure gradient (green) draws air toward the eye where the barometric pressure is lowest. In opposition, in the northern hemisphere, air is pulled to the right by both the Coriolis (purple) and centrifugal (orange) forces. Friction (red) acts to reduce the wind speed. The net balance of these forces results in surface winds that spiral inward toward the centre of the storm as indicated by the dashed blue line. The black line represents an "isobar," which is a contour of equal pressure at an arbitrary distance from the eye. Diagram not to scale.

Source: Modified from http://www.hurricanescience.org/

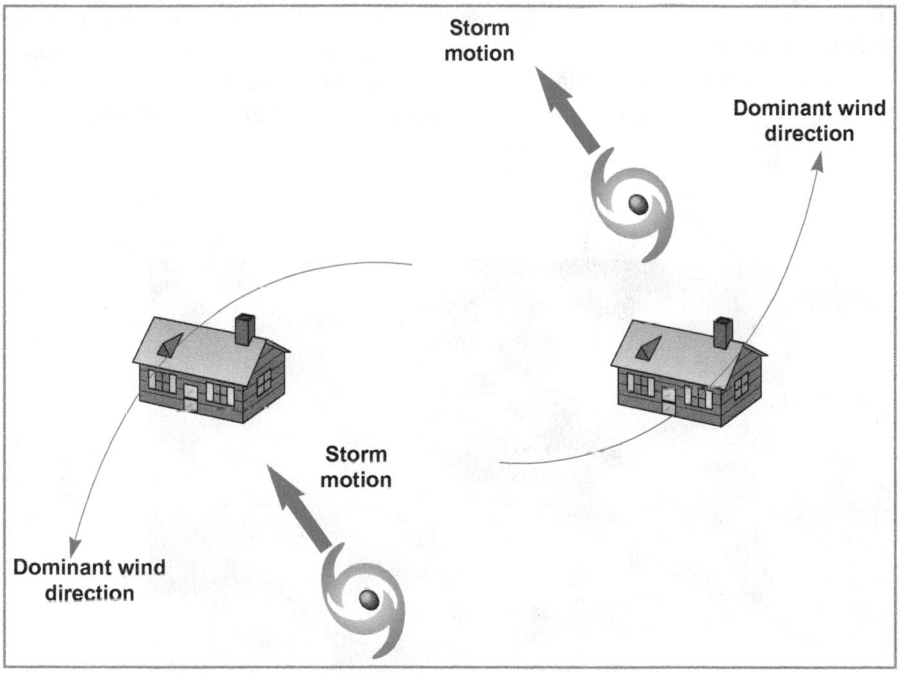

Figure 10.11

Change in wind direction before (left) and after (right) the passage of the eye of a hurricane.

Source: © National Oceanic and Atmospheric Administration.

the North Atlantic, most hurricanes are in the final stage of their lives. Their paths curve eastward, blown by the clockwise winds around the Bermuda High, sometimes reaching all the way to the British Isles (Figure 10.20). In a different scenario, some hurricanes undergo a transformation process known as **post-tropical transition** and unexpectedly gain strength.

LO3

Post-Tropical Transition

In the North Atlantic, when hurricanes venture to latitudes beyond 30°N and 40°N, they move into cooler air and stronger air streams, and accelerate. Some of them undergo a post-tropical transition, a topic of intense research in meteorology in recent years. During post-tropical transition, the well-organized, symmetric cyclonic structure (Figure 10.9d) deforms and becomes less compact. An asymmetric structure develops where rain bands are mostly concentrated on the west side and the strongest winds and ocean waves occur on the east side. This explains why Atlantic Canada most often experiences the heavy rains associated with post-tropical cyclones rather than their most punitive winds (Figure 10.12). Occasionally, a post-tropical cyclone merges with an existing depressionary weather system, and gains strength. Hurricane Hazel is a classic example of this phenomenon.

LO4 Winds and Storm Surges

Not all coastal residents are hit by the same hazards during a hurricane; they vary along the coastline (Figure 10.13). In the northern hemisphere, if you are on the "right side" of the tropical cyclone, you experience the speed of the storm body *plus* the wind speeds (for example, 30 km/h + 160 km/h = 190 km/h). If you are on the "left side," you feel the wind speed *minus* the storm motion (for example, 160 km/h – 30 km/h = 130 km/h). Also, storm surges tend to develop about 15–30 km to the right of the hurricane path as the winds come off the ocean, pushing seawater onto the land. Storm surges are mounds of water rising mainly due to wind action and, to a lesser extent, to suction created by the low pressure area associated with the hurricane eye.

Most deaths related to tropical cyclones are associated with storm surges occurring when a cyclone nears and moves onto land (Figure 10.14). Why do impacting waves kill so many people? One cubic metre of water weighs 1000 kg and water is almost incompressible. Being hit by a wall of water is not much different from being hit by a solid mass.

The worst time for a storm surge to come onshore is during the already high sea level of an astronomical high tide. On 4 October 1869, the arrival of a hurricane in the Bay of Fundy coincided with the new Moon being at its closest point to Earth in its orbit. The combination of the storm surge and the high spring tide resulted in the water level rising nearly two metres higher than previous records. Several people and animals from coastal farming communities were lost at sea. This event is remembered as the "Saxby Gale" after Lieutenant Stephen Saxby of the British Royal Navy. Lieutenant Saxby, a naval instructor and amateur astronomer, had predicted a year earlier that astronomical forces could produce extremely high tides in the North Atlantic Ocean on October 5.

Hurricane Camille is one of three category 5 hurricanes to hit the United States in the twentieth century. Camille brought winds gusting over 320 km/h that hit the state of Mississippi in 1969 with a surge of 7.3 m; this caused many of the 256 fatalities. Fatal sites included the three-storey brick buildings of the seaside Richelieu apartment complex where, instead of evacuating, 32 party-hearty people held a "hurricane party"

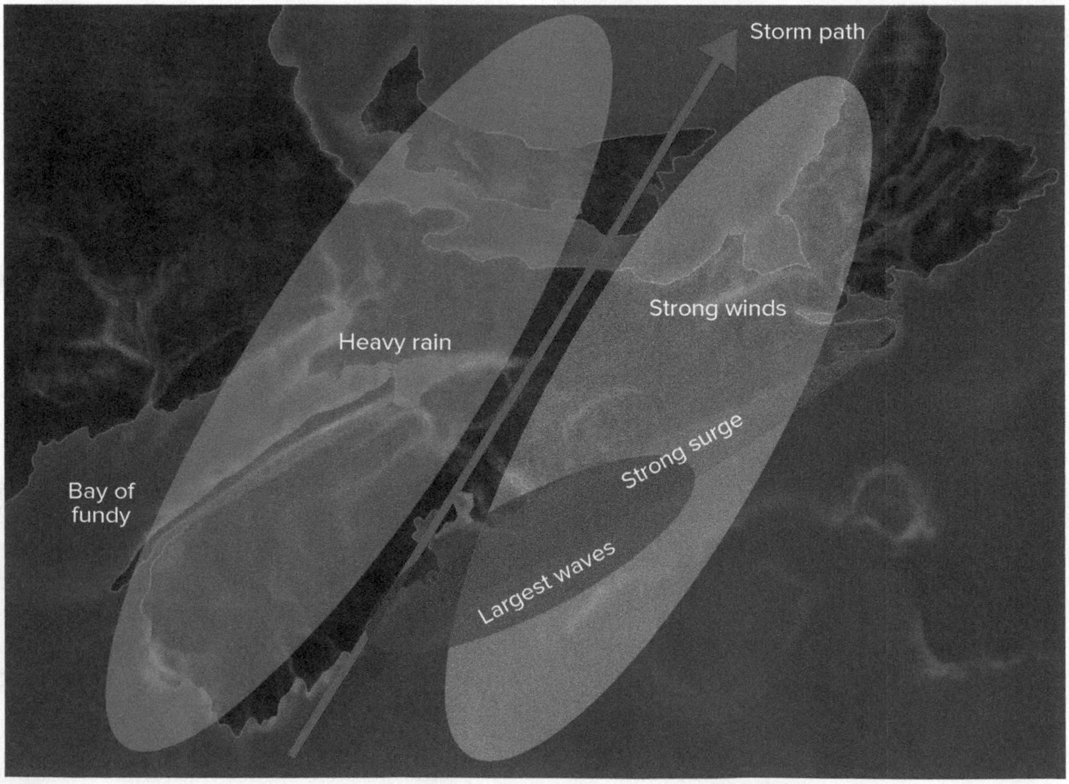

Figure 10.12

Threat areas associated with post-tropical storms in Nova Scotia and Prince Edward Island.

Source: Environment Canada.

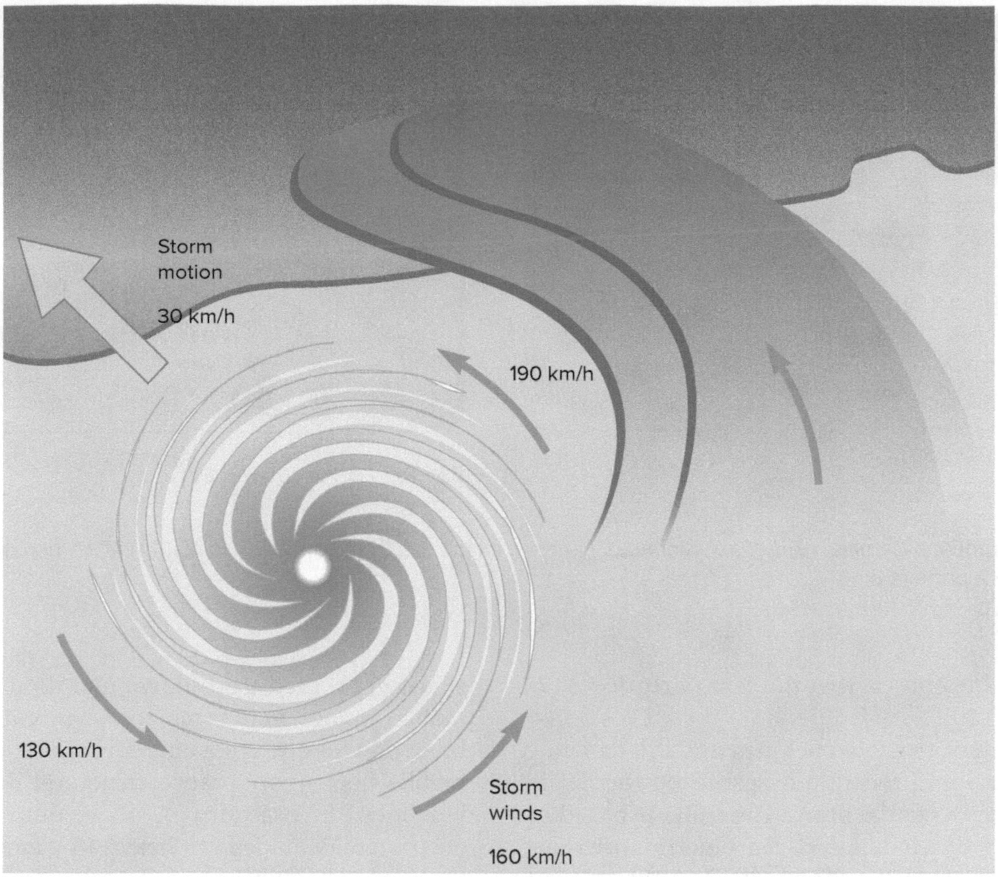

Figure 10.13
Tropical cyclones hit the coastline with different wind speeds. Storm motion (in this example, 30 km/h) and wind speed (in this example, 160 km/h) may combine or subtract.

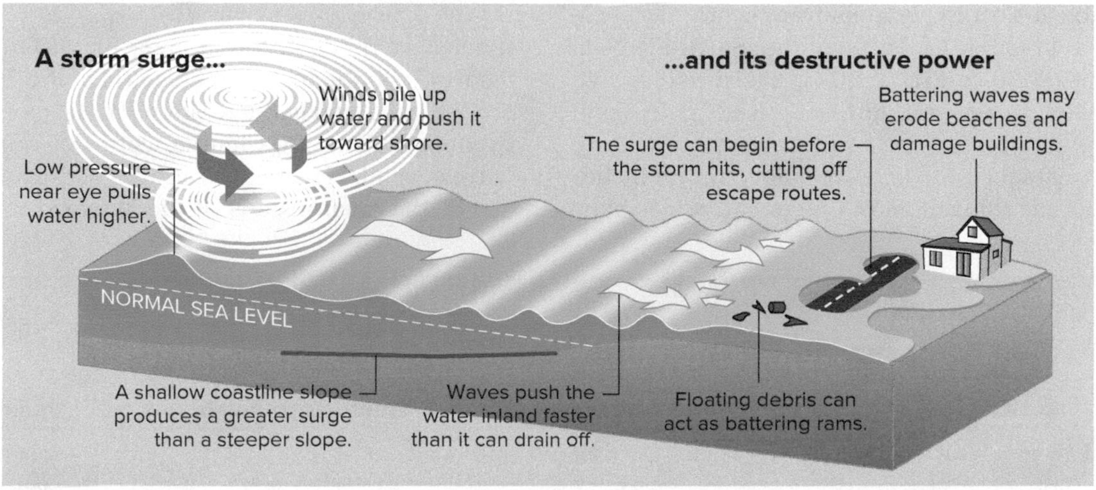

Figure 10.14
Storm surge.
Source: NOAA.

(a) (b)

Figure 10.15
Storm surge of Hurricane Camille. (a) Before. Richelieu Apartments in Pass Christian, Mississippi. (b) After. Remains of the building where 30 of 32 partiers died.
Source: United States Geological Survey (USGS).

to celebrate the event—it was the last party for 30 of them (Figure 10.15).

The strength of tropical cyclones and the damages they inflict were until recently assessed by the Saffir-Simpson damage-potential scale. The scale is based on three parameters: wind speed, barometric pressure, and storm surge elevation (Table 10.3). Although successfully used for decades, there are problems with the scale. Barometric pressure is an imperfect proxy for wind speed; this was necessary in the 1970s and 1980s when measurements from reconnaissance aircraft were not routinely available, but it is not justifiable anymore. Storm surge elevations are not reliable indicators of hurricane intensity as they vary according to bathymetry and topography.

To establish a more rigorous framework, the scale was revised in 2011 to become the Saffir-Simpson Hurricane Wind Scale (Table 10.3), based exclusively on wind speed. In general, in the revised scale, damage rises by about a factor of four for every category increase. In category 1, winds damage tree branches and unanchored mobile homes. Category 2 winds blow shallowly rooted trees down and do major damage to mobile homes and some roofs. In category 3, winds blow down large trees and strip foliage, destroy older mobile homes, and cause structural damage to small buildings. In category 4, all commercial signage is destroyed; damages are heavy to windows, doors, and roofs of well-built homes. In category 5, damages are catastrophic to all buildings. Because of their damaging power, hurricanes of category 3 to 5 are called major hurricanes.

How Hurricanes Get Their Names

Hurricanes go by different names in different parts of the world. In the Indian and South Pacific Oceans, they are cyclones, and in the western Pacific Ocean, they are **typhoons,** from the Chinese word *t'ai fung,* meaning "strong wind." Hurricanes are named after Hurakan, one of the creator gods of the Mayans, who blew his

TABLE 10.3

Saffir-Simpson Hurricane Wind and Damage-Potential Scales

	Wind speed (km/h)	Minimum pressure (kPa)	Storm surge height (m)	Damages
Category 1	119–153	≥98.0	1.0–1.7	Minimal
Category 2	154–177	96.5–97.9	1.8–2.6	Moderate
Category 3	178–208	94.5–96.4	2.7–3.8	Extensive
Category 4	209–251	92.0–94.4	3.9–5.6	Extreme
Category 5	≥252	<92.0	>5.6	Catastrophic

breath across the water and brought forth dry land. Hurakan was later introduced in the Carib mythology as Hurican, the god of evil. Nowadays, the diverse manifestations of this angry god are given human names. Andrew, Camille, Hugo, Iniki, Katrina, Mitch, Rita, and their kin share family traits, but each has its own personality. Each hurricane "lives" for enough days that we get to know its individual characteristics.

It is unclear how the practice of naming hurricanes started, but the approach has gained wide acceptance because it is quicker to use and less subject to error than latitude–longitude identification methods. Historians point to Clement Wragge (1852–1922), a pioneer of Australian meteorology, who named cyclones after women and local politicians he particularly disliked. The practice was revived during World War II when American Air Force and Navy meteorologists named events after their wives. The system was formalized in 1953 by the United States Weather Service. Until 1979, only women's names were used. Since then, the World Meteorological Organization has overseen the use of pre-selected lists of alternating male and female names, recycled every six years (Table 10.4). The 2015 list will be used again in 2021. The names for each year total 21; the letters Q, U, X, Y, and Z are not used. If more than 21 named tropical storms and hurricanes occur in a year, then additional names are taken in order from the Greek alphabet: alpha, beta, gamma, delta, epsilon, zeta, etc. This was necessary in 2005. Names attached to extreme events are retired: there will not be another hurricane Katrina, Sandy or Juan. The names Katrina and Sandy have been replaced by Katia and Sara. In consideration of the devastating impact of Hurricane Juan in the Maritimes in 2003, the name Juan has been replaced by Joaquin. This is the only time Canada has requested the retirement of a hurricane name.

Hurricanes in the North Atlantic Ocean

Hurricanes in the North Atlantic Ocean are large, mobile, and long lasting (Table 10.5). Each year anywhere from 4 to 28 tropical storms and hurricanes originate in the North Atlantic–Caribbean Sea–Gulf of Mexico region, out of which an average of 4 affect Canada (Table 10.6). Storms reaching Canada are most often weakened and have lost their hurricane status.

TABLE 10.4

World Meteorological Organization List of Atlantic Hurricane Names

2015	2016	2017	2018	2019	2020
Ana	Alex	Arlene	Alberto	Andrea	Arthur
Bill	Bonnie	Bret	Beryl	Barry	Bertha
Claudette	Colin	Cindy	Chris	Chantal	Cristobal
Danny	Danielle	Don	Debby	Dorian	Dolly
Erika	Earl	Emily	Ernesto	Erin	Edouard
Fred	Fiona	Franklin	Florence	Fermand	Fay
Grace	Gaston	Gert	Gordon	Gabrielle	Gonzalo
Henri	Hermine	Harvey	Helence	Humberto	Hanna
Ida	Ian	Irma	Isaac	Imelda	Isaias
Joaquin	Julia	Jose	Joyce	Jerry	Josephine
Kate	Karl	Katia	Kirk	Karen	Kyle
Larry	Lisa	Lee	Leslie	Lorenzo	Laura
Mindy	Matthew	Maria	Michael	Melissa	Marco
Nicholas	Nicole	Nate	Nadine	Nestor	Nana
Odette	Otto	Ophelia	Oscar	Olga	Omar
Peter	Paula	Philippe	Patty	Pablo	Paulette
Rose	Richard	Rina	Rafael	Rebekah	Rene
Sam	Shary	Sean	Sara	Sebastien	Sally
Teresa	Tobias	Tammy	Tony	Tanya	Teddy
Victor	Virginie	Vince	Valerie	Van	Vicky
Wanda	Walter	Whitney	William	Wendy	Wilfred

Source: National Weather Service, National Hurricane Center http://www.nhc.noaa.gov/aboutnames.shtml.

TABLE 10.5

General Characteristics of North Atlantic Hurricanes

Storm diameter	200–1300 km
Eye diameter	16–70 km
Surface wind speed	≥ 119 km/h
Direction of motion	Westward then northward, then eastward
Surface wind rotation	Counter-clockwise
Life span	1–30 days

TABLE 10.6

North Atlantic Tropical Storms and Hurricanes, 1899–2013

	Frequency (Year)	
Category	**Maximum**	**Minimum**
Tropical storms and hurricanes	28 (2005)	4 (1983)
Hurricanes	15 (2005)	2 (1982)
Major hurricanes (wind speed > 178 km/h)	8 (1950)	0 (many years)
U.S. landfalling tropical storms and hurricanes	8 (1916)	1 (many years)
Canadian landfalling tropical storms and hurricanes	5 (1996)	0 (many years)

Source: www.nhc.noaa.gov and the Canadian Hurricane Centre.

A notable exception is Luis, a category 3 hurricane, which made landfall on 11 September 1995 on the Avalon Peninsula of Newfoundland accompanied by 60–120 mm of rain and sustained winds of 195 km/h, causing extensive material damage. A total of 33 cyclones classified as hurricanes have made landfall in Canada between 1886 and 2013. No category 4 or 5 hurricane has made landfall in Canada since Confederation (Table 10.7).

The arrival of rotating tropical-weather systems is an annual media event in North America. Hurricanes form when sea-surface temperatures are warmest, and in the North Atlantic Ocean, this occurs in late summer. The warmest weather occurs earlier in the summer, but sea surface temperatures are highest at the end of summer because the ocean water with its high heat capacity absorbs solar energy all summer long. The peak of the North Atlantic hurricane season is between mid-August and late October (Figure 10.16). As the average temperature of the ocean increases from June to September, hurricane paths extend farther north along the Atlantic coastline and then gradually retract in October and November (Figure 10.17). All the strongest hurricanes affecting Canada struck in August, September, or October, except one (Table 10.7). The most common date for a storm to make landfall in Canada is September 15.

Meteorologists of the Canadian Hurricane Centre, located in Dartmouth, Nova Scotia, monitor all tropical and post-tropical storms and hurricanes predicted to enter a large response zone within 72 hours (Figure 10.18). The meteorologists assess the potential impact of these systems on Canada and issue weather forecasts for an area including Ontario, Quebec, New Brunswick, Nova Scotia, Prince Edward Island, and Newfoundland and Labrador, and extending 200 nautical miles (370.4 km) into Canadian Atlantic territorial waters.

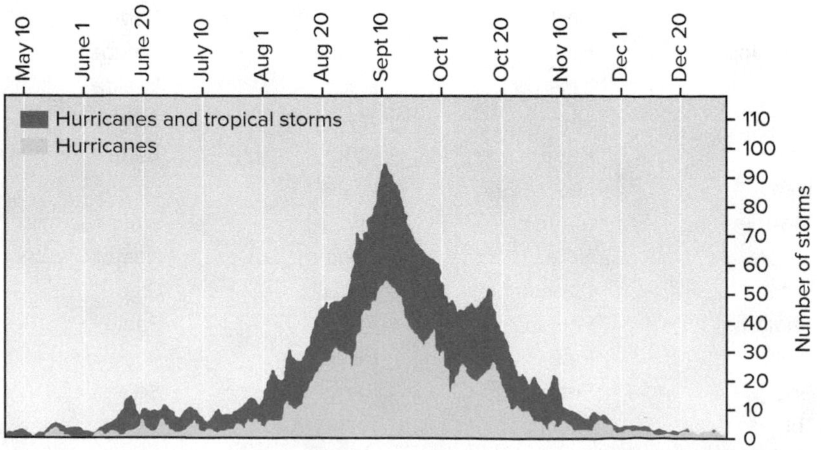

Figure 10.16

Monthly distribution of hurricanes and tropical storms in the North Atlantic Ocean between 1896 and 2006.

Source: http://www.nhc.noaa.gov/climo/images/peakofseason.gif.

TABLE 10.7

Hurricanes Making Landfall in Canada, 1886–2013

Date	Name	Category	Wind Speed [km/h]	Province Affected
11 Sep 1995	Luis	3	195	NF
22 Aug 1893	1893C	3	185	NS
29 Oct 1963	Ginny	2	167	PEI, NS, NB
25 Aug 1927	927A	2	167	NS
29 Sep 2003	Juan	2	158	NS, PEI
2 Aug 1908	1908B	2	158	NS
8 Oct 1891	1891F	2	158	NS, NF
18 Aug 1893	1893E	1	163	NF
27 Aug 1924	1924B	1	148	PEI, NS, NF
15 Oct 1896	1896E	1	148	NS
15 Oct 1891	1891I	1	148	PEI, NS, NF
19 Oct 2000	Michael	1	139	NF
8 Sep 1891	1891D	1	139	NS, NF
23 Aug 2009	Bill	1	137	NS, PEI, NF
12 Sep 2002	Gustav	1	130	NS
10 Sep 1969	Gerda	1	130	QC, NF
27 Sep 1937	1937G	1	130	PEI, NF, NS
25 Sep 1936	1936O	1	130	NS
25 Aug 1893	1893D	1	130	QC, NF
22 Aug 1892	1892B	1	130	NF
21 Sep 2010	Igor	1	129	NS
3 Sep 2010	Earl	1	129	NS, NF
15 Sep 1996	Hortense	1	120	NS
16 Aug 1971	Beth	1	120	NS, NF
21 Jul 1966	Celia	1	120	QC, NF, NS, NB
8 Oct 1962	Daisy	1	120	NS
29 Sep 1958	Helene	1	120	NF
17 Sep 1940	1940E	1	120	NF, NS
25 Aug 1935	1935A	1	120	NF
8 Aug 1926	1926B	1	120	NF, NS
5 Sep 1925	1925C	1	120	NF
27 Aug 1887	1887E	1	120	NS, NF
28 Sep 2008	Kyle	1	119	NF

Sources: 1886–2007: © Her Majesty The Queen in Right of Canada, Environment Canada 2014. Reproduced with permission; 2008–2014: National Aeronautics and Space Administration.

Hurricane Paths

The paths followed by many Atlantic hurricanes have been plotted in Figure 10.17. Hurricane paths are difficult to predict in detail because they adjust to other high- and low-pressure atmospheric systems they encounter. But in a broad sense, there are two main influences on paths. (1) At low latitudes, trade winds blow the tropical cyclone toward the west (Figure 8.4). (2) An extensive high-pressure zone called the Bermuda High commonly sits above the North Atlantic Ocean. Hurricane paths vary depending on the size and position of the Bermuda High. When the Bermuda High is small and to the north, hurricanes may curve northward around it and have little or no effects on coastlines (Figure 10.20a). However, when the Bermuda High is strong and extensive, it may guide hurricanes along the east coast of the United States (Figure 10.20b). Sometimes the Bermuda High drifts southwestward toward Florida and helps direct hurricanes into the Caribbean Sea and Gulf of Mexico (Figure 10.20c). When a hurricane travels far enough

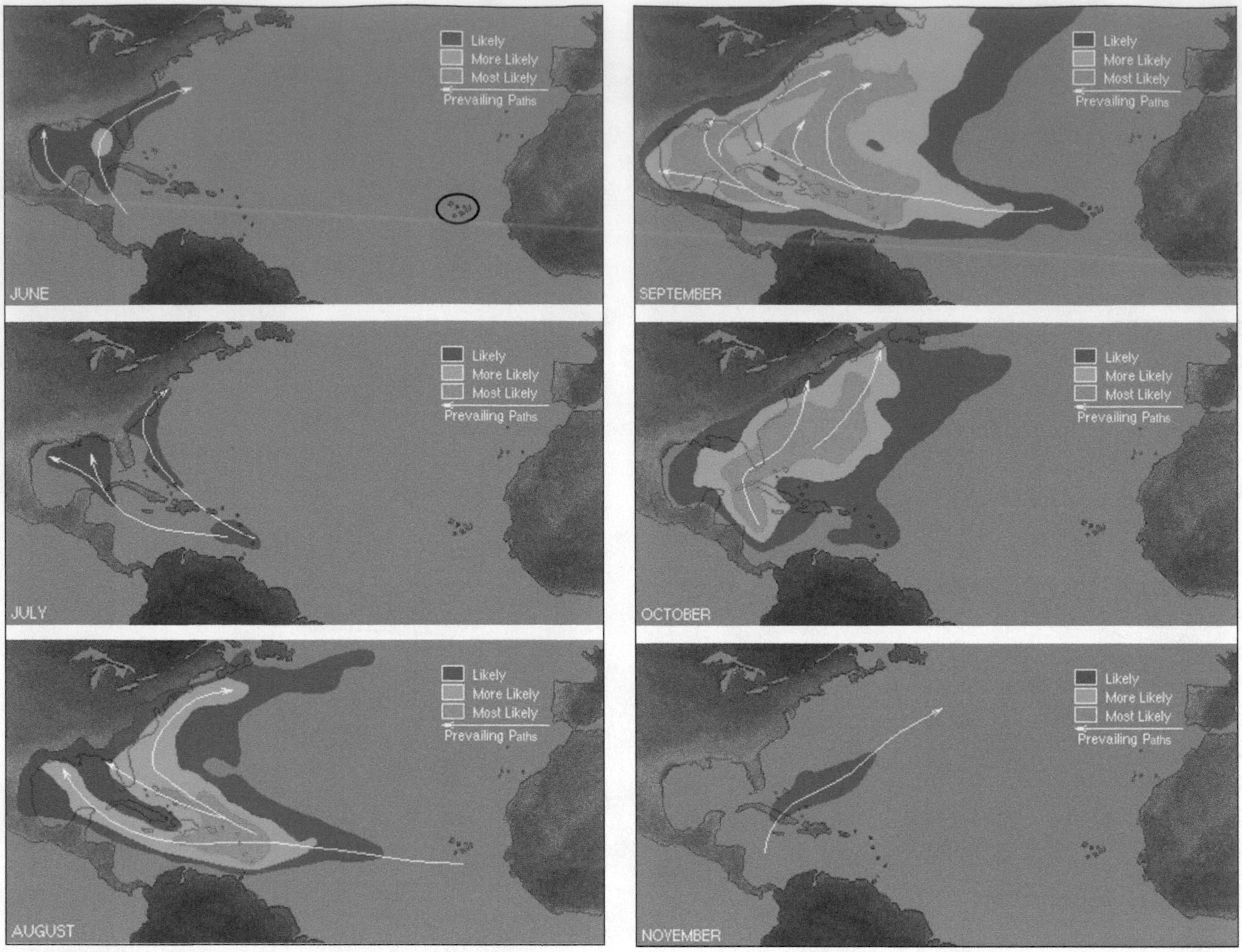

Figure 10.17
Typical hurricane paths for different months during the North Atlantic hurricane season. The location of the Cape Verde Islands is indicated by a circle.

Source: National Oceanic and Atmospheric Administration. http://www.nhc.noaa.gov/pastprofile.shtml; "Climatological Areas of Origin and Typical Hurricane Tracks per Month."

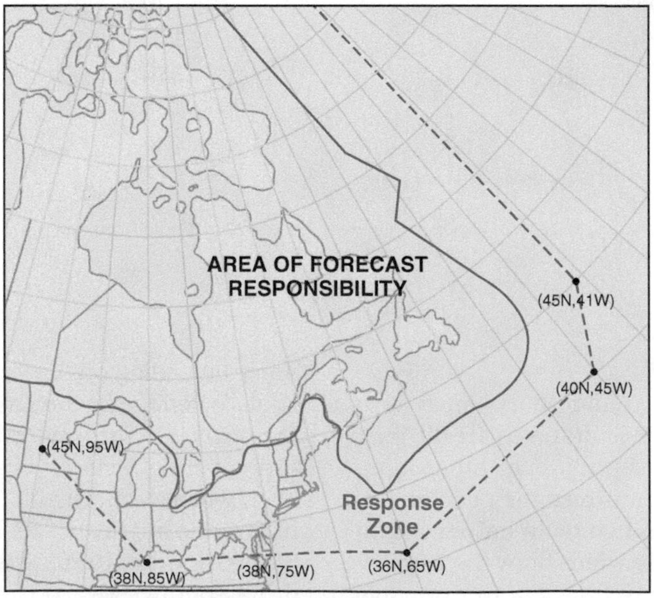

Figure 10.18
The response zone and area of forecast responsibility of the Canadian Hurricane Centre.

Source: National Oceanic and Atmospheric Administration. http://www.nhc.noaa.gov/pastprofile.shtml; "Climatological Areas of Origin and Typical Hurricane Tracks per Month"

HUMAN FOCUS

Chris Fogarty, Canadian Hurricane Centre Program Supervisor

Figure 10.19
Chris Fogarty at work analyzing the several data streams that allow precise hurricane tracking.

Source: Canadian Hurricane Centre forecaster Chris Fogarty analyzing a weather map, URL: http://www.ec.gc.ca/ouragans-hurricanes/default.asp?lang=en&n=487BDA78-1 © Environment Canada, 2014. Reproduced with permission.

I have had a lifelong fascination for weather. As a kid, I maintained a weather log book and presented several science-fair projects on meteorology. My focus on hurricanes started when doing my Master's degree at McGill University, where I studied how tropical cyclones transform as they move northward into the middle latitudes. After graduating, I joined Environment Canada. A first posting in Gander, Newfoundland, exposed me to the challenges of day-to-day weather forecasting. In the following years, my employer encouraged me to pursue my studies at the doctoral level at Dalhousie University where I worked on computer simulations of hurricane models. Beyond these virtual hurricanes, however, I had several close encounters with real hurricanes! I flew through storms, including Hurricane Juan, to record crucial data on winds, temperature, and humidity, against which models are tested.

In my current role as the Program Supervisor of the Canadian Hurricane Centre (Figure 10.19), off-season—in winter and spring—I am busy training weather forecasters and testing new ways of communicating weather information to the public. During the hurricane season, the Canadian Hurricane Centre is in close contact with the United States National Hurricane Centre in Miami. A potential hurricane is detected five days before it might reach Canada. Three days before, a special desk is staffed 24 hours a day and weather bulletins are issued every 6 hours. Daily teleconferences are held with representatives from Public Safety Canada and first responders. On the day of the storm, there can be considerable media interest and I am on hand to comment on the developing situation.

I have seen my career evolving from the science of storms toward more and more interaction with the public. I am particularly interested in developing indicators of uncertainty to accompany weather predictions and improving the accessibility of information, for example, via mobile phone technology. I believe a better informed society will take a longer-term view to extreme weather and plan ahead to reduce vulnerability.

Source: Text reprinted by permission of Chris Fogarty.

to the north, the westerlies that prevail at mid-latitudes will push it to the northeast (Figure 8.4).

The position and strength of the Bermuda High is part of the **Atlantic Multidecadal Oscillation (AMO),** which describes the shifting of atmospheric pressures over the ocean (Figure 10.35). The AMO may strengthen and weaken on a timescale of decades, causing some coastlines to be repeatedly struck by hurricanes for a decade and then escape attack for another decade. For example, in the 1950s, the Atlantic coast of the United States and Canada was hammered by major hurricanes, but in the 1960s and 1970s, it was the Gulf of Mexico coast that was hit most frequently.

LO5 CAPE VERDE-TYPE HURRICANES

Atlantic hurricanes commonly begin as storms in the western Sahel region of Africa, which lies south of the Sahara Desert. Some of these storms strengthen rapidly and reach tropical storm status near the Cape Verde Islands (Figure 10.17). These Cape Verde-type tropical cyclones are blown across the Atlantic Ocean by the trade winds between 5°N and 20°N latitude. The great distances that they travel over water warmer than 27°C are a major factor in helping them grow to hurricane strength. Approaching North America, they commonly move north on clockwise-curving paths due to the general circulation around the Bermuda High (Figure 10.20).

Juan, September 2003

Juan formed off the coast of Africa on 14 September 2003, and travelled west across the Atlantic. It was classified as a tropical depression on 23 September southeast of Bermuda, then started its journey toward Canada along an unusually straight south–north path, becoming a tropical storm on September 25 (Figure 10.21). The next day, an eye developed and Juan was promoted to hurricane status. As the hurricane moved into the warm waters of the Gulf Stream, it strengthened and organized further. It made landfall near the picturesque village of Peggy's Cove at midnight on September 29 as a category 2 hurricane (Figure 10.22), causing widespread structural and vegetation damage in the metropolitan areas of Halifax and Dartmouth. In the following

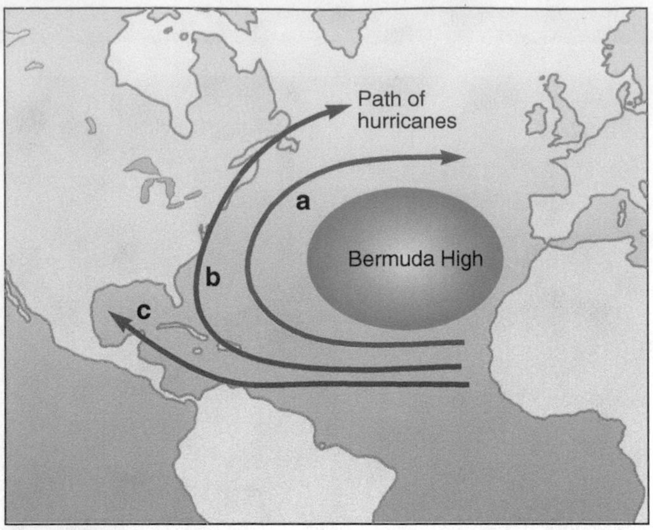

Figure 10.20

Paths of Cape Verde-type hurricanes are influenced by the size and position of a high-pressure zone, the Bermuda High. (a) A small Bermuda High allows hurricanes to stay over the Atlantic Ocean and miss North America. (b) A large Bermuda High may guide hurricanes along the eastern coast of the United States and Canada. (c) When the Bermuda High moves south, it directs hurricanes into the Caribbean Sea and Gulf of Mexico.

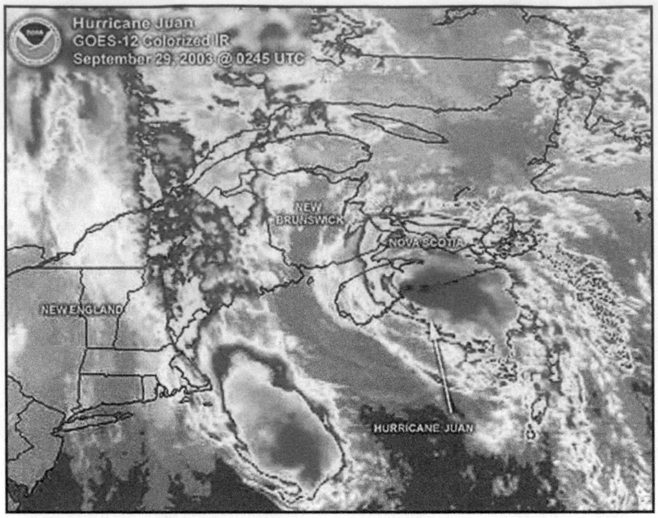

Figure 10.22

Satellite image of Hurricane Juan taken at 11:45 p.m. on 28 September 2003, just before it made landfall.

Source: National Oceanic and Atmospheric Administration. satellite image of Hurricane Juan Source: URL: http://ec.gc.ca/hurricane/default.asp?lang=En&n=8B94BBA4-1.

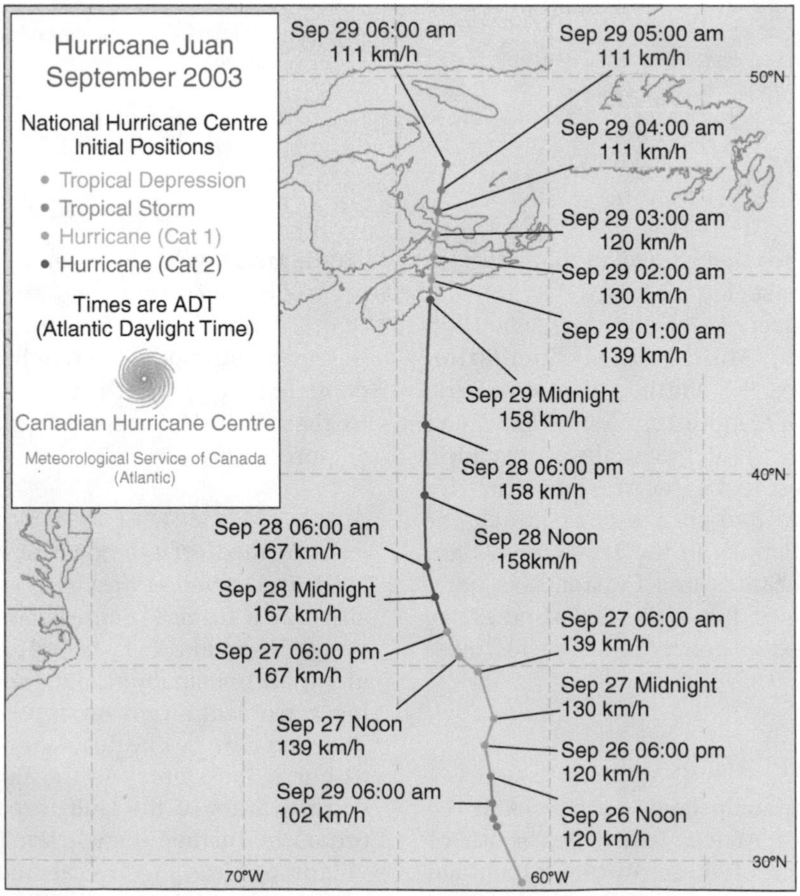

Figure 10.21

The path of Hurricane Juan, September 2003.

Source: The track of Juan through Nova Scotia and Prince Edward Island, URL: http://www.ec.gc.ca/ouragans-hurricanes/default.asp?lang=en&n=222F51F7-1

few hours, Juan continued its course due north through rural central Nova Scotia to Prince Edward Island (Figure 10.23), the storm centre passing directly over the Confederation Bridge. It finally started to lose strength when it reached the Gulf of St. Lawrence.

The Canadian Hurricane Centre started to monitor Juan when it transitioned from depression to storm on September 25. By September 27, meteorologists forecast a landfall over or just west of the City of Halifax the evening of the next day. Warnings were issued to alert the population of strong winds and heavy rainfalls. Although no large-scale evacuations were made, local evacuations for low-lying areas were issued on the evening of September 28.

With almost 100 000 trees, Point Pleasant Park in Halifax is a forest within a city. It also offers a perfect vantage point from which curious onlookers would be able to see the hurricane approaching shore. Resisting public pressure, the authorities closed the park to the population. This preventive measure probably saved several lives as between 60 000 and 75 000 trees were uprooted by Juan, leaving the park totally devastated.

The storm surge accompanying Juan set a new record water level in Halifax Harbour (Figure 10.24). Boulders the size of garbage cans were hurled from the harbour to the adjacent boardwalks and piers by the surge. Four independent unfavourable circumstances contributed to the record: (1) a new Moon on September 25, (2) the position of the Moon at its closest point to the Earth in its orbit, (3) the timing of the daily high tides along the Atlantic coast of Nova Scotia, and (4) hurricane-force winds. The first two points are reminiscent of the Saxby Gale.

Although the population was very disciplined and took cover during the hurricane, Juan still took eight lives. Three fatalities occurred where people generally feel the safest—in their home. These indirect deaths were caused by a house fire started by candles during a power outage.

CARIBBEAN SEA– AND GULF OF MEXICO–TYPE HURRICANES

Hurricanes can form above the very warm waters of the Caribbean Sea and Gulf of Mexico at the Intertropical Convergence Zone (ITCZ). The convergence zone occurs where the trade winds meet near the equator (Figure 8.4). The southwestward-blowing trade winds of the northern hemisphere converge near the equator with the northwestward-blowing trade winds of the southern hemisphere. The location of the ITCZ moves with the tilt of the Earth's axis. The average position of the ITCZ is about 5°N latitude, but in January, it mostly lies south

Figure 10.23
Hurricane Juan devastated rural central Nova Scotia.

Source: Saint John's Anglican Church, Oyster Pond NS © Environment Canada, 2011. Photo taken by Chris Fogarty and Jim Abraham. Reproduced with the permission of the Minister of Public Works and Government Services, 2011.

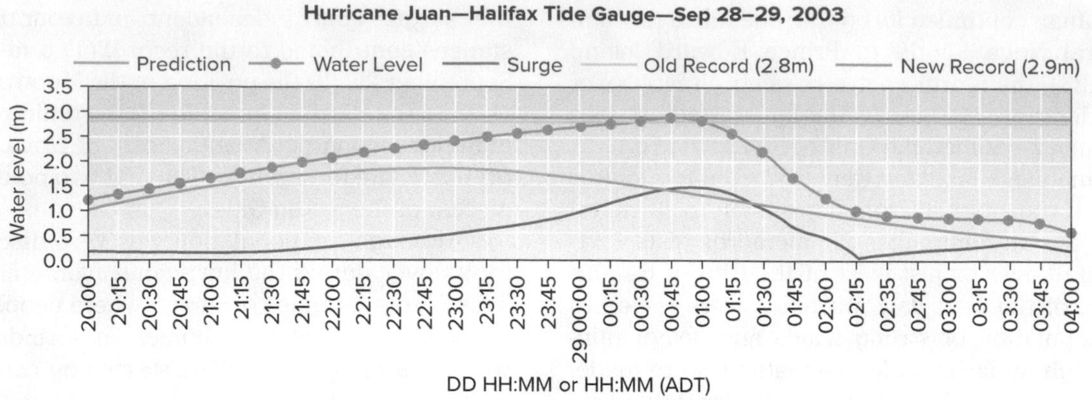

Figure 10.24

Tide gauge data recorded in Halifax Harbour during the passage of Hurricane Juan (orange line). The green line is the predicted water level from astronomical tides. The red line is the difference between the green and the orange line, and corresponds to the storm surge itself. The storm surge raised the previous record water level by 10 cm (dark blue line).

Source: Tide gauge for Hurricane Juan, URL: http://www.ec.gc.ca/ouragans-hurricanes/default.asp?lang=en&n=BAAEAC12-1 © Environment Canada, 2014. Reproduced with permission.

of the equator, and, by July, all the ITCZ is north of the equator. Where the airflows converge, a low-pressure area can form with thunderstorms, a large core, and rising moist air. These elements can combine to create a rotating tropical cyclone that can strengthen to a hurricane, such as Katrina in 2005 and Sandy in 2012.

Barbarians At The Gate: Katrina (2005) and Sandy (2012)

In recent years, two hurricanes have devastated major urban centres in the United States: Katrina brought much damage and suffering to New Orleans in 2005, and superstorm Sandy inflicted a terrible blow to New York City in 2012.

Water has always been part of life in New Orleans. The original French settlement was built on Mississippi River delta swampland surrounded by huge bodies of water. It is the nature of deltas to subside; this continuing phenomenon has already lowered part of the city to six metres below sea level. Three centuries of floods brought by the river and hurricanes have led to spending billions of dollars to build levees to try to keep water out. As levees are built higher and the city sinks lower, a bowl has been created (Figure 10.25), with lake and river water levels higher than city land levels.

On 24 August 2005, a tropical air mass over the Bahamas grew powerful enough to be given a name—Katrina. Two hours before reaching Florida on 25 August, Katrina had grown to be a hurricane. Katrina lost strength crossing Florida, but after reaching the warm waters of the Gulf of Mexico, the storm grew rapidly, with wind speeds reaching 280 km/h and its

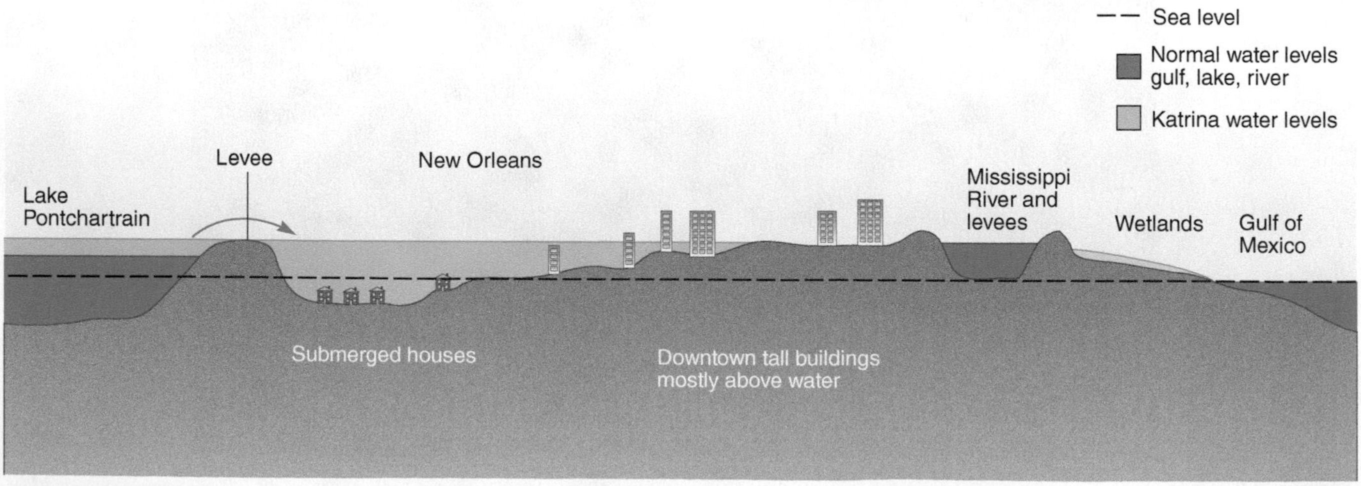

Figure 10.25

New Orleans sits in a bowl between the levees of the Mississippi River and Lake Pontchartrain. Much of the city is below sea level. The land continues to sink, so levees are built higher. The normal lake level is 1.2 m above sea level.

size nearly doubling (Figure 10.5). By 26 August, computer models identified New Orleans as a probable target with a 17% chance of a direct hit. As 27 August dawned, residents saw that Katrina had moved closer. More warnings were issued. People began shuttering their homes, grabbing prized possessions, and fleeing. On the morning of 28 August, the situation looked even worse and a mandatory evacuation was ordered for 1.2 million residents. All lanes of major highways were converted to one-way traffic out of the area and were filled with evacuating vehicles.

Katrina came ashore with incredible violence on 29 August 55 km east of New Orleans near the border between the states of Louisiana and Mississippi (Figure 10.26). Katrina brought enough water inland to breach the precarious levee system, in dire need of maintenance and upgrade, and to overflow canals, flooding low-lying areas that make up 80% of New Orleans (Figure 10.27). Was Katrina a "natural" disaster?

Figure 10.26
Katrina's powerful storm surge lifted boats out of the sea and deposited them inland. Note the several sunken boats in the background.
Source: FEMA photo provided by IP.

At least 100 000 people did not evacuate from New Orleans; more than 1500 of those died there. Who were they? "The carless, the homeless, the aged and infirm, and those die-hard New Orleanians who look for any excuse to throw a party" as described by J.T. Bourne of National Geographic who adds: "Thousands drowned in the murky brew that was soon contaminated by sewage and industrial waste. Thousands more who survived the flood later perished from dehydration and disease as they waited to be rescued." The most vulnerable had been left behind.

It is a sad thing to say, but there were no surprises before, during, or after Hurricane Katrina passed alongside New Orleans. A hurricane like Katrina had been anticipated for decades. The storm, the evacuation difficulties, the levee failures, the flooding, the destruction, and the deaths had all been accurately predicted for many years. In the words of essayist Christopher Hitchens, New Orleans ". . . suffered from a lethal combination of being built below sea level and neglected by the Bush administration . . ." Katrina remains the costliest natural disaster in U.S. history, with damages estimated at US$135 billion.

Hurricanes are natural hazards that you see coming. Hurricane Sandy began in the western Caribbean Sea on 22 October 2012, and quickly developed into a category 1 hurricane the next day. Sandy started its rampage in Jamaica (24 October), then continued on to hammer Haiti and Cuba (25 October). As it moved northward off the eastern coast of North America it did not take the usual path and curve toward the right out into the greater Atlantic Ocean (Figure 10.17); that path was blocked by a high-pressure atmospheric ridge over Greenland causing Sandy to move westward, combining with a stalled arctic front and increasing the fury of the total storm event. Soon, predictions revealed that the New York City area was in its path (Figure 10.28).

Figure 10.27
Water flows over a failed levee into New Orleans on 30 August 2005.
Source: Jocelyn Augostino, FEMA.

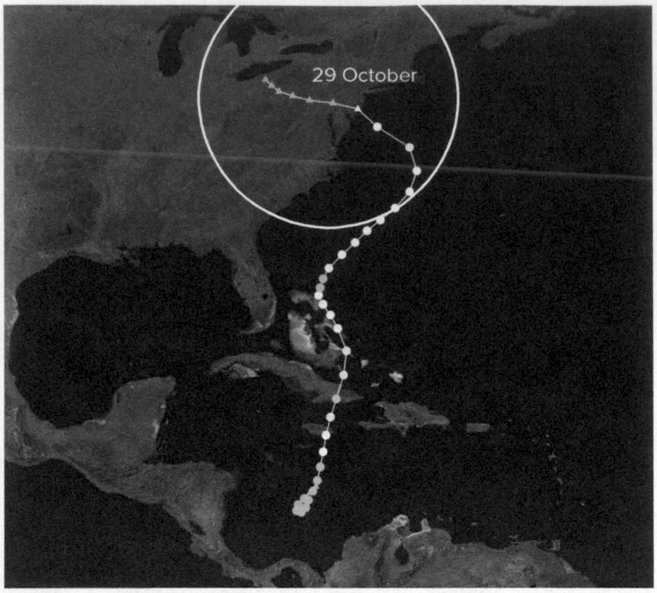

Figure 10.28
The path of hurricane Sandy, October 2012. The points show the location of the storm at 6-hour intervals. The circle indicates the approximate size of the storm at landfall on 29 October. Blue and green dots correspond to tropical depression and tropical storm status, respectively. Other colours indicate the hurricane category (see Table 10.3).
Source: Modified from Wikimedia Commons.

Figure 10.29
The eerie sight of a crane damaged by Sandy's high winds and left dangling from the seventieth floor of a skyscraper under construction in Manhattan.
Source: ADS/Alamy/GetStock.com.

Response was decisive and coordinated. On 28 October, President Barack Obama declared a state of emergency in the District of Columbia and the states of Delaware, Maryland, Massachusetts, New York, and Rhode Island. New York City Mayor Michael Bloomberg ordered evacuations in low-lying areas of the city. These calls were largely respected by the population. Lessons had been learned from Katrina.

Sandy's landfall occurred on the evening of 29 October about eight kilometres southwest of Atlantic City, New Jersey, with wind speeds of 150 km/h (Figure 10.29). The storm had weakened to a post-tropical cyclone just before hitting the coast. The biggest problem was the storm surge; landfall was made at high tide and helped push an already high sea level another four metres higher, across the coastline and inland, flooding streets, tunnels, and subway lines in New York City and cutting off power in many places. For the record books: Sandy is the largest Atlantic hurricane ever, with a an approximate diameter of 1800 km. It is the second costliest hurricane in U.S. history causing about $60 billion in direct damages and business interruption. Out of respect for the citizens of devastated neighbourhoods, the 2012 New York City marathon planned for 4 November was cancelled.

While municipal engineers in New Orleans have merely reinforced and raised existing levees, and added new pumping stations around the city, the urban planners of New York are encouraging people to develop creative ideas to improve the resilience of their city to future storms. One such project under consideration is BigU (Figure 10.30). BigU is a protective berm 16 km long that would encircle the southern tip of Manhattan while providing quality community space such as gardens, open-air markets, and museums. Decorated with art and well-lit, it would provide an attractive walkway through several neighbourhoods at all times of the day in "the city that never sleeps"! Some of its elements would be mobile and could be lowered temporarily for added storm protection.

FORECASTING THE HURRICANE SEASON

William M. Gray of Colorado State University has had reasonable success forecasting the number of named tropical storms in the North Atlantic region based on several variables (Figure 10.31). (1) When the western Sahel region of Africa is wet, its greater number of thunderstorms provides more nuclei for hurricanes. (2) The warmer the sea-surface temperatures, the more energy is available to help tropical depressions grow into hurricanes. (3) Low atmospheric pressure in the Caribbean region aids the formation of tropical cyclones. (4) If La Niña conditions are present in the Pacific Ocean, then west-blowing trade winds assist hurricane movement over warm water. But if El Niño conditions exist, then east-blowing high-level winds tend to disrupt and break apart tropical cyclones. Forecasting, however, remains challenging. Chris Fogarty of the Canadian Hurricane Centre comments

Figure 10.30
The BigU berm would help protect Manhattan's financial district against flooding while enhancing New York City's waterfront.
Source: BigU project.

on the 2013 pre-season forecast: "We were thinking 30% above normal, but it ended up 70% below normal".

Wherever they begin over the Atlantic, tropical cyclones reach hurricane strength above the warm waters of the westernmost Atlantic Ocean, Caribbean Sea, and Gulf of Mexico. The annual probabilities of a hurricane over the waters of this region are sobering (Figure 10.32). Many of these hurricanes will extend their paths of destruction all the way to Canada's Maritime Provinces.

Tropical Cyclones in the Indian and Pacific Oceans

CYCLONES IN THE BAY OF BENGAL

In the twentieth century, seven of the nine most deadly weather events in the world were cyclones striking Bangladesh. The nation has densely populated a comparatively small area of less than 150 000 km^2. The delta country is low lying, mostly 30 cm or less above sea level. When cyclones bring surges of seawater 6 m high, they can flood 35% of the nation. Bangladesh has a 575 km long coastline shaped like a funnel that catches the cyclones roaring up and over the warm waters of the Bay of Bengal. On 12–13 November 1970, during the high tides of a full Moon, a cyclone arrived with a surge of 7 m and winds of 255 km/h. The tall waves drove into the low-lying delta land, killing about 400 000 people and as many large farm animals. On 30 April 1991, a cyclone packing winds of 235 km/h unleashed a surge of 6 m into Bangladesh, drowning 140 000 people and 500 000 large farm animals, and leaving 10 million people homeless.

The new millennium brought similar tragedy in neighboring Myanmar. During a typical month of May, farmers in the low-lying Irrawaddy delta would be working with their water buffalo to plow fields in preparation for planting rice. But in 2008, May was not typical; it brought Cyclone Nargis with its 210 km/h winds and storm surge of water up to 3 m high that pushed inland up to 55 km. Cyclone winds and flooding killed more than 100 000 people, with another 50 000 missing and

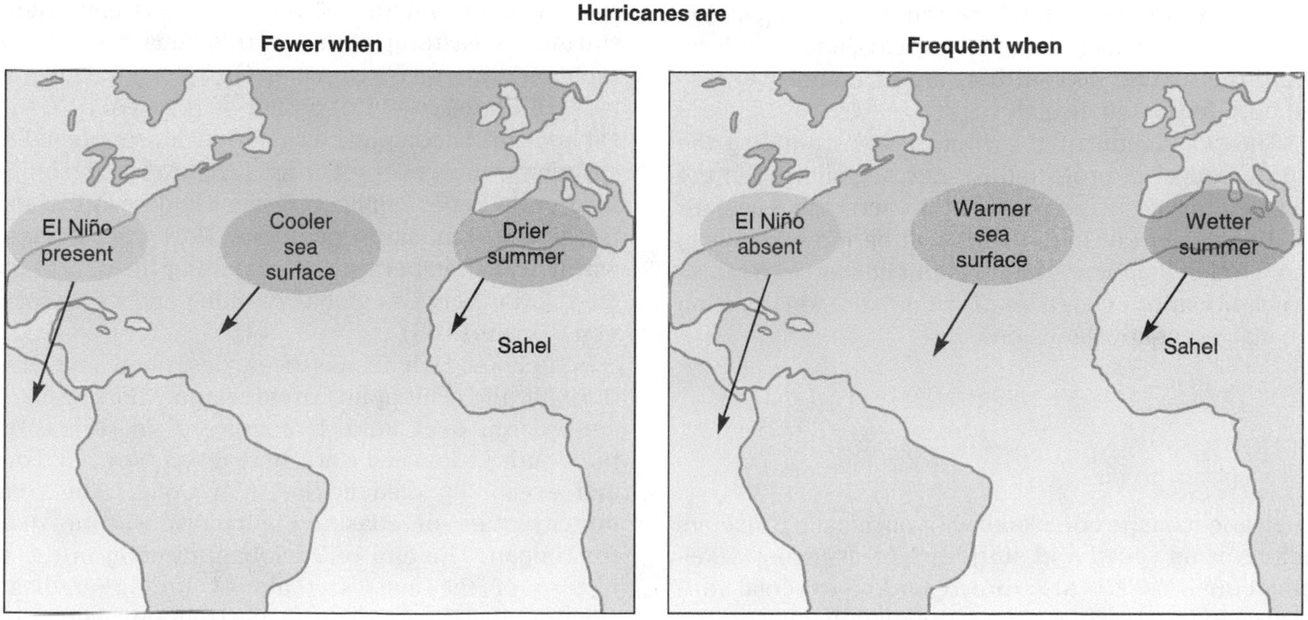

Figure 10.31
The frequency of North Atlantic Ocean hurricanes is affected by climatic conditions.

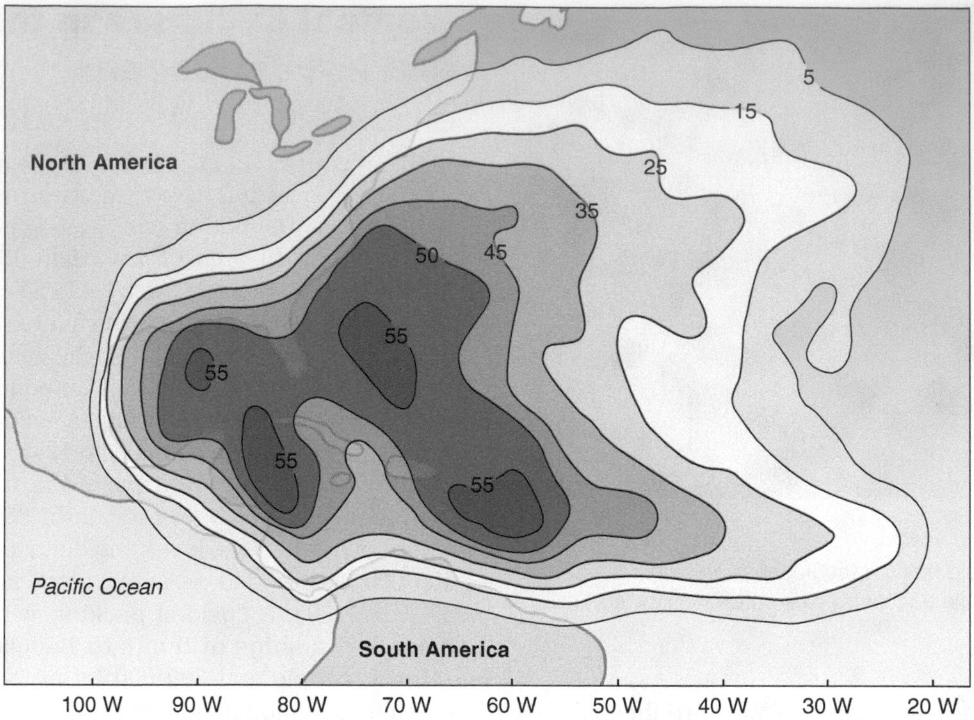

Figure 10.32

Annual probability of a named storm in each area during the June to November season for tropical storms and hurricanes, 1944–1999.

Source: © Chris Landsea of NOAA.

3 million homeless. Cyclone Nargis left behind flooded fields, destroyed rice stocks and seeds for planting, and about 150 000 dead water buffalo. Myanmar's "rice bowl" and shrimp farms were unproductive for months. Damages were greatest where the natural vegetation had been cut down to create more fields, and were least where the natural coastal barriers of mangrove trees had been left untouched.

The population of the countries surrounding the Bay of Bengal is projected to increase sharply in the next generation, exposing millions more to cyclones like Nargis. As low-lying lands will be more seriously inundated in the future, many might choose to relocate to neighbouring countries, fuelling already existing regional geopolitical tensions.

TYPHOON HAIYAN, PHILIPPINES, NOVEMBER 2013

Hurricane damage correlates with physical parameters such as wind speed and surge height. In many developing countries, it is also directly linked to social variables such as poverty and high population density. The case of typhoon Haiyan (known locally as Yolanda), which struck the Philippines in November 2013, combines both aspects.

The physical traits of Haiyan are impressive and scary. First detected on 2 November as a low-pressure system in the middle of the Pacific Ocean, Haiyan started its easterly path towards Asia and attained typhoon status on 5 November. On 7 November, it made landfall on the island of Samar as a category 5 tropical cyclone, accompanied by the strongest one-minute sustained winds ever recorded (315 km/h). The intensification of Super Typhoon Haiyan had been fueled by "ideal" environmental conditions—low wind shear and warm ocean temperatures—reigniting the debate over the relation between global warming and storm formation (Figure 10.33).

Typhoon Haiyan has been described as "slicing through the Philippine archipelago", losing hardly any energy over land. It continued its course over the South China Sea until it reached North Vietnam and eventually died in Southern China. The flimsy infrastructure of coastal Philippines was no match for Haiyan. The city of Tacloban, directly in the trajectory of the eye, was almost totally eradicated (Figure 10.34). Scenes of destruction were reminiscent of those of the 2004 Indian Ocean tsunami.

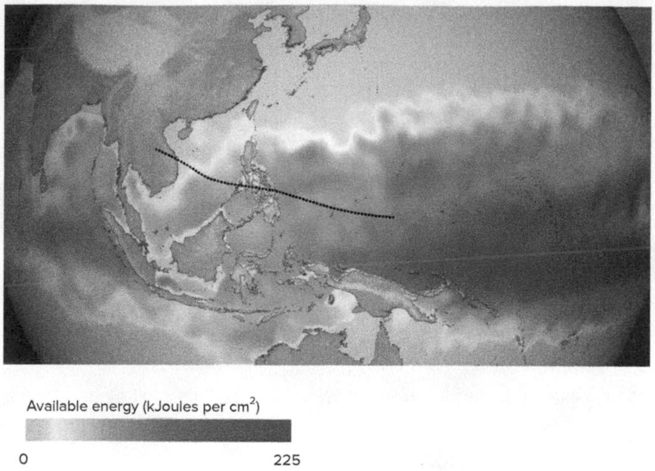

Figure 10.33
Total amount of heat energy available through the water column of the Pacific Ocean for typhoon Haiyan to absorb and strengthen, between 28 October and 3 November. Regions coloured pink or purple provide sufficient energy to fuel storm intensification. The black line is the projected typhoon's path at that time.
Source: NOAA.

Figure 10.34
The City of Tacloban was destroyed by the strong winds and the five metre high storm surge accompanying typhoon Haiyan.
Source: AP Photo/Bullit Marquez/The Canadian Press.

As summarized by the non-governmental organization OXFAM: "Typhoon Haiyan not only killed thousands and made millions homeless. It also struck an already poor region, pushing families deeper into poverty, and making them more vulnerable to the next disaster."

HURRICANES AND THE PACIFIC COAST OF NORTH AMERICA

Each year about 15% of Earth's tropical cyclones of hurricane strength form in the eastern Pacific Ocean, mostly offshore from southern Mexico, Guatemala, and El Salvador (Figure 10.6). There are about 25% more hurricanes per year in the eastern Pacific Ocean than in the North Atlantic, the Caribbean Sea, and the Gulf of Mexico. Why don't Pacific Ocean hurricanes strike the west coast of North America as often as Atlantic Ocean hurricanes strike the east coast? First, the trade winds blow most of the hurricanes westward out into the Pacific Ocean. Second, there is a marked difference in seawater temperatures. Along eastern North America, the northward-flowing Gulf Stream current brings warm water from the Gulf of Mexico up along the Atlantic Coast, while western North America is bathed by cold water of the California Current coming down from Alaska (Figure 8.6). The cold-water current acts as a hurricane defence line. The cold water drains the energy out of any hurricanes that dare to move across it.

Freda, October 1962

The worst hurricane that ever affected Canada's west coast, Freda, was born near the Philippine Sea in Asia on 28 September 1962. During its 8000 km, two-week journey across the Pacific Ocean, Freda was promoted to typhoon (October 4) and then declined back to tropical storm (October 8) and depression (October 10). When approaching the Pacific coast of North America, however, Freda underwent post-tropical transition and merged with another depression. Invigorated with renewed energy, it rapidly gained strength. Freda first struck the northern California coast, its area of influence stretching from San Francisco to northern British Columbia, making it one of the largest storms of the twentieth century. On October 12, Freda's low-pressure minimum was centred on Vancouver Island, following another storm that had raged in the region only a day and a half earlier. Victoria and Vancouver were seriously battered. World-renowned Stanley Park in Vancouver lost of third of its trees during the storm. In total, Freda was responsible for 46 fatalities in the United States and 7 in Canada, with hundreds injured. Damages in British Columbia are estimated at $500 million in 2003 dollars. In addition to the serious destruction Freda caused, a long-time resident of Port Moody, British Columbia, recalls a shortage of roof shingles following the event. Many owners could not get matching colours, resulting in a lot of multicoloured roofs.

IN GREATER DEPTH

Global Warming and Hurricane Frequency and Intensity

Using satellite observations available since 1970, no detectable worldwide trends in hurricane frequency have been documented. But has the intensity of hurricanes increased? Several recent studies state that total energy release by hurricanes is increasing, and these authors attribute the increase to global warming. They point to increasing sea-surface temperatures, to higher concentrations of water vapour in the lower atmosphere, and, since 1950, to hurricane seasons that have been lengthening by approximately 5 days per decade in the Atlantic Ocean and 10 days per decade in the northwest Pacific Ocean.

Other respected scientists point to natural oscillations in ocean and atmosphere circulation that in turn cause hurricanes to vary in multidecadal cycles. For instance, in the North Atlantic Ocean, they infer a causal relationship between the trends of the Atlantic Multidecadal Oscillation (AMO) (Figure 10.35), hurricane intensity (Figure 10.36) and hurricane paths (Figure 10.37). A cold AMO phase correlates with fewer hurricanes, most of them directed at the Gulf of Mexico. A warm AMO correlates with seasons of intense hurricanes preferentially propagating along the Atlantic coast. Note, however, how limited are current observations, which cover only two complete cycles of the AMO.

Will global warming bring more hurricanes like Juan to Atlantic Canada in the future? Data about the frequency and intensity of hurricanes in Atlantic Canada in the past are inconclusive, due to changes in observing systems such as satellites. It is important to understand the past to even begin to predict the future. Natural ups and downs in hurricane frequency can also make the detection of human-induced trends difficult to filter out. It is known, however, that the sea level is rising in the region due to a combination of factors including land subsidence, the melting of ice caps and glaciers, and increasing global water temperatures. Higher sea levels expose the coast to a higher likelihood of flooding due to storm surges. The relationship between global warming and hurricane intensity is hotly debated now, but as data sets improve in quality and duration in the next few decades, these questions should be answered.

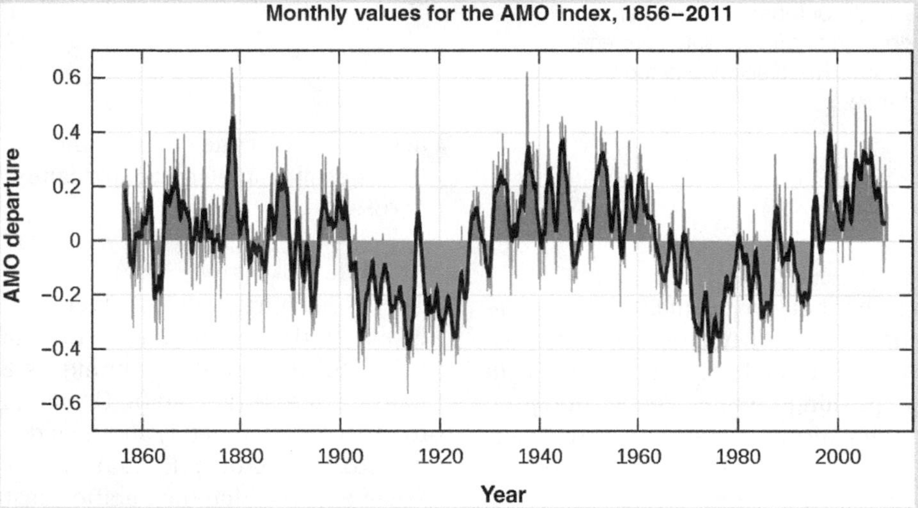

Figure 10.35

Atlantic Multidecadal Oscillation (AMO) time series with a 12-month moving average, exhibiting a pattern of alternating periods of colder (blue) and warmer (red) water.

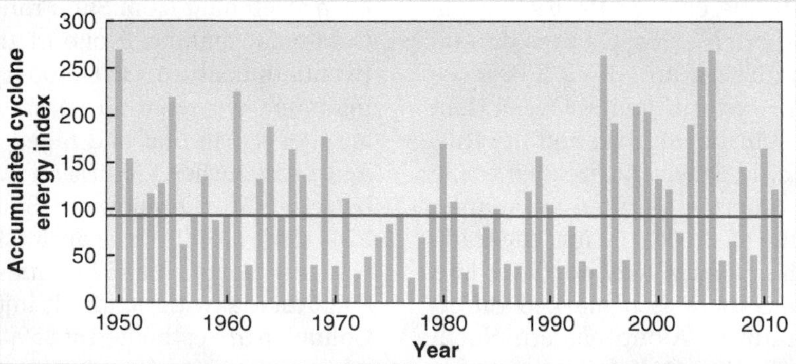

Figure 10.36

Accumulated Cyclone Energy (ACE) index of Atlantic hurricanes compared to the 1950 to 2000 median (red line). The ACE is a measure of hurricane intensity. Each cyclone's energy is calculated every six hours of its existence and then summed to yield its total energy release. The ACEs of all the cyclones during a season are totalled to determine the energy release of that entire season. The 1970–1994 interval is below average and 1995 and ongoing is above average. The most energetic year was 2005 when an unprecedented four hurricanes reached category 5.

Source: © NOAA.

continued

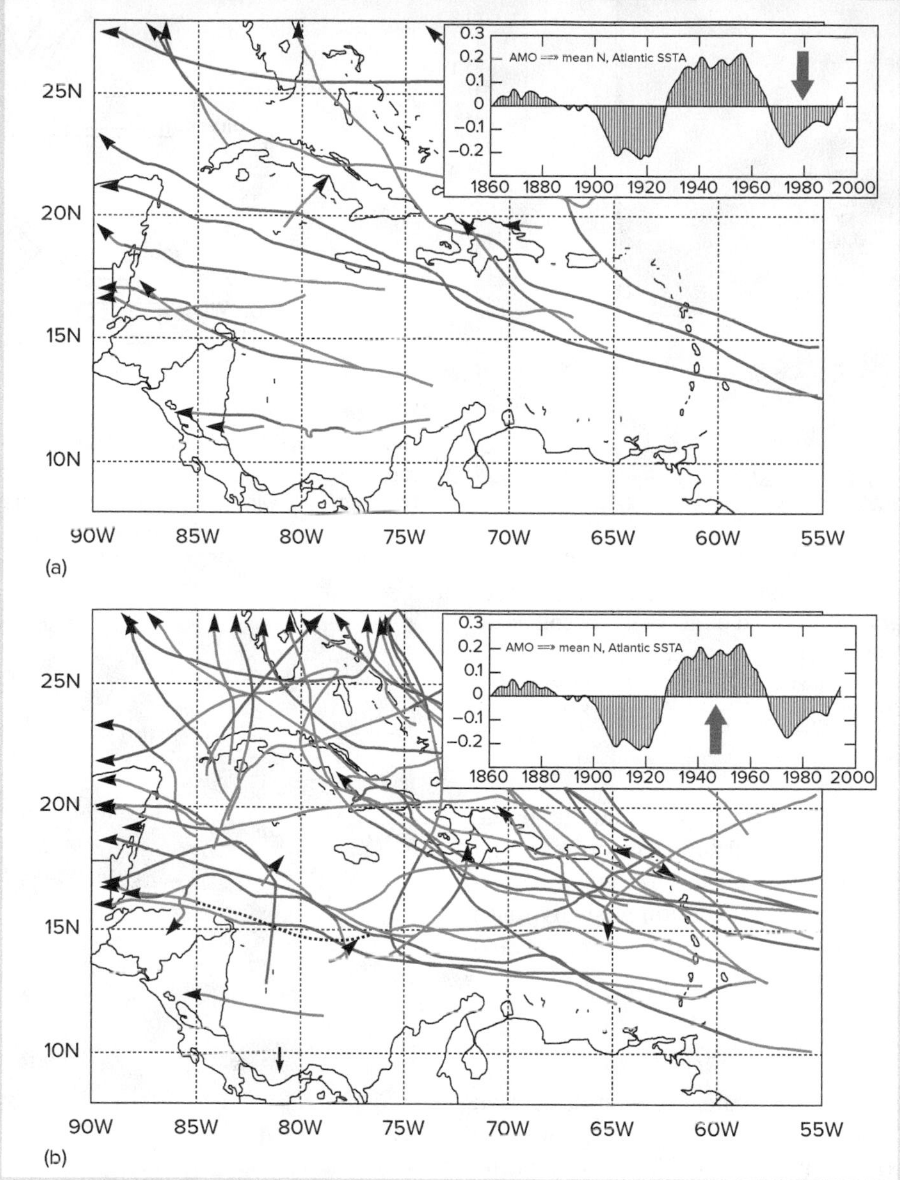

Figure 10.37

Paths of hurricanes in the North Atlantic Ocean during (a) cold and (b) warm AMO phases.

Source: NOAA.

LO6 Reduction of Hurricane Damages

The effort to reduce the impact of hurricanes on society includes concrete actions in both the short term and the long term. In the event of a hurricane approaching, advanced weather forecasts alert people early enough to take cover and to help save lives. As important are long-term mitigation measures, including land planning and building codes, introduced to reduce hurricane damage.

LAND-USE PLANNING

Decisions made about land use before development takes place can prevent a lot of damage. Think of the destruction that could be avoided if authorities designated low-lying coastal land for use only as parks, farm fields, golf courses, nature preserves, or other purposes

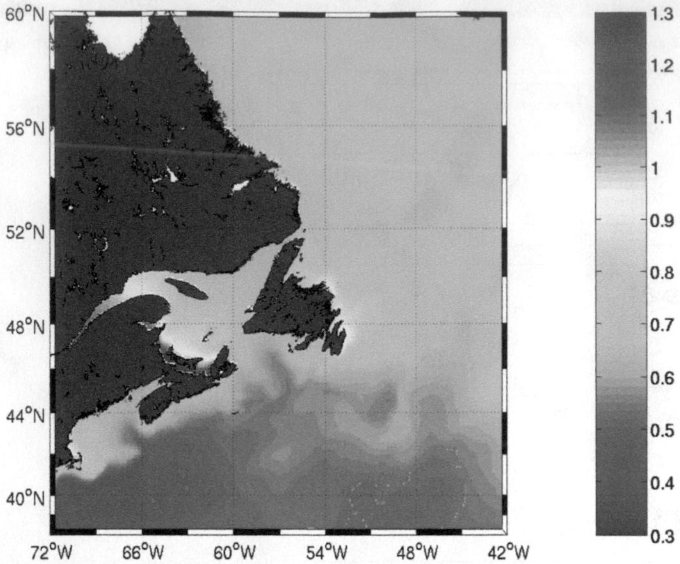

Figure 10.38
Predicted maximum levels of extreme storm surges in Atlantic Canada in metres, over a time period of 40 years, based on an analysis of past events.

Source: N.B. Bernier and K.R. Thompson (2006), Predicting the frequency of storm surges and extreme sea levels in the northwest Atlantic. *J. Geophys. Res.*, 111, C10009, doi:10.1029/2005JC003168.

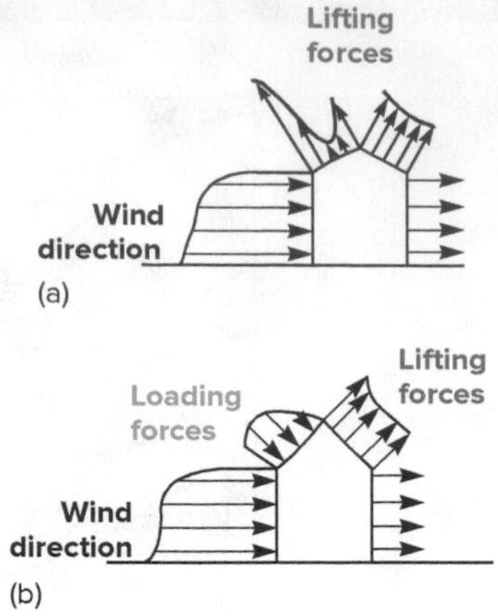

Figure 10.39
Distribution of forces due to wind on a house. (a) Suction forces act to lift low-pitch roofs. (b) For steeper roofs, loading forces on the windward side counterbalance lifting forces.

Source: Modified from Rowe (2003) *Roof Damage by Hurricane Force Winds in Bermuda—The Fabian Experience,* September 2003.

Figure 10.40
Roof eave damaged by the high winds associated with the passage of Hurricane Fabian, Bermuda.

Source: Modified from Rowe (2003) Roof damage by hurricane force winds in Bermuda— The Fabian experience, September 2003.

where flooding will not lead to disasters. At the same time, higher and more protected land could be zoned for house and building construction. To inform decision makers, researchers from Dalhousie University recently produced the first map of storm surge hazard in Atlantic Canada (Figure 10.38).

BUILDING CODES

In 1994, two years after Hurricane Andrew destroyed countless mobile homes in the Florida peninsula, tougher building codes were enacted. The mobile-home industry filed a lawsuit in an unsuccessful attempt to stop the stiffened rules. Nevertheless, when Florida was hit by four hurricanes in 2004, countless old mobile homes were destroyed, but the new ones built to meet the tougher standards fared well. The Florida Manufactured Housing Association admitted that it had been wrong to oppose the new rules.

When hurricane winds destroy a building, commonly, the roof is first lifted off. Then, with walls standing exposed and less supported, the winds proceed with their destruction. When hurricane winds push against the outside of buildings, the wind energy needs to be passed from the roof down through the walls to the ground to prevent damage or destruction. This goal can be achieved by using several strategies to design better buildings. For example, (1) build roofs with a high pitch (Figure 10.39). Eliminate or strengthen eaves that project from roofs, making it easier for winds to lift off the roofs (Figure 10.40). (2) Strap roofs to walls. Inside the attic where the roof meets the walls, add numerous hurricane straps to help hold the roof to the walls. The straps are heavy belts of material similar to those used on suitcases or backpacks. Each strap is wrapped around a roof rafter or truss and continues wrapping onto a heavy wood wall stud; each hurricane strap is fastened by several nails. (3) Ban the common practice of using rapid-fire staples to secure thin asphalt roofing sheets onto plywood. Hurricane winds easily strip off these lightweight, flexible materials, and thus gain entry to the house.

IN GREATER DEPTH

What to Do Before, During, and After a Hurricane

The Canadian Hurricane Centre, in collaboration with Environment Canada, is responsible for issuing hurricane warnings for land and sea (Figure 10.41). Marine weather reports are especially important as hurricane fatalities often include sailors caught in rough seas. Hurricanes are forecast one or two days before they strike. Preparation is the key to reducing risk.

Before

Move people and livestock from exposed coastal areas and areas prone to flooding to higher ground. If your home is well built and safely located, take cover at home. Stock water and food that needs little cooking or refrigeration. Check battery-operated equipment. Opening windows on one side of the house during a hurricane to save the roof is an urban myth! Close all windows. Protect them with storm shutters or board them up. Remove or secure all items around your home (porch furniture, gardening tools, bicycles, etc.) that could fly in high winds. Secure all boats.

During

Keep well informed of the storm progression by listening to the radio. If the eye of the hurricane passes directly over your region, resist the temptation to venture outside. Quiet conditions will prevail only a few minutes before winds pick up again. Use the telephone only for emergency calls.

After

Inspect your property. Clean out debris. In the unfortunate event of damages, take pictures for insurance claims. Service damaged septic tanks first as they are a health hazard. Pump out flooded basements gradually to avoid structural damage to buildings.

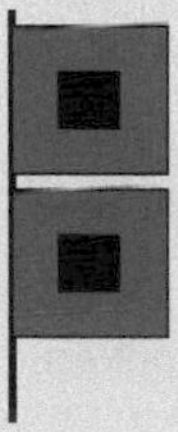

Figure 10.41
The hurricane warning marine flags are two square red flags each with a black square in the middle.
Source: National Weather Service Marine Forecasts COASTAL WARNING DISPLAY PROGRAM http://www.nws.noaa.gov/om/marine/cwd.htm.

SUMMARY

- Tropical cyclones are weather systems that convert the energy of warm ocean waters into wind and rain. They are called cyclones, hurricanes, or typhoons in different parts of the world. Four requirements must be met for a hurricane to form: (1) surface seawater temperature of at least 27°C, (2) warm and humid air, (3) weak upper-level winds, and (4) a substantial Coriolis effect to deflect surface winds. These conditions are encountered in the oceans between latitudes of 5° and 20°. Hurricanes spin in a counter-clockwise fashion in the northern hemisphere and a clockwise fashion in the southern hemisphere.
- Hurricanes go through four stages of development, gradually becoming more structured and powerful. (1) A low-pressure disturbance forms from a cluster of thunderstorms. (2) Winds begin to flow in an organized pattern and the system becomes a depression. (3) The system reaches the status of tropical storm when winds in excess of 63 km/h converge to its centre. (4) When winds reach 119 km/h, a strong updraft prevents them from reaching the centre. An eye forms and the system reaches hurricane status.
- Hurricanes decline rapidly after they make landfall, being deprived of their main source of energy, warm water. However, at mid-latitudes, some hurricanes undergo post-tropical transition, merge with other depressions, and temporarily regain strength.
- Even though weather forecasters track hurricanes several days before they make landfall, hurricanes, together with earthquakes, are the deadliest natural disasters worldwide. Storm surges and torrential rains associated with hurricanes can kill thousands of people in low-lying coastal areas.
- Atlantic Canada experiences the effects of hurricanes, most often after their transition to post-tropical cyclones, on average four times a year.

Terms to Remember

Atlantic Multidecadal Oscillation (AMO)
hurricane
post-tropical transition
surges

Questions for Review

1. Rank the following in order of increasing strength: hurricane, tropical depression, tropical storm, tropical disturbance.
2. Why do hurricanes require an ocean water temperature of at least 27°C to form?
3. Draw a cross-section through a hurricane and explain how it operates. Label the internal flow of winds. What is the "eye"? How is it formed and maintained?
4. Why do hurricanes rotate in a counter-clockwise fashion in the northern hemisphere and in a clockwise fashion in the southern hemisphere?

tropical cyclones
tropical depression
tropical disturbance
tropical storm
typhoons

5. Why are the strongest winds of a North Atlantic hurricane typically on the right side of the storm?
6. Draw a cross-section showing how a hurricane produces a sea surge that floods the land. How high can surges be?
7. Explain the sequence of events that turns an African storm into a hurricane hitting North America.
8. What factors control the path of a Cape Verde-type hurricane from Africa to North America?
9. What is the most common month for hurricanes to strike Canada? The United States? Why?
10. Why do hurricanes strike the Atlantic Coast of North America much more often than the Pacific Coast?
11. Many hurricanes form north of the equator in the North Atlantic, Caribbean Sea, and Gulf of Mexico. Why don't many hurricanes form south of the equator in the South Atlantic Ocean? Can a hurricane form at the equator?
12. Compare a tornado to a hurricane. Which has more total energy? Which has higher wind speeds?

Questions for Further Thought

1. Should buildings be allowed in low-lying coastal areas vulnerable to hurricanes? Should governmental relief funds go to homeowners who suffer losses from hurricane surges and waves?
2. If global ocean temperature continues to rise, what effect will it have on hurricane strength? On hurricane frequency?
3. What can be done to strengthen buildings to withstand hurricanes?
4. Compare how many hours in advance we know when a hurricane will strike with how many hours it takes to evacuate a large city.
5. What should authorities do when people refuse to comply with a hurricane evacuation order?
6. How would you react if confronted with a hurricane evacuation order? Is it difficult for people to accept emotionally that they may be endangered?
7. Where is investment to reduce the impact of hurricanes better directed? Toward early detection? Toward hurricane tracking? Toward building resilient infrastructure? Toward making emergency management plans?

Interesting Websites

- Canadian Hurricane Centre, Environment Canada
  http://www.ec.gc.ca/ouragans-hurricanes
- National Hurricane Center, National Oceanic and Atmospheric Administration, United States
  http://www.nhc.noaa.gov
- Hurricane Research Division, Atlantic Oceanographic and Meteorological Laboratory, National Oceanic and Atmospheric Administration, United States
  http://www.aoml.noaa.gov/hrd
- Hurricanes: Science and Society, Graduate School of Oceanography, University of Rhode Island
  http://www.hurricanescience.org/
- Animation on hurricane wind damage, National Hurricane Center, United States
  http://www.nhc.noaa.gov/aboutsshws.php

CHAPTER ELEVEN

11

Floods

Angry clouds and murky waters in Calgary, June 2013.
Source: Karin Michel.

Come hell or high water.
—American idiom, nineteenth century

Outline

LO1 Explain how streams adapt to excess water.

LO2 List the factors which favour the infiltration of water in the ground versus those that promote runoff.

LO3 Describe the different flood styles, and their relation to Canadian weather.

LO4 Describe flood control structures.

Environment Canada describes the events of June 2013 in Alberta as a "flood of floods". The misery started with a slow moving rainstorm that brought three days of torrential rains to southern Alberta. In the eastern flank of the Rockies, rainfall rates of 10 to 20 mm/h were recorded. The picturesque mountain village of Canmore lay first on the front line. A thick snowpack, late to melt in the spring, had saturated the subsurface, leaving the ground with no further infiltration capacity. Running off steep slopes, the rainwater transformed an existing creek into a raging stream that cut through town ignoring its original course, a process called **avulsion.** Bank erosion destroyed building foundations and left riverfront properties literally suspended in midair (Figure 11.1).

Much of the excess water eventually found its way into the Bow River, which saw its level rise dramatically. The high waters continued their course toward Calgary. Calgary is located at the confluence of the Bow and Elbow Rivers, each of which collects water from large watersheds swollen by the rain. Close to Calgary, the level of the Bow River is regulated by several hydroelectric dams and the Glenmore reservoir, which helped to dampen the influx. The Elbow River, on the other hand, is short and more susceptible to rapid variations in water flow. The amount of water flowing through these two rivers proved too much. The Bow River overtopped its banks, inundating Calgary's downtown core including the corporate headquarters of several of Canada's oil and gas producers (see photo of chapter opener). The floods in the City of Calgary made the international news but the waters did not stop there. High water levels moved downstream and affected towns as far away as Medicine Hat, in southern Saskatchewan.

Figure 11.1
Homes along Cougar Creek in Canmore, Alberta barely hang on, 20 June 2013.
Source: Craig Douce, Rocky Mountain Outlook.

There is little new in terms of water management to learn from these floods. In fact, the Bow River at Calgary has reached very high discharges (greater than 1500 m^3/s) five times in the last 134 years. There was a major flood as recently as 2005. What is becoming problematic is the combination of a human element and a climatic element: there are more and more people and infrastructure on the flood plain of the Bow, and climate models predict that intense rainfall events in the region will become more frequent in the future.

Pictograms prepared by the City of Calgary show the wide-ranging impact of the floods on the community—from disruption of public transportation to power blackouts, the immediate response, and the path to recovery (Figure 11.2).

Response was exemplary. Under the leadership of Calgary's charismatic mayor, Naheed Nenshi, and alongside official responders, neighbours helped neighbours, and total strangers helped total strangers. Until the Calgary flood, the Canadian Red Cross, an indefatigable presence at times of disasters small and large, had only mobilized highly-trained volunteers during emergencies. For the first time, they coordinated the actions of hundreds of spontaneous volunteers. Thanks to its network, the Red Cross organized the distribution of more than one million items such as brooms, plastic gloves, and garbage bags.

Recovery was strong and energetic. Return to a tentative "normal" situation was achieved within two weeks, in time for the one-hundred-and-first edition of the Stampede.

Now that water has flowed under the bridge (literally and figuratively), it is time to reflect and plan. All options to prevent future floods in Calgary are expensive. They include digging a diversion tunnel under the city, and building higher levees and larger reservoirs. The status quo is not an option.

Figure 11.2

Pictograms on the fallout, response, and recovery of the 2013 Calgary flood.

Source: Infographic courtesy of the City of Calgary.

Floods in Canada: A Worsening Situation?

The year 2013 was particularly taxing with major floods in Southern Alberta and Toronto. Is the situation regarding floods worsening in Canada? Statistics show an increasing number of floods through the decades of the twentieth century (Figure 11.3). This trend is a result of several factors. The floods tallied in these statistics are events identified as "natural disasters" and might be overrepresented in the second half of the century because of better reporting. Nevertheless, the statistics also reflect the very real trend of increased development on flood-prone lands following growth in the Canadian population. They might also signal long-term changes in climate.

Floods occur in every region of Canada and at any time of the year. However, the classic combination of snowy winters transitioning abruptly into balmy, wet springs causes a cluster of floods during the snowmelt period (Figure 11.4).

In general, floods in Canada cause few deaths but extensive damage (Figure 11.5). Only 1 of the top 40 deadliest Canadian disasters from 1900 to 2013 is indirectly related to flooding, Hurricane Hazel (Table 1.3). On the other hand, floods feature prominently among the costliest disasters, with 7 entries out of 18 (Table 1.4). A close look at fatality statistics reveals a different pattern before and after 1950 (Figure 11.6). Deaths due to flooding are probably underrepresented in the first half of the twentieth century. Most deaths in recent decades are isolated cases of people caught in their homes or cars by rapidly rising waters. The decade 1960–1969 was especially deadly, with people losing their lives in five separate events.

Yet Canadians like to be near rivers. They provide food and drink, business and transportation, arable land and irrigation, power, and an aesthetic environment. But being near rivers also means being subjected to floods. To live successfully with floods, we need to understand how streams and rivers operate and plan accordingly.

LO1 Rivers as Response Mechanisms

A **drainage basin** can be represented as a large net, open to the sky, catching rain droplets as they fall on the ground or channelling water from snowmelt. Rivers and streams are dynamic components that respond to changes happening in the drainage basin. Depending on topography and geology, different forms of river networks develop but they share a hierarchy in which water

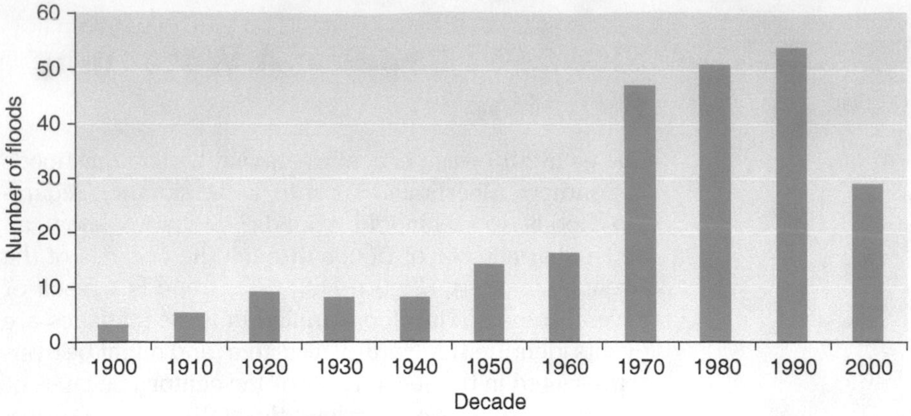

Figure 11.3
Number of floods identified as natural disasters in Canada per decade from 1900 to 2010.

Source: Number Floods Identified as Natural Disasters in Canada per decade, Canadian Disaster Database, http://cdd.publicsafety.gc.ca, Public Safety Canada. Reproduced with permission.

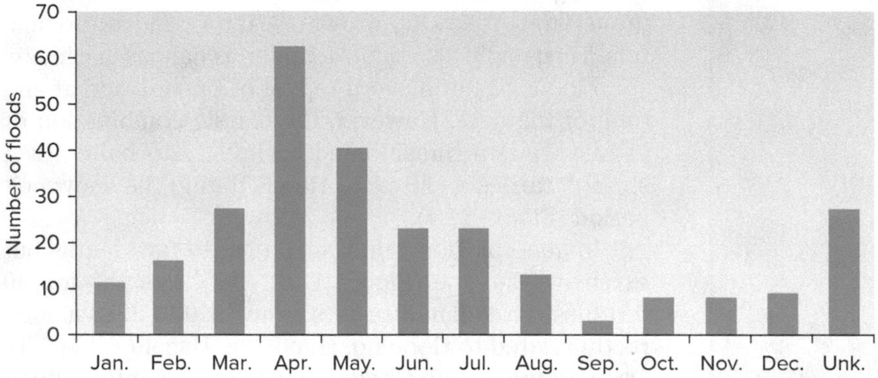

Figure 11.4
Number of floods identified as natural disasters in Canada per month of the year from 1900 to 2010. (Unk. = unknown or unspecified.)

Source: Number Floods Identified as Natural Disasters in Canada per month, Canadian Disaster Database, http://cdd.publicsafety.gc.ca, Public Safety Canada. Reproduced with permission.

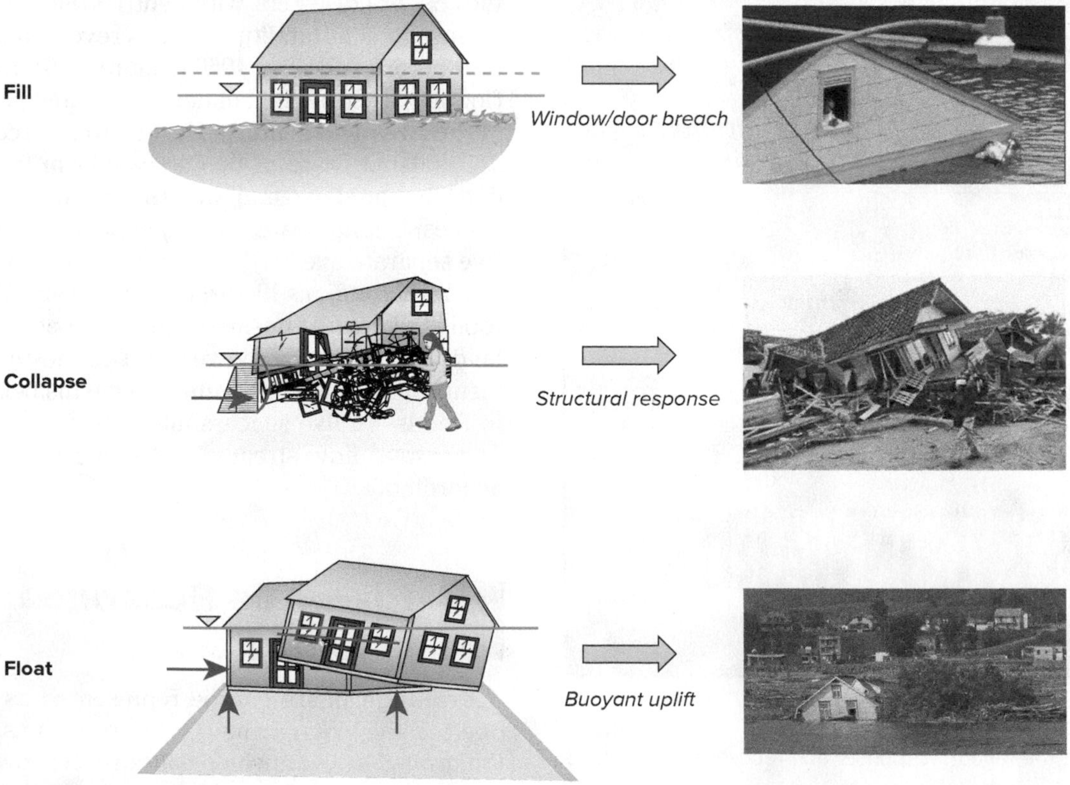

Figure 11.5
Different failure mechanisms of buildings subjected to floods.

Source: Becker, A.B. and Lence, B.J. (2007). "Wood Frame Building Response to Catastrophic Flooding in Aid of Emergency Planning and Mitigation." GEOIDE 9th Annual Scientific Conference, Halifax, Nova Scotia: June 6–8, 2007. Modified from Figure 6 in: Johnstone, W.M., Sakamoto, D., Assaf, H., and Bourban, S. (2005) "Architecture, Modelling Framework and Validation of BC Hydro's Virtual Reality Life Safety Model" in International Symposium on Stochastic Hydraulics (ISSH 2005), May 23–24, 2005, Nijmegen, Netherlands. Photo reproduced with the permission of Natural Resources Canada 2014, courtesy of the Climate Change Impacts and Adaptation Program.

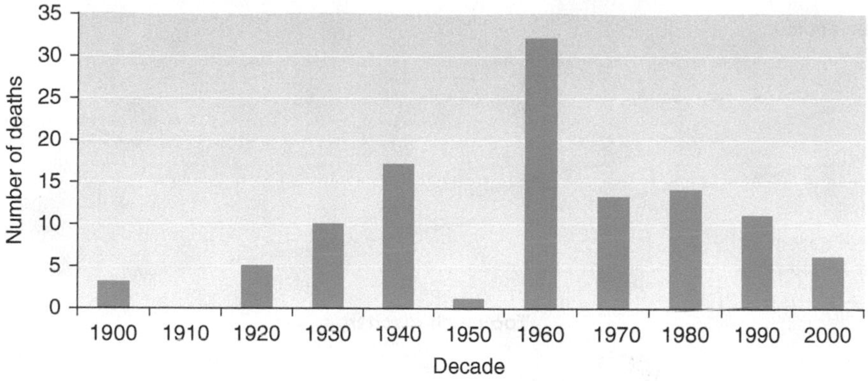

Figure 11.6

Number of flood fatalities in Canada per decade from 1900 to 2010.

Source: Number of Fatalities in Canada Per Decade, Canadian Disaster Database, http://cdd.publicsafety.gc.ca, Public Safety Canada. Reproduced with permission.

is conveyed from subtributaries to tributaries, then to the main stream (Figure 11.7). The drainage basin acts as a funnel, evacuating water to a single outlet.

THE EQUILIBRIUM STREAM

Within a drainage basin, numerous factors interact to make streams seek **equilibrium,** a state of balance in which any change causes compensating actions. To grasp the fundamentals of how streams work, a few key variables must be understood: (1) **discharge**—the rate of water flow expressed as volume per unit of time, (2) **load**—the amount of sediment moved, (3) **gradient**—the slope of the stream bottom, and (4) channel pattern—the **sinuosity** of the stream path.

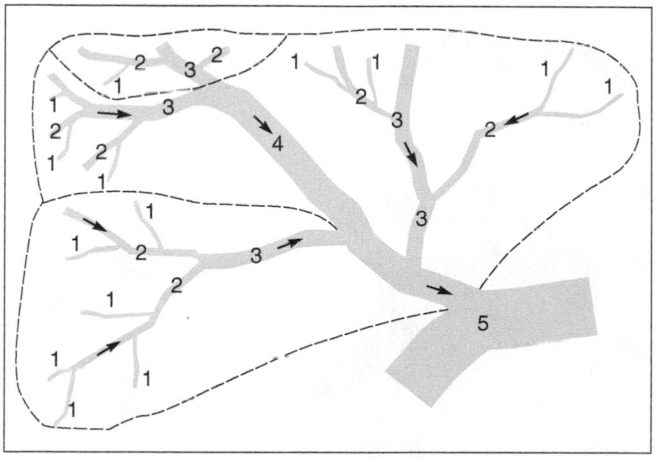

Figure 11.7

A tree-shaped drainage basin composed of four subbasins delineated by dashed lines. Primary, often ephemeral, streams (1) merge unto small subtributaries (2), larger subtributaries (3), tributaries (4), and finally into the main stream (5).

Source: Reproduced with the permission of Dr. Stephen A. Nelson, Tulane University.

The greater the discharge, the greater the load of sediment carried. Both discharge and available sediment are independent variables; that is, the stream has no control over how much water it will receive or how much sediment is present. Nonetheless, a stream moves the sediment present with the water provided. Excesses in discharge or load are managed by changing dependent variables, such as gradient and channel pattern.

Case 1—Too Much Discharge

If a stream has too much water, it will flow more rapidly and energetically. The move away from equilibrium triggers responses to correct the imbalance. (1) Some of the excess energy is used in eroding the stream bottom, reducing the vertical drop downstream and causing slower and less energetic water flow (Figure 11.8). (2) The sediment picked up by erosion adds to the load carried by the stream, thus consuming more of the excess energy. (3) The stream also responds by increasing the sinuosity of its channel pattern through meandering. A meandering stream cuts into its banks, thus using some of its excess energy to erode and transport sediment. Notice how the meandering pattern lengthens the flow path, lowering the stream's gradient and thus slowing water flow (Figure 11.9).

A close look at the meandering process tells us much of value (Figure 11.10). Water does not flow at even depth and power across a stream. Instead, a deeper, more powerful volume of water flows from side-to-side, eroding the river bank on one side and then on the other. This lengthens the path of the stream, decreases the gradient, and slows the water flow. Notice that deposition of sediment occurs on the inside bend of each **meander**, where water is shallower and less powerful. The meandering process can proceed so far that two erosional banks can merge and create a shortcut that straightens the river locally.

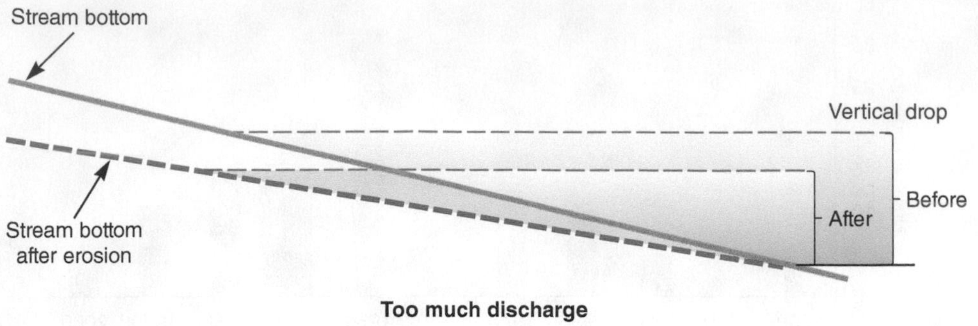

Figure 11.8
Schematic cross-section of a stream with too much discharge. The excess water erodes the bottom, flattening the gradient and thus slowing water flow.

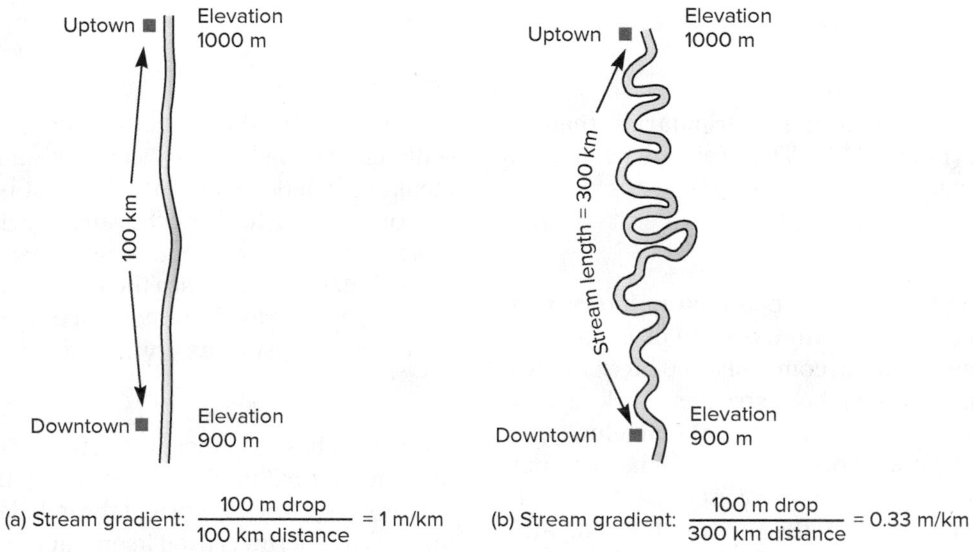

Figure 11.9
(a) A straight stream follows the shortest path between two points. (b) A meandering channel lengthens the stream, thus reducing the gradient and slowing water flow.

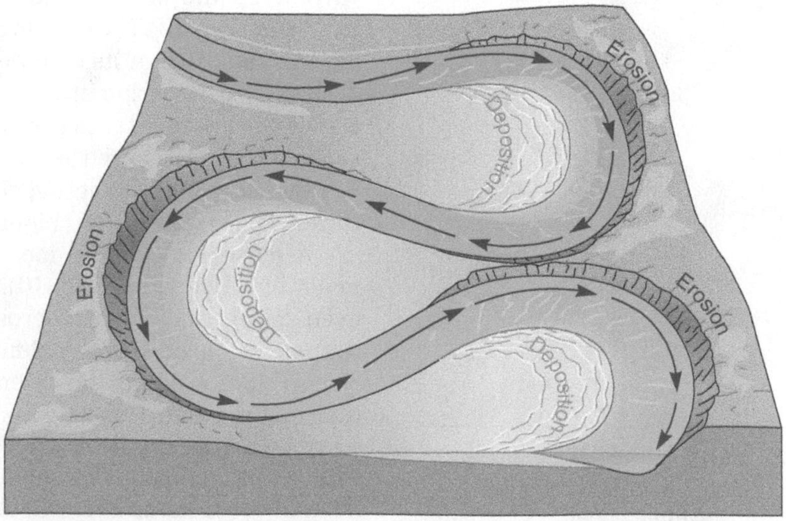

Figure 11.10
In a meandering stream, the inside bank grows as sediment is deposited, while the outside bank is eroded and steep. During a flood, fast moving water might eat into the outside bank, precipitating waterfront properties catastrophically into the stream below.

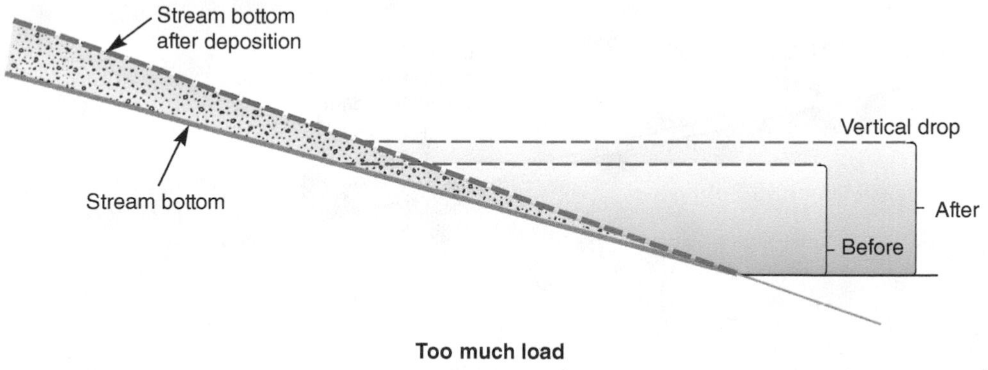

Figure 11.11
Schematic cross-section of a stream with too much load. Excess sediment is dropped on the stream bottom, increasing the gradient and thus speeding water flow.

Case 2—Too Much Load

If a stream is choked with sediment and has insufficient water to carry it away, this also triggers a counteraction. The excess sediment builds up on the stream bottom, increasing the gradient and causing stream water to flow faster and thus have more load-carrying capacity (Figure 11.11). The channel pattern responds by straightening to shorten the flow distance and increase gradient. The straighter stream still contains excess sediment, causing the water to pick its way through as a **braided stream** (Figure 11.12).

Figure 11.12
Braided stream on Axel Heiberg Island, Nunavut. A braided stream develops as water flows through excess sediment within a fairly flat valley. During periods of high discharge, the entire valley might be under water. During periods of low discharge, sediment is deposited as short-lived sandbars in ever-changing patterns.
Source: © Claire Samson.

Another situation related to "too much load" in a stream is the presence of a lake. For example, if a mass movement dams a stream, it adds excess load that the stream will attempt to carry away. The stream will gradually fill in the lake basin with its load of sediment until flow can reach the dam (Figure 11.13). When the stream is able to flow over the face of the dam, it does so with heightened erosive power, allowing it to carry away the landslide dam as well as the sediment in the lake. In a geological sense, lakes are temporary features that streams are striving to eliminate.

All streams operate in a state of delicate equilibrium maintained by ever changing gradients and channel patterns. Every change in the system triggers compensating changes that work toward equilibrium. Streams also change their equilibrium states from one season to another and in response to global changes in sea level and to tectonic events.

LO2 The Flood Plain

After rainfall, some water infiltrates through the soil and the rest runs off at the surface into streams and rivers. What factors determine the amount of **infiltration** versus **runoff** (Table 11.1)? More water is likely to infiltrate in porous, dry soils over a flat landscape covered with vegetation. This is especially true if the total amount of precipitation is spread over a relatively long period of time. On the other hand, intense precipitation over already-saturated soils on exposed, steep slopes promotes runoff.

Streams occupy less than 1% of Earth's land surface but convey excess water from all the land. When discharge temporarily exceeds their capacity to contain the flow, flooding occurs. Drainage basins with a high density of short streams are associated with a

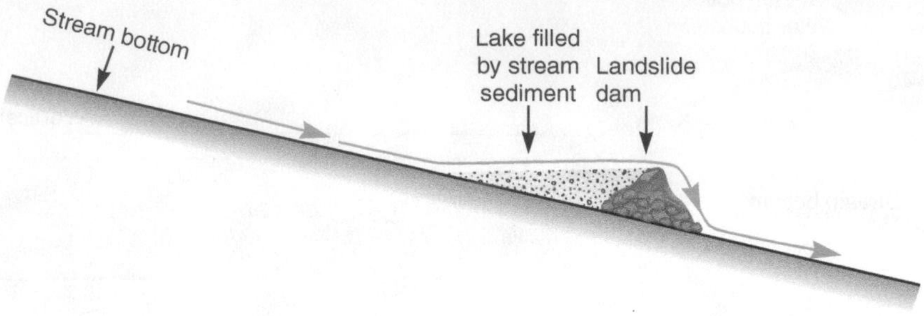

Figure 11.13
Schematic cross-section of a natural dam. Over time, a stream fills the lake with sediment and then flows across the infilled lake. Flow down the dam's steep face is at high velocity, causing erosion and transport of dam and lake sediment. In extreme cases, the natural dam might fail catastrophically.

TABLE 11.1

Factors Affecting Infiltration and Runoff

Infiltration	Runoff
← Increasing soil porosity	
← Increasing vegetation cover	
← Increasing duration of precipitation	
	Increasing amount of precipitation →
	Increasing soil saturation →
	Increasing slope steepness →

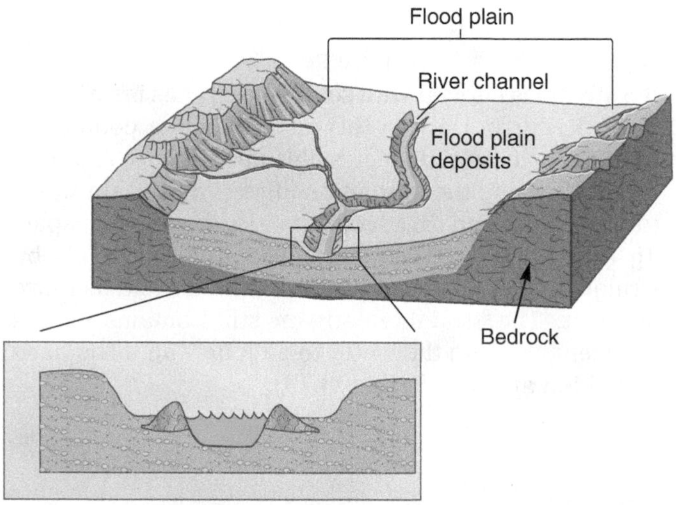

Figure 11.14
Flood plains are flat lands bordering a stream. During a flood, the stream overtops its banks and inundates the flood plain. In certain cases (see insert), a ridge of sediment is deposited when water spills over the banks and slows down, forming a natural levee.

higher potential flooding hazard because rainwater tends to be captured quickly into streams instead of infiltrating over a long distance.

Flood plains are the floors of streams during floods (Figure 11.14). With their thick sediment cover and sheltered surroundings, they offer several plant species a nurturing environment. Streams build flood plains by erosion and deposition, and reoccupy their flood plains during high-discharge events. Humans who decide to build on a flood plain are gamblers. They may win their gamble for many years, but the stream still rules the flood plain, and every so often it comes back to collect all bets.

Flood Frequency

Flooding is part of the natural rhythm of rivers. Everyone living near a stream needs to understand the frequency with which floods occur. Small floods happen every year or so. Large floods return less often—every decade, century, or longer—an illustration of the inverse relationship between frequency and magnitude mentioned in Chapter 1. A typical analysis of flood frequency involves a plot of historical data on flood discharge versus return period (Figure 11.15). The longer the historical record of floods in an area, the more accurately the curve can be drawn. With a flood-frequency curve, the return period of floods of a given size can be estimated by reading the period on the horizontal axis and the corresponding discharge value on the vertical axis.

Individual flood-frequency curves must be constructed for each stream because each stream has its own characteristic floods. A flood-frequency curve helps planners to decide what size flood (how many years of protection) to accommodate when determining how the land will be used.

IN GREATER DEPTH

Flood-Frequency Curves

We need to know how often a given-size flood may occur in order to intelligently develop land. The process used is statistical. If enough historical records exist for a river, then flood frequencies can be estimated.

A relatively simple method for constructing a flood-frequency curve begins by determining the peak discharge for each year. Ignoring the chronological order, rank the data in order from greatest discharge (M = 1), second greatest (M = 2), etc., down to the smallest. To plot a curve such as the one in Figure 11.15 for a river of interest, first estimate return periods for each year's maximum flood using the formula

$$\text{Return period} = \frac{(N + 1)}{M}$$

where N is the number of years of flood records, and M is the numerical rank of each year's maximum discharge. After calculating an estimated return period for each year, locate that value (in years) on the horizontal axis (which usually is a logarithmic axis as in Figure 11.15), then move upward until reaching the corresponding discharge value. Stop and plot a point marking the intersection of the return period and the discharge value. After plotting a discharge versus return period point for each year, draw a best-fit line through your plotted points.

The flood-frequency curve for the Red River in Manitoba is presented in Figure 11.15. The 1997 flood is the fourth highest (M = 4) in the records, which span 222 years from 1776 to 1997, inclusive (N = 222). Using the above formula, a flood of this size has an estimated return period of (222 + 1)/4 = 56 years.

How valuable are flood-frequency curves? Their reliability is directly related to the number of years of flood records; the longer the record, the better defined the flood-frequency curve. In this method, the return period for the largest flood on a river is the most suspect point; it is based on a sample population of one. Advanced statistical methods are available to help plot the upper segments of flood-frequency curves for the rare, extra-large floods.

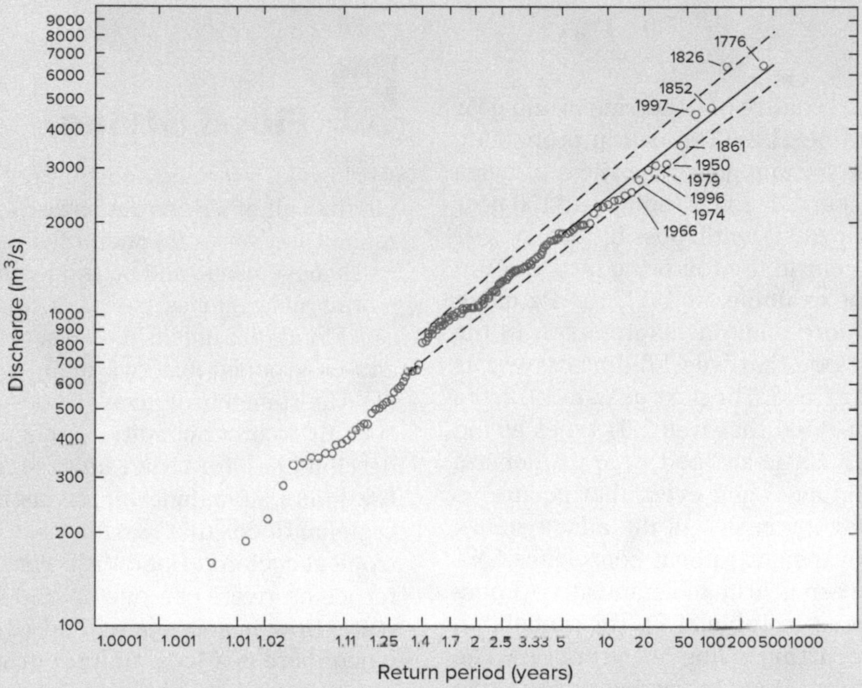

Figure 11.15

Flood-frequency curve for the Red River, Manitoba, for the years 1776, 1826, 1852 1861, 1875 to 1878, 1880 to 1885, and 1892 to 1997. (The ten largest floods are labelled.)

Source: Reproduced with the permission of Natural Resources Canada 2014, courtesy of the Geological Survey of Canada (Bulletin 548).

When designing roads, bridges, and buildings, it is seductive to plan only for the smaller floods and save large amounts of money on initial construction costs. In the long run, however, it is commonly cheaper to build to withstand large floods; this not only saves money but also eliminates much of the human suffering that occurs when homes and other buildings are flooded.

A designer needs to know the likelihood of a given size flood occurring during the expected usage time of a structure. A common standard for design near streams is protection from a 100-year flood. Flood frequency can be expressed as the statistical probability of discharges of a given size arriving in any year or number of years (Table 11.2). Based on yearly statistics, a

TABLE 11.2

Cumulative Probabilities of Floods (Percentage Chance of This Size Flood Occurring)

Return Period (Years)	Any 1 Year	10 Years	25 Years	50 Years	100 Years
2	50%	–	–	–	–
5	20	–	–	–	–
10	10	65%	94%	99.9%	–
20	5	40	71	90.5	–
50	2	18	40	63	86%
100	1	9.6	22	39	63
200	0.5	5	12	22	39
500	0.2	2	5	9.5	18
1 000	0.1	1	2.5	4.8	9.5
2 000	0.05	0.5	1.2	2.3	5
5 000	0.02	0.2	0.5	1	2
10 000	0.01	0.1	0.25	0.5	1

Source: B.M Reich Water Resources Bulletin, 9 (1973), 187–88.

100-year flood has a 1% chance of occurring in any year (second column in Table 11.2). The yearly probability of a flood is the same for any year regardless of when the last flood has occurred. Even though a "150-year flood" may occur one year, it is still possible for another of the same size to occur in the following year or even in the same year. For example, in 1971, the Patuxent River between Baltimore and Washington, DC, in the United States had a flood that was 1.6 times as big as its calculated 100-year flood. The next year, in 1972, the Patuxent River had a flood that was 1.04 times as big as its 100-year flood. A 100-year flood, or any other size flood, is a statistically averaged event that occurs by chance, not at regular intervals. As the adage states: "Nature has neither a memory nor a conscience." We must distinguish between yearly and cumulative probability (four right columns in Table 11.2). The probability of a 100-year flood occurring in any one year is 1%. The probability of a 100-year flood occurring once in two years is not simply 1% times two. The probability of the flood occurring in year one is 1% and the probability of it not occurring in year two is 99%. The probability that both these occur is 1% times 99% = 0.99%. Then there is the probability of no flood in year one (99%) and a flood in year two (1%) also giving a probability of 0.99%. The sum of these two probabilities is 1.98%, which is slightly less than 2%. Calculating the cumulative probability for more years is more complicated and shows a bigger reduction from the expected resut. Hence the probability that a 100-year flood will occur once in 100 years is not the naïve 100%, but actually only 63% (rightmost column of Table 11.2, sixth row). No flood has a 100% chance of occurring.

LO3 Flood Styles

Worldwide, river and coastal flooding affects more people than all other natural hazards. Floods are intricately related to several other natural disasters. They can trigger mass movements, and be triggered by mass movements, storms and cyclones, tsunamis, and volcanic activity.

Floods are unleashed by several phenomena, which can be grouped into two main categories (Table 11.3). (1) Hydrometeorological floods occur in relation to specific weather conditions. For example, a local thundercloud can form and unleash a flash flood in just a few hours. Abundant rainfall lasting for days can cause regional floods that last for weeks. The storm surges of tropical cyclones flood the coasts. The breakup of winter ice on rivers can pile up and temporarily block the water flow, in an ice-jam flood. (2) Flooding also occurs when there is a local natural obstruction to flow from mass movements, glaciers, or lahars.

In Canada, most floods are caused by hydrometeorological mechanisms, often working in combination.

TABLE 11.3

Flood Styles

1. Hydrometeorological floods	Rainfall Snowmelt Rain-on-snow Ice jam
2. Natural dams	

April and May are particularly vulnerable (Figure 11.4) when abundant rain coincides with the spring melt.

Hydrometeorological Floods

RAINFALL FLOODS

Rainfall floods occur when the rate of precipitation exceeds the infiltration capacity of the ground. Over this limit, any additional water finds its way into streams and rivers, which swell and soon overflow.

A rainfall flood can take the form of a dramatic flash flood, the result of torrential rainfall over a relatively small area. Flash floods develop in a matter of a few hours, sometimes unexpectedly. The hamlet of Buffalo Gap, Saskatchewan, holds the Canadian flash-flooding record. On 30 May 1961, 254 mm of precipitation—a mix of rain and hail—fell in less than one hour! An agent of the Saskatchewan Wheat Pool reported: "Pigpens, full and empty gas barrels, toilets, timbers, C.P.R. [Canadian Pacific Railway] ties, and telegraph poles went through the town like sailboats." A day after the storm, hail was still piled a metre deep.

Flash floods can be deadly. Several flood fatalities in recent years in Canada have occurred when cars were swept off the road by flood waters (Figure 11.16). Not enough people appreciate what a shallow-water flood can do to a car (Figure 11.17). Flowing water 0.3 m deep exerts about 2250 newtons of lateral force. If water 0.6 m deep reaches the bottom of a car, there will be a buoyant uplift of about 6500 newtons, which helps the 4500 newton lateral force in pushing or rolling the car off the road. Many automobile drivers and passengers are swept away by flood water less than one metre deep. In areas prone to sporadic flooding, authorities occasionally install flood gauges along the road to alert motorists to unexpectedly deep water accumulations (Figure 11.18).

Figure 11.16
Paved roads, especially those located in topographic lows, are vulnerable to sporadic flooding during heavy rain.
Source: © Claire Samson.

The 8 July 2013 Toronto Fast Flood

Southern Ontario, with its oppressive summer heat and high humidex ratings, both of which fuel thunderstorm activity, has witnessed a few deluges. From 19 to 20 July 1989, for example, 450 mm of rain fell in Harrow, near Lake Erie. More recently, in the late afternoon of 19 August 2005, a swarm of thunderstorms—with "fireworks" of 1400 lightning strikes per minute—inundated the City of Toronto with 153 mm of rain, accompanied by quarter- to golf-ball-sized hail, over a period of only three hours. An event of similar proportion occurred on 8 July 2013 when, within a few hours, Toronto Pearson International Airport and Toronto's downtown area received 126 mm and 97 mm of rain, respectively. The storm dumped a total of 6.1 billion litres of water—enough water to fill the Rogers Centre to the brim 38 times! The 2005 and 2013 storms, only eight years apart, brought rainfall in excess of the 1-in-100 year storm event, bringing the uncomfortable thought that we may be witnessing an intensification of severe weather due to climate change and underestimating the hazard. To add to the gravity of the situation, any disaster occurring in Toronto has the potential to affect a large number of people. According to the 2011 census, there are on average 945 people per square kilometre in the Toronto metropolitan area.

In several Toronto neighborhoods, the water and sewer system has been designed to specifications exceeding 1-in-100 years storm models. In addition, the city possesses many green spaces to promote rainwater infiltration, several of them created in the aftermath of Hurricane Hazel. Still, the 8 July 2013 storm proved too fierce. The Humber River overtopped, pushing great volumes of water into the city core. The Don Valley Parkway and several subway stations were completely flooded, and a commuter train became partially submerged, trapping the 1000 passengers on board (Figure 11.19).

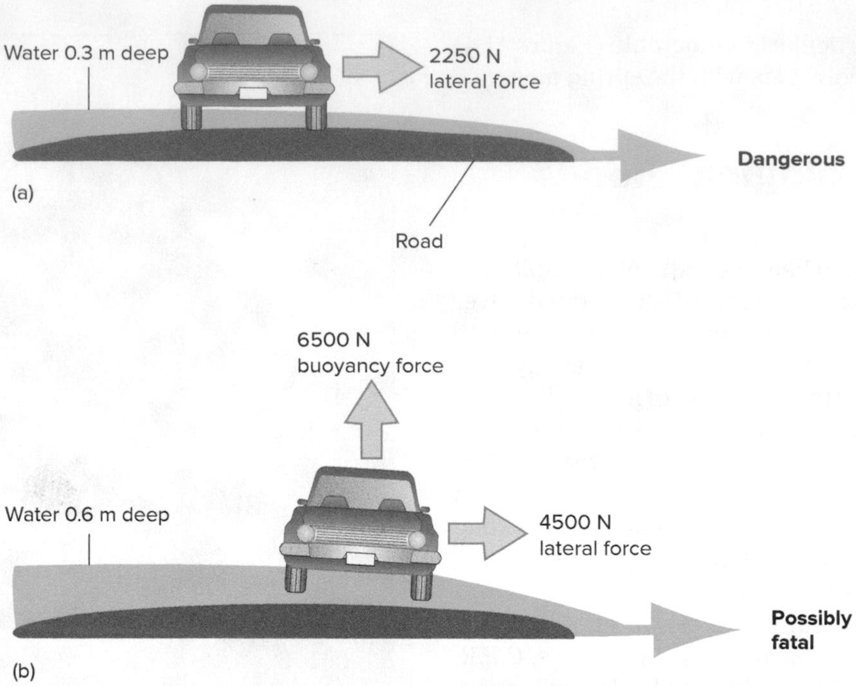

Figure 11.17

Do not drive through a flood. (a) Flood water 0.3 m deep exerts 2250 newtons (N) of lateral force. (b) Flood water 0.6 m deep both buoyantly lifts and laterally pushes a car.

Source: Modified from United States Geological Survey Fact Sheet 024-00.

Figure 11.18

Flood gauge in the middle of the Central Australian Desert. The Central Australian Desert is hot and dry, but prone to flash floods from rain thousands of kilometres away. Several major rivers, including the Diamantina River, do not have a permanent channel but are a collection of channels shifting in response to heavy rain.

Source: © Claire Samson.

Figure 11.19

First responders used watercraft to rescue trapped passengers from a partially submerged GO train.

Source: Mark Blinch/Reuters/Landov.

According to the Insurance Bureau of Canada, the bill for the 2013 tempestuous event exceeded $940 million, significantly more than the $590 million price tag that accompanied the 2005 storm (Table 1.4). In both cases, the vast majority of claims were from homeowners having to cope with flooded basements and sewer backups. To mitigate future disasters, the City of Toronto is encouraging residents to install flood-prevention devices on the internal plumbing of their homes. The City has also made a priority of preserving vegetation cover (including that provided by green roofs) even more to boost natural infiltration.

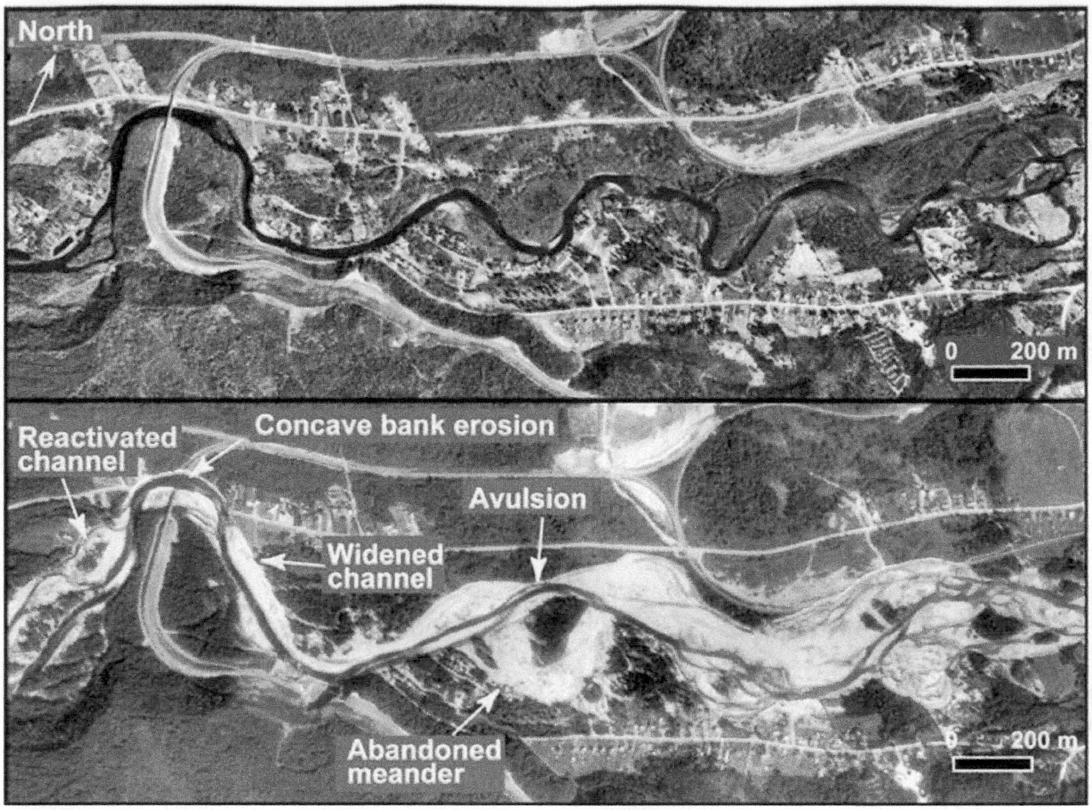

Figure 11.20
Pre-flood (top) and post-flood (bottom) Rivière à Mars, Saguenay region, showing different channel modifications due to excess flow.
Source: Natural Resources Canada.

The 1996 Saguenay Flood, Quebec

The Saguenay flood of 1996 illustrates the complex interaction between the forces of nature and human modifications to the environment.

On 18 July 1996, a large cyclonic depression started forming over the North Atlantic Ocean, offshore of New England. The weather system, shaped like a giant inverted comma, evaporated warm water from the Gulf Stream in the Atlantic Ocean and condensed rain droplets over the Saguenay region of Quebec. Between 19 and 21 July, the region received a total of 279 mm of rain, the equivalent of 10 buckets of water per square metre of soil. Such an extreme event causes rivers to adapt. In the Saguenay, they did this with a vengeance (Figure 11.20). Some rivers abandoned their current meanders. They re-occupied ancient channels, many of which had been diverted by urban intervention. Other rivers eroded their banks severely, sending waterfront properties down into widened channels.

The precarious situation was further complicated by the fact that the area is covered by a network of more than 2000 dams and earthen dikes. All this haphazard infrastructure is managed by various organizations, dedicated to different uses, and in various states of maintenance. Kenogami Lake was one of the many reservoir lakes whose level was artificially controlled by a dam. At the request of recreationists, the water level in Kenogami Lake had been kept high since the spring. At the onset of the crisis, there were only 160 cm between the lake and the crest of the dam. In the early hours of 20 July, technicians realized that the dam would not resist the influx of water into the reservoir much longer. They increased the evacuation of water, creating an artificial flood downstream in the Rivière aux Sables and Rivière Chicoutimi that was so strong it damaged several hydroelectric dams (Figure 11.21).

Figure 11.21
The City of Jonquière dam along Rivière aux Sables was breached during the 1996 Saguenay flood.
Source: Reproduced with the permission of Natural Resources Canada 2014, courtesy of the Geological Survey of Canada (Photo 1997-42L by Greg Brooks).

The floods created chaos in the region, with 1700 houses and 900 cottages destroyed. More than 15 000 people had to be evacuated from their homes. Ten people lost their lives, including two children who died when a mud flow buried their home. The house of Mrs. Jeanne d'Arc Lavoie-Genest, which resisted the flood, has been preserved in downtown Chicoutimi as a symbol of the resilience of the people of the Saguenay (Figure 11.22). May it also serve as a reminder for more cautious land use and urban development practices in the future.

SNOWMELT FLOODS

Snowmelt floods develop over several weeks. Technological advances, including satellite imagery and distributed networks of river gauges, allow better forecasts of the time and height of flood waters. In well-studied drainage basins, computer models can simulate the response of the different streams and rivers to different weather scenarios.

The floods of the Red River are classic examples of regional snowmelt floods, compounded with the occasional ice jam. Hydrologists knew in December 1996 that the 1997 spring melt in the Red River valley would be problematic. On 23 April, almost two weeks before the actual peak in water level, Manitoba provincial authorities ordered a mandatory evacuation of thousands of homes in the Red River Valley, a decision still questioned. For several residents, the forced evacuation meant that they were relegated to the role of bystanders and could not do anything to save their homes.

Better forecasting of snowmelt floods has reduced the loss of life. But it is interesting to note the twin trends of better forecasting and better engineering offset by ever-greater dollar losses during big floods. We know more, yet suffer greater damages.

RAIN-ON-SNOW FLOODS

Rain-on-snow floods are a combination of rainfall and snowmelt floods. They are likely to occur in the fall along the West Coast, or during a mild spell in winter or in spring elsewhere in Canada, when temperatures are hovering around 0°C. Two factors coincide to create the problem: rain adds to the snowmelt to generate a large quantity of water, and, at the same time, the frozen soil is almost impermeable. The result is excess water pooling at the surface.

Another problem is associated with rain-on-snow. A water-saturated snowpack becomes very heavy and can form a dangerous load on structures. We have seen this situation before: just imagine replacing volcanic ash with wet snow in Figure 5.18!

ICE JAM FLOODS

Ice jams are a spring "classic" in many drainage basins across Canada. With the return of milder temperatures, river ice breaks into pieces and moves downstream

Figure 11.22
The house of Mrs. Jeanne d'Arc Lavoie-Genest, nicknamed "La petite maison blanche" ("the small white house") now stands alone in a park. The neighbouring houses were washed away during the 1996 Saguenay flood.
Source: © Pascal Tremblay.

with the current. Problems occur when the pieces start to pile up, obstructing the flow of water. Water levels rise upstream and the river may overtop its banks. Ice jams of several kilometres in length are common.

Rivers flowing from south to north—the Red River of Manitoba, the Mackenzie River in the Northwest Territories, and the St. Lawrence River and several of its tributaries in Ontario and Quebec—are particularly vulnerable to this style of flood. Break-up starts earlier in the south, sending large pieces of ice toward the north where the still-frozen ice acts as a plug. The supply of ice upstream and the thickness of the intact ice are the key variables in this scenario. Several other factors can compound the problem. Bends and other variations in the shape, depth, and gradient of the river channel can create favourable circumstances for the formation of ice jams, as can human-made obstacles such as bridges and piers (Figure 11.23).

At critical times in the St. Lawrence River, ice breakers continually fracture the ice to prevent the onset of a jam. In smaller rivers, a mix of blasting and ice cutting is used to breach the ice cover. Recently a new tool has been added to the arsenal: the Amphibex icebreaking machine. The Amphibex, designed and built in Canada, resembles a backhoe on a barge (Figure 11.24). It can venture onto water and ice, and reach problematic areas where it breaks ice blocks into smaller, more mobile, pieces.

The 2003 Ice Jam Flood, Badger, Newfoundland

The town of Badger, Newfoundland, is located at the confluence of the Exploits, Red Indian, and Badger rivers, and flooding in the area is entirely due to ice jam events. The list of years afflicted by damaging floods is long: 1903, 1916, 1943, 1977, 1983, 1985, and 2003. The year 2003 was exceptionally trying as ice jams clogged all three rivers at once. On 15 February of that year, frigid water submerged more than half the town, necessitating the evacuation of 1200 residents. The combination of water and ice caused extensive damage (Figure 11.25). With water levels higher than one metre in certain neighbourhoods, large chunks of floating ice smashed through the windows of several buildings. The temperatures on the days following the flood were very cold. Water froze hard, causing further damage and delaying cleanup operations.

Since 2005, the latest radar satellite technology has been applied to monitor ice on the Exploits River. Satellite images are acquired two to three times a week. Software has been developed to automatically classify water and non-consolidated and consolidated ice (Figure 11.26), and to detect changes in ice cover between successive images. These interpreted images are released three to five hours after their acquisition. With this information at hand, authorities can prevent excessive accumulations of ice, usually by a program of ice-breaking explosions.

WORLD DISTRIBUTION OF HYDROMETEOROLOGICAL FLOODS

It is interesting to examine the flooding styles of the world's largest drainage basins (Figure 11.27). Rainfall floods occur most often (20 of 38) and include the record flood of 1953 in Brazil when the Amazon River reached a peak discharge of 370 000 m^3/s. Rainfall floods are mainly concentrated between latitudes of 35°N and 35°S, and are associated with torrential tropical rains. Snowmelt floods dominate in the northern latitudes. Canada contributes four data points to this inventory:

Figure 11.23
Ice blocks jamming against bridge pilings on Hay River, Northwest Territories, spring 2007.
Source: Robyn Andrishak, Research Engineer, University of Alberta.

Figure 11.24
An Amphibex machine ready for action!
Source: CP PHOTO/Winnipeg Free Press/Wayne Glowacki.

Figure 11.25
The residents of Badger, Newfoundland, experienced the destructive power of water and ice during the ice jam flood of 15 February 2003.
Source: CP PHOTO/The St. John's Telegram/Keith Gosse.

the drainage basins of the St. Lawrence, Nelson, and Mackenzie rivers, and that of the international Yukon River flowing from the Canadian Rockies to the Bering Sea through Alaska. All are characterized by snowmelt flooding.

Natural Dams

The category "Natural dams" groups several flooding mechanisms in which an obstacle blocks the flow of water. This blockage can result from mass movement, lava flows (Figure 11.13), or the advance or retreat of glaciers.

The complex relationship between lava and ice can take several forms. Under the surface, subglacial volcanic activity can trigger the rapid melting of glaciers (see "Jokulhlaup of 1996" in Chapter 6). On the surface, thick lava flows might block the melt streams from nearby glaciers. A colossal example is a feature called "The Barrier," located in Garibaldi Provincial Park in British Columbia (Figure 11.28). "The Barrier" is a crumbly rock wall that formed when lava flows were stopped by a glacier during the last eruption of Mount Garibaldi, some 13 000 years ago, and cooled in place. When the glacier melted away, water ponded behind the lava dam, forming Garibaldi Lake. "The Barrier" is 300 m high and 2 km wide. If it were to fail entirely, Garibaldi Lake would be released, causing extensive damage downstream. A more immediate hazard is the possibility of debris flows (Figure 11.29). The most recent debris flows occurred in 1855 to 1856 and prompted the relocation of a small village built at the foot of

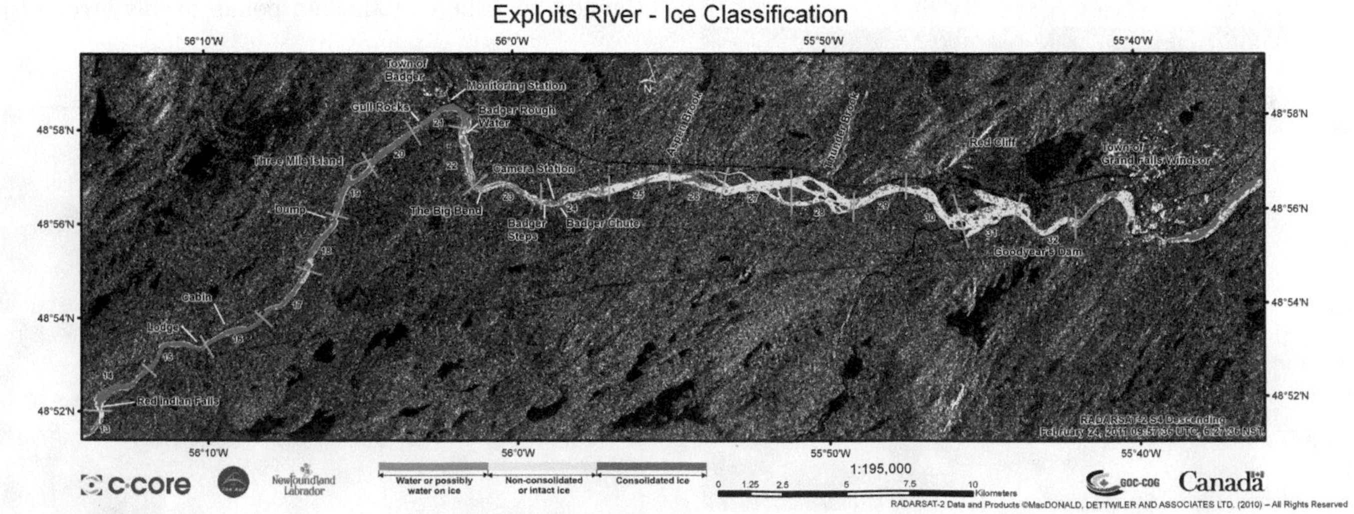

Figure 11.26
Ice blocks shown through a radar satellite image of the Exploits Rivers, Newfoundland, on 24 February 2011. The image is colour-coded to identify water (blue), and non-consolidated (yellow) and consolidated (red) ice.
Source: Reprinted by permission of Water Resources Management Division, Department of Environment and Conservation, Government of Newfoundland and Labrador.

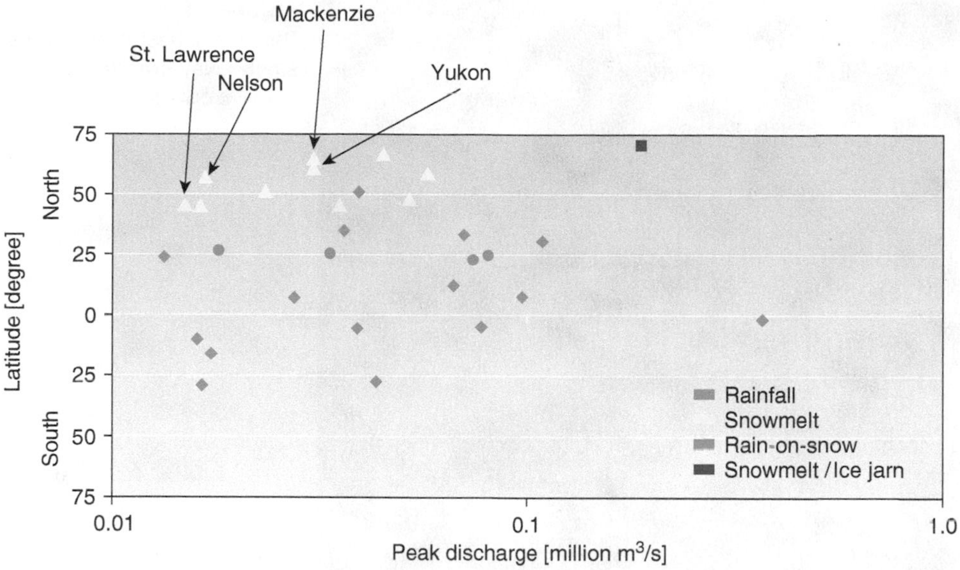

Figure 11.27

Geographical distribution and peak discharges for 38 of the world's 45 largest drainage basins.

Sources: O'Connor and Costa, 2004, USGS Circular 1245; Dery et al, 2005, *Journal of Climate*.

Figure 11.28

"The Barrier" formed when lava flows solidified against a large glacier.

Source: Reproduced with the permission of Natural Resources Canada 2014, courtesy of the Geological Survey of Canada (Photo 2001-308 by Lionel Jackson).

Figure 11.29

Plunging view from the top of the "The Barrier" into Rubble Creek, which has been the site of several debris flows.

Source: © Claire Samson.

the cliff. Hikers exploring the area can regularly hear the sound of small boulders detaching from "The Barrier." Camping is not permitted at the base, along a small stream very fittingly called "Rubble Creek" (Figure 11.30).

In some cases, very large glacial lakes are formed when deep valleys are blocked by tall glaciers for an extended period of time. These lakes can overflow, or breach their ice dams or retaining moraines.

When natural dams fail catastrophically, they trigger **outburst floods.** Outburst floods are the sudden release of large quantities of water with peak discharges typically one order of magnitude greater than that of hydrometeorological floods. Their force of impact causes enormous damage downstream. Table 11.4 lists the 11 known historical floods with peak discharges equal to or greater than 100 000 m^3/s. Although not quite as common as hydrometeorological floods, natural dam floods account for 4 out of 11 entries. All natural dam floods listed were outburst floods.

Figure 11.30
One of the best mitigation strategies is to stay safely away from a hazardous location.
Source: © Claire Samson.

Table 11.4

Largest Historical Floods

Date	Flood/River	Country	Peak Discharge [million m^3/s]	Flood style
1841	Indus River	Pakistan	0.54	Landslide dam
1953	Amazon River	Brazil	0.37	Rainfall
1918	Katla	Iceland	0.30	Jokulhlaup
1963	Amazon River	Brazil	0.25	Rainfall
1976	Amazon River	Brazil	0.24	Rainfall
≈1450	Columbia River	United States	0.22	Landslide dam
1967	Lena River	Russia	0.19	Snowmelt and ice jam
1962	Lena River	Russia	0.17	Snowmelt and ice jam
1948	Lena River	Russia	0.17	Snowmelt and ice jam
1870	Yangtze	China	0.11	Rainfall
1986	Russell Fiord	United States	0.10	Ice dam

Hydrometeorological floods
Natural dams

Source: J.E. O'Connor and J E. Costa, 2004, United States Geological Survey Circular 1254.

LO4

Mitigation of Flood Hazards

Mitigation strategies to reduce society's vulnerability to flood hazards have been of two main types: structural and non-structural.

Structural mitigation initiatives include the erection of major infrastructures such as floodways, dams, and flood barriers; building **levees** along rivers to contain flood water inside a taller and larger channel; and engineering projects to increase the water-carrying ability of a river channel via straightening, widening, deepening, and removing debris.

Non-structural responses include more accurate flood forecasting through use of satellites and high-tech equipment, zoning and land-use policies, insurance programs, evacuation planning, and education.

Figure 11.31
The 1950 Red River flood on the campus of the University of Manitoba.
Source: University of Manitoba Archives & Special Collections, Winnipeg Tribune Photograph Collection, "Flood 1950" (PC 80, 339-I).

THE RED RIVER FLOODWAY, MANITOBA

The Red River flows northward. The meandering river drains parts of South Dakota, North Dakota, and Minnesota before crossing the U.S.–Canada border into Manitoba where it joins with the Assiniboine River in Winnipeg, before reaching Lake Winnipeg. The list of historical floods on the Canadian side of the Red River basin reads like a litany. There were major floods in 1776, 1826, 1852, 1861, 1916, 1950, 1979, 1997, 2009, and 2011. Less serious floods occurred in 1882, 1897, 1904, 1948, 1956, 1966, 1969, 1974, and 1996. As described by John McCormick of *Newsweek*, "On the northern plains, nature is less an enemy than a sparring partner, trading rounds in a grudge bout that never ends."

Why are floods so common along the Red River? (1) The Red River valley is geologically young, only about 9000 years old, and the river has not yet carved a deep valley. (2) The valley is underlain by an impermeable reddish clay layer, which gave the river its name. This clay blocks the infiltration of water into the ground. (3) The slope of the riverbed is very low, averaging a drop in elevation of only eight centimetres per kilometre. The lack of slope causes slow-flowing water to pool into a broad and shallow lake on the flat prairie during high-water flow. (4) River flow increases as winter snow melts. The meltwater runs northward into still-frozen lengths of the river, where ice jams obstructs water flow.

The 1950 Red River Flood

The winter of 1950 had been long and severe, covering southern Manitoba under a thick blanket of snow and ice. The spring was equally miserable and late in coming. By April, snow was starting to melt and water levels in the Red River were rising. They were already 8.2 m above normal when, on 5 May, a blizzard struck the region. The precipitation, combined with strong winds, caused several **dikes** protecting Winnipeg to collapse, turning 1600 km^2 of land into an enormous lake (Figure 11.31). A state of emergency was declared and 107 000 people were evacuated from Winnipeg (one-third of the city's population!) with the help of the Canadian Army and the Red Cross. The Red River stayed above **flood stage** for 51 days. When the waters finally subsided, Winnipeggers were left with 10 500 damaged buildings (Figure 11.32).

The Red River Floodway was built between 1962 and 1968 in response to the flood of 1950. The project cost $63 million at the time. The federal government

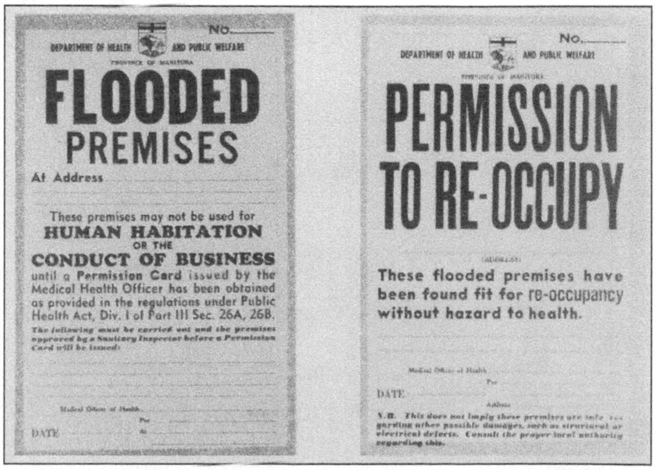

Figure 11.32
Notices issued by the Manitoba Department of Health and Public Welfare during the 1950 Red River flood.
Source: Used with permission of the Library and Archives Canada nlc010739.tif.

contributed 55% of the funds, and Manitoba 45%—a significant investment for a province with a modest economy. Premier Duff Roblin showed strong leadership and vision in championing the project against considerable opposition.

The Floodway is simply a trench in the earth diverting excess water, but a trench of gigantic proportions! The 48 km long, 140 m wide channel circumvents Winnipeg to the east, extending from the St. Norbert inlet structure to the Lockport outlet structure (Figure 11.33). The project necessitated the excavation of 75 million cubic metres of earth. At the time, the excavation of the Floodway was the second-largest earthmoving project in the world, next to the Panama Canal.

Under normal circumstances, the Floodway is empty. However, when the Red River starts to overflow its banks and poses a potential threat within Winnipeg, the gates of the inlet structure are partially raised to limit the amount of water flowing in the river through the city and redirect the excess flow into the Floodway (Figure 11.34). In recent years, it has been necessary to use the Floodway every two to three years in the spring. In 1997, the city narrowly avoided a disaster.

Figure 11.33
(a) The St. Norbert inlet structure and (b) the Lockport outlet structure of the Red River Floodway.
Source: © Claire Samson.

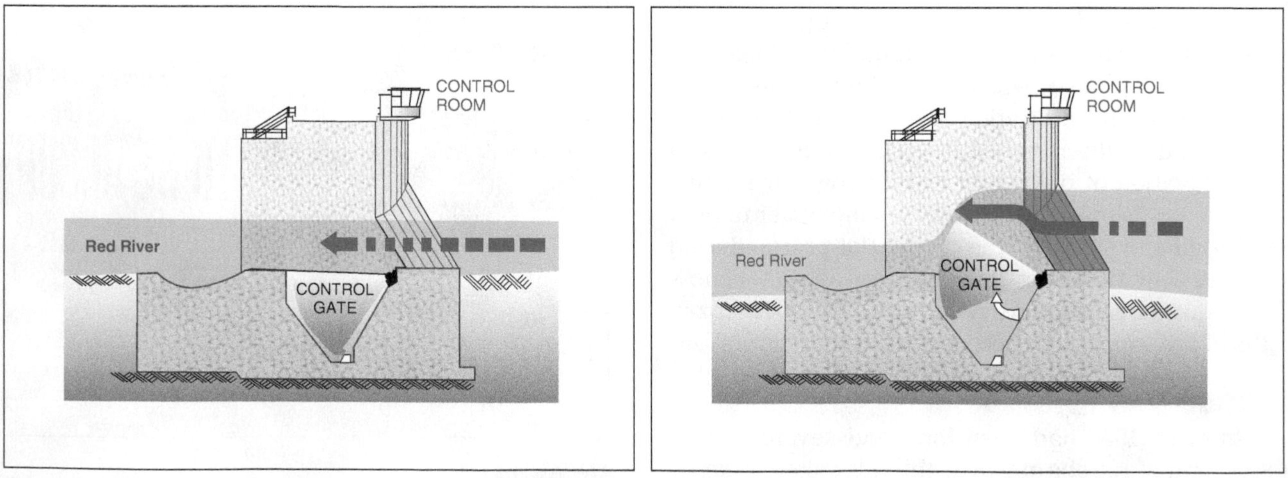

Figure 11.34
Operation of the inlet control structure of the Red River Floodway.
Source: Images courtesy of the Manitoba Floodway Authority.

The 1997 Red River Flood

In 1997, several variables combined to unleash record floods, which were forecast weeks in advance. (1) The fall 1996 rainfall in the Red River drainage basin was about four times greater than average. (2) Cold temperatures in winter 1996 began earlier than normal, thus freezing the water saturated in the soil into an impermeable layer. (3) The winter of 1996 was exceptionally snowy. At the end of the season, the snowpack had reached a record thickness of 250 cm. The situation became catastrophic when a late-winter blizzard dropped an additional 50 cm of snow on 4–6 April.

On 8 April 1997, the average regional temperature was −13°C, but on 18 April, it was 14°C. Snow and ice melted, and the water everywhere overwhelmed the capacity of the Red River. As the flood waters slowly flowed northward, they inundated farmland and towns. The flood reached its maximum at the U.S.–Canadian border around 26 April, and continued to progress further north. A new lake formed, centred on the town of Morris, south of Winnipeg, that reached 40 to 50 km in width and over 100 km in length (Figures 11.35 and 11.36). Winnipeggers, however, were protected by the floodway infrastructure that they had wisely invested in. At the peak of the crisis in Manitoba on 4 May, the Red River Floodway was diverting about 1400 m^3 of water per second around the city (Figure 11.37). It was, however, barely containing the flow. An additional rise of 60 cm in water level would have overwhelmed Winnipeg's network of dikes, including the strategic West dike, which protects the southern edge of the city.

Figure 11.35
Satellite image of the 1997 Red River flood.

Source: Reproduced with the permission of Natural Resources Canada 2014, courtesy of the Canada Centre for Remote Sensing and Canadian Space Agency.

The Red River Floodway Expansion Project

What if the Red River reaches a water level higher than in 1997? Studies estimate that a 1-in-700-years flood would necessitate the evacuation of 450 000 Winnipeg residents, and cause damages in the order of $12 billion. This realization prompted the recent expansion of the Floodway, which included widening the main channel by 60 m, necessitating the replacement of nine bridges, major improvements to the inlet and outlet structures (Figure 11.33), and the extension of dikes. One-in-700-years flood protection was achieved in Spring 2009 when the capacity of the Floodway was increased to 4000 m^3/s from its original capacity of 1700 m^3/s. The upgraded Floodway was immediately put to the test: the Spring 2009 flood was only slightly smaller than the 1997 flood, and the second largest since 1852! The Floodway performed impeccably, reducing the water level of the Red River flowing through downtown Winnipeg by more than three metres. A total of 2800 people were evacuated in 2009 in comparison to ten times that figure in 1997.

Figure 11.36
The town of Morris, Manitoba, surrounded by water during the 1997 Red River flood. The ground surface in Morris is lower than the level of flooding. A ring-dike protects the town from flood waters.

Source: Reproduced with the permission of Natural Resources Canada 2014, courtesy of the Geological Survey of Canada (Photographer: Greg Brooks).

Figure 11.37
The Red River Floodway at the inlet structure, in operation during the 1997 flood. The inlet structure is in the centre of the photograph and the flow in the Floodway channel is toward the top of the photograph.

Source: Reproduced with the permission of Natural Resources Canada 2014, courtesy of the Geological Survey of Canada (Photo 2000-18 by Greg Brooks).

DAMS

The construction of dams is a common method used to lessen the threat of flooding. Dams act as dampers by holding water in large reservoirs and releasing it at a safe rate. The presence of a dam gives a feeling of protection that invites many people to settle in the "protected" flood plain lying downstream. But dams do not provide absolute flood control. They offer some flood protection—if their reservoirs are not filled to capacity and if they do not fail. All dams have life spans limited by the durability of their construction materials and style, and the rate at which stream-delivered sediment fills in their reservoirs.

THE LONDON FLOOD BARRIER, ENGLAND

Although located up the Thames estuary, some 50 km inland from the sea, central London has been flooded repeatedly. It happened last in 1928 when 14 people drowned. A similar event is unimaginable today. Beside major museums, art galleries, and institutional buildings, central London includes the "City," the world's premier financial district. It also features cultural icons such as Big Ben and the Tower of London.

What makes London vulnerable to flooding? (1) Central London is built on a bed of clay and is gradually subsiding under the weight of its infrastructure. Several highly populated neighbourhoods are barely above sea level. (2) Tectonic forces are inexorably tilting southeast England downward into the sea. The net result is a rise of the tide levels relative to the land of 60 cm per century. Storm surges are a particular threat. When they coincide with high astronomical tides, large quantities of water enter the Thames estuary, which acts as a bottleneck, causing a rapid increase in water level.

Since 1984, London has been protected by the Flood Barrier (Figure 11.38). This major infrastructure consists of 10 concrete buttresses spread across the 500 km width of the Thames. Not unlike the inlet structure of the Red River Floodway (Figure 11.34), the most important features of the barrier—the radial gates—are normally submerged, allowing maritime traffic on the Thames. When dangerous weather conditions are forecast, the gates are raised, some three to four hours before the predicted peak of the incoming surge. The gates effectively form a continuous steel wall facing downriver, ready to stem the high tide.

Some years the barrier is not used. On the other hand, in December 2013 and January 2014, it was used a record of 28 times! Engineers estimate that the barrier will provide sufficient protection until 2060 or 2070.

LEVEES AND SANDBAGGING

Natural levees (Figure 11.14) offer some protection against floods by increasing the height of stream banks and confining water within the channel. Engineers have replicated the concept and several waterways are bordered with artificial levees to protect their adjacent flood plains (Figure 11.39). Higher levees, however, create higher river levels. Levees prevent rivers in flood from flowing laterally to spread out their water; instead, they are confined and forced to rise vertically until they eventually overtop the levees. As levees become saturated, the river finds weak spots, compromising the levees by wave attack, overtopping, failing by slumping, and undermining by subsurface erosion (Figure 11.40). Levee failure was a major cause of damage in New Orleans during Hurricane Katrina (Figure 10.27).

There is a continuing debate regarding the value of levees. On one side, critics suggest that the cost of

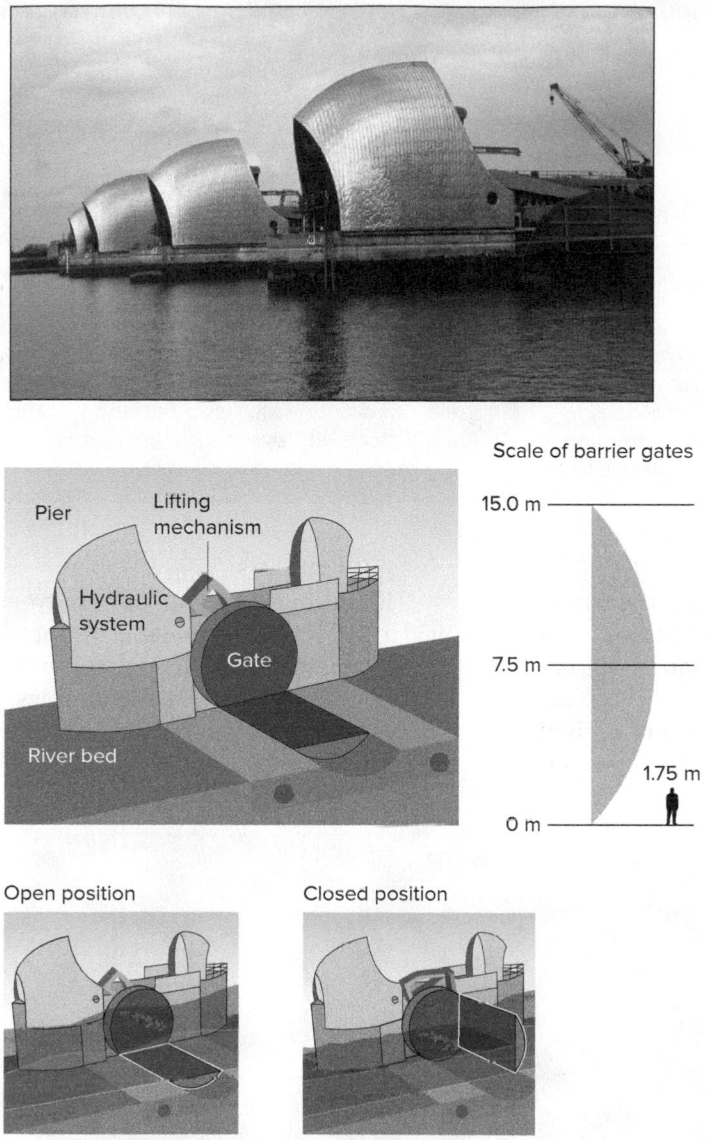

Figure 11.38
The London Flood Barrier. Under normal conditions, radial gates are kept underwater so they do not interfere with maritime traffic. It takes 75 to 90 minutes to raise them.
Source: Claire Samson (photograph) and British Broadcasting Corporation (sketches).

building more levees and dams may be higher than the value of the buildings they are protecting. Plus, the presence of structures advertised to control floods creates a sense of security that stimulates further development of the flood plain—development that likely will be flooded. These critics recommend lowering or removing levees along farmland to increase wetland habitat and restore the flood plain. Allowing floods to spread out and dissipate their energies over a wide expanse of land would also lower flood heights in the levee-protected major cities and towns.

However, proponents of levees say that the billions of dollars in flood damages would have been many billions more without the levees. When a big flood is on the way, a common response is to build temporary levees quickly using hastily filled bags of sand and mud. Some of the sandbag levees do lessen damages but others do not. Even when sandbag levees fail, it is commonly observed that there is a real therapeutic value gained by people working together in a project for the common good.

CHANNELIZATION

Humans try to control flood waters by making channels clear of debris, deeper, wider, and straighter. A typical

IN GREATER DEPTH

What to Do Before, During, and After a Flood

Before

If you live in a flood-prone area, consider taking a few practical steps to make your home more resilient. For example, put sealant around basement windows and at the base of ground-level doors. Install drains moving rainwater away from the building. Install a sump pump and zero-reverse-flow valves in basement floor drains.

If a flood is forecast and there is enough time, turn off the basement furnace and the outside gas valve. Electricity and water do not mix! Safeguard all electrical equipment. Move valuables above ground level.

If there is immediate danger of flooding, shut off the electricity. Plug basement sewer drains and toilet connections with a wooden stopper.

During

Listen to the radio to stay informed of the latest developments.

Never cross a flooded area. If your car stalls in rising waters, abandon the car.

After

Be aware of potential electrical shocks when re-entering your home. Wear rubber boots.

Flood water can be heavily contaminated with sewage and other pollutants, posing a serious health hazard. Dispose of any food items if they have been exposed to flood waters. Do not move back into your house until every flood-contaminated room has been thoroughly cleaned, disinfected, and surface dried. Because some items (appliances, carpets, furniture, etc.) require specific care, you might need the help of a qualified professional.

channelization project involves clearing the channel of trees, debris, and large boulders to reduce channel roughness and then increasing the channel capacity by digging it deeper, wider, and straighter by creating shortcuts across meander bends. All these activities make it easier for water to flow through the channel.

The Brutalist architectural movement of the years 1950 to 1975, with its angular geometries and expanses of raw concrete, coincided with several channelization projects worldwide. In several cities, rivers had their floors lined with concrete and their banks encased in the same material (Figure 11.41). The objective was to

Figure 11.39
A massive levee protects the capital city of Vientiane in Laos against floods from the Mekong River. The levee has created space for a riverfront pedestrian walkway.

Source: © Claire Samson.

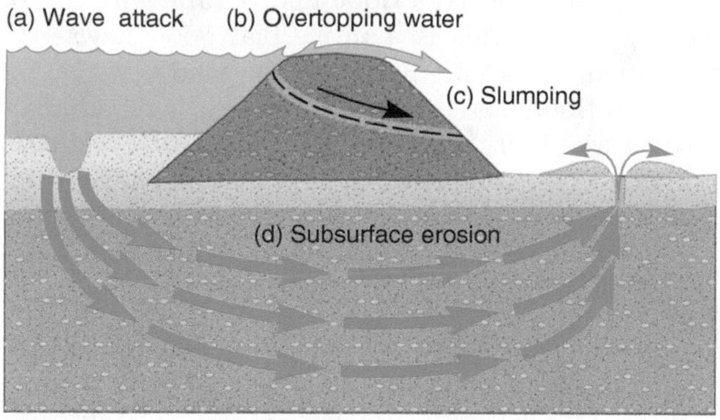

Figure 11.40
Levees are attacked by several processes: (a) wave attack, (b) erosion by overtopping, (c) slumping of the levee mass, and (d) subsurface erosion.

counteract erosion and firmly stabilize the channel in place. This came, however, at the cost of obliterating the habitat of all riverine plants and animals.

The pendulum has swung with the emergence of the environmental movement. The realization of the importance of the riparian zone—the delicate interface between land and river—for biodiversity has led to the "renaturalization" of several rivers. Slabs of concrete have been replaced by more discreet gabion baskets and rock berms. Residents are rediscovering their rivers along water's-edge trails. The soul of a community is better served by a tree-lined stream than by a concrete ditch.

Urbanization and Floods

As more people move near rivers and streams, they encounter unexpected problems. Yet some of the problems are the results of human activities that increase both flood heights and frequencies.

HYDROGRAPHS

A **hydrograph** plots discharge versus time, recording the passage of water volumes flowing downstream (Figure 11.42). There is a time lag for rainwater to flow over the ground surface and reach a stream channel, but stream surface height usually rises quickly once surface runoff reaches a channel; that is, the rising limb of the hydrograph is steep. When a flood crest passes downstream, stream level does not fall as rapidly as it rose. This is due to the stream being fed water by underground flow of rain that soaked into the ground and moved slowly to the stream; as a result, the falling limb of the hydrograph has a gentle slope.

The flood hydrograph in Figure 11.42 is typical of rural areas, but what happens in an urban setting? Humans cover much of the ground with houses and other buildings, pave the ground for streets and parking lots, and build storm-sewer systems to take rainwater runoff directly to streams. Covering the ground with an impervious seal prevents rainwater from soaking into the ground and causes rainwater to flow rapidly across the surface, thus reaching the stream even more quickly.

Figure 11.41
The Mapocho River flowing through downtown Santiago, Chile, is a raging torrent during the rainy season and is reduced to a trickle in the dry season. The river is contained in a bed of concrete to prevent erosion, an eyesore in this otherwise elegant city.
Source: Eszter Sára Kóspál.

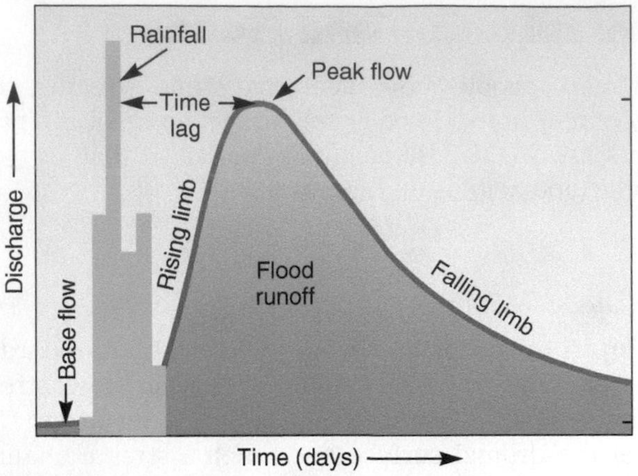

Figure 11.42
A hydrograph showing discharge (vertical axis) versus time (horizontal axis). Precipitation is drawn in green. Commonly, water flow in a stream increases rapidly from surface runoff, as shown by a steep rising limb reaching a peak flow. From the peak, discharge decreases slowly as infiltrated rain flows underground and continues to feed the stream.

Figure 11.43 shows flood hydrographs from similar size rainstorms in Brays Bayou in Houston, Texas, both before and after urbanization in the drainage basin. The rainstorm of October 1949 mostly soaked below the surface and its water flowed slowly underground to feed the stream. Following urbanization, the rainstorm of June 1960 produced a flood hydrograph with a very different shape. This is a proverbial good news–bad news situation for city dwellers. The good news is that the urban flood lasted only 20% as long; the bad news is that it was four times as high. The roofing and paving that accompany growing urbanization cause many areas to receive more severe floods.

FLOOD FREQUENCIES

Another way of looking at flood runoff within urban areas is to see how urbanization affects the frequency of floods. Roofing and paving the ground increase the surface runoff of rainwater, thus causing higher stream levels in shorter times; that is, runoffs become flash floods. Figure 11.44 shows the effects of building storm sewers (percentage of area sewered) and of roofing and paving (percentage of area impervious). The various curves corresponding to different urbanized conditions appear to the left of the curve for an unurbanized setting, that is, at shorter flood return periods.

Even well-planned communities can experience unanticipated floods. As population grows and development moves up a river basin, the increase in ground covered by buildings, roads, and parking lots means that floods will occur more frequently. Remember that wherever urbanization is increasing, the floods of tomorrow will be larger than the floods of today.

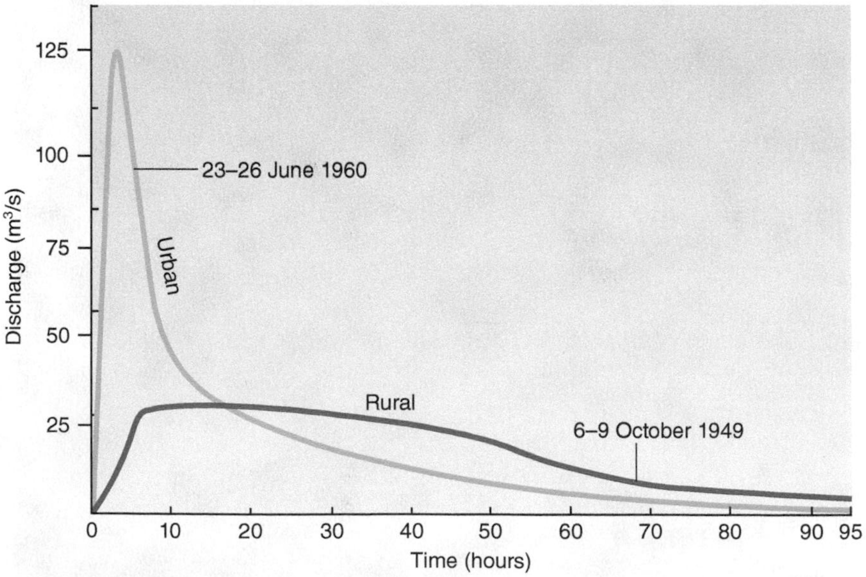

Figure 11.43
Flood hydrographs for similar-size runoffs in Brays Bayou in Houston, Texas, before and after urbanization. In the rural setting, much of the rainfall soaks into the ground. After urbanization, the roofs and pavement covering the land prevent infiltration, and most rain runs over the surface of the ground quickly, creating much higher floods.
Source: K. Young, *Geology: The Paradox of Earth and Man.* Boston: Houghton Mifflin, 1975.

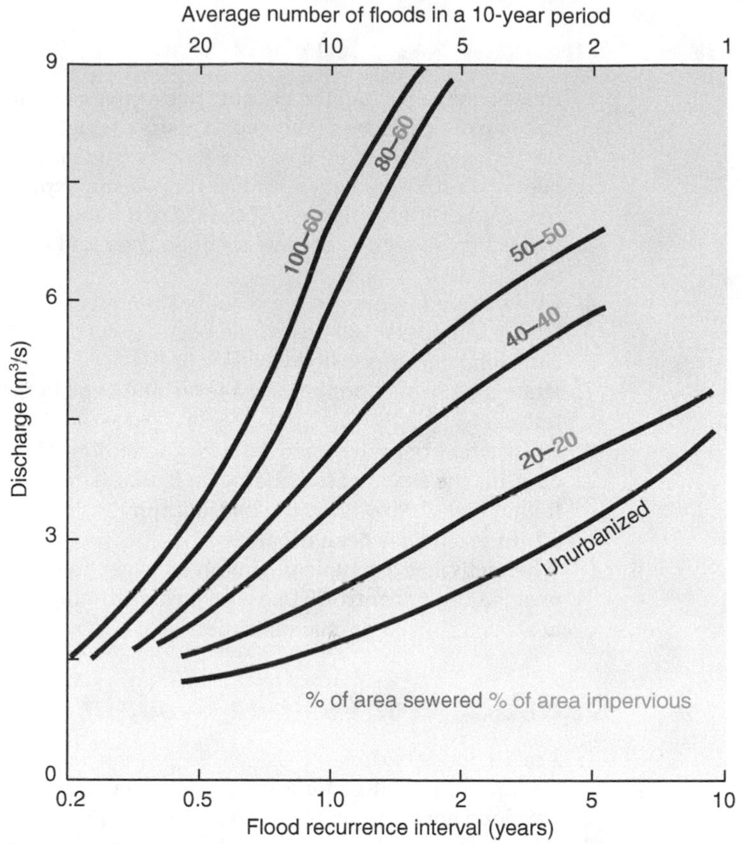

Figure 11.44

Flood-frequency curves for small drainage basins in various stages of urbanization. Floods occur more frequently as storm sewers, roofs, and pavement increase. For example, a discharge of three cubic metres per second has a return period of four years in the unurbanized setting. The same discharge has shorter return periods as urbanization intensifies: 1.75 years (20–20); 0.9 years (40–40); 0.7 years (50–50); 0.5 years (80–60); 0.45 years (100–60).

Source: L. B. Leopold, "Hydrology for Urban Land Planning," in United States Geological Survey Circular 554, 1968.

SUMMARY

- Floods occur when the infiltration capacity of the soil is exceeded. The surplus water reaches streams and rivers, which swell and overflow their banks.
  - Hydrometeorological floods are caused by excess rainfall or snowmelt, or both. Rainfall floods are mostly associated with torrential tropical rains. Snowmelt floods affect northern countries and tropical countries with high mountain ranges, especially in the spring. They are the dominant flood style in Canada's large drainage basins.
  - Natural dams—earth material displaced during mass movements or by glaciers, for example—can block the flow of water. When natural dams fail catastrophically, high-impact, devastating outburst floods are triggered.
- Flood plains are flattish areas used as stream floors during floods. Streams routinely adopt new courses in their flood plains. Development on flood plains is risky as nature eventually takes back its rights.
- Small floods happen frequently; large floods happen uncommonly. Statistical analysis of successive flooding episodes is used to assess the return period and severity of floods in a given area.
- Humans have occupied flood-prone land for millennia. Efforts to control river flow in the long term have had various levels of success. Levees keep elevating river channels perilously higher and higher above the flood plain. Some dams gradually choke under excess sediments. On the other hand, small-scale channelization and large-scale floodways and barriers have been effective in handling high water flow in times of crises.
- Urbanization has increased society's vulnerability to floods. In rural settings, a heavy rain supplies water to a stream quickly by overland runoff and slowly by infiltration. After urbanization occurs, pavement seals off most of the ground, increasing the amount of surface runoff. The result is flooding of a greater frequency and severity than a region's pre-urbanization history would have predicted.

Terms to Remember

avulsion
braided stream
dikes
discharge
drainage basin
equilibrium
flood plains
flood stage
gradient
hydrograph
infiltration
levees
load
meander
outburst floods
runoff
sinuosity

Questions for Review

1. Draw a map showing the channel pattern of a stream having excess discharge. Explain the processes involved to restore equilibrium.
2. Geologically speaking, lakes are temporary features. Draw a cross-section of a lake and use stream equilibrium processes to explain how lakes are gradually removed over long periods of time. Are human-made reservoirs also temporary?
3. Draw a cross-section of a meandering river and its flood plain. Label where it is safe to build.
4. Draw a flood-frequency curve and explain its use in planning.
5. How often does a 100-year flood occur on a stream?
6. How long does flooding last?
7. Draw a cross-section through a levee and explain the processes pushing it toward failure.
8. Draw a hydrograph record for a two-week-long flood in a rural setting. What controls the shape of the hydrograph; that is, what is happening on the rising and falling limbs? Now draw the hydrograph resulting from the same-size rainstorm after the land has been urbanized.
9. What activities are typically involved when humans modify stream channels to provide flood "control"? Use equilibrium stream processes to explain the changes in stream flow after channelization.

Questions for Further Thought

1. Are all floods bad?
2. List appropriate uses for a flood plain. List inappropriate uses. Should urban development on flood plains be halted?
3. Why are some urban areas currently receiving more frequent floods and higher peak flows than at any time in their history?
4. What kind of damage can floods cause to buildings?
5. How can communities increase their resilience to floods?
6. Are floodways like the Red River Floodway in Winnipeg, a good idea for everyone?
7. What can be the adverse consequences of flooding on health?

Interesting Websites

- Floods, Environment Canada
  https://www.ec.gc.ca/eau-water/default.asp?lang=En&n=08D7890E-1
- Red River Floodway Expansion Project, Manitoba Floodway Authority
  www.floodwayauthority.mb.ca
- Water Resources of the United States, United States Geological Survey
  http://www.usgs.gov/water/
- European Flood Awareness System (EFAS), European Commission
  https://www.efas.eu/

CHAPTER TWELVE

12

Fire

SOLAR ENERGY

Helitorch burning-out operation (use of a backfire) on a forest fire north of Thunder Bay, Ontario, 2006.

Source: Mitch Miller/Ontario Ministry of Natural Resources.

"On a trail you set a fire and the following year, when you return to the same trail and there's new growth, that's where all the moose are. As I burned there in the fall, I would return in the spring—maybe five moose."

—Member of a First Nations community in northwestern Alberta, recorded by T.A. Ferguson, and reported in Henry T. Lewis and Theresa A. Ferguson (1988) "Yards, Corridors, and Mosaics: How to Burn a Boreal Forest." *Human Ecology* 16(1): 55–77.

Outline

- Forest Fires: A Canadian Overview
- What Is Fire?
- The Need for Fire
- The Fire Triangle
- The Stages of Combustion
- The Spread of Fire
- Forest and Wildland Fuels
- Fire in the Canadian Boreal Forest
- Fire Suppression
- Home Design and Fire
- Climate Change and Forest Fires
- Summary

LO1 Explain the causes and consequences of forest fires in Canada

LO2 Formulate the relationship between photosynthesis and fire.

LO3 Explain how plant material burn.

LO4 List the factors promoting the spread of fire and explain how they are captured in the Canadian fire-danger rating system.

LO5 Describe several fire suppression strategies.

Fire is so familiar; it is both friend and foe, slave and master. Fire is a natural force, yet it has been used by humans for many thousands of years. Humans developed the ability to artificially generate fire, and the control and use of fire has been a major factor in the development of the human race. The control of fire for warmth allowed humans to migrate into cold climates and build diverse and successful civilizations. Fire for cooking greatly increased the number of foods available and improved their taste, ease of digestion, nutrition, sanitation, and preservation. Fire has long been used to drive game out of hiding while hunting and to scare away predatory animals at night. Fire has aided agriculture by clearing the land of trees and creating fertilizer with its ashy residue. With the help of fire, humans have been able to expand farmland and pasture against both climatic and vegetational gradients.

The possibilities of fire have also stimulated creative thinking, which in turn has spurred human development. One invention has followed another. The use of fire to harden materials led to the creation of pottery, cookware, weapons, and more. The ability to produce ever-higher temperatures led to smelting and use of metals. The use of fire also provided the benefits of sterilization, which advanced public health. Controlled fire inside machinery supplies much of the energy that underlies our civilization. The heat from the burning of oil, coal, and natural gas is converted into the electrical and mechanical energy that powers our industries, lights and heats our homes, and allows us to travel quickly from one part of the world to another.

LO1 Forest Fires: A Canadian Overview

Wildfire is common throughout the forested regions of Canada. Although it is often depicted as a destructive force, it is a natural ecosystem process that is essential to the health of many forests. Fire, for example, provides the heat that is required to melt the waxy resin that seals the serotinous cones of jack pine, prevalent throughout the boreal forest. It also burns the dead pine needles and moss that grow beneath jack pine stands and thereby prepares a fertile bed on which the seeds released from those cones can germinate. The exclusion of fire from the boreal forest would lead to a reduction in the abundance of jack pine and other species, and set the forest on an unnatural path.

Canada has approximately 10% of the world's forests. Figure 12.1 paints an intricate spatial and temporal portrait of forest fires in our country. A complex interplay

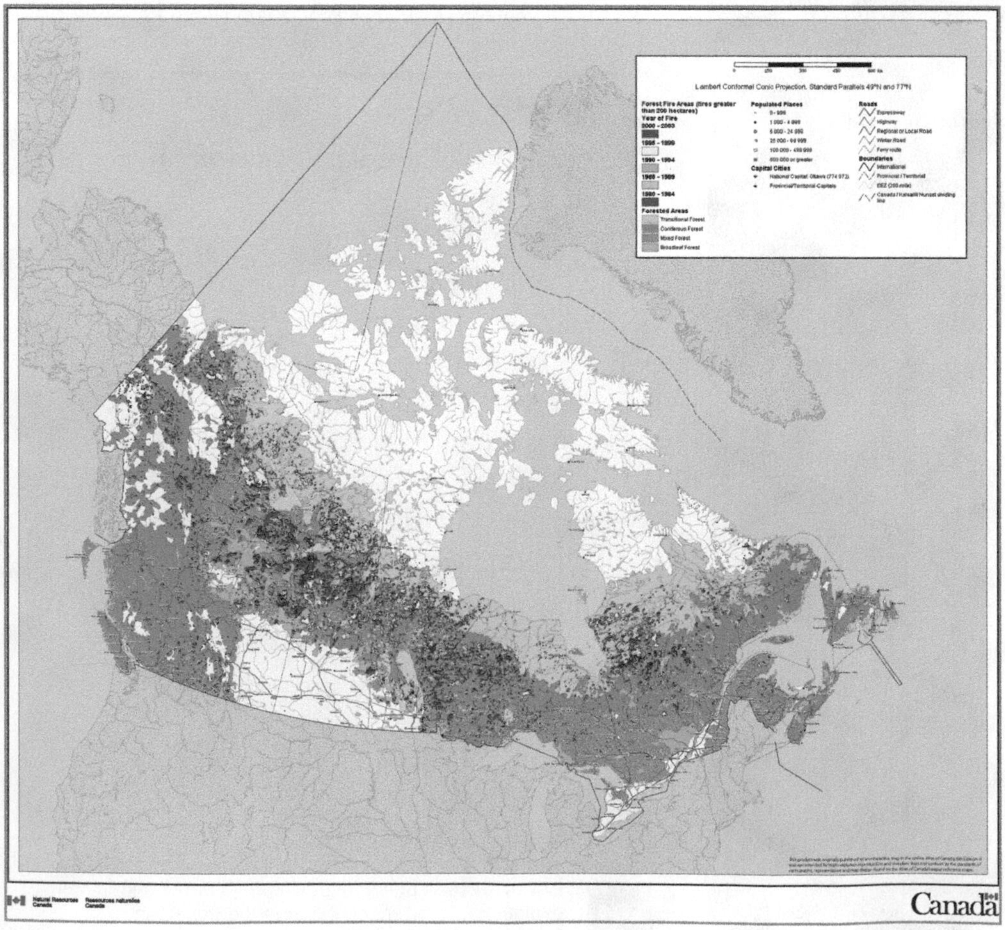

Figure 12.1
Map of forest fires greater than 1000 hectares (ha), 1980–2003.
Source: The Atlas of Canada.

of several variables is responsible for the distribution of fires shown on the map. Biological factors include insect infestations and the distribution of tree species. Weather plays a key role, as do fire management practices. This complex mix of social, economic (Figure 12.2), and ecological costs and benefits of fire pose significant challenges to fire and forest managers who seek to achieve an appropriate balance of the beneficial and detrimental effects of fire. Climate change will make it even more difficult for them to achieve this balance in the future.

Most of the fires that occur in Canadian forests are caused by people, but lightning-caused fires account for most of the area burned (Figures 12.3 and 12.4). The year 2012, for example, is typical in this respect (Figure 12.5). Lightning-caused fires tend to arrive in clusters generated by the passage of thunderstorms (Figure 12.23), and they can overtax the capabilities of fire-suppression resources to a greater degree than human-caused fires, which tend to occur at a more uniform rate over time. Also, most human-caused fires occur near populated areas or along roads or railways where they are more readily detected. Lightning fires, some of which occur in more remote areas where they burn undetected for longer periods, are typically larger and more difficult to control when the suppression forces arrive at the scene (Figure 12.6).

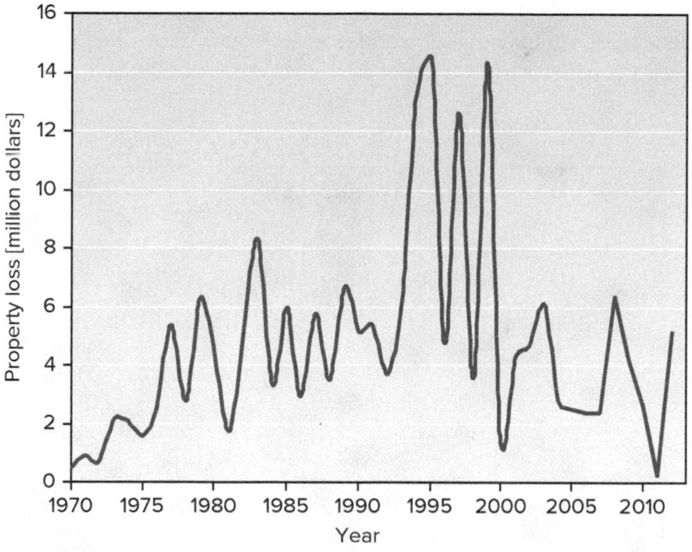

Figure 12.2
Value of property destroyed by forest fires in Canada, 1970–2012.

Source: "Graph: Value of property destroyed by forest fires" Canadian Council of Forest Ministers 2014, Natural Resources Canada, 2014. Reproduced with the permission of the Minister of Natural Resources Canada, 2014.

LO2

What Is Fire?

Fire is the rapid combination of oxygen with carbon, hydrogen, and other elements of organic material in a reaction that produces flame, heat, and light. In effect, the burning of forest vegetation is the **photosynthesis** reaction in reverse.

In the photosynthesis reaction, plants take in water (H_2O) and carbon dioxide (CO_2), and use solar energy to build organic material, their tissue. Oxygen is given off as a by-product of the reaction. The molecules of plants are tied together by chemical bonds between atoms. These bonds store some of the Sun's heat as chemical potential energy. An example of the photosynthesis reaction is:

$$6CO_2 + 6H_2O + \textit{energy from the Sun} \rightarrow C_6H_{12}O_6 + 6O_2$$

The organic molecule ($C_6H_{12}O_6$) in this equation is glucose, which approximates that of cellulose, the main component of wood.

In the combustion reaction, plant material is heated above its **ignition temperature** and oxygen begins

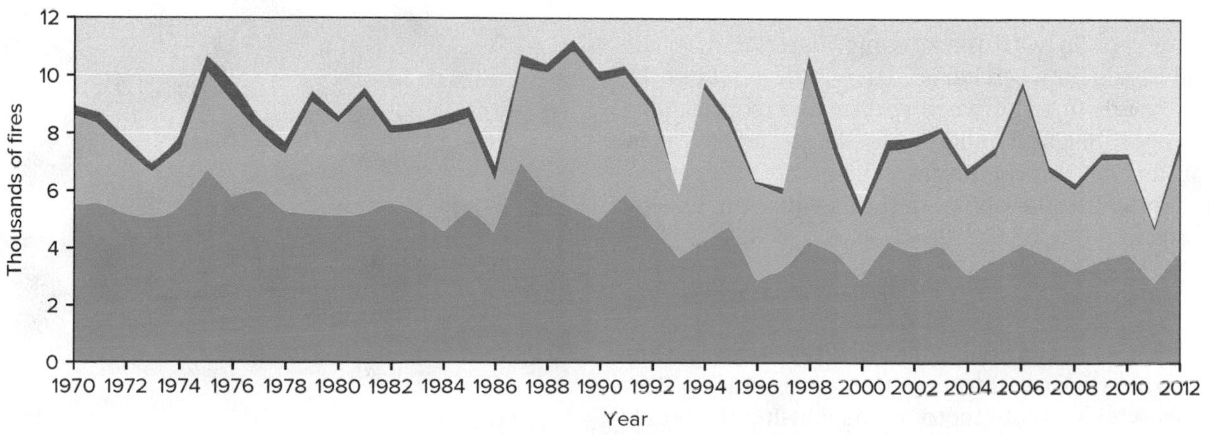

Figure 12.3
Number of forest fires in Canada (1970–2012) by cause: human activities (blue), lightning (green), and unknown (red).

Source: "Number of fires (1970–2012) ", Canadian Council of Forest Ministers 2014, Natural Resources Canada, 2014. Reproduced with the permission of the Minister of Natural Resources Canada, 2014.

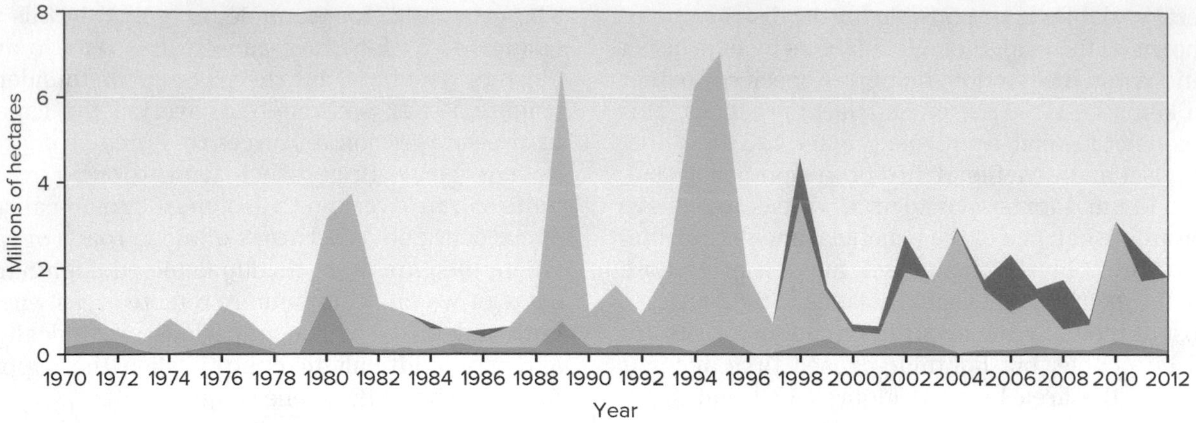

Figure 12.4
Area burned across Canada (1970–2012) by cause: human activities (blue), lightning (green), and unknown (red).
Source: "Area burned (1970–2012)", Canadian Council of Forest Ministers 2014, Natural Resources Canada, 2014. Reproduced with the permission of the Minister of Natural Resources Canada, 2014.

Cause	Number of fires	Area burned (hectare)
Human Activities		
Recreation	1282	36 535
Resident	1076	10 164
Forest industry	98	3 119
Railways	97	40 361
Other industry	451	3 729
Incendiary	613	2 549
Miscellaneous known causes	346	12 488
Lightning	3536	1 672 122
Unknown cause	367	7 454

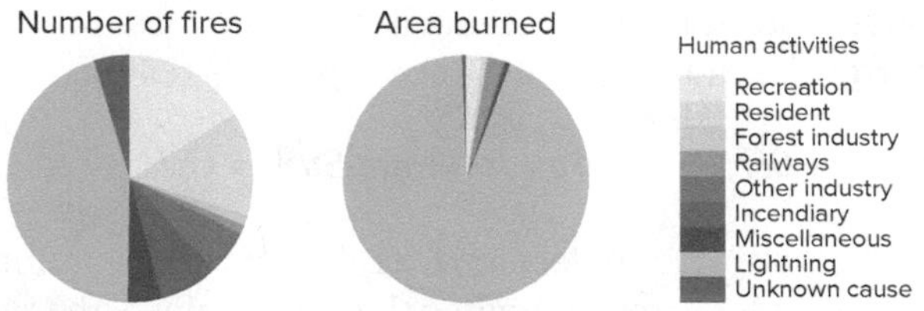

Figure 12.5
Canadian forest fires by cause, 2012.
Source: Source: "Canadian forest fires by cause, 2012", Canadian Council of Forest Ministers 2014, Natural Resources Canada, 2014. Reproduced with the permission of the Minister of Natural Resources Canada, 2014.

combining rapidly with the organic material. The old chemical bonds between carbon and hydrogen are broken, new bonds form between carbon and oxygen, and between hydrogen and oxygen, and the stored energy is given off as heat during the fire. The combustion equation is identical to the photosynthesis equation, except that it runs in the opposite direction:

$$C_6H_{12}O_6 + 6O_2 \rightarrow 6CO_2 + 6H_2O + \textit{released energy (heat)}$$

In effect, the solar energy stored by plants during their growth is returned to the atmosphere during fire. Earlier, we viewed plate tectonics as causing the build-up of stresses that are released during earthquakes; by analogy, photosynthesis causes the build-up and storage of chemical potential energy in plants that is released during fires.

Figure 12.6
A tree that was struck by a lightning that travelled down its trunk and ignited a fire in the duff layer at the base, Fort Frances District, northwestern Ontario.
Source: © Jennifer Beverley, Canadian Forest Service.

IN GREATER DEPTH

Historical Canadian and American Forest Fires

Most Canadian forest-fire management agencies were established in the early 1900s in response to tragic forest fires that burned large areas and took many lives in Canada and the United States during the nineteenth century and the early part of the twentieth century. Many of these fires followed a common pattern: under adverse weather conditions, small unattended fires merged and grew out of control.

The 1825 Miramachi fire burned more than 1214000 hectares of uncut forest and spruce budworm–killed stands in the Miramichi river valley in the province of New Brunswick and the state of Maine. Many small logging and settler fires that had been left to burn unattended, a severe summer drought, and high winds supported the spread and merging of many of those fires into a large fire that killed 160 people.

The Peshtigo fire burned 1530000 hectares in eastern Wisconsin and western Michigan in October 1871. Many uncontrolled logging and settler fires that were burning under severe drought, high temperature, and strong wind conditions grew together and burned through red and white pine stands, some hardwoods, and large slash areas. More than 1500 lives were lost.

In 1910, the Rainy River fire started when three railway locomotive fires and one settler fire joined to eventually burn 121500 hectares in northwestern Ontario and Minnesota. The fire resulted in the loss of 42 lives in the United States.

The 1916 Cochrane and Matheson fire in northeastern Ontario formed when many small unattended fires fed by a prolonged drought, high temperatures, and strong winds joined to burn 344000 hectares of predominately spruce and jack pine stands. The 233 lives lost make this the worst forest fire ever experienced in Canada.

A poignant sculpture on the waterfront of Haileybury on the shores of Lake Timiskaming commemorates the great fire of 1922 in this area (Figure 12.7). Again, in this case, small fires started by farmers to fertilize the land had merged into an uncontrollable blaze.

Figure 12.7
Sculpture commemorating a family taking refuge in a lake to escape the flames during the 1922 Haileybury fire.
Source: Franctasy/Flickr, licensed under Creative Commons license 2.0.

The Need for Fire

Through photosynthesis, plants grow and collectively produce large volumes of trunks, branches, leaves, needles, grasses, and other organic material. The mass of organic material is recycled by the combined effects of slow decomposition through rotting and digestion and rapid burning through wildfire. Decomposition requires warmth and moisture to operate efficiently. In a tropical rain forest with abundant warmth and moisture, rotting can decompose the dead vegetation and recycle the nutrients for the production of new plant material via photosynthesis; there is no need for wildfire to recycle materials (except in cases such as after a hurricane destroys large numbers of trees). In the deserts, there is little moisture for either plant growth or decomposition, so fire does not need to be frequent.

In many environments, fire is necessary to recycle nutrients and regenerate plant communities. Fire-dependent ecosystems include grasslands, seasonal tropical forests, the boreal forest, and the Mediterranean-climate shrublands. In Mediterranean climates, such as in California, Australia, and South Africa, the wet winters are too cold and the warm summers too dry for rotting to recycle the products of photosynthesis; consequently, wildfire must be frequent. In these areas, fire is necessary for the health of plant communities. Many of the plant species must have the smoke and/or heat of fire to germinate their seeds, to control parasites, and to influence insect behaviour. Thus fire is necessary; it is nature's way of cleaning house.

AUSTRALIA

Australia is bedevilled by bushfires, major conflagrations swept by high winds through eucalyptus forests that are fire adapted and fire maintained. Eucalyptus makes good wood for a fireplace, but in a natural setting, the trees may become so hot that their sap boils and whole trees explode in flame. This presents obvious problems for houses and towns in the path of a eucalyptus-fuelled bushfire. The bluegum eucalyptus is described by Robert Sward:

Deadly beauty,
Much to admire.
Until it falls
Or catches fire.

The worst bushfires in Australia's history correlate with drought and wind. Many of these weather episodes occur when an El Niño circulation system is operating in the oceans (Figure 9.14). When the ocean waters off Australia are cooler, evaporation and precipitation are reduced. The lessened rainfall creates drought that can extend through an entire southern hemisphere winter. Bushfire conditions may start with a high-pressure system off southern Australia. As the high-pressure zone moves slowly eastward, it induces air masses over the central desert to blow southeastward from the Interior toward the heavily populated southeastern region of Australia. As the winds descend from the desert, they warm, producing temperatures around 40°C, humidities of less than 20%, and speeds of at least 60 km/h.

The El Niño of 1982–1983 was particularly strong, and the Australian summer was the driest in recorded history. On 16 February 1983, strong, hot, dry winds from the Interior were reinforced by the jet stream in the upper atmosphere. Adelaide, the capital of South Australia, and Melbourne, the capital of Victoria State, were ringed by fires pushed by the southeastward-blowing winds. In mid-afternoon, a cold front swept through the area, dropping temperatures by 10°C. However, the cooler winds did not subdue the fires but instead changed their direction of movement to the northeast and increased their speed. The winds were blowing 70 km/h with gusts up to 170 km/h, and the fire front advanced at speeds up to 20 km/h. The **firestorms** were so strong that their winds snapped tree trunks. When the fires were finished, 76 people were dead, 3500 had suffered injuries, and 2500 houses and 20 towns were gone. The livestock toll was also great; more than 300 000 sheep and 18 000 cattle perished along with uncounted numbers of native animals.

The bushfire hazard is ever present. Hot, dry, fast winds returned to Sydney in January 1994 and December 2001, again leaving dead bodies and hundreds of incinerated homes behind. In January 2003, a lightning-started fire pushed by 60 km/h winds entered the capital city of Canberra, killing 4 people and destroying 380 houses.

In the world before global travel and trade, eucalyptus was confined to Australia, but it has been exported in abundance to many areas where it thrives. The eucalyptus fire hazard is now a significant threat in Southern California, North Africa, India, and the Middle East.

LO3

The Fire Triangle

A fire may begin only when **fuel,** oxygen, and heat are present in the right combination. These three critical components are referred to as the fire triangle

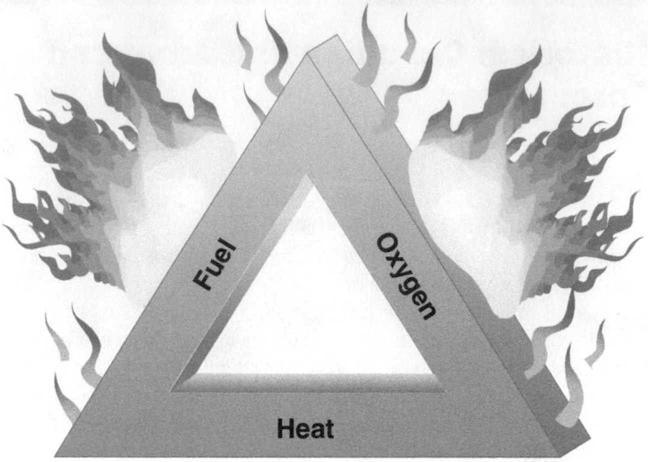

Figure 12.8
The fire triangle. When all three sides are present, a fire results; eliminate one side and the fire cannot burn.

(Figure 12.8). Oxygen makes up 21% of the atmosphere, so as long as a steady supply of air is available, heat and fuel are the most important factors. During summers and droughts, heat warms and dries vegetation, making it easier for a lightning strike to ignite a fire. Given the common presence of oxygen and heat, the occurrence of fires is limited mainly by the amount of fuel available.

Any combustible material is fuel. Common categories of fuel include grasses, shrubs, trees, and **slash**—the organic debris left on the ground after logging or windstorms. As the human population spreads into wildlands, houses have become a fifth category of fuel.

The fire triangle is useful in visualizing how to fight a fire. Remove one of the sides of the fire triangle, and the fire collapses:

- Firefighters spray water on a fire to reduce its *heat.*
- Air tankers drop reddish-orange viscous fluids (commonly referred to as fire retardant) in front of a fire to coat the unburned vegetation and block *oxygen* from contacting the plant. Dry chemical extinguishers using "Purple K" (potassium bicarbonate) kill fires by disrupting chemical reactions.
- Firefighters commonly bulldoze and remove vegetation to eliminate *fuel.* Fuel also may be reduced by setting **backfires** (Figure 12.9 and photo of chapter opener). A backfire is lit by firefighters in front of the advancing wildfire. As the wildfire draws in oxygen, it also draws in the backfire, thus eliminating fuel in front of the advancing wildfire.

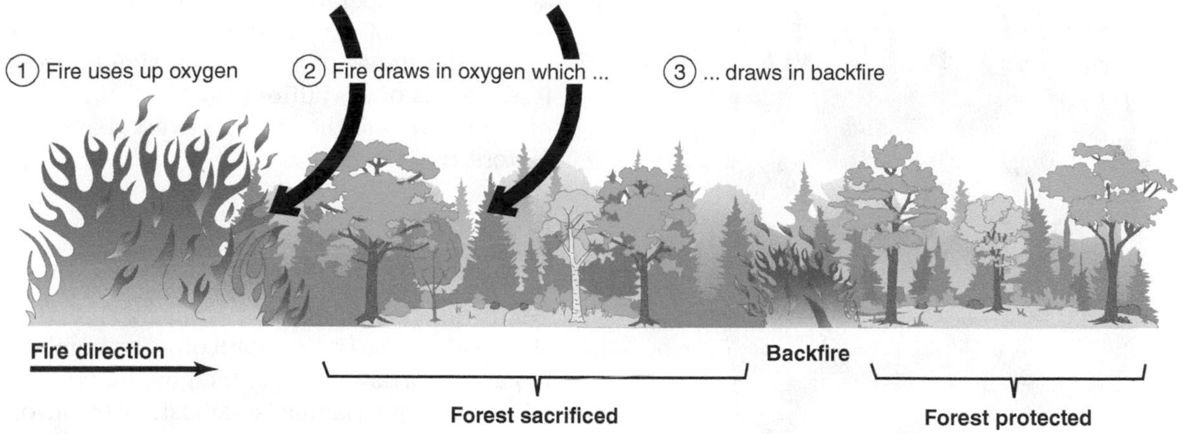

Figure 12.9
How to fight a fire with fire: light a backfire in front of an advancing wildfire.

Vegetation of varying heights makes it easy for fire to climb from grasses to shrubs to trees similar to climbing up the rungs of a ladder (Figure 12.10). The presence of these **ladder fuels** allows small ground fires to quickly carry upward into tall trees and create major wildfires. How can the ladder fuel threat be reduced? Cut and prune vegetation to create vertical separations between layers.

With the emergence of humans and their ability to both make fires and fight the flames, the old natural balance has changed. No longer does fuel supply simply accumulate until ignited by a lightning strike. Now humans extinguish many small fires, causing the build-up of tremendous volumes of dead-plant fuel that can ignite and cause fires bigger than we can handle. Humans interfere with the natural cycle of plant growth and fire, but they don't control it.

Figure 12.10
Ladder fuels. Vegetation of varying heights allows fire to climb from grasses to treetops.

The Stages of Combustion

The three stages of **combustion**—(1) preheating, (2) flaming combustion, and (3) smouldering and glowing combustion—are well known to anyone who starts logs burning in a campfire or fireplace. The preheating phase is usually accomplished by lighting newspaper or kindling with a match to dry out the logs and raise their surface temperature. Flaming combustion follows, during which logs are engulfed in high flames, burn quickly, and give off a lot of heat. Finally, during smouldering and glowing combustion, the active flames disappear but embers continue to release radiant heat.

Before a fire breaks out, a preheating phase occurs. In this phase, water is expelled from plants, wood, or fossil fuels by nearby flames, drought, or even a long summer day. The water in wet wood has such a high capacity to absorb heat that wet wood is extremely difficult to ignite. To burn, wood not only needs to be dry, but also have its temperature raised considerably. For example, the cellulose in wood remains stable even at temperatures of 250°C; however, by 325°C, it breaks down quickly, giving off large amounts of flammable hydrocarbon vapours, together with water vapour, tar, and mineral residues, in the process of **pyrolysis.** If oxygen is present when the temperature is raised, the gases can ignite and combustion begins.

In flaming combustion, the flammable gases produced by pyrolysis burn quickly at the surface of the wood and produce large amounts of heat; logs expand in volume and cracks form that release gases to the surface to feed the flames. Where cracks do not form, the

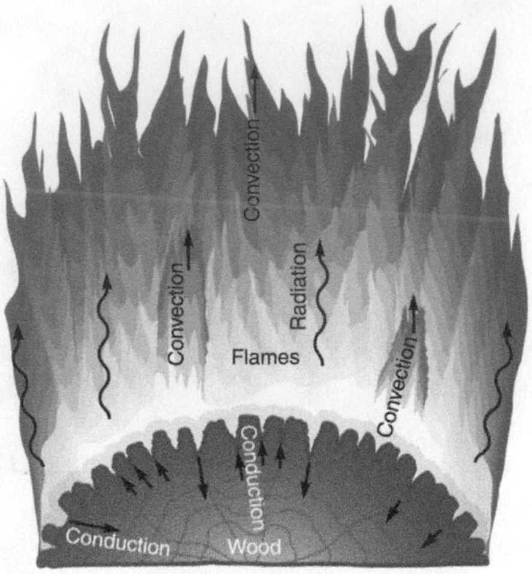

Figure 12.11
Schematic cross-section of a burning log. Heat moves inward by conduction, decomposing the cellulose and lignin of wood into gases (pyrolysis) that move through cracks to fuel flames at the log surface. Heat flows outward by (1) conduction from hotter to cooler areas, (2) radiation from flames and hot surfaces, and (3) convection of hot, lightweight buoyant gases that rise upward.

wood will "pop" and throw out sparks. Flaming combustion is the stage of greatest energy release in any fire (Figure 12.11).

Because of the poor conduction of heat in wood, the interior of a log remains below the combustion point even when the exterior is engulfed in flames. For a log to burn completely, there must be enough outside heat (from embers below, adjoining burning wood, etc.) conducting into the heart of the log. The process of combustion gradually dies off during smouldering when the remaining pyrolized gases are consumed with little or no flames, and terminates with glowing combustion. In glowing combustion, burning occurs more slowly and at a lower temperature as the fire consumes the solid wood instead of pyrolized gases.

All the stages of a fire occur simultaneously in different areas of a wildfire (Figure 12.12). The character of a wildfire and the area it covers depend on several factors, described next.

LO4 The Spread of Fire

Wildfires occur in different styles: (1) they may move slowly along the ground with glowing combustion playing an important role, (2) they may advance as a wall of fire along a flaming combustion front, or (3) they may race through the treetops as a crown fire.

The spread of fire depends on (1) fuel—the types of plants or other material burned, (2) weather—especially the strength of winds, (3) topography—the shape of the land, and (4) behaviour within the fire itself.

FUEL

The energy released in a fire strongly depends on the chemical composition of the plants and organic debris. For example, the eucalyptus family of trees and shrubs has a high oil content that allows easy ignition and intense heat of burning. Some trees invite fire by shedding their bark in long, thin strips; the dry strips of bark are kindling that ignites easily and burns quickly. Fire, however, is not a problem for the plant species. Most eucalyptus varieties are designed to burn hot and quickly; it is then that their fruit opens and releases unburned seeds to germinate in the fire-cleared ground. The fast-moving fires may burn down trees, but many of the resilient plant species simply send up shoots from their stumps or roots, and grow to full-size trees again in several years.

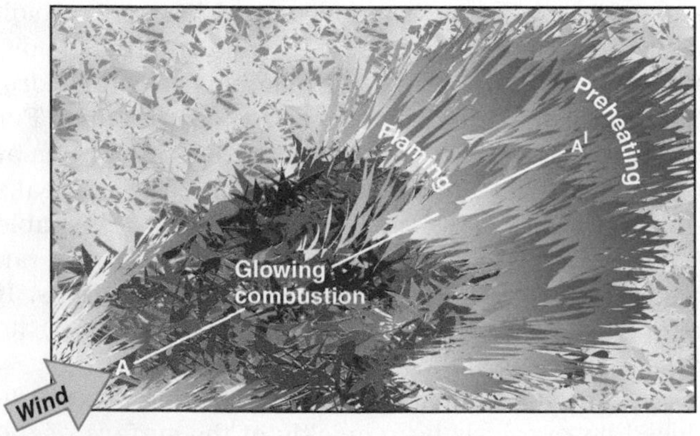

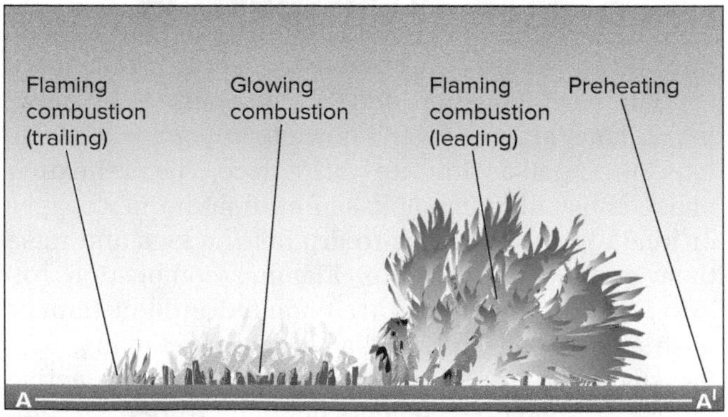

Figure 12.12
(a) The stages of fire are shown in horizontal or map view. (b) Line AA' on the map is shown in cross-section view.

Another example is **chaparral,** which is abundant in California. Chaparral leaves contain aromatic oils that discourage insects and other animals from eating them. But these same oils are flammable. In fact, chaparral is one of the most flammable plant groups in the world, and it is a plant community whose generations are in equilibrium with fire. Chaparral plants respond to fire in different ways. Some are "sprouters"; after fire destroys their surface vegetation, shoots spring forth from fire-resistant stems or roots, beginning the next crop of plants (Figure 12.13). Some are "seeders"; they encase their seeds in shells that open only after the intense heat of fire destroys the outer coat, thus freeing the seed to later absorb water and germinate. Some other plant seeds respond to the smoke of a fire. For example, nitrogen dioxide (one of the gases in smoke) induces complete germination of some seeds in as short a time as 30 seconds. Thus, the very fire that burns away a dense plant cover releases and germinates seeds on ground made bare by the same fire. The brush removal by the fire also allows the seedlings to get the sunlight they need to grow.

Figure 12.13
Some chaparral plants are destroyed by fire aboveground, but they resprout after a fire.
Source: Photo by Pat Abbott.

WEATHER

The probability that a lightning discharge that strikes a tree and travels down its trunk to the ground (Figure 12.6) will ignite a fire depends on the moisture content of the organic layer at the base of the tree. The chance that a discarded cigarette or hot metal fragment from a railway brake shoe will ignite a fire depends upon the moisture content of the dead grass or pine needles on which they fall. Since fuel moisture is influenced by temperature, relative humidity, rainfall, and wind, weather has a very significant influence on fire occurrence and fire behaviour processes as well as fire management operations.

Weather affects fire on national, regional, and local scales. Much of Canada is influenced by a predominately westerly flow of weather systems off the Pacific Ocean so sea surface temperature in the Pacific influences weather and fire activity across large parts of Canada. From time to time, upper atmospheric flows are interrupted by ridges of high pressure that steer moisture-bearing storm systems north and south of the ridge and contribute to the drying of downstream regions. On a local scale, lightning can ignite fires and daily weather has a profound influence on any fires that do occur.

Fuel moisture levels influence fire behaviour but once the fuel is dry enough to support sustained combustion, short-term changes in wind speed and direction have the most dramatic impact. Fire spread rates are particularly sensitive to wind, and large fires are usually the product of one or more wind-driven isolated events, each of which may persist for one or more days. Many of the worst fires in history were accompanied by strong winds. Winds bring a continuous supply of fresh oxygen, distribute heat, push the flames forward, and bend them toward preheated plants and other fuel. If winds are absent, a vertical column of convected heat dominates, and the fire may move very slowly (Figure 12.14a, type I). If winds are fast, they push the fire front rapidly ahead and prevent a vertical convection column from forming (Figure 12.14f, type VI). Strong, gusty winds and fire whirls both pick up flaming debris and burning embers, called **firebrands,** and drop them onto unburned areas, starting new blazes. Firefighters commonly use strategies based on the fire triangle (Figure 12.8) and try to deprive the fire of its heat or fuel or oxygen. This strategy works well for small- to moderate-size **fuel-driven fires.**

But catastrophic firestorms are **wind-driven fires.** When the winds blow, the fire goes, and only a change in the weather will stop it.

Days when the relative humidity is low and temperatures and wind speeds are high are cause for concern for forest-fire managers, particularly if such days are preceded by prolonged periods of drought and accompanied by daytime heating or frontal thunderstorms. It is therefore not surprising that fire management agencies devote a great deal of time and effort to monitoring weather, and they make very extensive use of weather forecasts to help predict when and where fires will occur, and how they will behave in the days ahead.

TOPOGRAPHY

The topography of the land has numerous effects on fire behaviour. Before a fire, the topography sets up microclimates that result in different plant communities that will burn with different intensities. Winds blowing over rugged topography develop turbulence. Canyons with steep slopes and dense vegetation cause high levels of radiant heat that consume virtually all the organic matter in the canyon (Figure 12.14g, type VII). Fire burns faster up a slope because the convective heat rising from and above the fire front dries out the upslope vegetation in an intense preheating phase; in effect, a chimney is created up the slope, allowing fire to move quickly (Figure 12.15).

FIRE BEHAVIOUR

The strength of a fire is partly determined by its own actions. Firestorms are fires powerful enough to generate their own winds. The vast quantities of heat given off by a fire create unstable air. Heat-expanded air is less dense and more buoyant; thus, it rises in billowing convection columns (Figure 12.14a–e, types I–V), leaving behind a local low-pressure area at the Earth's surface. The low pressure, in turn, pulls jets of air down toward the ground. These interacting movements of air cause abrupt and significant changes in wind speed near the fire. They can produce dramatic increases in fire spread and intensity, and thereby pose both control and safety problems for firefighters. In rare occasions, the rising columns of hot, unstable air may spin off fire whirls (Figure 12.16). Winds sucked into the base of a fire whirl bring oxygen to feed the flames, while huge quantities of heat race up the column, venting above as in a megachimney. Fire whirls are commonly 10 to 50 times taller than their diameters, and they may spin at speeds of 250 km/h. Fire whirls may carry fiery debris and drop it kilometres away, starting new fires.

A fatal example showing the strength of a fire whirl occurred on 24 April 2000 near Winkler, Manitoba. A fire burning 90 000 bales of flax straw spun off a fire whirl that lifted a man and his pickup truck and carried them 50 m away before dumping their remains onto a field.

Forest and Wildland Fuels

The rate of spread, depth of burn, and other important characteristics of a forest fire are heavily influenced by the type of forest vegetation or fuel in which it is burning. Some forest types (e.g., coniferous species such as jack pine and black spruce) burn readily while others (e.g., aspen and other hardwood species) usually burn very slowly with little flame. It is therefore not surprising that forest-fire specialists often view forest vegetation in terms of its fuel properties.

Fire behaviour specialists who study the burning of wood chips, wooden dowels, and dead pine needles in the laboratory have identified many chemical and physical properties of the fuel particles and the fuel bed that influence how quickly a fire will spread. Some of the fuel attributes they have identified as being important include the chemical composition, specific heat capacity, fuel particle length, fuel particle cross-sectional area, fuel loading (mass of fuel per unit area), bulk density, and of course, moisture content. Although such fuel-type characteristics can be measured in the laboratory, it is difficult to measure them in the forest and it would simply be impossible to do so in front of an active wildfire. They have therefore developed **fuel models** that are used to classify *forest types* as *fuel types* that are relatively homogeneous with respect to important fuel attributes.

The Canadian Fire Behaviour Prediction (FBP) system has 16 fuel types that are divided into 5 general categories: coniferous, deciduous, mixed-wood, slash, and open. The coniferous fuel types include C-1 spruce-lichen woodland (Figure 12.17), C-4 immature jack or lodgepole pine, and C-7 ponderosa pine/Douglas fir (Figure 12.18). The slash category includes S-1 jack or lodgepole pine logging slash and the open category includes O-1b standing grass.

Fire behaviour specialists conduct experimental burns under different weather conditions and develop mathematical models that can be used to predict the rate of spread and other fire behaviour characteristics as a function of the **fire-danger rating** codes and indices. How reliable are these models? Post-fire tree mortality analysis is an important validation step to assess the accuracy of the predictions. Sean Michaletz and Ed Johnson of the University of Calgary are investigating the link between fire behaviour and tree mortality, and

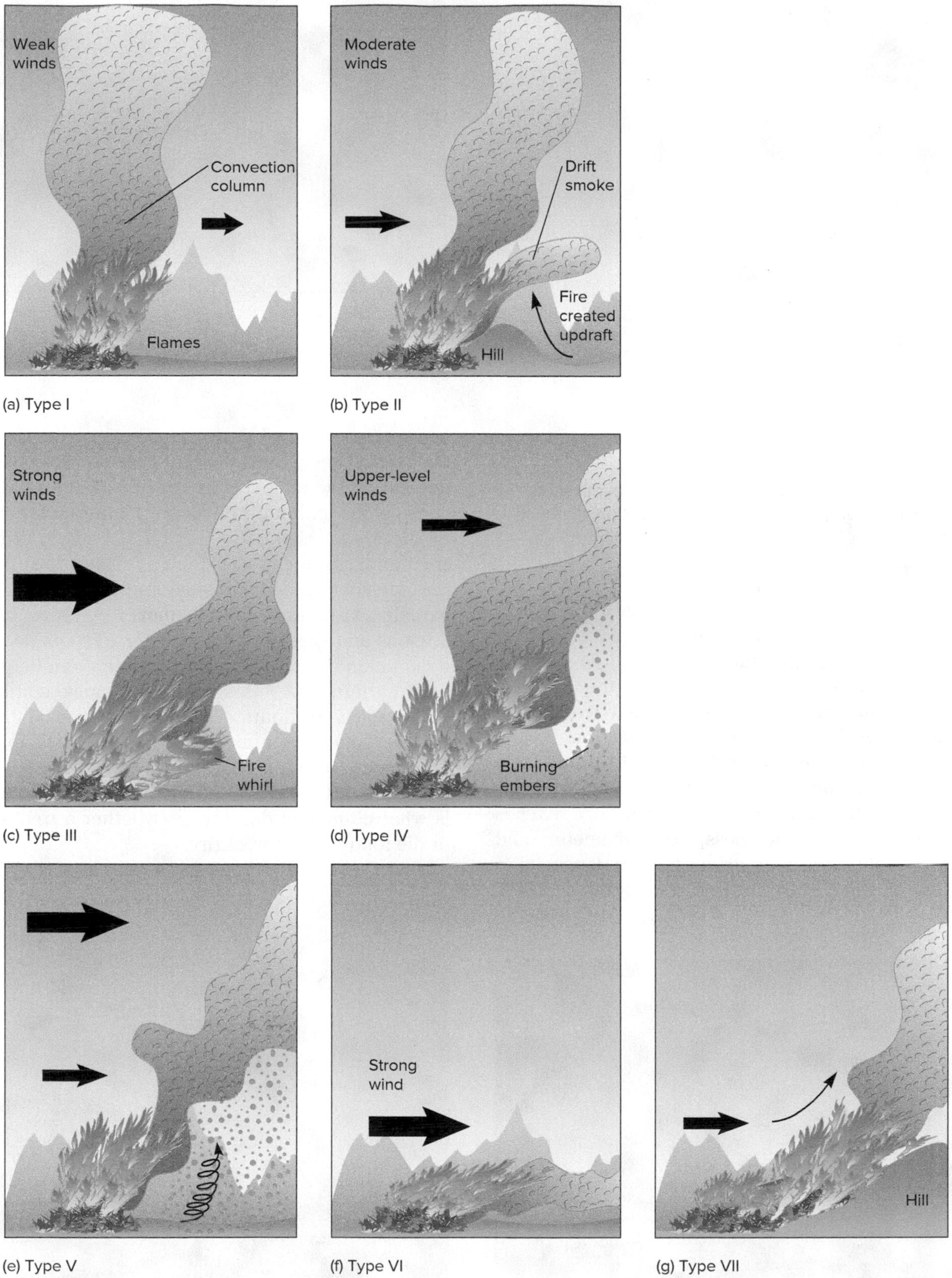

Figure 12.14
Some fire types. (a) Type I has a tall convection column and weak winds that push the column at a moderate rate of spread. (b) Type II has a tall convection column that moves rapidly upslope. (c) Type III has a powerful convection column pushed by surface winds; fire whirls are spun off. (d) Type IV has a convection column distorted by upper-level winds; glowing embers are dropped. (e) Type V has a convection column bent by winds of differing speeds. (f) Type VI is a wind-driven fire that spreads rapidly; the winds are too strong for a convection column to function. (g) Type VII shows the effects of topography.

Figure 12.15
How fires burn on slopes. (a) An upright match burns slowly downward, similar to fire on top of a hill. (b) A sloping match burns rapidly upward, similar to fire up a hill.

Figure 12.16
Fire whirls form as rising hot air spins and carries the flames upward.

have developed software tools to evaluate the impact of the several biophysical variables involved. Forest fires kill trees through heat transfer (Figure 12.19). During a forest fire, heat transfer into the tree can injure the stem, crown, and roots. Heat transfer to the stem occurs by radiation and convection. As the stem surface increases in temperature, heat conducts through the bark and into the interior of the stem, causing localized cell death when the temperature reaches 60°C or more. Bark thickness, stem diameter, and stem water content are important factors determining the extent of stem injury in fires. Heat transfer to the crown also occurs by radiation and convection, with convection being the dominant process. Crown injuries depend on the temperature and residence time of the rising plume of hot air and also the thermal properties of the crown elements (branches, buds, and leaves) such as mass and water content. Thick foliage might provide some protective shielding to branches, which explains variations in tree mortality rates between seasons and species. Heat transfer to roots occurs via conduction through soil. Smouldering can be particularly harmful to roots since it can cause soil heating that persists for hours or even days, causing cell mortality even at temperatures below 60°C. The extent of injuries in the stem, crown, and roots, and how these interact to affect whole-tree carbon and water budgets, is what ultimately determines whether a tree will live or die following a forest fire.

Figure 12.17
C-1: spruce-lichen woodland fuel type.
Source: Photo by Marc Shandoro.

Figure 12.18
C-7: ponderosa pine/Douglas fir fuel type.
Source: Photo by Nikname.

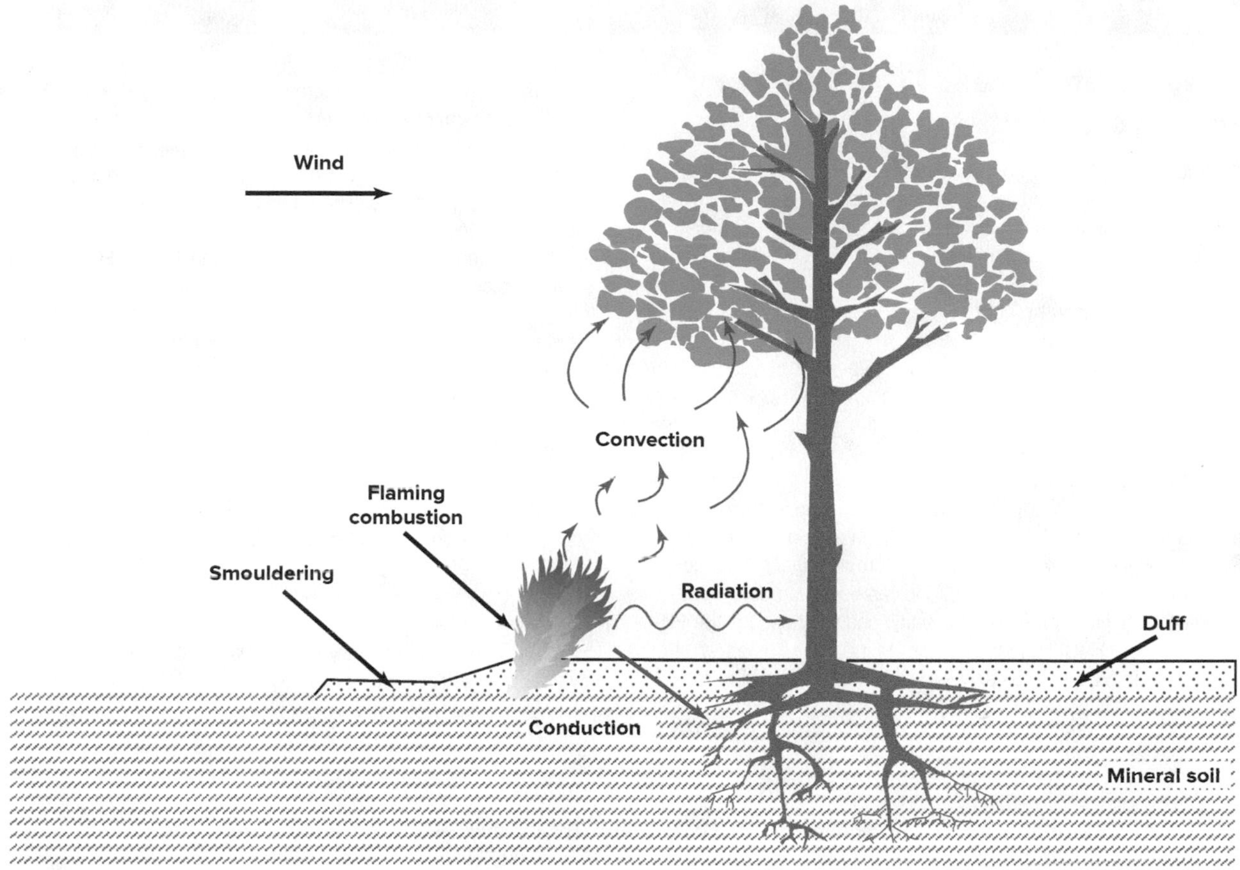

Figure 12.19
During a forest fire, heat injures the stem and the crown of a tree by radiation and convection, and the roots by conduction.
Source: Modified from Michaletz and Johnson, Scandinavian Journal of Forest Research, 2007.

Fire in the Canadian Boreal Forest

The Canadian boreal stretches from the Alaska–Yukon border to the east coast of Newfoundland as part of the circumpolar boreal forest that spans the globe. It is a predominately coniferous forest that is populated by white and black spruce and tamarack, with balsam fir and jack pine in the east and lodgepole pine in the west. White birch, trembling aspen, balsam poplar, and other deciduous tree species occur there, primarily in mixed-wood stands. The forest floor is usually covered with a duff layer that, depending upon its moisture content, can support smouldering combustion (high moisture content) or flaming combustion (low moisture content).

Fire is most common in the southern half of the boreal forest, where large stand-replacing fires, which can burn tens or hundreds of thousands of hectares, destroy existing stands and initiate the growth of new even-aged stands in their wake. The boreal forest is home to many forest insects, one of which is the spruce budworm. Spruce budworm population levels surge and subside over time throughout the boreal forest in cycles that have yet to be fully understood. When these populations surge, they destroy balsam fir and other conifers, which then serve as highly flammable fuel.

Lightning is common across the boreal forest and serves as a source of ignition to ensure fire continues its important natural role. Lightning fires tend to occur in spatial and temporal clusters that fire managers often refer to as fire flaps. Lightning fires are usually ignited in the duff layer where they may smoulder for several days until the top of the duff layer and the surface litter layer become dry enough to support the spread of a surface fire (Figure 12.24). As the surface fire grows in intensity, the energy that it releases preheats the lower branches of the pine and spruce trees, sporadically causing individual trees to burst into flame—what fire specialists refer to as torching (Figure 12.24b). If the surface fire continues to grow in intensity and there are sufficient ladder fuels present to help the fire move from the surface into the crowns, then more and more crowns become actively engaged

IN GREATER DEPTH

The Canadian Forest Fire–Danger Rating System

Weather affects fire behaviour both directly (fire speed rates increase as the wind speed increases) and indirectly (fires spread more quickly and burn more intensely as fuel moisture content decreases). Fuel moisture rises and falls from day to day in response to variations in temperature, relative humidity, wind speed, and rainfall. Fire behaviour is therefore influenced by not only the current weather but also the cumulative effect of past weather on the current fuel moisture content. Forest-fire researchers have therefore developed fire-danger rating systems that distil daily temperature observations into relatively simple measures of the impact of weather on fuel moisture, fire occurrence, and fire behaviour.

Canadians are familiar with the "humidex," which is used to describe how uncomfortable they will feel given the temperature and relative humidity during the summer months (Figure 9.18). The Canadian Forest Fire Danger Rating System (CFFDRS) is, in essence, a forest-fire manager's "humidex."

The CFFDRS includes six codes and indices based on daily observations of rainfall, temperature, relative humidity, and wind speed. The Fine Fuel Moisture Code (FFMC) is a measure of the moisture content of litter and other cured fine fuels such as dry needles and dead leaves on the forest floor, and is used to predict when and where people-caused fires might occur. The Duff Moisture Code (DMC) is a measure of the moisture content of the moss and underlying decomposing organic layer (what fire managers refer to as the **duff** layer) and is coupled with measures of lightning activity to predict daily lightning fire occurrence. The Drought Code (DC) is an index of the moisture content of the deep organic layers and is used to predict how deep fires will burn and how much time and effort will be required to extinguish them.

Fires spread faster as the Initial Spread Index (ISI) increases. They consume more fuel as the Buildup Index (BUI) increases. The Fire Weather Index (FWI) is a measure of fire intensity and also serves as an aggregate measure of fire danger that is used to communicate the need for caution to the public (Figure 12.20). Most Canadian forest-fire management agencies use the FWI to set the pointer on signs communicating the level of fire danger day by day in forested areas (Figure 12.21). Maps of the CFFDRS codes and indices portray fire danger on provincial (Figure 12.22) and national scales.

A new fire-danger rating code, the sheltered duff moisture code (SDMC), has been introduced recently. The SDMC is a measure of the moisture content of the duff layer at the base of a tree, the point at which a lightning strike is most likely to reach the ground and ignite a fire. Since higher SDMC values denote drier duff layers, lightning that strikes a high-SDMC area is more likely to ignite a fire than lightning that strikes a low-SDMC area. The two maps in Figure 12.23 indicate that most of the lightning-caused forest fires in the province of Ontario on 9 August 2001 were ignited by lightning that struck high-SDMC areas.

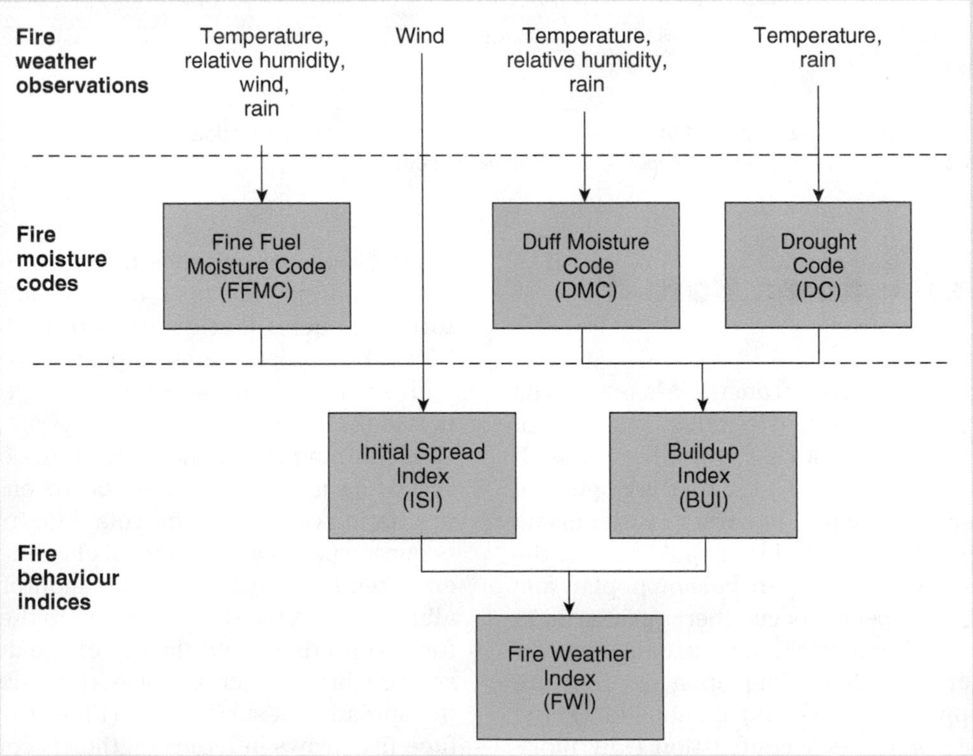

Figure 12.20

Structure of the Canadian Fire Weather Index system.

Sources: The reproduction of "Structure of the Canadian Fire Weather Index System" from the CWFIS website http://cwfis.cfs.nrcan.gc.ca/background/summary/fwi, and "Map of the Fire Weather Index across Canada on May 18, 2007" from CWFIS website http://cwfis.cfs.nrcan.gc.ca/maps/fw

continued

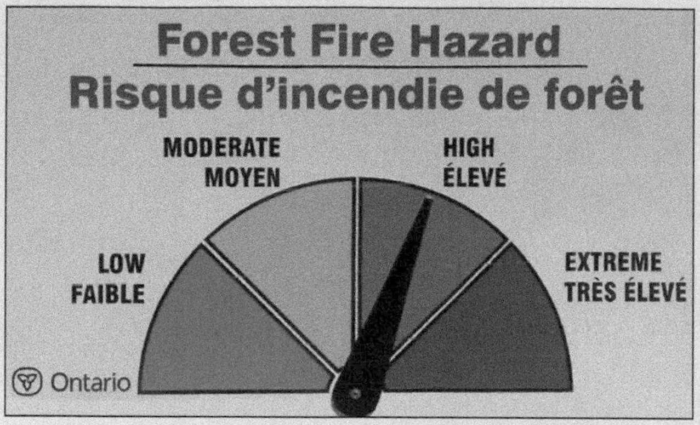

Figure 12.21
Roadside fire prevention sign to communicate current fire danger to the public in Ontario.

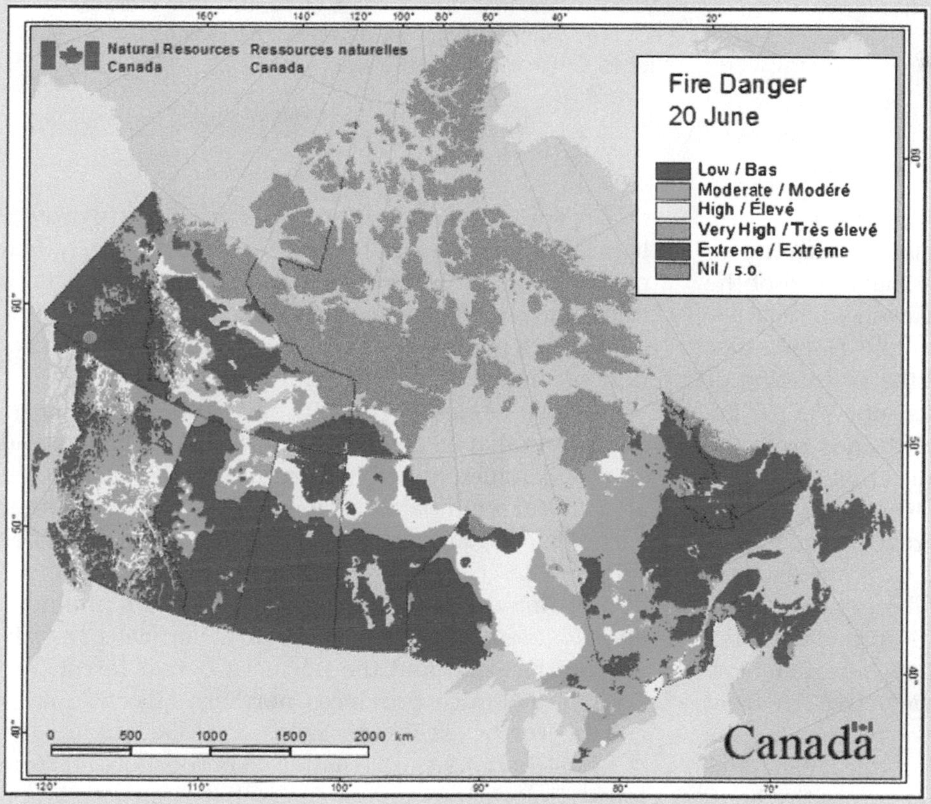

Figure 12.22
Map of the Fire Weather Index across Canada on June 20, 2014. In summer 2014, the Northwest Territories experienced one of its worse fire seasons ever.

continued

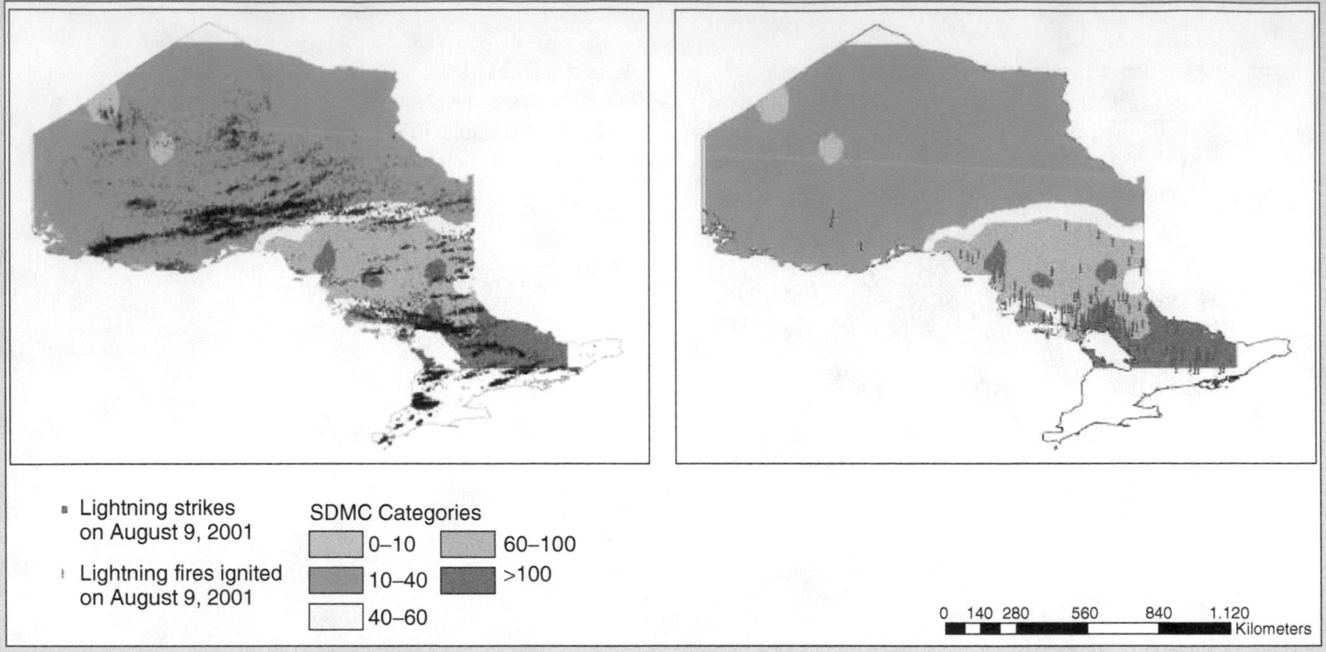

Figure 12.23

Lightning activity and lightning fire occurrence in Ontario on August 9, 2001. The map on the left is colour coded to indicate the sheltered duff moisture code (SDMC) category and where lightning occurred that day. The map on the right indicates that most of the lightning fires that day occurred where lightning struck areas that had a high SDMC.

Source: B.M. Wotton of the Canadian Forest Service.

in a slow-moving crown fire (Figures 12.24c–e). If winds are strong enough, they will cause fire to penetrate the crowns and accelerate the spread of the surface fire, which will then torch even more trees. Winds above the crowns will bend the flames that extend above crowns and enhance the preheating of unburned crowns (Figure 12.25). This supports the initiation of an active crown fire that extends from the surface through the crown with flames that can reach 30 m or more in height and begins to move as a continuous crown fire front that can spread as quickly as 50 m per minute or more (Figure 12.26). As winds push burning dry needles, dead leaves, and other fine debris ahead in fluidized waves, they pull firebrands into the fire plume or convection column. The winds then blow those flaming firebrands ahead of the active fire front where they drop and ignite spot fires well ahead of the main fires, often more than a kilometre ahead. This allows the crown fire to spread easily across fire lines, roads, and small lakes and rivers.

Forest firefighters first attack fire on its perimeter, gradually working their way inward. When a wide enough corridor along the perimeter has been cleared, they might allow the central part of the fire to die off naturally and redeploy their efforts elsewhere. Firefighters cannot attack crown fires but they sometimes deploy sprinklers connected to power pumps to protect homes and cottages that lie in the fire's path. They then pull back and curtail their suppression activity until rain and/or a change in wind direction or speed slow the fire to a point where it is safe enough to deploy firefighters on the fire perimeter.

Large, intensely burning fires often form large mushroom-shaped convection columns that can extend several kilometres into the atmosphere where they affect local wind patterns and inject smoke and other particulates that can be transported long distances (Figure 12.27). People living in eastern Canada often observe intensely orange sunsets. These are produced by smoke emitted from forest fires burning in northwestern Ontario, and the northern boreal forest portions of the Prairie provinces, northern Alberta, Yukon, and the Northwest Territories.

First Nations people suffer disproportionally from forest fires in the boreal forest but destruction and evacuation of remote northern First Nations communities rarely make the news. Sad to say, damage affecting wealthy people living closer to urban centres does. Would people across Canada have heard of the Slave Lake fire in 2011 if Prince William and the Duchess of Cambridge had not toured the fire-ravaged town during their royal tour of Canada?

Figure 12.24
Sequence of photographs illustrating the development of a crown fire in an immature jack pine forest in the Blind River district northeast of Sault Ste. Marie, Ontario. (a) Shortly after ignition, (b) early stages of torching, (c) early stages of crown fire, (d) advancing crown fire, and (e) established crown fire.
Source: B.J. Stocks, Canadian Forest Service, Natural Resources Canada.

Figure 12.25
Crown fire in an immature jack pine forest.
Source: © David Martell.

Figure 12.26
Crown fire in the boreal forest near Red Lake, Ontario.
Source: B.J. Stocks, Canadian Forest Service, Natural Resources Canada.

FIRESTORM 2003, BRITISH COLUMBIA

The forests of British Columbia are shaped by the predominately eastward flow of weather systems off the Pacific Ocean that interact with mountain ranges aligned in a north–south direction to produce areas with above-average rainfall, dry rain shadows, and changes in elevation. This broad range of climatic and topographic features supports very diverse forests;

Figure 12.27
Established convection column over a forest fire in northern Ontario.
Source: © Queen's Printer for Ontario, 2014. Reproduced with permission.

Canada is divided into 194 ecoregions and 46 of them are located in British Columbia. British Columbia's renowned temperate rainforests, which dominate much of Vancouver Island, Haida Gwaii, and the coast of mainland British Columbia, for example, are characterized by very large Douglas fir and Sitka spruce trees that seldom burn. Much of the southern Interior, on the other hand, is covered by grasslands, lodgepole pine, and ponderosa pine stands that burn readily under hot dry conditions. In this area, seventy years of fire suppression, a reduction in the use of prescribed fire attributed to a number of factors including public concern about smoke, and a lack of adequate funds and trained personnel contributed to fuel build-ups that resulted in the encroachment of forests onto grasslands and the increased presence of Douglas fir in the understory of many forest stands.

The 2003 fire season was the worst ever experienced in British Columbia (Figure 12.28). It is a stark example of what can happen when people live near flammable wildland urban interface (WUI) areas, that is, localities where infrastructure is built close to or within undeveloped land. More than 2500 fires burned more than 260 000 hectares across the province, but those figures alone reveal little of the human cost of several significant fires that occurred in WUI areas in the southern Interior. Three pilots involved in fire operations lost their lives, 334 homes were destroyed, and more than 45 000 people were evacuated. Many businesses were disrupted and some were destroyed. The economic loss is estimated to have been roughly $400 million.

Environment Canada described the weather conditions that set the stage for the 2003 fire season in these terms:

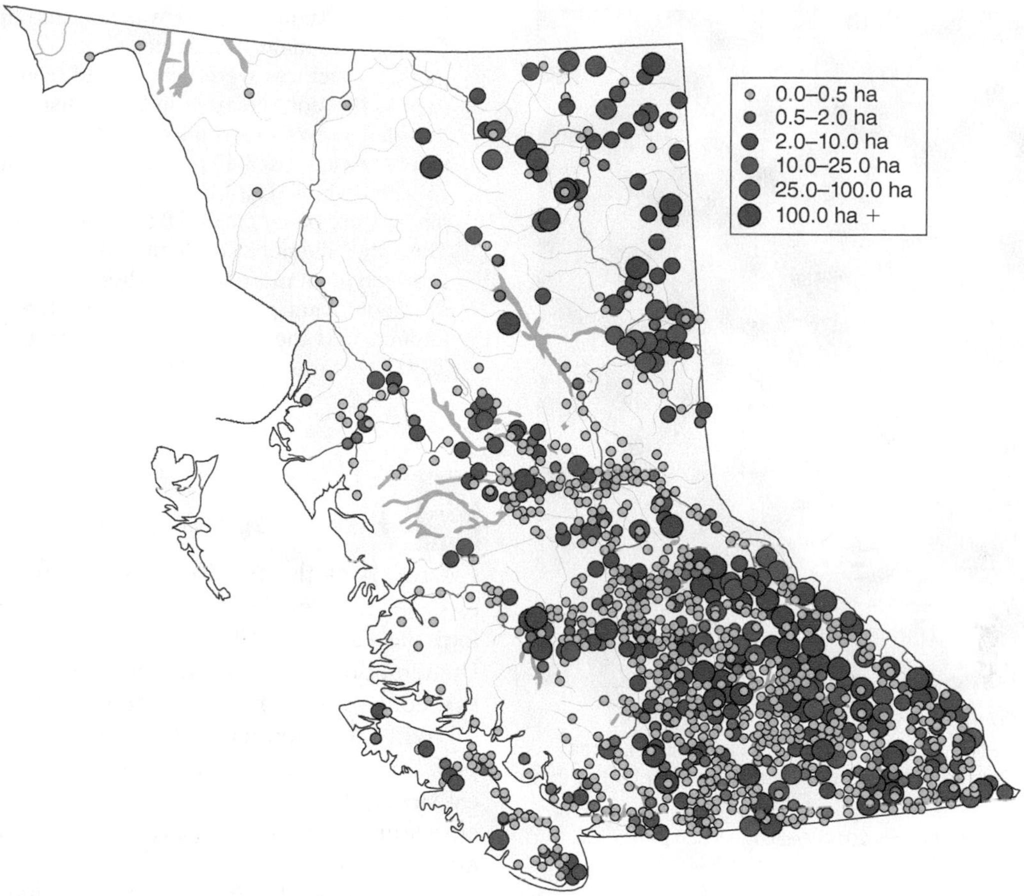

Figure 12.28
Distribution of forest fires in British Columbia in 2003. Note the high concentration of fires in the southeast of the province. This area is considered by many to pose the greatest challenge to forest-fire managers in Canada.
Source: © Province of British Columbia. All rights reserved. Reprinted with permission of the Province of British Columbia. http://www2.gov.bc.ca

> During most of the summer, a large Pacific high-pressure area anchored near the coast kept [precipitation] away from British Columbia. At some weather stations in the Interior, temperatures soared to 40°C. In Kamloops, temperatures rose above 30°C on 19 days in July and 20 days in August; normal for each month is 11 [days]. Kelowna recorded the driest June–August period since records began in 1899 and set a record with 44 consecutive rainless days. On the coast, Victoria had its driest summer since record keeping began in 1914 with a paltry 8.2 mm of rain. The forests in the south were tinder dry and the forest floor volatile—a spark away from igniting. Then came flashes of dry lightning, strong gusty winds, and a bit of human carelessness. (*Firestorm 2003—Provincial Review,* 18)

The 2003 Okanagan Mountain Park fire, which many Canadians think of as the Kelowna fire, was the most destructive Canadian forest fire in recent history (Figure 12.29). The fire burned more than 250 homes

Figure 12.29
Okanagan Mountain Park fire, August 2003.
Source: *The Daily Courier,* Kelowna BC.

Figure 12.30

To ensure public safety, the Ontario Provincial Police closed Highway 101 in Northern Ontario during the Wawa #18 fire in May 2010.

and at one point nearly one-third of the residents of Kelowna had been evacuated from their homes. What follows is based on the Fire Review Summary prepared by the Protection Branch of the British Columbia Ministry of Forests.

> The fire was ignited by lightning at 1:55 a.m. and reported at 2:05 in the morning of 16 August, and it grew to 5 hectares in size by 3:00 that morning. When the fire was first reported, it was 6 km from the nearest structures in Narmata and 10 km from the nearest homes in Kelowna. Air tankers worked the fire until 11:15 a.m. when it was reported to be a relatively low intensity Rank 1 fire. When the air tankers returned to their base for refuelling they were dispatched to other, higher-priority fires. The winds picked up at about 12:30 p.m. and spot fires materialized north of the main fire. Helicopters bucketed those spot fires, and air tanker action resumed at 1:55 p.m. Air tanker operations continued until 7:05 p.m. but ceased then due to flight crew safety concerns regarding low visibility due to smoke and falling light levels. The fire was reported to have burned through the retardant dropped by air tankers consistently throughout the day. Suppression action continued on the following days but the fire continued to grow and reached more than 9000 hectares by 20 August.
>
> On 21 August the fire was spotting up to 100 m in front of the main fire. It began threatening Kelowna and 21 structures were lost. A cold front was forecast to pass through the area on 22 August and at 2:00 p.m. that day, crews were pulled off the northeast flank for safety reasons. At 4:45 p.m. the fire blew up, pushed by 75 km/h winds. Burning firebrands the size of dinner plates were being carried 6 to 8 km from the main fire. The winds did not subside until 3:00 a.m. on 23 August, at which point more than 250 homes had been lost. The first significant precipitation fell on the fire on 8 September, and the fire was eventually extinguished at 25 912 hectares.

LO5 Fire Suppression

Canada is at the forefront of advanced technologies (see In Greater Depth box: Combat Weapons) and logistics (Figure 12.30; see Human Focus box: Vincent Demers, Forest Firefighter) in fire suppression. Forest fire control is a provincial and territorial responsibility, with the Canadian Interagency Forest Fire Centre playing a coordinating role. Teams of experienced forest firefighters are occasionally mobilized to help their colleagues from another province facing an exceptionally severe fire.

As a general rule, to make optimal use of limited fire suppression resources, forest fires happening in the north are not fought as aggressively as those occurring farther south unless a community or important infrastructure element, such as one associated with fuel oil extraction or mining, is at risk. The boundary between the fire management zones—intensive (highest level of intervention), intermediate, and extensive (little or no intervention)—varies according to provinces.

Attitudes and strategies toward fire suppression are evolving. During the twentieth century, people were taught to hate fire and to stamp it out quickly. Fire-suppression tactics and equipment improved during that century, resulting in dramatic reductions in the number of hectares burned. Over the decades, forests were transformed by the fire-suppression practices. Forests that once held 75 big trees per hectare were accustomed to having ground fires move quickly through grasses and thin litter on the forest floor without harming most of the big trees. However, after years of limiting fires, some of these forests now support 750 to 7500 big trees per hectare plus an understory of shrubs. When lightning ignites fires in these dense forests, the flames burn slowly and intensely, killing the big trees. The widespread recognition of the fire problem for dense and crowded forests led to a dilemma: Should dense forests be thinned? Should natural fires be allowed to burn?

IN GREATER DEPTH

Combat Weapons

Forest fire intensity is ranked according to the amount of heat energy released per second for a metre of fire front (Figure 12.31). This system is distinct from the CFFRS (see In Greater Depth Box: The Canadian Forest Fire–Danger Rating System), although closely related. The fire intensity classes have been defined using empirical data from experimental fires and wildfires, and describe fire behaviour rather than hazard levels. They are used to define the "preparedness level" required and to pre-position the necessary firefighting assets to control and extinguish fires before they reach an unmanageable size. The higher the intensity, the more equipment will be pre-positioned to quickly attack the fire before it spreads. It is important to be quick at the initial attack.

Fires with an intensity of less than 10 kW/m are benign and usually do not sustain themselves. Fires with an intensity between 10 and 500 kW/m can be suppressed by firefighters using hand tools such as axes, shovels, and chain saws (Figure 12.32). Hoses spraying water under pressure are normally required to extinguish fires with an intensity between 500 and 2000 kW/m, together with the support of helicopters carrying water buckets (Figures 12.33 and 12.34). Fires with an intensity between 2000 and 4000 kW/m call for the intervention of air tankers. Finally, fires with an intensity greater than 4000 kW/m are so ferocious that the safest course of action is often to wait for an amelioration of the weather conditions.

Canada is a world leader in the design and commercialization of air tankers, the ultimate weapon for initial attack against fierce fires. The first generation of air tankers were modified military aircraft. Since the 1940s, Canadair Ltd. from Montreal, Quebec (now Bombardier) has manufactured aircraft specially designed for aerial firefighting. Canadair Ltd. was the first to design an aircraft specifically for the purpose of fighting forest fires.

Figure 12.32
A firefighter working with an axe.
Source: Photo courtesy of SOPFEU.

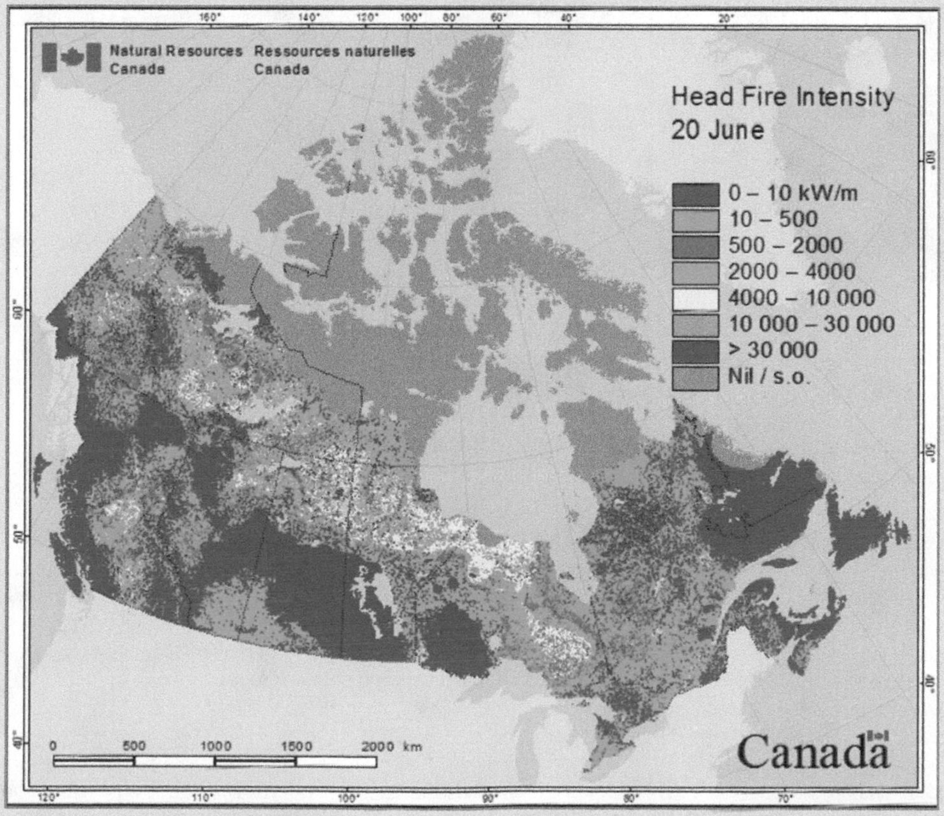

Figure 12.31
Map of fire intensity across Canada on June 20, 2014.
Source: Canadian Wildland Fire Information System, Natural Resources Canada. Reproduced with the permission of the Minister of Natural Resources Canada, 2014.

continued

Figure 12.33
A firefighter extinguishing a fire with high-pressure water.
Source: Photo courtesy of SOPFEU.

Figure 12.35
The Bombardier 415 aircraft drops foam retardant on the front of the fire to suppress flames and cool the fire to a level so ground operations can intervene to fully extinguish the fire.
Source: Photo courtesy of SOPFEU.

Figure 12.34
A helicopter carrying a water bucket for aerial firefighting.
Source: Photo courtesy of SOPFEU.

Figure 12.36
Two small (12.7 cm wide by 7.6 cm high) probes located on each side, underneath the Bombardier 415 aircaft hull, are used to scoop water into its reservoirs in approximately 12 seconds.
Source: Bombardier.

The first CL-215 scooping aircraft was delivered in 1971. The Bombardier 415 aircraft, the newest version of the CL-215 firefighter, flew its first flight on December 6, 1993. In its firefighting configuration, the Bombardier 415 aircraft capitalizes on the concept of rapid initial attack with its ability to scoop water near a fire. It can also be configured for other utility roles, including maritime search and rescue, surveillance, and personnel transport.

The Bombardier 415 aircraft operates in four Canadian provinces and has been exported to five countries. It is the current standard in the field (Figure 12.35). Operated by a crew of only two pilots and a few ground technicians, its capability to land on water and unpaved runways makes it suitable for missions in the remote locations where forest fires often strike. The Bombardier 415 aircraft is highly manoeuvrable and can scoop water on any body of water (lakes, rivers, even the open sea) that is 1350 m long by 90 m wide and 2 m deep, clear of floating debris. The aircraft needs only to make contact with water for 10 to12 seconds for a full pickup while skimming at a speed of 130 km/h. Water is scooped into the 6100 L reservoir through two small probes located on each side, underneath the aircraft hull (Figure 12.36). The water is later dropped on the target from an altitude of 30 to 35 m above treetop level at a typical speed of 200 km/h. By varying altitude and the sequence of opening of the drop doors, the pilot can spread the water with precision so that it poses little threat to ground crews and infrastructure. Water can also be mixed with firefighting foam. Dropped on unburned vegetation, the foam acts as a retardant; used directly on the fire, the foam reduces flame height and intensity.

The combination of rapid refilling, precision dropping, and the use of water–foam mix makes the Bombardier 415 aircraft a mighty tool in the fight against fires, in both natural and urban environments.

HUMAN FOCUS

Vincent Demers, Forest Firefighter

I had my first job as a forest firefighter as a summer student and forest firefighting has become my lifetime passion. I have since become a forest engineer and have assumed roles of increasing responsibility. I am currently the team coordinator for major fires at SOPFEU, the agency for the protection of forests against fire in the Province of Quebec (Figure 12.37).

Fighting fires brings people together in very much the same way as war or a competitive sport. Firefighters are typically deployed in small teams of four people on the ground, with several teams being active in different sectors of the same fire. A semi-permanent base is set up, usually in an existing logging camp. A structure—the incident command system, developed in the United States for disaster management—is put in place to oversee operations, logistics, finances, and planning.

Fires tend to be detected between the middle of the afternoon until the evening, when temperature is hot, humidity is low, and thunderstorm activity at its highest. Firefighters and their equipment (pumps, hoses, chain saws, shovels, etc.) are usually transported by helicopter to their sector. Their first task is to find a source of water for the pumps. Depending on the intensity of the fire, their work is supported by helicopters lifting water buckets and/or air tankers. Firefighters wear lightweight fire retardant clothing, gloves, boots, and helmets. Everyone carries a GPS and a radio, and maintains verbal contact with their teammates, the aircraft, and the base. Often working in close proximity to open flames, with experience firefighters develop an acute situational awareness and are sensitive to changes in heat, wind, and smoke, and their impact on fire behaviour (Figure 12.38). Air pilots must know where everyone is on the ground to discharge water safely away from them.

From my vantage position at the base, I am orchestrating operations that can involve as many as 150 firefighters supported by a dozen aircraft, in the case of a major fire. My responsibility is to coordinate efforts, ensure that all resources are optimally deployed, and monitor the situation. Time is of the essence here as rapid response can prevent adjacent small fires from merging and escalating into larger fires. Some fires, however, become too fierce to combat. Teams are pulled back, and they wait for rain.

Figure 12.37
Vincent Demers briefing a team of forest firefighters.
Source: Photo courtesy of SOPFEU.

Figure 12.38
Direct intervention in close proximity to open flames.
Source: Photo courtesy of SOPFEU.

CALIFORNIA VERSUS BAJA CALIFORNIA: PAY NOW OR PAY LATER

Many people hold the view that humanity is separate from the environment. Many seek to control nature for their own benefit. This includes building houses wherever it strikes their fancy. Fires? No problem, we will just extinguish them before they cause any damage. But what is the long-term effect of short-term suppression of fires? An interesting study by fire ecologist Richard Minnich addressed this question using satellite imagery to determine the number and size of all chaparral fires in Southern California, United States, and contiguous northern Baja California, Mexico, from 1972 to 1980. The life cycle of the chaparral plant community takes it through a sequence of fire susceptibility. Younger plants do not burn easily, but after 40 years of growth, an increased proportion of dead-plant material acts as fuel, allowing fire to burn readily and intensely.

In the United States, fires are fought energetically and expensively. The goal is to not let fire interfere with human activities, no matter how much money it costs. Fires that break out during the cooler, wetter months are quickly extinguished. As a result, most of the chaparral is allowed to grow older and more flammable. Then, when the hot and dry winds come blowing from the continental Interior (commonly in September, October, and November), firestorms are unleashed that firefighters are powerless to stop, and great numbers of hectares burn. Southern California has fewer fires but larger ones (Figure 12.39).

In Mexico, many fires are simply allowed to burn with little or no human interference. The fires are smaller because older chaparral is commonly surrounded by younger, less flammable plants. This distribution creates an age mosaic that mixes volatile, older patches with younger, tougher-to-burn growths. Fires are more numerous in Baja California, but they are smaller and more of them occur during the cooler, wetter months (Figure 12.39).

For the period from 1972 to 1980, the percentage of chaparral area burned in the United States and Mexico was about the same. This is despite the enormous expenses and valiant efforts made in the United States to suppress fire. The U.S. fire-control efforts have reduced the number of fires but not the amount of area burned. In Southern California, the monster firestorms pushed by dry, hot winds burn tremendous numbers of hectares, killing people and destroying thousands of buildings.

Home Design and Fire

Not all of the death and destruction from fires can be called "natural disasters." Poor decisions about landscaping, home design, and construction materials are partly to blame (Figure 12.40). Many homes are made of wood or roofed with wooden shake shingles. Wooden decks extend out over steep slopes and help fire to concentrate

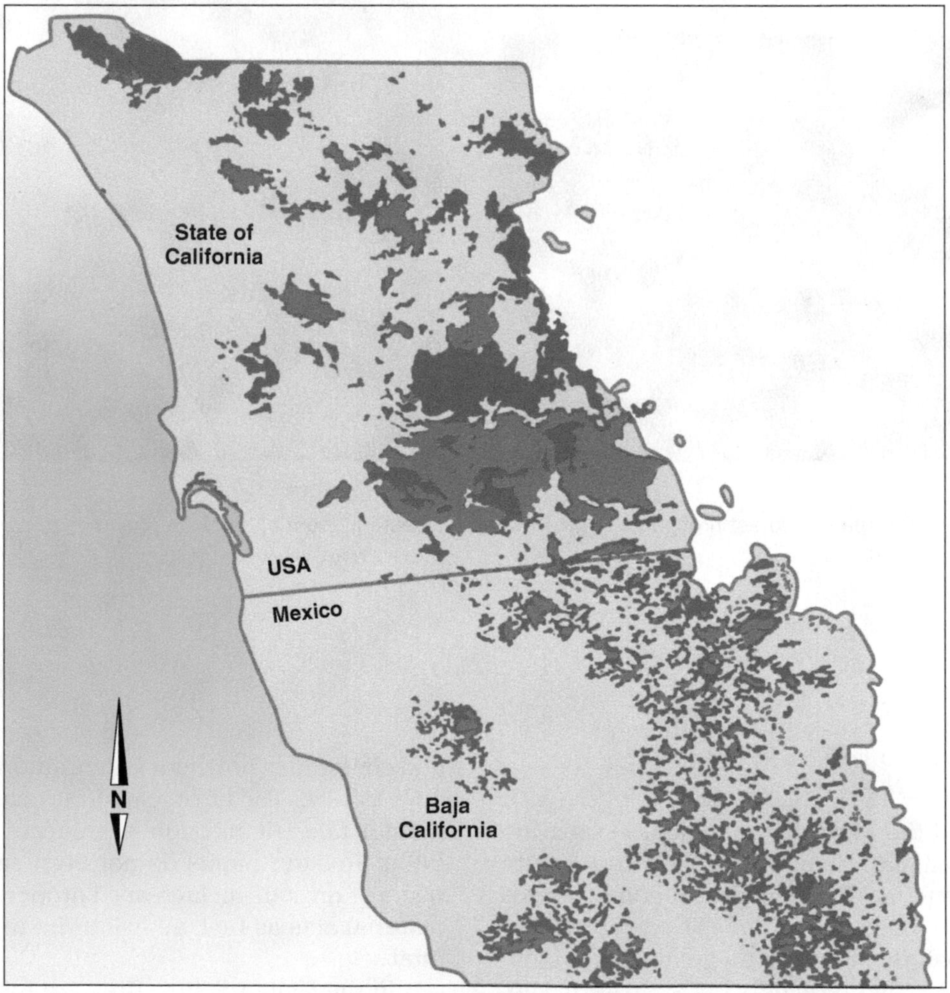

Figure 12.39
Fire burn areas in California and Baja California between 1938 and 1972. Notice the huge areas burned by some California fires. See the larger number of burn areas in Baja California but their smaller sizes.
Source: © Richard A. Minnich, University of California—Riverside.

Figure 12.40
Twelve mistakes, or how to sacrifice your house to the fire gods. (1) House is located on a slope. (2) House is made of wood. (3) Wooden deck hangs out over the slope. (4) Firewood is stored next to the house. (5) Roof is made of flammable wood shingles. (6) Tree limbs hang over roof. (7) Shrubs continue up to house. (8) Large, single-pane windows face the slope. (9) Unprotected louvers face the slope. (10) No spark arrester is on top of chimney. (11) Narrow road or driveway prevents access of fire trucks. (12) Wooden eaves extend beyond walls.
Source: © National Fire Protection Assoc.

Figure 12.41
Houses designed to withstand fire remain unharmed while their million-dollar neighbours are nothing but ashes, near Las Flores Canyon in Malibu, California.
Source: © Patrick Downs, *L.A. Times*

heat, igniting the houses. Natural and planted vegetation commonly continue from wildland right up to houses or even drape over houses' roofs. All of these flammable materials act to convey fire into and through houses.

A house can catch on fire in different ways. (1) Flames can travel to the house by burning through vegetation or along a wood fence. (2) Flames do not have to reach the house; they can generate enough radiant heat to ignite the exterior of the house or even the curtains hanging inside windows. (3) Firebrands carried by wind can be dropped on or next to the house. All it takes to ignite a house is one vulnerable point where combustion can occur. Now stand outside, look at your house and ask yourself—what could catch on fire? How could you eliminate the hazard?

It is possible to build a house and landscape the property so that a fire will pass by (Figure 12.41). The houses that flames pass by commonly have clay or concrete tile roofs, stucco exterior walls, double-pane windows, few overhanging roofs or decks, and cleared vegetation extending at least 10 m from the house (Figure 12.42). Houses built on slopes need even larger areas of cleared space. If you plan to build a house in the woods or along a WUI area, the decisions you make about construction materials and landscaping may well determine whether your house will end up as fuel for flames or remain your home (Table 12.1).

Climate Change and Forest Fires

Since climate influences forest vegetation, and weather influences fire occurrence and fire behaviour processes, climate change is expected to have a significant effect on fire activity in the forested regions of Canada and elsewhere.

Fire researchers are studying the effects of climate on fire occurrence and fire behaviour. Some of their understandings of the these effects are described in the form of mathematical relationships between, for example, the average number of people-caused fires per day in a region and the Fine Fuel Moisture Code, one of the components of the Canadian Fire Weather Index system described above (Figure 12.20). A 2014 study by Douglas Woolford of Wilfrid Laurier University and co-workers, for example, has established a significant statistical relationship between lightning-caused fires and fire weather for Northwestern Ontario. This region of Ontario was selected for the study because of the availability of both reliable climate data and reliable fire data over several decades. It would be unwise to extrapolate these findings to other regions without a careful examination of local particularities.

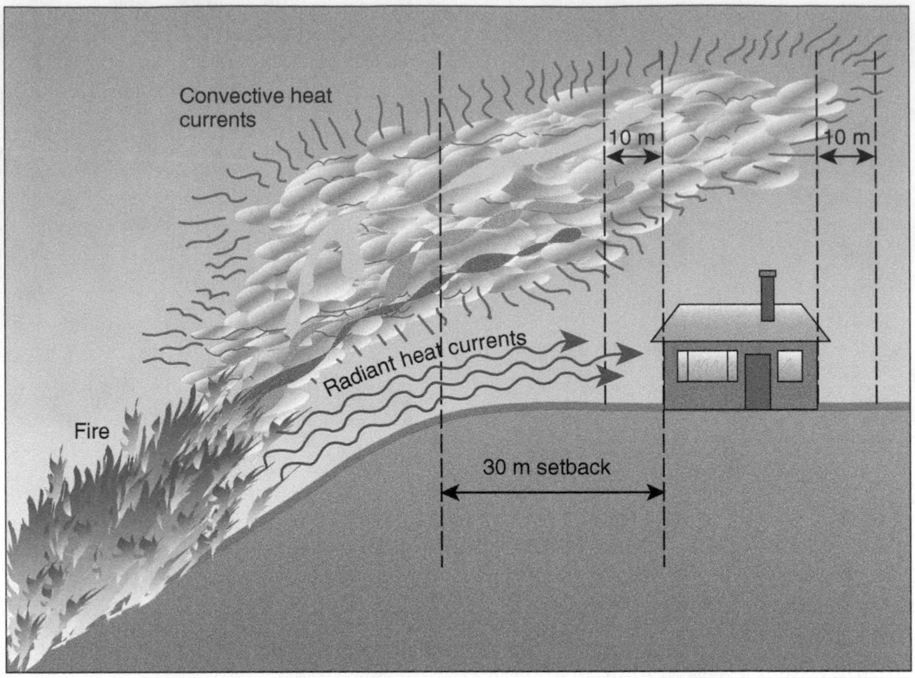

Figure 12.42
Buildings at the top of a slope need setbacks to help avoid the increased heat flow by convection and radiation. The defensive space includes a vertical zone around the building that has no tall trees.
Source: © San Diego County.

TABLE 12.1

How to Protect Your House from Wildfire: A Must-do List

Roof The roof is the most vulnerable part of your house because of wind-blown burning embers. Build or reroof with lightweight materials that will not burn. Remember to remove branches hanging over your roof and sweep off accumulated leaves, needles, and other plant debris. Place screens over all vents.

House Build or remodel with fire-resistant materials. The ultimate foolishness is to build a wood house among abundant trees and shrubs.

Decks The undersides of above-ground decks, balconies, and eaves must be covered with fire-resistant materials.

Windows Use only double- or triple-paned windows to reduce the potential of breakage during a fire. Eliminate wood shutters. Beware of the new-style white plastic window frames; they have melted and allowed fire into homes.

Flammables Be sure to place natural-gas tanks and firewood piles at least 10 m from your house.

Trees Hold back fire from your house by (1) reducing the number of trees in densely wooded areas and (2) cutting off branches hanging close to the ground so grass fires cannot climb up to the treetops.

Yard Create as defensible a space as possible by (1) replacing fire-loving plants with fire-resistant plants and (2) removing all dry grass, dead brush, and leaves near your home, and farther away if you are on a slope. Replace wood fences with concrete block or metal fences.

Community planning Place golf courses, grass ball fields, and open-space parks between houses and the wildland so they can serve as fire breaks or buffers.

Fire researchers work with climatologists to project how the fire-danger rating indices for an area will change under different CO_2 scenarios and how such changes in fire danger will likely influence fire activity under climate change. Some of the early studies indicated that fire-season severity (which is based on the Fire Weather Index) will increase by roughly 45% under doubling CO_2 conditions, and the fire seasons will increase in length. It is important to note, however, that the impact of climate change on fire-season severity is expected to vary regionally, with some areas experiencing increased activity and others decreased activity. Other studies have focused on fire occurrence and predicted people-caused fire occurrence might increase by roughly 20% under those same conditions. The area burned by lightning fires is expected to increase as well. Collectively, these studies suggest that fire weather will intensify, more fires will occur, and a greater area will burn (Figure 12.43).

Large forest fires are a relatively rare occurrence in moisture-charged tropical rainforests. In Indonesia, there are more fires under the dry El Niño conditions and fewer fires during the heavy precipitations associated with La Niña. In 1997–1998, under a strong El Niño, forest fires of an unprecedented intensity devastated Kalimantan and Sumatra. Probably initiated by traditional slash-and-burn agriculture, several minor fires merged into large fires, and the situation spiralled out of control. Fires burned for months, leaving a total of 45 600 km^2 of rainforest devastated. They triggered smog of multinational proportions, covering a large area of South East Asia, and produced carbon dioxide emissions equal to the overall emissions from Europe for a year. These events ring alarm bells, reminding us of the fragility of the rainforest ecosystems. What will happen if climate change brings abrupt temperature rises in the equatorial regions?

IS THERE ANY EVIDENCE CLIMATE CHANGE HAS ALTERED CANADIAN FOREST-FIRE REGIMES?

Both temperatures and forest-fire activity have been rising in parts of Canada in recent decades and many observers are quick to point to increased forest-fire activity as an early sign of climate change. Unfortunately, although climate change is widely believed to be contributing to increased forest-fire activity in Canada, it is very difficult to determine the extent to which such increases are or are not due to climate change.

Fire occurrence and fire-behaviour processes are influenced not only by fuel, weather, and topography but also by people who establish homes and cottages in WUI areas, build forest-access roads, harvest forest stands, and engage in human activities that lead to people-caused fire occurrence. People also attempt, with considerable success, to suppress many of the fires that do occur. It is therefore difficult to assess the extent to which fire activity in a particular area is or is not influenced by climate change.

It is challenging to establish clear causal relationships when several variables are intermingled with climate data. For instance, two insects are proliferating in Canadian forests at present, the mountain pine beetle in the west and the spruce budworm in the east, and infested forests are highly flammable. The insect populations are thought to fluctuate on the scale of approximately half a century: they grow for a few decades and then shrink for the next few decades. This periodicity is on the same order as several climate cycles. And, to further complicate the issue, climate is also one of the variables influencing insect life cycles! Careful studies and observations over long time periods are required to unravel these complex relationships.

A few studies, however, have attributed increased warming during the fire season and increased area burned in the fire-prone regions of Canada to human emissions of greenhouse gases and sulfate aerosols. More recently, researchers identified areas in the forests of the Northern Rockies of the United States in which large fire activity appears to be related to increased spring and summer temperatures and an earlier spring snowmelt. Such results lend credence to the belief that climate change will have a significant impact on Canadian forest-fire regimes.

POTENTIAL IMPACT

The projected increases in fire activity that are expected to result from climate change will have significant social, economic, and ecological impacts on Canadian forests and the people who live and work in and near them. Given the current structure and composition of our forests, land-use patterns, and fire management strategies, it is reasonable to assume that more timber will be lost to fire and that more communities, particularly small, relatively isolated communities in the north, will be threatened by fire. Some studies have suggested that increased burning will release more greenhouse gases, which in turn may lead to even more warming, while others have suggested that burning of parts of Canada's northern boreal forest may lead to more Sun being reflected by the snow during the winter months, thereby mitigating warming. Some have suggested that our forests should be used to sequester carbon while others have expressed concerns that such strategies are short-sighted; as the fuel builds up, this approach will simply delay and exacerbate the inevitable. Clearly, there is an urgent need to develop a better understanding of forests and fire, and how they will be shaped by, and in turn influence, climate change.

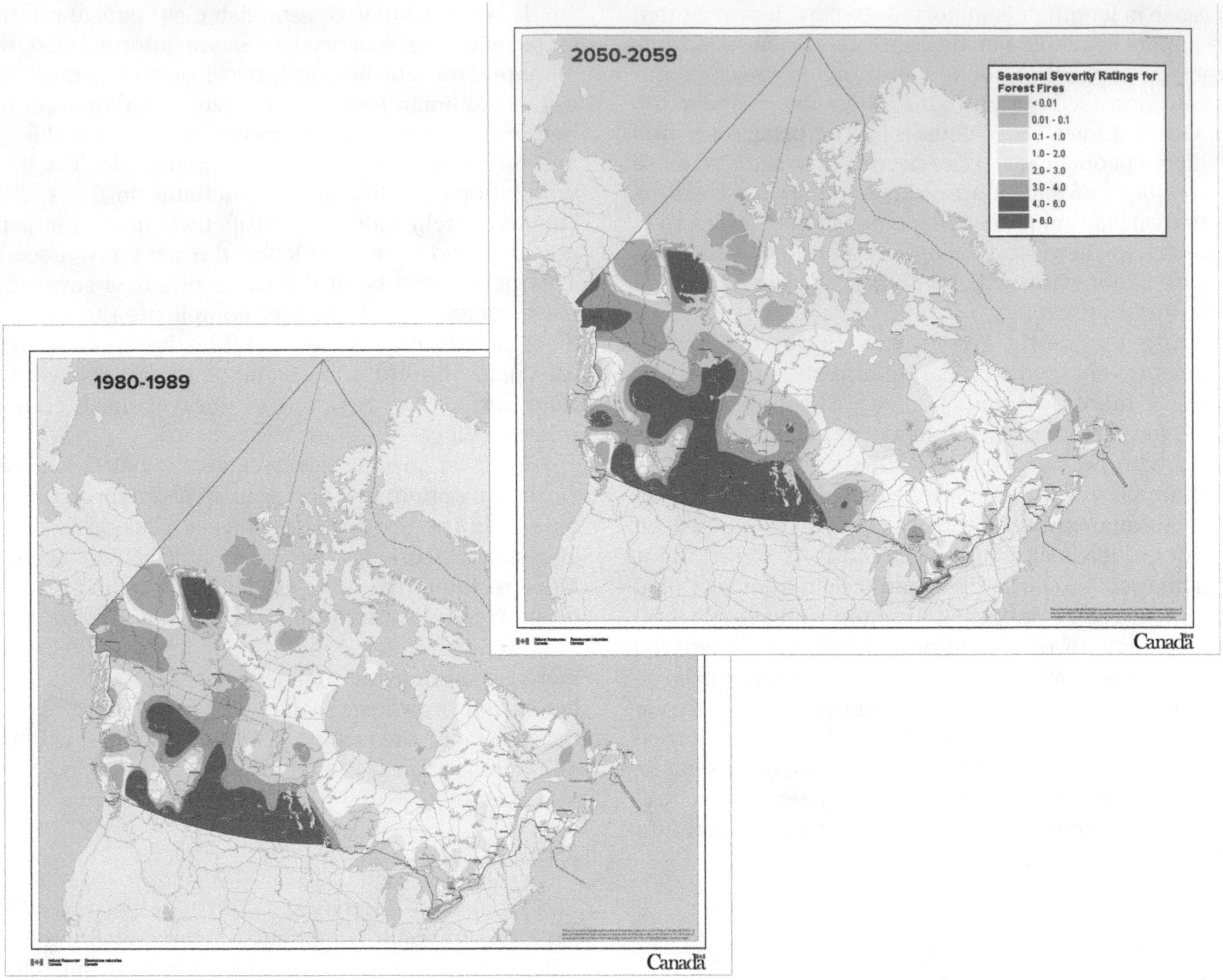

Figure 12.43

Forest fire seasonal severity levels; historical (1980–1989) and projected (2050–2059) data based on global generation circulation models. The seasonal severity levels are a measure of fire danger conditions for a complete fire season.

Source: The Atlas of Canada.

SUMMARY

- Fire is the rapid combination of oxygen with carbon, hydrogen, and other organic material in a reaction that produces flame, heat, and light. Fire is photosynthesis in reverse.
- Fire is a natural process that is essential to the health of many ecosystems, including Canada's forests. Fire recycles nutrients and plays a key role in the reproductive cycle of some plants.
- Combustion develops in three stages, which can occur simultaneously in different areas of a wildfire:
  1. In the preheating stage, water is expelled from wood, plants, or fossil fuels by flames, drought, or hot weather.
  2. In the flaming combustion stage, when temperatures exceed 325°C, wood breaks down and

gives off flammable gases. If oxygen is present, these gases can ignite and combustion begins. Released heat keeps the wood surface hot through conduction, radiation, and convection.

3. After the active flames pass, smouldering and glowing combustion slowly reduce the solid wood to ash.

- The spread of fire depends on:
  - the types of plants or fuel burned.
  - strong winds bringing oxygen and pushing flames forward. Intense fires create their own winds.
  - topography, which helps control plant distribution, and channels fire in preferential directions. A steep slope acts like a chimney that fire races up.
- Fire threats are greatest in areas with big contrasts between wet and dry seasons. A wet season triggers voluminous plant growth. Then dry conditions dehydrate plants, making it easier for ignition to occur.
- Given the type of vegetation and meteorological conditions, fire specialists use mathematical models to predict fire behaviour. Results are communicated to the public using a simple index that rates fire hazard as low, moderate, high, or extreme.
- Buildings can be constructed to withstand fire. Traditional structures can be made safer by eliminating flammable vegetation and woodpiles near them, avoiding wood-shingle roofs and overhanging wood balconies or decks, and using double-pane glass in windows and doors.
- Fires cannot be prevented, only deferred. Allowing natural fires to burn helps prevent build-ups of extensive debris that can fuel a firestorm.
- In Canada, a majority of forest fires are caused by people but lightning-caused fires, occurring mostly in remote areas where immediate remedial action is difficult, account for most of the area burned.
- Several climate-change scenarios predict that forest-fire activity will intensify in the future.

Terms to Remember

backfires
chaparral
combustion
duff
fire
firebrands
fire-danger rating
firestorms
fuel
fuel models
fuel-driven fires
ignition temperature
ladder fuels
photosynthesis
pyrolysis
slash
wind-driven fires

Questions for Review

1. How many forest fires occur in Canada each year and how much area do they burn on average?
2. Why do lightning-caused fires burn a disproportionate amount of the area burned by forest fires in Canada?
3. Write an equation to represent the chemical reaction that occurs when a fire burns woody material.
4. Compare fire to photosynthesis.
5. Explain the process of pyrolysis.
6. What is the difference between flaming combustion and glowing combustion?
7. Will a typical wildfire burn faster upslope or downslope? Why?
8. Explain how a wildfire can create its own winds.
9. Explain how to build a campfire. Explain the fire processes occurring at each stage of your campfire.

Questions for Further Thought

1. What difficulties are presented when duff catches fire?
2. Make a detailed list of actions you could take to make your current residence safer from fire.
3. If you were designing your dream house on your dream lot, what features could you incorporate into the house and landscape design to better protect your house from destruction by fire?
4. Evaluate the wisdom of quickly suppressing a local wildfire during a time of cold weather with low wind speeds.
5. Should homeowners in houses surrounded by flammable vegetation in wildlands pay the same fire insurance premiums as homeowners in the city?
6. Prescribed fire is sometimes used to reduce hazardous fuel build-ups but the smoke emitted bothers many people. Discuss how fire and forest managers might resolve such problems.

7. Suppose Canadian governments decided to sequester carbon in our forests. How might that affect forest-fire management and Canadian firefighters?
8. Should we aggressively promote the exploitation of the Canadian boreal forest and provide employment for northern communities, or should we leave the forests untouched and wait for fires to destroy them?

Interesting Websites

- Fire (under Forest Topics), Canadian Forest Service, Natural Resources Canada
  http://fire.cfs.nrcan.gc.ca
- Canadian Wildland Fire Information System
  http://cwfis.cfs.nrcan.gc.ca/home
- Canadian Interagency Forest Fire Centre
  www.ciffc.ca
- Current BC Forest Fire Info, Government of British Columbia
  www.bcforestfireinfo.gov.bc.ca
- Global Fire Monitoring Center
  www.fire.uni-freiburg.de

CHAPTER THIRTEEN

13

Mass Movements and Snow Avalanches

Rock bolts hold earth materials in place on a steep slope like giant thumbtacks, Kii Peninsula, Japan. This engineering work is part of remediation efforts following a debris flow. The Kii Peninsula, on the eastern shore of Japan, is exposed to typhoons. They bring with them heavy rain, which can trigger mass movements.
Source: Claire Samson.

Fall seven times and stand up eight.

—Japanese proverb

Outline

- The Role of Gravity
- External Conditions of Slope Instability
- Internal Conditions of Slope Instability
- Classification of Mass Movements
- Falls
- Slides
- Flows
- Complex Events
- Subsidence
- Snow Avalanches
- Mitigation
- Summary

LO1 Explain the various causes of mass movement, with an emphasis on the roles played by water and clay.

LO2 Classify mass movements.

LO3 Explain the various causes of snow avalanches, especially those related to snowpack conditions.

LO4 Distinguish the features of slab and point-release avalanches.

LO5 Give examples of several mitigation strategies against mass movements and snow avalanches.

Large volumes of material move downslope under the pull of gravity, and some do so catastrophically, as we will explore in this chapter. In Canada, major mass movements, displacing in excess of 1 million cubic metres of material—that is, a volume equivalent to 1000 m long by 100 m wide by 10 m deep—occur on average once every 10 years. In addition, thousands of smaller mass movements occur every year, most often in the spring and fall, highlighting the role of water as a contributing factor. Broad patterns can be identified on the first-ever landslide susceptibility map of Canada, recently compiled by Peter Bobrowsky and Maria Jose Dominguez of Natural Resources Canada (Figure 13.1). The authors integrated several variables, including slope angle, vegetation, precipitation, and geology, and expert opinions to define six susceptibility levels from 1 (lowest risk) to 6 (highest risk). As expected, the areas of highest risk are mountainous regions in British Columbia and Yukon. More surprisingly, the flat prairies show high landslide susceptibility levels. The risk there is linked to the presence of loose surficial sediments prone to movement, especially down river valleys. Another problematic group of surficial materials, **sensitive clays**, are responsible for high landslide susceptibility levels along the Saint-Lawrence River Valley (Figure 13.22). Overall, the Canadian Precambrian Shield is very stable.

Due to their high frequency, mass movements are Canada's most deadly and destructive geological hazard. Since confederation, more Canadians have died from mass movements than from all other natural hazards combined. Mass movements cost the Canadian economy between $200 million and $400 million annually. Snow avalanches are most frequent in the Rockies where they have a significant impact: the closure of the Trans-Canada Highway through mountain passes results in economic losses of $1 million per hour.

A large array of mitigation measures, however, is deployed against mass movements and snow avalanches to reduce risk, and this effort has been largely successful. The last disaster to make the "top ten" list of deadly mass movements and snow avalanches, the Saint-Jean-Vianney lateral spread, occurred in the 1970s (Table 13.1).

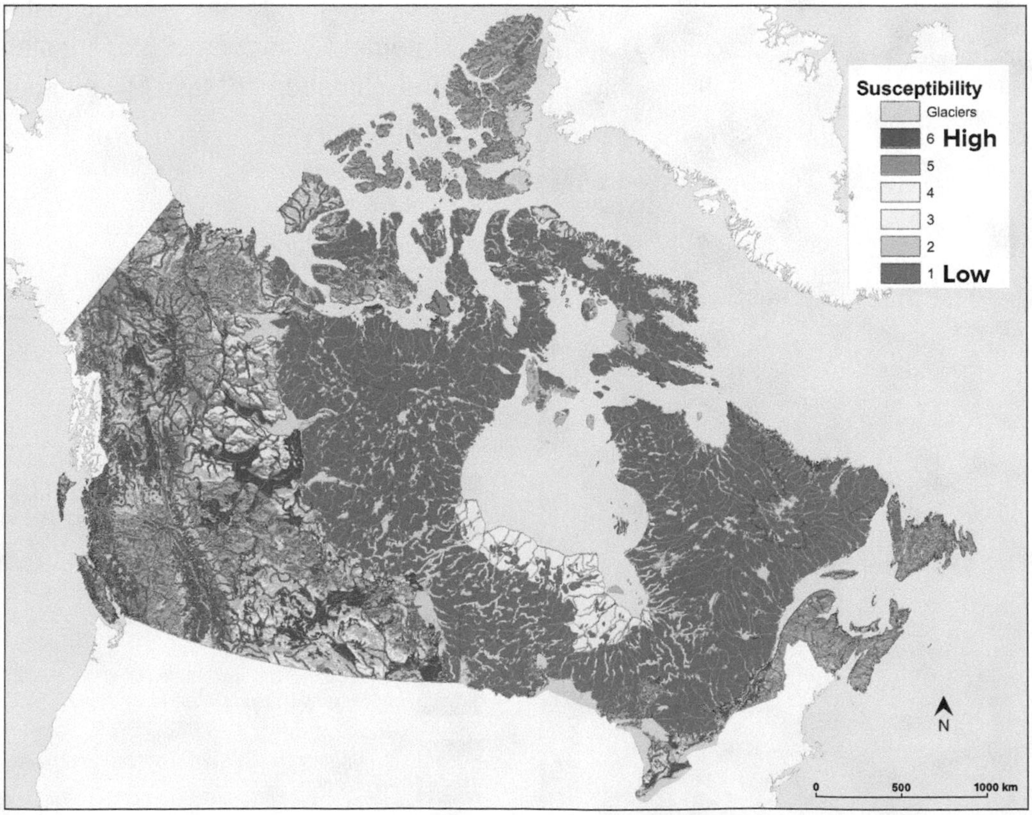

Figure 13.1
Landslide susceptibility map of Canada.
Source: Natural Resources Canada.

TABLE 13.1

Ten Deadliest Mass Movements and Snow Avalanches in Canada 1840–2013

Fatalities	Date	Event	Location
75	23 Apr 1903	Rock avalanche	Frank, AB
62	5 Mar 1910	Snow avalanche	Rogers Pass, BC
56	22 Mar 1915	Rock avalanche	Jane Camp, BC
50	19 Sep 1889	Rockfall	Quebec City, QC
35	6 Jul 1891	Debris flow	North Pacific Cannery, BC
33	26 Apr 1908	Lateral spread	Notre-Dame-de-la-Salette, QC
32	17 May 1841	Rockfall	Quebec City, QC
31	4 May 1971	Lateral spread	Saint-Jean-Vianney, QC
28	18 Nov 1911	Submarine mass movement and tsunami	Grand Banks, NF
26	18 Feb 1965	Snow avalanche	Grandduc Mine, BC

Source: Ten deadliest mass movements and snow avalanches in Canada 1840–2013, Atlas of Canada, reproduced with the permission.

LO1 The Role of Gravity

Gravity is relentless. It operates 24 hours a day, every day of the year. Given enough time, gravity would pull all the land into the seas. Over the great lengths of geological time, all slopes can fail; all slopes should be viewed as inherently unstable. Slope failures may be overpowering, catastrophic events, such as when the side of a mountain breaks loose and roars downhill. Or hill slopes may just quietly deform and yield to the unrelenting tug of gravity in the very slow-moving process known as creep.

Gravity pulls materials downslope with a force that can be measured in newtons (N). For example, consider a boulder with a mass of 1 kg resting upon a 30° slope (Figure 13.2). Gravity pulls the boulder toward the centre of the Earth with a force equal to the boulder's mass times the gravitational acceleration ($1 \text{ kg} \times 9.8 \text{ m/s}^2 = 9.8 \text{ N}$), but the ground is too solid to allow the boulder to move down vertically. Trigonometric relations allow the force acting on the boulder to be decomposed into a component parallel to the slope and a component perpendicular to the slope. The parallel component, the driving force, is directed downslope, toward open space. It is calculated as $9.8 \text{ N} \times \sin(30°) = 4.9 \text{ N}$. The perpendicular component is calculated as $9.8 \text{ N} \times \cos(30°) = 8.5 \text{ N}$. Before the boulder moves downhill its mass must overcome inertia and friction. Inertia is the tendency of a body to remain at rest until an external force is applied. **Friction** is the resistance to motion of a body that keeps it from moving over another body. Friction comes in large part from the roughness of surfaces that make sliding, flowing, or rolling difficult. The rough surface could be the ground or some weak rock layer at depth. All that is needed is some initial energy to overcome inertia and friction to begin the boulder's movement. Initial energy could come from an earthquake, a heavy rain, a bulldozer, or the footstep of a sheep.

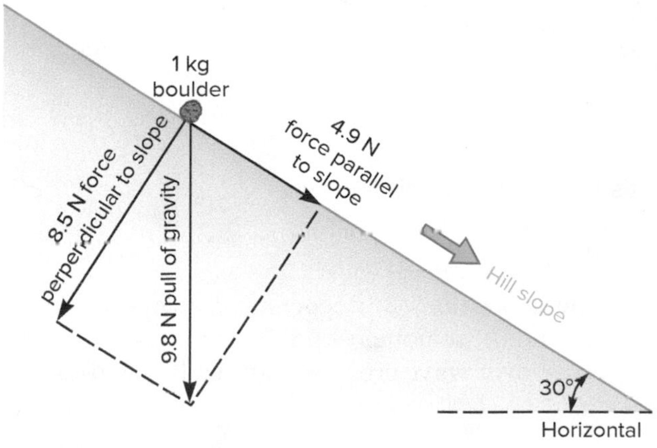

Figure 13.2
Gravitational forces acting on a 1 kg boulder sitting on a 30° slope.

In a typical mass movement, the centre of gravity of a portion of the land surface moves downward and outward (Figure 13.3). There is a tear-away zone upslope where material has pulled away and a pileup zone down-slope where material has accumulated.

External Conditions of Slope Instability

It is useful to distinguish between the underlying conditions of instability and the immediate causes of mass movements. The sum of all the underlying conditions

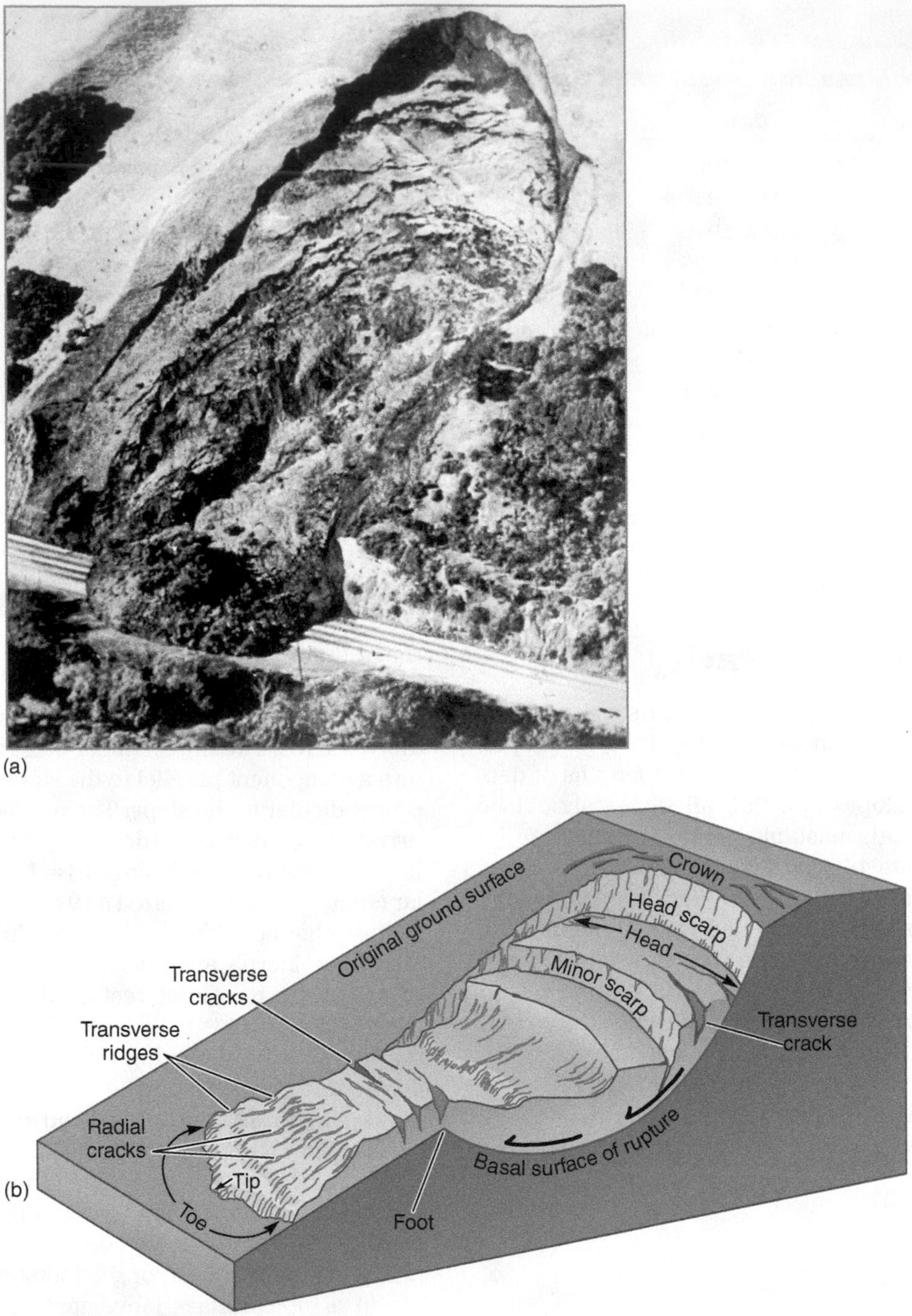

Figure 13.3
(a) Rotational slide showing downward-and-outward movement and (b) associated topographic features.
Source: © United States Geological Survey.

of instability can push a slope to the brink of failure, and then an immediate cause will trigger the movement. Common triggers for mass movements include heavy rains, earthquakes, thawing of frozen ground, and more and more frequently, the construction projects of humans.

External conditions that increase the odds of a slope failure include (1) adding mass high on a slope, as by sediment deposition, (2) steepening the slope, as by road cutting, and (3) removing support from low on a slope, as by stream or wave erosion (Figures 13.4 and 13.5).

WATER IN ITS EXTERNAL ROLES

Water plays many important roles in mass movements, both externally and internally. Rainfall is an external

Figure 13.4
Overhanging limestone block, Bruce Peninsula, Ontario. For several thousands of years following the end of the last glaciation, waves from Lake Huron have eroded the base of the block. Present-day water levels are several metres lower than they were at the time.
Source: © Claire Samson.

factor; rain falls from the atmosphere. Rain runoff causes external erosion that sets masses moving on slopes. It undercuts bases of slopes, causing hillsides to fail.

Water is also at work in the repeated, pounding action of waves along the shore, a main contributor to coastal erosion. In Atlantic Canada, rates of erosion are typically on the order of less than 1 m per year, although they can reach up to 10 m per year where the coast is composed of poorly consolidated earth materials (Figure 13.5). Historically, several islands off the coast of Nova Scotia have been lost to this process. The rises in sea level predicted by several climate change scenarios might exacerbate the problem in years to come.

Figure 13.5
The distinctive red sandstone of the north shore of Prince Edward Island is gradually being eroded away by wave action.
Source: © Claire Samson.

Rip currents can aggravate erosion locally. Rip currents develop when especially powerful waves bring water ashore. When too much water builds up near the shoreline, it will create a "channel" so it can flow back offshore, bringing with it a large quantity of sediments (Figure 13.6a). Rip currents can be narrow or as wide as hundreds of metres. They are common near human-built structures such as jetties and piers. These strong currents can flow up to 2.5 m/s.

Rip currents can be killers. Drowning deaths occur when people pulled offshore cannot stay afloat or swim out of the current (Figure 13.6b). Rip currents frequently form along seashores, but they also form in the Great Lakes. During the seven-year period from 2002 through 2008, the United States National Oceanic and Atmospheric Administration documented 61 deaths in the Great Lakes. Deaths occurred in Lakes Michigan (36), Erie (11), Superior (10), Huron (3), and Ontario (1).

Internal Conditions of Slope Instability

Beneath the surface, inside the materials underlying a slope, long-term processes are weakening the Earth and preparing it for failure. Internal conditions of slope instability include (1) the presence of clay, (2) water in different roles, (3) decreases in **cohesion**, and (4) adverse geological structures.

THE PRESENCE OF CLAY

The materials most commonly associated with earth failures are the **clay minerals**. Clays are the most abundant of all sediments. They form during **chemical weathering** when acidic fluids, such as CO_2-charged water and organic acids, decompose silicate minerals and form new atomic structures under conditions of low temperature and pressure. Clay crystals are very small. From a top view, they are nearly equidimensional (Figure 13.7a). But a side view shows a much thinner dimension that is split into even thinner subparallel sheets, like the pages in a book (Figure 13.7b). The book-like structure typically forms in the soil zone where water strips away elements, leaving many unfilled atomic positions in crystal structures. This is like building a Tinker Toy or Lego structure, then having a tremendous number of pieces removed. As clay minerals take in new elements and lose others, they increase and decrease in strength, they expand and contract, and they may absorb water and later have it removed. The changing conditions cause variations in the strength of clay minerals from month to month and year to year. At times when a hill containing clay minerals is weaker gravity has a better chance of provoking a slope failure.

(a)

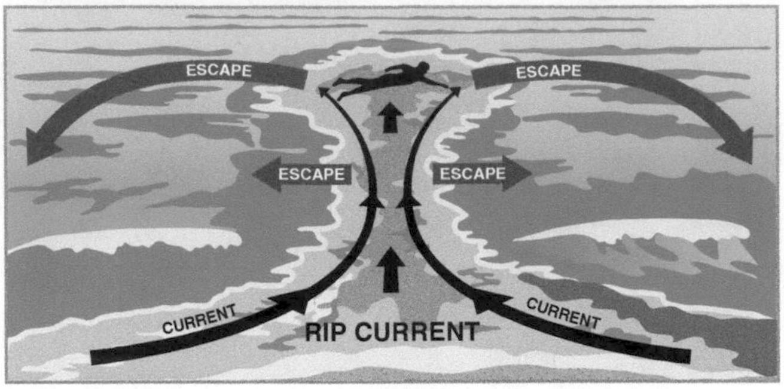

(b)

Figure 13.6
(a) A rip current forms as water pushed ashore by Hurricane Jeanne cuts through a beach sand bar and flows back to sea, September 2004. (b) Rip currents pull material away from the shore in a narrow corridor perpendicular to the coast. If you are caught in a rip current, swim parallel to the shore to escape.
Source: (a) Courtesy of National Weather Service, Melbourne, Florida; (b) Drawing from NOAA.

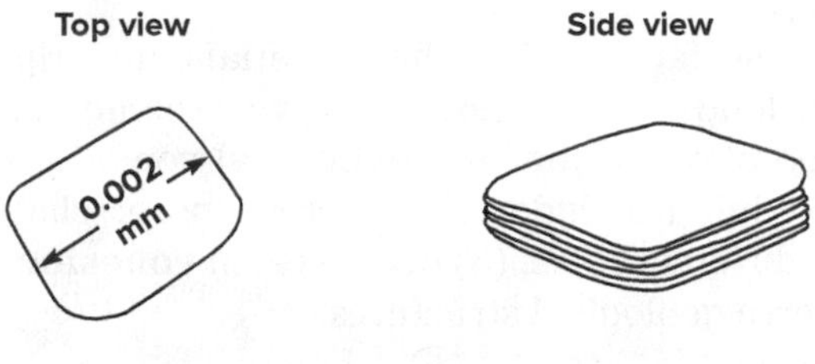

(a)

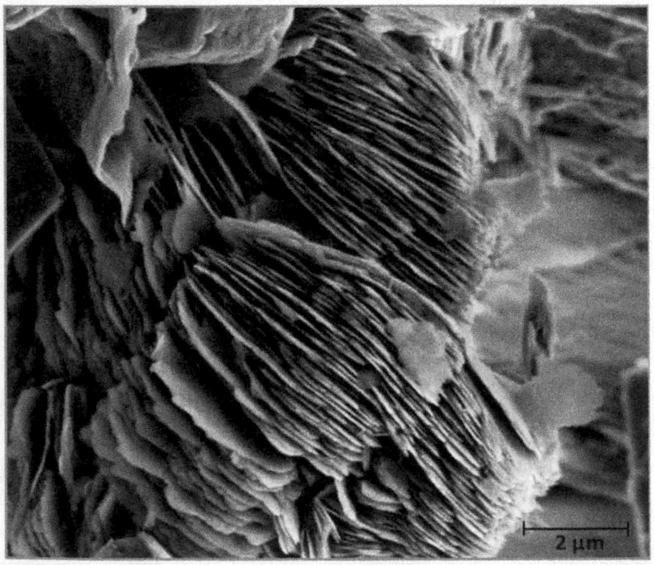

(b)

Figure 13.7
(a) Schematic views of the exceedingly small size and structure of a clay mineral. (b) Scanning electron microscope image of the book-like structure of kaolinite clay.

A spectacular type of mass movement, the **lateral spread**, is associated with sensitive clays, known also as "quick" clays. Sensitive clays begin as fine rock flour scoured off the landscape by massive glaciers and later deposited in nearby seas. The clay and silt sediments are assembled in a structure filled with water. Sea salts holds the solid components together as a weak solid (Figure 13.8a). When glaciers retreat, the Earth's surface rebounds (see Chapter 2), lifting these clay sediments above sea level where they become exposed to rain. Freshwater passing through the uplifted sediments dissolves and removes much of the sea salt "glue," leaving sensitive clay with (1) a weak dispersed structure, (2) grains mostly less than 0.002 mm in diameter, (3) water contents commonly in excess of 50% (Figure 13.8b). What has been solid earth can literally turn to liquid and flow away. To believe this, you really need to see it. Check out the video entitled "The Quick Clay Landslide at Rissa—1978" (1998, Norwegian Geotechnical Institute) at www.ngi.no/en/Areas-of-research-and-development/Soil-and-rock-slides/. It is mind boggling to watch solid earth suddenly turn to fluid and flow off, carrying houses with it.

WATER IN ITS INTERNAL ROLES

Water weakens earth materials in a variety of ways.

1. **Weight of Water:** Water is heavier than air. Sedimentary rocks commonly have porosities of 10 to 30%. If these void spaces are filled with water, the weights of materials are dramatically increased; thus, the driving forces acting upon slope materials are also increased and mass movements may begin.

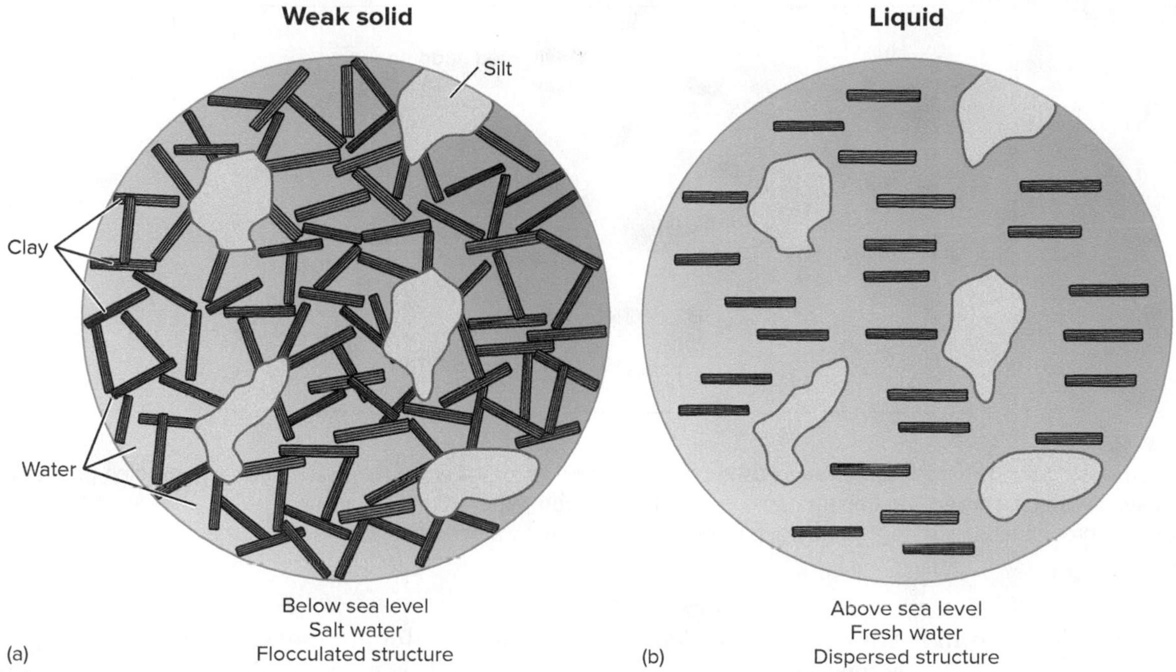

Figure 13.8
Sensitive clays. (a) In the flocculated structure, salt glues platy clay minerals together to form a weak solid. (b) In the dispersed structure, the clay minerals are suspended in water and the mix behaves as a liquid.

2. **Adsorption and Absorption by Clay Minerals:** The strength of a rock is usually governed by the 10 to 15% of material with the finest grain size, which is often the clay fraction. Clay minerals may have their strength lessened by water that is (1) adsorbed to the exterior of clays, thus spreading the grains apart, and (2) absorbed between the interlayer sheets, with resultant expansion. Water attaches easily to clay minerals because of its unique distribution of charges. Water is a molecule formed by two hydrogen (H^+) atoms linking up with one oxygen (O^-) atom. The two positive charges from the hydrogen atoms should cancel the two negative charges from the oxygen atom to create an uncharged or neutral molecule. But water is a bipolar molecule (Figure 8.10) with its hydrogen atoms on one side (the positive side) and its oxygen on the other side (the negative side). Since clay surfaces are negatively charged, water molecules tend to attach their positive sides to clay minerals (Figure 13.9).
3. **Cement Dissolution:** Water flowing through rocks can dissolve some of the minerals that bind the rock together. The removal of cement decreases the cohesion of rocks.
4. **Subsurface Erosion:** Water flowing underground can not only chemically dissolve minerals but also physically erode loose material. Subsurface erosion, also known as piping, can create extensive systems of caves (Figure 13.10). A network of caves obviously makes a hill weaker and is critical in the formation of sinkholes.
5. **Pore-Water Pressure:** As sediments pile up on the surface, their weight puts ever more pressure on sediments and pore water at depth. Sediment grains pack into smaller and smaller volumes, while water, which is nearly incompressible, simply stores built-up pressure. This effect has been referred to as a "hydraulic jack" that progressively "lifts up" sediment until the pull of gravity can start a massive failure. Many mass movements are due to abnormally high **pore-water pressures**.

   Quicksand occurs where sand grains are supersaturated with pressurized water. If water-pressurized sand is on a slope, it will flow away; but if it sits on a flat surface, water flows upward through it, helping lift the sand grains. The pull of gravity on the sand grains is effectively cancelled, leaving the sand with no strength or ability to

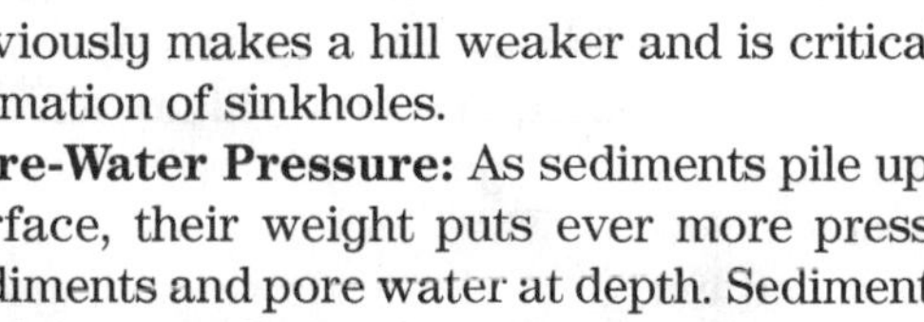

Figure 13.9
The positive side of water molecules attaches to the negatively charged surface of clay minerals.

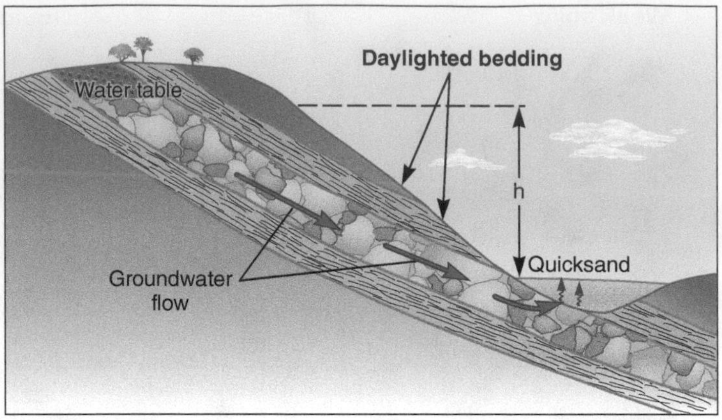

Figure 13.10
Schematic cross-section showing groundwater pushed by a high column of water (h) flowing through and eroding poorly consolidated rock sandwiched between two impermeable layers. This erosion will eventually create a network of caves. Water is reaching the surface through loose sands. The uplifting force of the escaping water equals the weight of the sand grains, thus creating quicksand.

carry a load (Figure 13.10). It becomes quicksand. Despite what some old movies show, quicksand does not suck people or other objects down. It is rather like stepping in a high-viscosity liquid. Stand there long enough and you will sink below the surface. What should you do if you get caught? If the water is not too deep, fall backward and spread your arms out; this distributes your weight broadly, like a boat on water, and you will not sink. If you can float on water, you surely will float on the denser quicksand. Then call to your companions to pull you out, or if alone, slowly slide your way backward, keeping your weight broadly distributed as you pull your legs from the quicksand's grasp.

6. **Water Table Height:** Rain, streams, and lakes all supply water to the subsurface. Gravity pulls surface water down to saturate open spaces in subsurface rocks with **groundwater**. A groundwater body is not a lake or pond-like volume of water. Instead it is water that invades fractures in rocks, pores between sand grains, voids left after shells are dissolved, and other holes. The top of the groundwater body is the **water table**. Below the water table is the saturated zone, and above is the unsaturated zone where groundwater is sparse. During droughts, water tables may drop hundreds of metres below the ground. During rainy intervals, the water table may reach the ground surface. The material close to the ground—**soil** or weathered **bedrock**—is more porous, so a rising water table results in proportionally more water in the near subsurface. This water acts as a lubricant, so there is an increased likelihood of mass movements.
7. **Congelifraction:** Water infiltrates fractures within rock. When liquid water changes to ice, its volume expands. Additional tension is applied on the fracture wedges, forcing them to open further. Repeated over several melting and freezing cycles, **congelifraction** can lead to the disintegration of rock.
8. **Stress-Relaxation Process:** When rocks are buried to depths of hundreds, thousands, and tens of thousands of metres, they are compressed into smaller volumes by the weight of the overlying materials. But this process also works in reverse. When deeply buried rocks are uncovered by erosion and exposed at the surface, the removal of great weight allows the compressed rocks to relax and expand. The expansion in volume produces fractures and increases in **porosity**. The stress-relaxation process reduces the strength of rocks, opening up passageways and storage places for water to attack and further weaken the rocks.

ADVERSE GEOLOGICAL STRUCTURES

Many hill slope masses are weak due to pre-existing geological conditions. For example, (1) rocks may be crumbly and not cemented together well, (2) a clay layer may provide a basal failure surface, (3) soft rock layers may slide off strong rock layers, (4) fractures may split and separate rock, or (5) an ancient fault may act as a failure surface.

Ancient failure surfaces are weaknesses that tend to be reused over time. When a mass first breaks loose and slides downslope, it tends to create a smooth, slick layer of ground-up materials beneath it. The slick layers become especially slippery when wet. It is wise to avoid building on these sites, but if building is necessary, then these slick surfaces need to be recognized, dug up, and destroyed.

The orientation of rock layering within a hill may create either a strong or a weak condition. Where rock layers are subparallel to the slope or where they dip at angles less than that of the hill slope, then the stage is set for slippage and mass movement (Figures 13.11 and 13.35). This condition is known as daylighted bedding because large cross sections of the ends of the shallow-dipping rock layers are exposed to daylight (Figure 13.10). Conversely, where rock layers dip into the hill at a steep angle, it is difficult for a slide to initiate and break free. The two situations are commonly observed on both sides of the same valley (Figure 13.11). On which side of the valley would you recommend selecting a building site?

Figure 13.11
Dipping layers create a less-stable condition on the side of the valley where they are subparallel to the slope than on the side where they are subperpendicular to the slope.
Source: © Claire Samson.

LO2 Classification of Mass Movements

Rate of movement and water content vary markedly in different types of **mass movements** (Figure 13.12). Slow-moving masses cause tremendous amounts of destruction and property damage, but rapidly moving masses not only destroy, but also kill. Rapidly moving mass movements have been responsible for large numbers of deaths worldwide (Table 13.2).

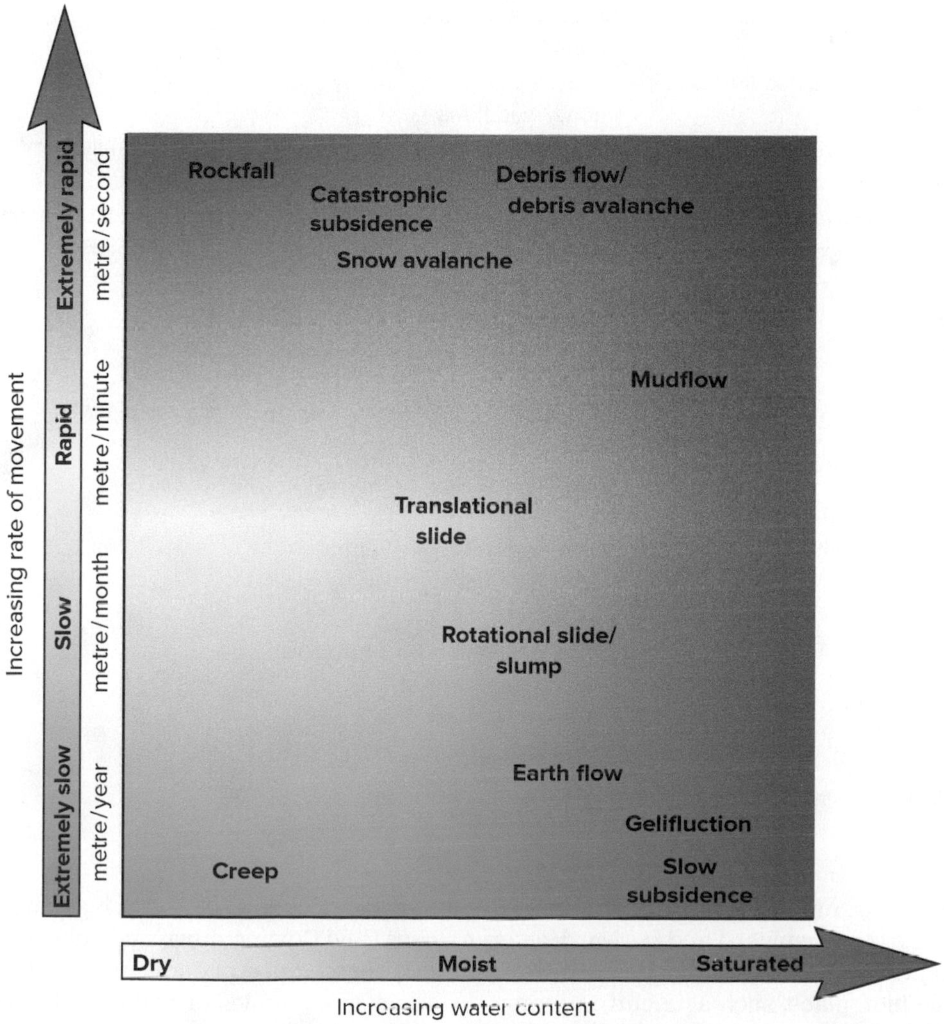

Figure 13.12
Rate of mass movement versus water content.

TABLE 13.2

Most Catastrophic Mass Movements, 1900–2013 (mass movements triggered by natural causes and involving 500 or more fatalities are included)

Date	Country	Event or Location	Type of Mass Movement	Trigger	Volume of Displaced Material or Area Affected	Fatalities
1919	Indonesia	Kalut	Lahars	Volcanic eruption	185 km^2	5110
1920	China	Haiyuan	Landslides	Earthquake	?	100000
1920	Mexico	Rio Huitzilapan	Debris flow	Earthquake	?	600–870
1921	Kazakhstan	Alma-Ata	Debris flow	Snowmelt	?	500
1933	China	Deixi	Landslides	Earthquake	150 million m^3	9300
1939	Japan	Mount Rokko	Slides, mudflows	Heavy rain	?	505
1941	Peru	Huaraz	Debris flow	Failure of moraine dam	10 million m^3	4000–6000
1949	Tadzhikistan	Khait	Rock slide	Earthquake	?	7200
1958	Japan	Kanogawa	Slides, debris/mud flows	Heavy rain	?	1094
1962	Peru	Nevados Huascaran	Complex event	?	13 million m^3	4000–5000
1966	Brazil	Rio de Janeiro	Slides, avalanches, debris/mud flows	Heavy rain	?	1000
1967	Brazil	Serra das Araras	Slides, avalanches, debris/mud flows	Heavy rain	?	17000
1970	Peru	Nevados Huascaran	Complex event	Earthquake	100 million m^3	18000
1985	Columbia	Nevado del Ruiz	Lahars	Volcanic eruption	?	23000
1987	Ecuador	Reventador	Landslides	Earthquake	75–110 million m^3	1000
1994	Columbia	Paez	Landslides	Earthquake	250 km^2	1971
1998	Honduras, Guatemala, Nicaragua, El Salvador	Hurricane Mitch	Landslides, debris flows	Hurricane	?	10000
1999	Venezuela	Vargas	Landslides, debris flows	Heavy rain	?	30000
2001	El Salvador	Las Colinas	Landslides, lateral spreads	Two earthquakes	?	585
2005	Pakistan, India	Kashmir	Complex event	Earthquake	>80 million m^3	25 500
2006	Philippines	Leyte	Rockslide, debris avalanche	Heavy rain	15 million m^3	1100
2008	China	Sichuan	Landslides, rock avalanches, debris flows	Earthquake	?	20000
2010	China	Gansu	Mud slides	Heavy rain	?	1765

Source: Modified from Schuster, 1996.

The main types of mass movement are downward, as in falling or subsiding, or downward and outward, as in sliding and flowing (Figure 13.13). Falling is downward from a topographic high place, such as a cliff or mountain, whereas subsiding is downward via collapse of the surface. Sliding occurs where a semi-coherent mass slips down and out on top of an underlying failure surface. Flowing occurs when a moving mass behaves like a viscous fluid flowing down and out over the countryside.

These types of movements will be examined in a series of examples of **falls** and **flows**, **slides** and **subsides**. Although in popular language mass movements are often described using the generic term "landslide," in geotechnical engineering, the term "slide" refers

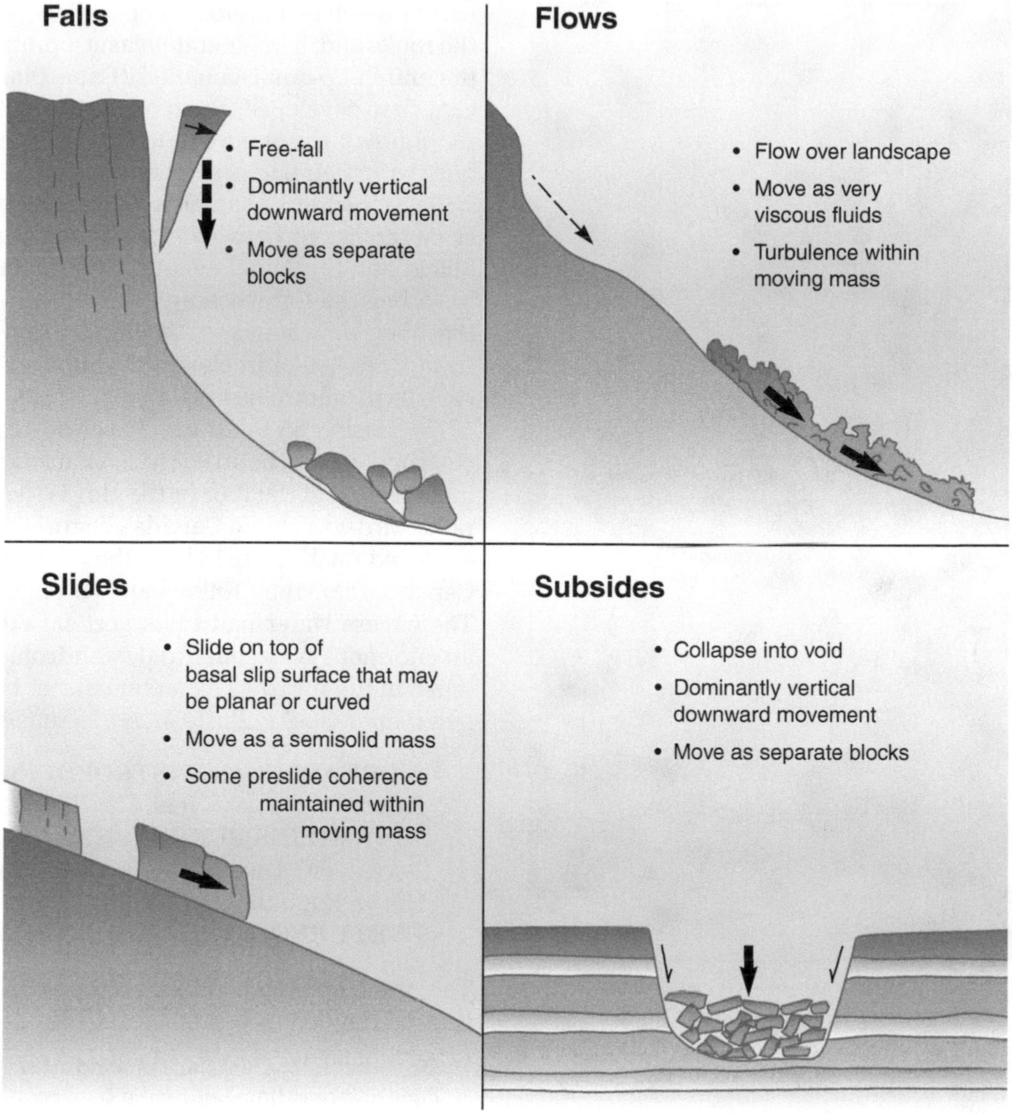

Figure 13.13
Classification of mass movements.

specifically to a mass movement associated with a more or less well-defined failure surface. In slides, there is limited deformation within the moving material, whereas in flows the material is thoroughly deformed during movement. In practice, mass movements often exhibit characteristics from two or more types. Those mass movements are classified as complex events.

Falls

Rock masses are commonly fractured in three nearly perpendicular directions (Figure 13.14). Each fracture is a weakness that separates a block of rock. Where vertical fractures are well developed, some blocks of rock might pivot forward about a fixed point near their base—not unlike giant dominoes—a rotational movement called **topple**. Falls occur when elevated rock masses separate along fractures, rock layers, or other weaknesses. When a mass detaches, it mostly falls downward through the air via free-fall and then, after hitting the ground, moves by bouncing and rolling. The most common triggers for falls—heavy rain and frost wedging—are related to the external roles of water. In mountainous regions, heavy rain and frost wedging combine to detach boulders from rock faces. Large chunks of rock fall to the base of the cliffs where they accumulate to form **talus slopes** (Figure 13.15).

1841 AND 1889 ROCKFALLS, QUEBEC CITY

Quebec City, founded in 1608, occupies a majestic location on top of a steep cliff, overlooking the St. Lawrence River where it narrows to a width of just over one kilometre. In fact, the name "Quebec" comes from the Algonquin word meaning "narrow strait." The

Figure 13.14
A block of sea-cliff sandstone gets ready to fall on Moonlight State Beach in Encinitas, California. Do you see the three mutually perpendicular fractures that allow this block to separate from the cliff?
Source: © Pat Abbott.

Figure 13.15
Arrow points to unstable material on steep talus slopes in Banff National Park.
Source: © Claire Samson.

early French explorers saw sparkling quartz crystals in the rocks and, in their enthusiasm, optimistically named the cliff "Cap-aux-Diamants" (Cape Diamond). Quebec City first developed along a narrow ribbon of land on the shore of the St. Lawrence River where houses were built with their backs right on the cliff.

The Cap-aux-Diamants is the result of the large-scale collision between the Precambrian Canadian Shield and the Appalachians. Sedimentary rock layers have been deformed so extremely by tectonic forces that they now stand vertically to form a cliff ranging from 60 to 100 m in elevation (Figure 13.16). This precarious geometry has resulted in 53 slope failures since 1775, causing 88 fatalities, 70 serious injuries, and the destruction of 20 houses. The 1.5 km long stretch of land immediately at the foot of the cliff is the deadliest natural hazard corridor in Canada's history. A major rockfall occurred on 17 May 1841 in the central portion of the Cap-aux-Diamants, following two days of heavy rain. The excess water had filled vertical crevices, causing an enormous rock mass to detach from the cliff and to crash in the narrow Champlain Street below. The local newspaper *Quebec Daily Mercury* ran as headlines:

> **A DREADFUL CATASTROPHE!**
> Fall of Rock Last Evening in Champlain Street.
> **30 FAMILIES BURIED BENEATH!**
> Seventeen Dwellings Crushed—Result of Late Heavy Rainfalls.
> **FORTY PEOPLE KILLED OR MISSING**

The newspaper also published the account of survivor George Hayden:

> Mr. George Hayden was standing near Mr. Berrigan's door for some time before the fatal rock descended. 'It is useless for us to deny,' said he last night, 'that we had not ample warning given us of a disaster. I was standing talking with poor Nolan and Farrell, who are now dead, and with Perry, when portions of the rock fell at intervals of about five minutes, first in small quantities, then more profusely. After the second slide occurred, I said it was time for us to move, and managed to get away. Nolan might have done the same, but ran into his house to call his wife.'

After the tragedy, the federal government bought and demolished several houses standing in particularly vulnerable locations. A retaining wall was built to hold back the rocks. Several crevices were filled with cement to prevent the infiltration of water. These measures proved insufficient.

On 19 September, 1889, after 12 hours of torrential rain, a major rockfall occurred only metres from the site of the 1841 failure. Several vertical crevices burst open as water exerted excess pressure on their walls. Tonnes of rock fell in Champlain Street, filling it with 10 m of rubble and flattening seven houses (Figure 13.17).

(a)

(b)

Figure 13.16

The south portion of the Cap-aux-Diamants is characterized by subvertical slivers of rock detaching along well-defined planar surfaces. (a) A temporary fence preventing falling rock from reaching the road has been replaced by (b) a permanent protective wall.

Source: (a), (b) © Claire Samson.

(a)

(b)

Figure 13.17

Site of the 1889 Quebec City rockfall. (a) Historical photograph by Louis-Prudent Vallée. (b) Current site stabilized using steel mesh.

Source: (a) Musée de la civilisation, fonds d'archives du Séminaire de Québec. Éboulis du Cap Diamant. Louis-Prudent Vallée, photographe. 1889. N° Ph1986-0014 (b) © Claire Samson.

The problem might have been exacerbated by the presence of a defective drain, which channelled water on a vulnerable point along the escarpment.

The engineer of the City of Quebec at the time, M.C. Baillargé, had studied the Cap-aux-Diamants extensively. His geological cross-section, published in 1893, clearly shows the vertical crevices—some of them 35 m deep and 1 m wide at the surface—and is still the reference today (Figure 13.18). Following the 1841 rockfall, Baillargé had recommended that an extensive series of buttresses be built at the base of the cliff, a recommendation rejected in favour of less-costly measures. Baillargé had also identified a particularly unstable zone along the Cap-aux-Diamants, precisely the area that failed in 1889. Today, it is the responsibility of each landowner to ensure that proper mitigation measures are taken (Figure 13.19). The City of Quebec grants as much as $80 000 to landowners undertaking stabilization work.

Figure 13.19
This combined car shelter and buttress on Sault-au-Matelot Street at the base of the escarpment provides extra support while respecting the style of Old Quebec City, a UNESCO World Heritage Site.
Source: Courtesy of Jacques Locat, Laval University.

Slides

Slides are movements above one or more failure surfaces (Figure 13.13). Failure surfaces are typically either (1) curved in a concave-upward sense in **rotational slides** or **slumps** or (2) nearly planar in **translational slides**. The slide mass maintains some degree of coherence as it moves down.

ROTATIONAL SLIDES

Rotational slides move on top of curved failure surfaces (Figure 13.3b), the head typically moving downward and rotating backward (Figure 13.20). Water falling or flowing onto the head of the slide mass ponds in the basin formed by the backward tilt. The trapped water

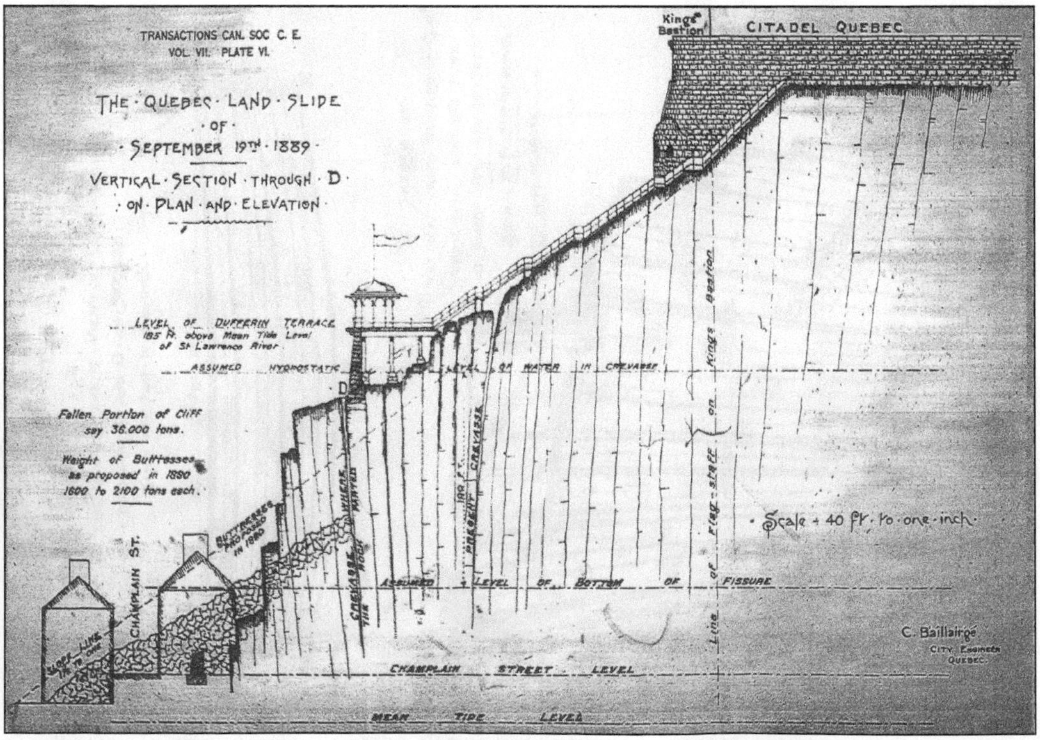

Figure 13.18
Structural cross-section of the 1889 rockfall site highlighting numerous vertical crevices.
Source: Used with permission of Canadian Society of Civil Engineering.

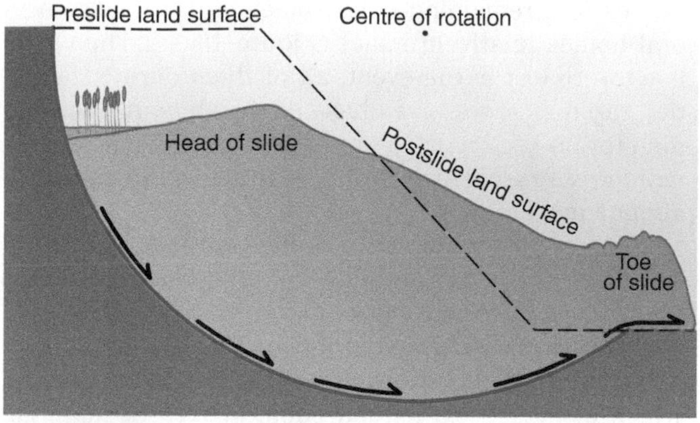

Figure 13.20

A rotational slide with movement around a centre of rotation. The basal failure surface (red line) can be approximated by setting one point of a pair of compasses at the centre of rotation and swinging an arc. Notice the backward-tilted head and bulged toe.

sinks down into the slump mass, causing more instability and movement. Because the scarp at the head of a slump is nearly vertical, it is unstable, thus setting the stage for further mass movement. The toe of a slump moves upward a short distance, riding out on top of the landscape.

TRANSLATIONAL SLIDES

In translational slides, masses move down and out by sliding on surfaces of weakness. Translational slide masses behave in different fashions: (1) They may remain basically coherent as block slides, (2) the sliding mass may deform and disintegrate to form a debris slide, or (3) lateral spreading may occur where the underlying material fails and flows, thus causing the overlying coherent material to break apart and move.

1971 Lateral Spread, Saint-Jean-Vianney, Quebec

The Ottawa and St. Lawrence River valleys have extensive deposits of sensitive clay, known locally as Leda clay (Figures 13.21 and 13.22). Leda clay formed in the Champlain Sea, a body of water that occupied the depression surrounding the massive glaciers present in the area during the last glaciation, between 13 000 and 10 000 years ago. When the glaciers retreated, the land rebounded and the Champlain Sea gradually shrank, leaving the marine clays exposed above the surface, vulnerable to leaching by rainwater.

Saint-Jean-Vianney was a suburban community of 1300 people living in modern bungalows, neatly aligned on a grid plan in the Saguenay region of Quebec.

Figure 13.21

Leda clay (light grey) and sand lenses (dark grey), Ottawa River Valley, Ontario. These beds are not in their original horizontal form, but have been folded by soft sediment deformation processes.

Source: Reproduced with the permission of Natural Resources Canada 2014, courtesy of the Geological Survey of Canada (Photo 2008-160).

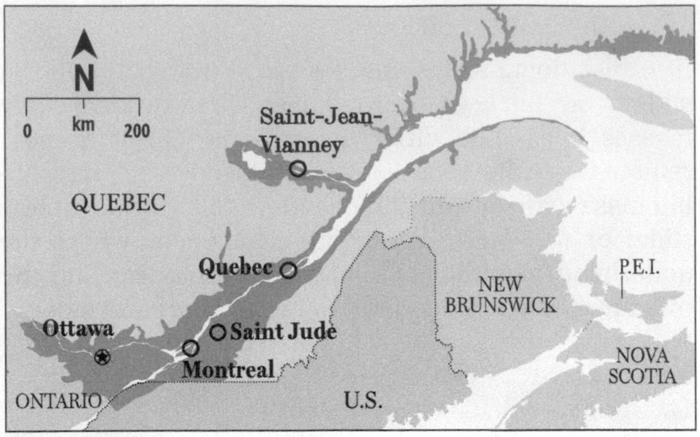

Figure 13.22
Location of Leda clay deposits.
Source: © Richard Johnson.

On 4 May 1971, late in the evening, hockey fans were in front of their television sets watching the playoff game between Montreal and Chicago when the ground opened beneath their feet.

The winter of 1970–1971 had brought a record snowfall to the St. Lawrence River Valley, spring melting had occurred rather slowly, and it had rained hard in April. All of this contributed to saturate a layer of sensitive clay in the subsurface. At 10:45 p.m., in a matter of minutes, the clay liquefied, losing all strength. The lateral spread started on the bank of a small creek, and progressed rapidly inland, in classical **retrogressive sliding** behaviour. The liquefied material dropped 30 m to form a canyon approximately 1500 m long by 400 m wide. Large rafts of earth material slid down into the depression, remaining coherent enough to carry several homes relatively intact (Figure 13.23). Thirty-one lives were lost in the event, all of them during the initial, rapid retrogressive phase of the slide. A man running for his life reported having to run on what seemed moving stairs, corresponding to a rate of movement of about 5 m/s.

The exact trigger of the Saint-Jean-Vianney lateral spread remains unclear, although some indications point to engineering work taking place to channel a small underground creek in the area. One thing is sure: aerial photographs show that the 1971 lateral spread, which displaced 7.6 million cubic metres of material, occurred within the scar of an earlier, much larger slide that moved 200 million cubic metres of material (Figure 13.24). The former lateral spread had probably been triggered by the 1663 Charlevoix earthquake (see Chapter 4). This crucial point had been overlooked by urban planners. Saint-Jean-Vianney is now abandoned. The federal government declared the site unfit for habitation, and all residents were relocated.

2010 Lateral Spread, Saint-Jude, Quebec

Mass movements do not have to be huge to be fatal. Late on 11 May 2010, a localized lateral spread swallowed the home of the Préfontaine-Charbonneau family, killing the parents and their two daughters (Figures 13.25 and 13.26). Although the volume of earth material displaced

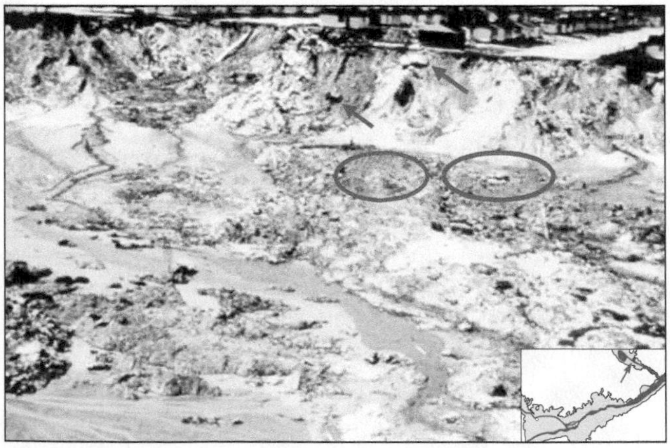

Figure 13.23
During the Saint-Jean-Vianney lateral spread, several homes (indicated by arrows and circles) slid on a semi-liquid mix of clay, snow, and water into a broad depression. Amazingly, a few of them remained structurally intact, having been carried on "rafts" of coherent material.
Source: Reproduced with the permission of Natural Resources Canada 2014, courtesy of the Atlas of Canada.

Figure 13.24
Aerial photos of Saint-Jean-Vianney, Quebec, dating from 1972. Compare the extents of the 1971 (blue) and 1663 (red) lateral spreads.
Source: National Air Photo Library, Centre for Topographic Information, Natural Resources Canada, Image A23076.

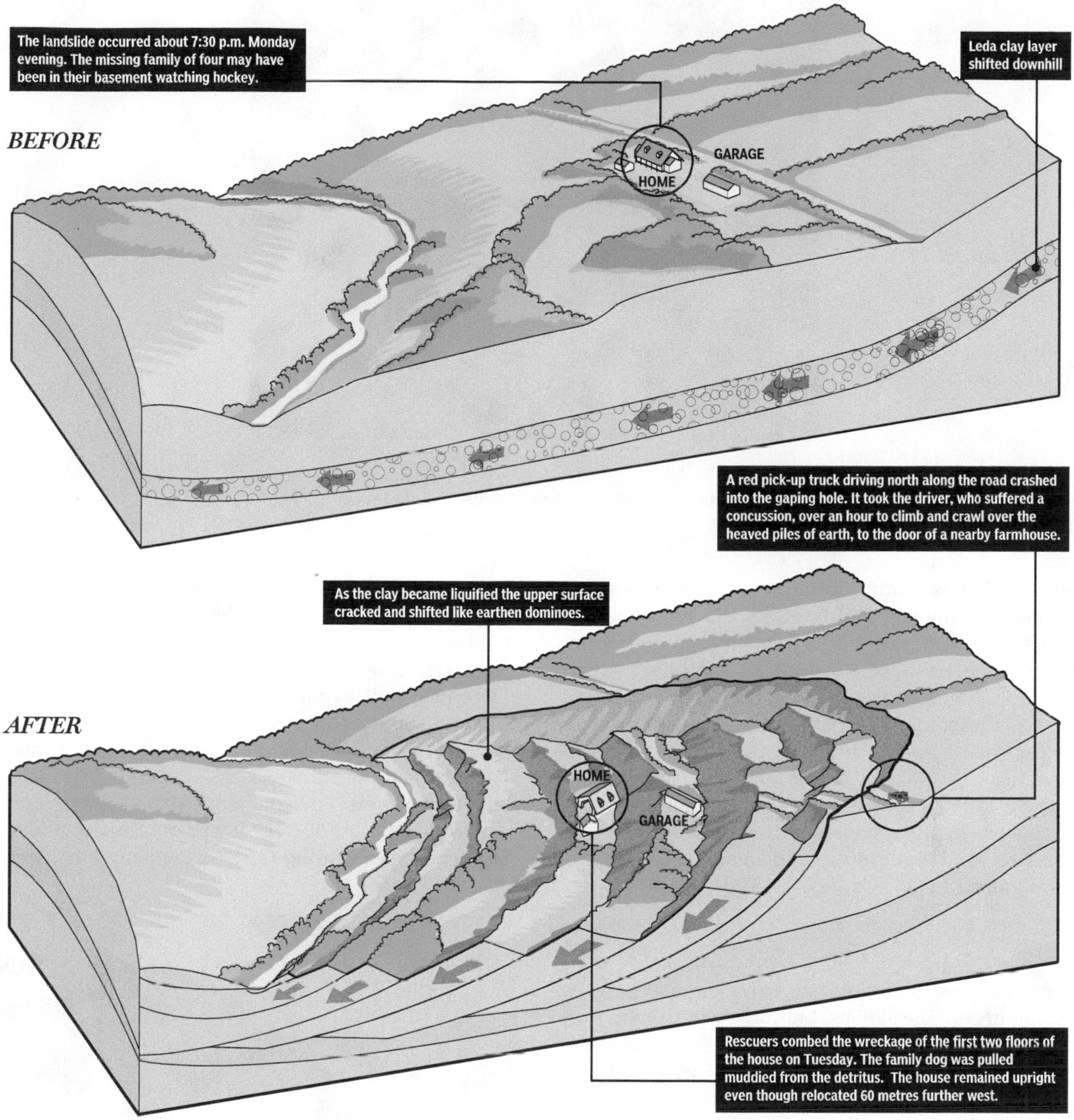

Figure 13.25
Anatomy of the 2010 Saint-Jude lateral disaster. A creek ran through the valley below the home, hinting that erosion might have played a major role in the disaster.
Source: © Richard Johnson.

at Saint-Jude (520 000 m^3) is much less than the volume displaced in Saint-Jean-Vianney in 1971 (7 600 000 m^3), there are chilling similarities between the two tragic events. In both cases victims were at home at night, watching a hockey playoff game, unaware of their external environment. Both mass movements occurred in the spring, when much water was present in the soil.

Flows

Flows are mass movements that behave like fluids. The materials within flows range from massive boulders to sand to clay to mixtures of them all. Water content varies from dry to wet and sloppy. The velocities of flows range from barely moving creep and gelifluction to

Figure 13.26
Wreck of the pickup truck that plunged into the depression created by the St-Jude lateral spread.
Source: THE CANADIAN PRESS/Graham Hughes.

speeds of 75 m/s. Within the moving masses, internal movements dominate, and failure surfaces are absent or short lived. Many names have been used to describe flows, on the basis of the type of material moving downslope (for example, mudflow) or according to particle size (for example, earthflow for fine soils; **debris flow** for coarse soils). However, all are characterized by fluid-like behaviour. Their classical morphology includes a starting zone where the initial failure occurs, a narrow track, and a widening runout zone where the moving material finally stops and accumulates, often in lobes (Figure 13.27).

CREEP

Gravity induces materials to move in many ways, including **creep**, the slowest but most widespread form of slope failure. Creep is an almost imperceptible downhill flow of the soil and uppermost bedrock zones. Creep is most commonly seen by its effects on objects, such as telephone poles and fences that lean downslope or trees whose trunks have deformed due to growing upward while rooted in material that is slipping downhill (Figure 13.28a). The soil zone slips in ultraslow movements as individual particles shift and move in response to gravity; the upper bedrock zone yields to the pull by curving downslope (Figure 13.28b).

By what mechanisms do soil and rock actually move? The volume of soil does not stay constant but instead expands and contracts. Several processes cause expansion. (1) Soil has a high percentage of void space or porosity. When water filling these pores freezes, it expands in volume by 9%, swelling the soil volume and lifting the ground surface upward. (2) When soil rich in expandable materials, such as some types of clay minerals, is wetted, it absorbs water and expands. (3) Heating by the Sun causes an increase in volume. Contraction occurs when soil (1) thaws, (2) dries, or (3) cools. Soil expands perpendicular to the ground surface and contracts vertically downward under the pull of gravity, causing a net downslope movement of particles (Figure 13.29).

In periglacial environments such as Arctic Canada, a particular type of soil creep, gelifluction, develops in **permafrost**. During the short summer, the first few

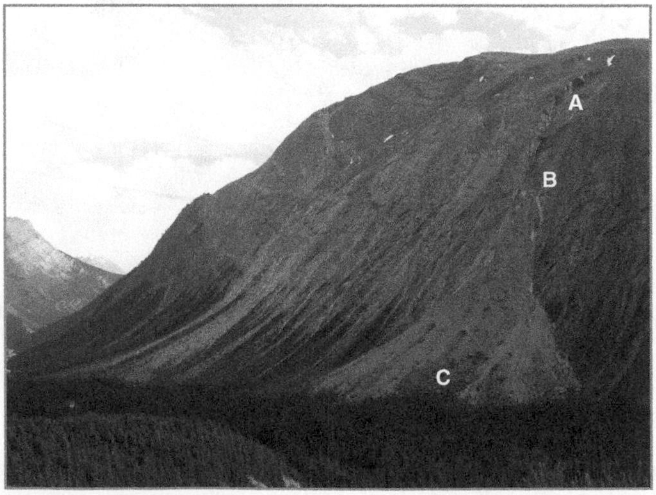

Figure 13.27
Rockslide and rock flow draping a mountain flank in Banff National Park. The failure was initiated as a slide (area A) and continued as a flow (areas B and C). A: starting zone, B: track, C: runout zone.
Source: © Claire Samson.

(a)

(b)

Figure 13.28
(a) Block diagram of a slope showing the effects of creep. Soil moves slowly, and bedrock deforms downhill. (b) Creep has deformed rock layers near Marathon, Texas.
Source: NOAA.

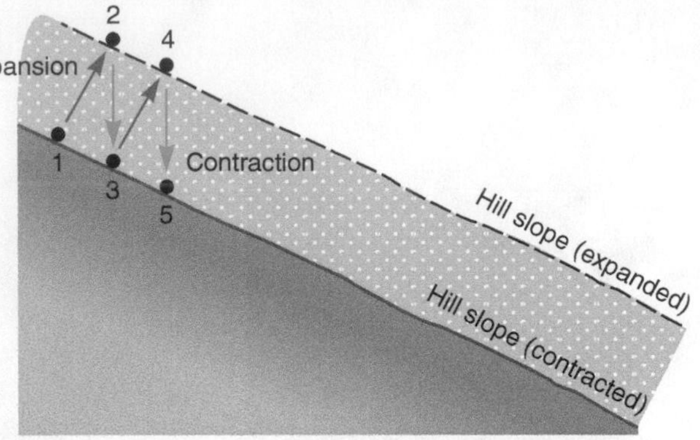

Figure 13.29
How creep works. Surface materials expand perpendicular to the hill slope (e.g., from point 1 to point 2). They contract (e.g., from point 2 to point 3) under the pull of gravity, which points toward the centre of the Earth. The result is a net downslope movement.

centimetres of permafrost melt. Unable to infiltrate the permanently frozen ground beneath, the excess water saturates surface sediments. These waterlogged sediments show little strength or cohesion. They tend to flow down even along barely perceptible slopes (Figure 13.30). Gelifluction is a slow process with typical rates of movement on the order of a few centimetres per year, and is unlikely to cause direct harm. Permafrost behaviour is nevertheless an important issue when designing infrastructure in northern regions.

STURZSTROMS

Mass movements with volumes in excess of 1 million cubic metres commonly travel long distances; some travel up to 25 times farther than their vertical fall. These long-runout flows, called **sturzstroms** (in German, *sturz* means "fall" and *strom* means "stream"), have been observed moving at rates up to 280 km/h, even running up and over sizable hills and ridges lying in their paths.

Figure 13.30
A dark band of water-saturated sediment slowly moves downhill by gelifluction toward a small lake (Lac de Gras, Northwest Territories).
Source: © Claire Samson.

1881 Elm Sturzstrom, Switzerland

With the advent of compulsory education in Europe in the nineteenth century, there arose a demand for **slate** boards to write on in classrooms. To help satisfy this need, some Swiss farmers near Elm became amateur miners, quarrying slate from the base of a nearby mountain. By 1876, an arcuate fissure formed about 360 m above their quarry, opening about 1.5 m wide. By early September 1881, the quarry had become a V-shaped notch about 180 m long and dug 60 m into the slope. At this time, the upslope fissure had opened to 30 m wide, and falling rocks were frequent and coupled with ominous noises coming from the large overhanging rock mass. These signs caused the miners to halt work. The inhabitants assumed the rock mass would fall down; but they did not think it would also flow up a steep slope and down their mountain valley to bury 115 of them. But it did.

On 11 September 1881, the Elm event unfolded as a drama in three acts: the fall, the jump, and the surges (Figure 13.31). Act 1, the fall, was described by Mr. Wyss, the Elm village teacher, from the window of his home:

> When the rock began to fall, the forest on the falling block moved like a herd of galloping sheep; the pines swirled in confusion. Then the whole mass suddenly sank.

Apparently, the formerly rigid mass of rock had already begun to disintegrate during its free fall. In act 2, the jump, the fallen mass hit the flat floor of the slate quarry, completely disintegrated, and then rebounded with a big jump forward, also described by teacher Wyss:

> Then I saw the rock mass jump away from the ledge. The lower part of the block was squeezed by the pressure of the rapidly falling upper part, disintegrated, and burst forth into the air . . . The debris mass shot with unbelievable speed northward toward the hamlet of Untertal and over and above the creek, for I could see the alder forest along the creek under the stream of shooting debris.

The bottom surface of the jumping mass was sharply defined. Eyewitnesses could see trees, houses, cattle, and fleeing people under the flying debris. The upper surface was not so sharply defined; it was a cloud of rocks and dust. Residents of Untertal who saw the jumping mass coming toward them ran uphill to save themselves. This turned out to be the wrong choice, as part of the flying debris hit their hill slope, fluidized, and flowed upslope 100 metres, overtaking and burying them. At the same time, some dogs and cows instinctively moved sideways, thus avoiding the debris flow.

In act 3, the surges, the disintegrated mass of rock was now fully in contact with the ground and flowed rapidly down the valley floor. Its motion was described by Kaspar Zentner, who barely eluded the flow:

> The debris mass did not jump, did not skip, nor did it fly in the air, but was pushed rapidly along the bottom like a torrential flood. The flow was a little higher at the front than in the rear, having a round and bulgy head, and the mass moved in a wave motion. All the debris within the stream rolled confusedly as if it was boiling, and the whole mass reminded me of boiling corn stew. The smoke and rumble was terrifying. I now ran breathlessly over the bridge and bent around the corner of Rudolf Rhyner's house. Then I turned back and held myself firmly against the house. Just as I went past the corner the whole mass shot right past me at a distance less than one metre away. The debris flow must have been at least four metres high. A single step had saved me. During the last jump I noticed that small stones were whirling around my legs like leaves in the wind. The house crunched, moved and seemed to be breaking apart. I fled on hands and knees through the garden until I got to the street. I was then safe. I had no pain anywhere and no stones had hit me. I did not feel any particular air pressure.

Although the moving mass at Elm looked and behaved like a "torrential flood" and a "boiling stew," it was not a watery mass but a dry one whose internal fluid was dust and air. Visitors who later viewed the mass of deposited debris remarked how similar its appearance was to a lava flow. The facts are these: a mass of broken rock with a volume of 10 million cubic metres dropped 600 m and then flowed 2.23 km as a dry mass moving at 180 km/h.

Movement of Sturzstroms

How do such large masses of debris move so far and so fast, and behave so much like a fluid? Numerous hypotheses have been proposed. (1) Some rely on water to provide lubrication and fluid-like flow, but some observed flows are masses of dry debris, as at Elm. (2) Other hypotheses invoke the generation of steam to liquefy and fluidize the moving mass, or (3) they call for frictional melting of material within the moving mass. Both ideas (2) and (3) fail because some long-runout deposits contain blocks of ice or lichen-encrusted boulders, showing that no great amount of internal heat was generated nor was internal friction ever at a very high level. (4) A popular hypothesis suggests the falling mass traps a volume of air beneath it and then rides partially supported on a carpet of trapped air that enables it to travel far and fast. This idea has never been verified and seems most unlikely. For example, after its early airborne jump, the Elm sturzstrom was described as being in contact with the ground, and in fact, it dug up pipes buried a metre below the surface. Additional problems for the air-cushioned flow hypothesis are deposits with identical flow features on the ocean floor, and on the Moon and Mars, where no or very little atmosphere is available.

So it appears that neither water, heat, nor a trapped cushion of air is necessary for a long-runout debris flow. A remarkable fact helps guide the formulation of another hypothesis. After the Elm mass fell, the hunks of debris stayed in their same relative position (Figure 13.31). How is this relationship to be explained? A provocative hypothesis involving acoustic energy within the moving mass has been proposed by U.S. geophysicist Jay Melosh. Apparently, an immense volume of falling debris produces much acoustical energy within its mass. The jostling and bumping back and forth of fragments produces acoustic (sound) energy that propagates as internal waves. The trapped acoustic waves may act to fluidize the rock debris, in a process called **acoustic fluidization**.

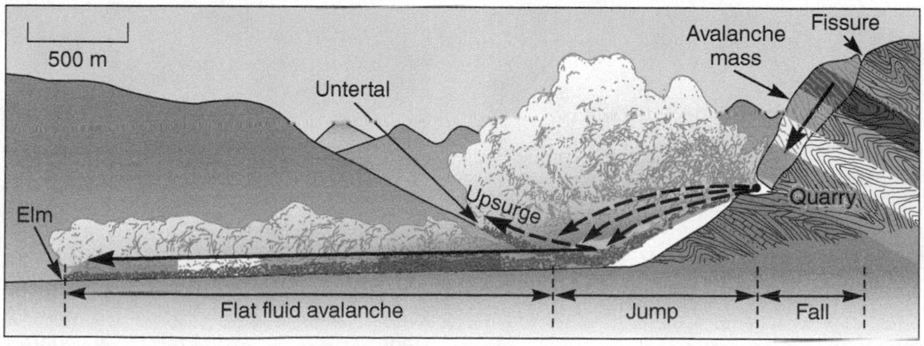

Figure 13.31
Cross-section of the 1881 Elm sturzstrom. The debris deposited on the valley floor maintained the same relative positions it had in the bedrock layers of the mountain.

Complex Events

Many mass movements involve combinations of topple, fall, slide, and flow at different times and places along their travel route, and are referred to as complex events.

DEBRIS AND ROCK AVALANCHES

Debris and rock avalanches form when a massive rockfall explodes on contact with a slope. They are a transitional type of mass movement, initiated as rockfalls and evolving into a rapid flow of material.

1903 Frank Slide, Alberta

The town of Frank, Alberta, occupied a beautiful site in the Crowsnest pass, near the Alberta–British Columbia border in the Rockies. The coal mining boom town had opened only in 1901, and had been promoted to investors as "the world's richest coal mine" and a metropolis-to-be. Frank boosted a population of 600 people, many of them young men attracted by the prospect of working at the mine for a handsome salary of $22 a week. Frank's place in history changed on 29 April 1903 when residents were startled at 4:10 a.m. by the noise coming down from Turtle Mountain (Figure 13.32). A 90-million-tonne mass of dipping limestone layers slid down their basal surface, dropped 1 km into the river valley, shattered, and then flowed 3 km across the valley and climbed 130 m up and over the terraced valley wall on the opposite side (Figure 13.33). The whole event lasted only 100 seconds, but it pulverized the southern end of town, killing about 75 people, including several families buried in their sleep. Fortunately, the colossal mass movement missed Frank's downtown area, where most residents lived, by a few hundred metres (Figure 13.34). Of the approximately 100 people living on the path of the slide, only 23 survived. Frank historians Monica Field and David McIntyre write:

> In the row of homes hit by the slide, fate determined who would live, and who would die. The Bansemer home was largely intact, and within it, Mrs. Bansemer and seven children were alive. (. . .) Alexander Leitch, his wife Rosemary and their four sons were killed, buried in the debris. But daughters Jessie and little Rosemary (May) survived. (. . .) Another daughter, baby Marion, was thrown through a window. Not seriously hurt, she was found on the rocks, surrounded by broken glass.

Eyewitnesses included the engineer of a train backing up to the coal mine when he heard the rock breaking high up on Turtle Mountain. He quickly switched to full speed ahead and chugged to safety as he watched miners at the loading dock sprinting for their lives only to be overrun and killed. The 17 miners who were working underground during the night shift felt a powerful air blast that knocked them off their feet and blew all the lights out. They soon realized that they were trapped underground in a precarious situation—the entrance of the mine being blocked by rocks and timber, and the lower mine tunnel rapidly filling with water. Their only option was to dig themselves out. Based on their extensive knowledge of the mine, they decided to follow a coal seam that they knew outcropped on the side of the mountain. After digging through six metres of coal and three metres of limestone, they all reached the surface safely, barely recognizing the landscape around them.

The Frank "slide" (technically, a debris avalanche) has held an enduring fascination for the general public.

Figure 13.32
A glider's view of the Frank slide. Glider pilots use the scarred Turtle Mountain as a landmark to orient themselves.
Source: Gerald Ince.

Figure 13.33
Debris covers approximately three square kilometres at the base of Turtle Mountain. The size of the boulders scattered at the base of attests to the violence and destruction of the rock avalanche.
Source: © Claire Samson.

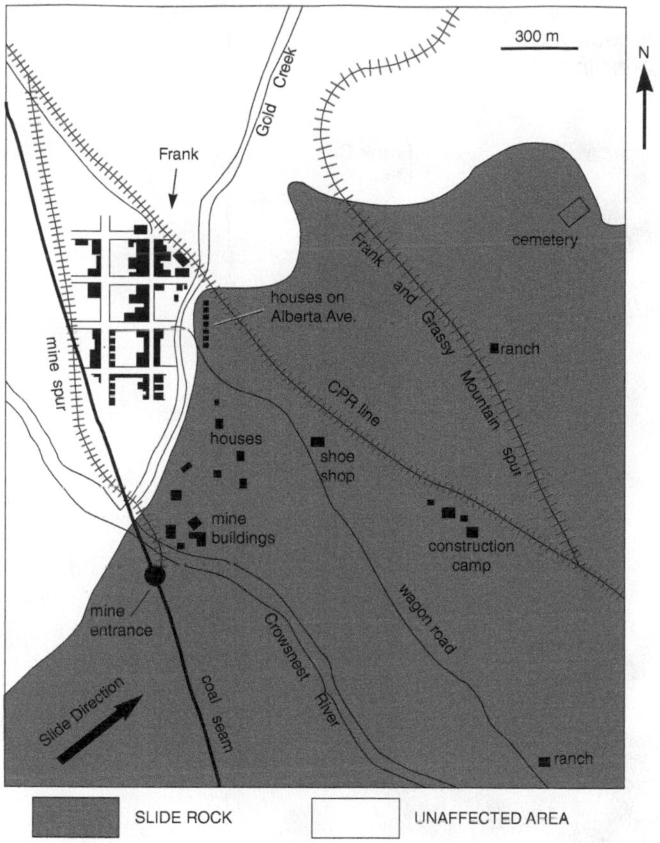

Figure 13.34

Map of the slide area in 1903. The town of New Frank has been rebuilt north of the railway line (not shown).

Source: Kerr, J.W. 1990. Frank Slide. Barker Pub. Ltd.

Several myths surround the event. Is it true that the safe of the local branch of the Union Bank of Canada (containing $500 000 in U.S. silver dollars ready for payday) still lies somewhere beneath the rubble? Did a First Nations chief really visit the Mayor of Frank the evening before the slide to warn him of the incoming danger? Historians know the first supposition is a myth: the bank, located downtown, was not damaged in the event. The second myth has some elements of truth: small pieces of rock fell regularly from Turtle Mountain. First Nations people called it "The Mountain That Moves." They would not camp beside it, and had warned residents about the potential danger. According to Field and McIntyre, First Nations people had certainly hiked to the summit where it is believed that a network of fissures was already in evidence.

Simple geological cross-sections provide clues to the causes of the tragedy (Figure 13.35). Turtle Mountain is an anticline, a hill formed by deformed layers of rocks folded in the form of an arch (think of the shape of capital letter "A"). The top of the mountain is made of very hard layered limestone whereas the base is made of soft shale and a coal seam. On the side of the mountain facing Frank, the limestone layers are oriented parallel to the slope, an adverse geological setting as we saw earlier in this chapter. The debris avalanche was triggered when rocks failed at the contact between layers, and dipping limestone blocks slid down their basal surface. Secondary causes point to water in its internal roles. They include the slow action of rain water infiltrating between layers, gradually dissolving the limestone, and dramatic changes in weather conditions—a quick freeze—the night of the event. In spring 1903, a very thick snowpack had accumulated on top of Turtle Mountain. A few days before the slide, a heat wave was melting it fast, filling fissures with water. The rapid freezing of that water into ice might have put extra pressure the fissures. Did mining activities play a role? On one hand, the mine was seismically active and miners had reported small tremors in the months leading to the slide (tremors are not uncommon in underground mines as the rock mass adjusts to changing stress (Figure 4.39)). On the other hand, the mine itself was left relatively intact after the slide. R.G. McConnell and R.W. Brock of the Geological Survey of Canada, mandated by the Department of the Interior to investigate the disaster offer a nuanced conclusion:

> The rock slide cannot, therefore, be considered as due to a single cause, but rather, like so many phenomena in nature, to a combination of causes, cumulative in their effects. The chief of these were the structure and condition of the mountain, aided by exceptional atmospheric and other natural conditions, and also, possibly, by slight readjustments in the lower strata attendant on mining operations.

The town of Frank has been relocated a short distance away and the debris avalanche site is now an organized tourist attraction with the Frank Slide Interpretive Centre, audiovisual program, and self-guided hiking trails.

1965 Hope Slide, British Columbia

In the early morning of 9 January 1965, four people in three vehicles were driving in the isolated Nicolum Valley, a few kilometres southeast of the village of Hope in British Columbia when a small snow avalanche blocked the highway. As people debated what course of action to take, a massive landslide engulfed them. In a few seconds, more than 46 million cubic metres of rock from the high mountain ridge forming the north side of the valley crashed down, filling up the valley floor with up to 70 m of debris. Water from the nearby Outram Lake was splashed violently onto the mountain wall on the opposite side of the valley and the lake was completely buried (Figure 13.36). Two of the victims were never found.

Local seismograph stations recorded the vibrations associated with the event. First, scientists assigned them to two minor earthquakes (at 11:56 and 14:59

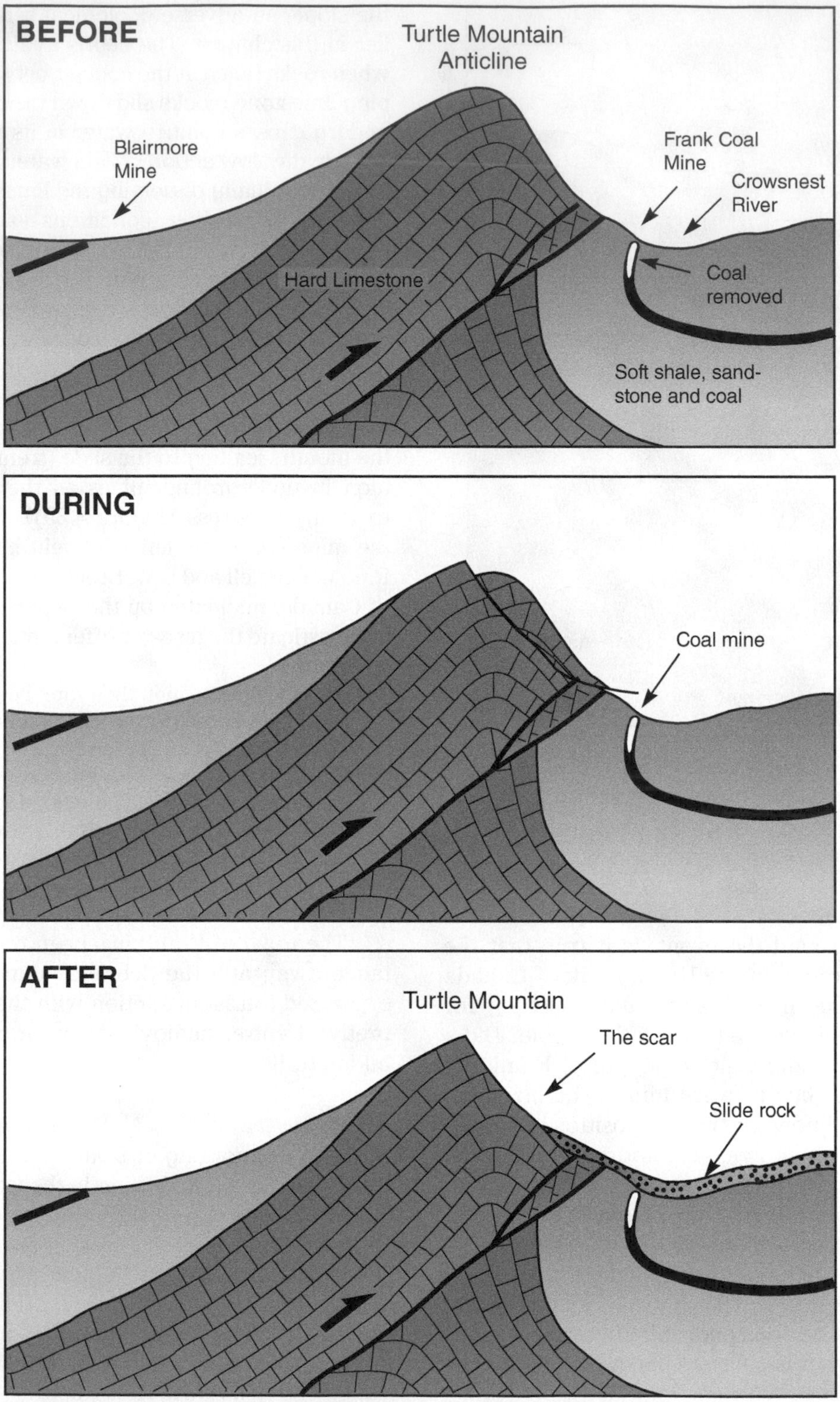

Figure 13.35
Geological cross-sections of Turtle Mountain before, during, and after the 1903 rock avalanche.
Source: Kerr, J.W. 1990. Frank Slide. Barker Pub. Ltd.

Universal Time), the second of which triggered the event. A re-examination of the data some 30 years later by Dieter Wiechert and co-investigators reversed the cause and the effect! They reinterpreted the seismic signals as the signatures of two mass movements, a small "precursor" landslide, followed three hours later by the main Hope slide.

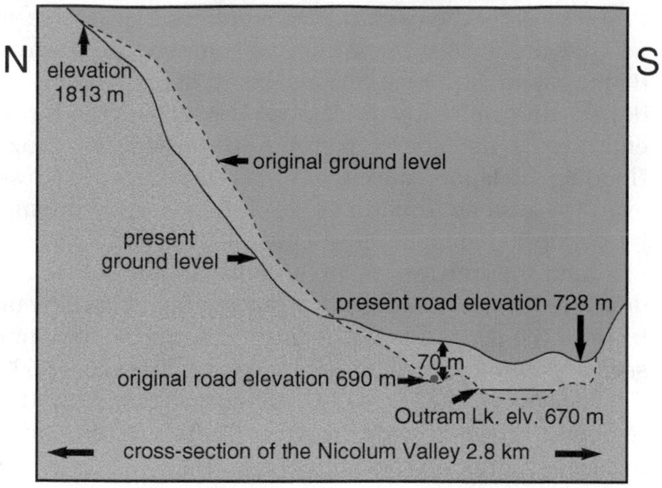

Figure 13.36
North-south cross-section through the Nicolum Valley at the Hope slide site, British Columbia.

Today, the site of the Hope slide looks amazingly fresh, with a large field of angular boulders scattered at the foot of Johnson Peak, a reminder of the briefness of the human experience in relation to geological processes (Figure 13.37). The Hope-Princeton highway has been rebuilt at an elevation 38 m higher than the original road.

Subsidence

In subsidence, the ground moves down (Figure 13.13). The surface either sags gently or drops catastrophically as voids in rocks close.

SLOW SUBSIDENCE

Although hardly an issue in Canada, in many areas of the world, the ground surface is slowly sinking as fluids are removed below the surface (Table 13.3). When water or oil are pumped up to the surface, the removal of fluid volume and the decrease in pore-fluid pressure cause rock grains to be crowded closer together; this results in subsidence of the ground surface.

TABLE 13.3

Cities Most Affected by Subsidence

City	Maximum Subsidence (m)	Area Affected (km^2)
Mexico City, Mexico	10	3 000
Tokyo, Japan	4.5	3 000
New Orleans, Louisiana	3	175
Houston, Texas	2.7	12 000
Shanghai, China	2.7	120
Taipei, Taiwan	1.9	130
Bangkok, Thailand	1	800
London, United Kingdom	0.3	300
Venice, Italy	0.3	150

Groundwater Withdrawal, Mexico City

The Valley of Mexico has been a major population centre for many centuries. People need water so the Aztecs, and later the Spanish, built aqueduct systems to bring water in from the surrounding mountains. In 1846, it became widely recognized that a large volume of groundwater lay beneath the city. The convenience of abundant freshwater lying underfoot led to drilling wells to make large withdrawals of underground water. But people are using more of the underground water each year than rainfall can resupply, so the land subsides. In the centre of the city the land sank about 10 m between 1846 and 1954. The city centre now lies lower than the level of nearby Lake Texcoco.

How can land subsidence be stopped? Stop pumping out groundwater. Can the land subsidence in Mexico City be reversed? No. Groundwater withdrawal is now banned in the city centre and has been moved to new wells in the north and south of the valley. Land subsidence of two to eight centimetres a year is now occurring in the new areas of groundwater withdrawal. Supplying the water needs of 20 million people is not easy in an area where the evaporation rate is greater than the precipitation rate.

Figure 13.37
Panoramic view of the Hope slide site, British Columbia.
Source: © James Hall.

Figure 13.38
Venice is built on the subsiding ground of a river delta. Notice how the former doorway has been bricked shut to keep out the sea.
Source: © MedioImages/Getty Images.

Long-Term Subsidence, Venice, Italy

Venice is one of the most improbable cities in the world. It began during the collapse of the Roman Empire in the fifth century CE when local people moved into marshes and islands in a malaria-ridden lagoon to gain some protection from invading armies from the north. The city is built on soft sediments that compact and sink under the weight of its buildings at the same time that the global sea level is rising. From 400 to 1900 CE, Venetians struggled to stay above water as the sea rose about 13 cm per century (Figure 13.38). They built up the islands using boatloads of imported sand and slowed the sinking of buildings by driving wood poles down into the sediment to make more stable foundations. In the twentieth century, the rate of sea level rise doubled to about 25 cm per century due in part to pumping up groundwater from the 1930s to the 1970s. Projections for the twenty-first century suggest the sea will rise another 50 cm. What can Venetians do to save their sinking city? One proposal is to spend billions of dollars to install movable floodgates across the three entrances to the lagoon to stop Adriatic seawater from flooding the lagoon during high tides and storms. However, these same floodgates would harm the economy by disrupting shipping and cause health problems by blocking the outflow of pollutants. Should Venetians do as their ancestors did and keep bringing in sediment to raise the ground level? A third proposal is to pump seawater or carbon dioxide into a sand mass lying 600 to 800 m below the city in an attempt to "pump up" the region by about 30 cm in 10 years. There is no easy and permanent solution for this sinking city.

CATASTROPHIC SUBSIDENCE

Most **limestone** formed in warm, shallow seas in the geological past by the accumulation and disintegration of shells and skeletons of organisms that remove calcium (Ca), carbon (C), and oxygen (O) from seawater to make their skeletal material of calcium carbonate ($CaCO_3$). Some other organisms build limestone directly as reefs. Today, limestones in several parts of the world have naturally acidic freshwater flowing through them, dissolving them and forming extensive networks of caves. During a drought or due to pumping, the removal of underground water creates voids, or spaces, in these caves. In turn, this can lead to the formation of **sinkholes** (Figure 13.39). Cover-subsidence sinkholes develop gradually when a near-surface sandy layer sags and fills the void. Cover-collapse sinkholes are more spectacular and dangerous! With no water left to provide support and hold up their roofs, they collapse catastrophically.

1981 Winter Park Sinkhole, Florida

Much of the Florida peninsula is underlain by limestone that is covered in most areas by 15 to 30 m of muddy sands. When the water table is lowered due to drought or by humans making excessive withdrawals by overpumping wells, caves in limestone may be drained of water. If the water is removed, the weakened caves may collapse (Figure 13.40). The risk is such that all counties in Florida have been mapped for sinkhole hazards.

On 8 May 1981, a small depression on the ground in Winter Park, Florida, grew to a 45 m diameter sinkhole within 15 hours. Before a week was up, the sinkhole was 100 m across and 34 m deep (Figure 13.41). The cover-collapse sinkhole claimed one house, several Porsches from a repair shop, and the deep end of the municipal swimming pool.

Figure 13.39

(a) Cover-subsidence and (b) cover-collapse sinkholes.

Source: www.sinkhole.org

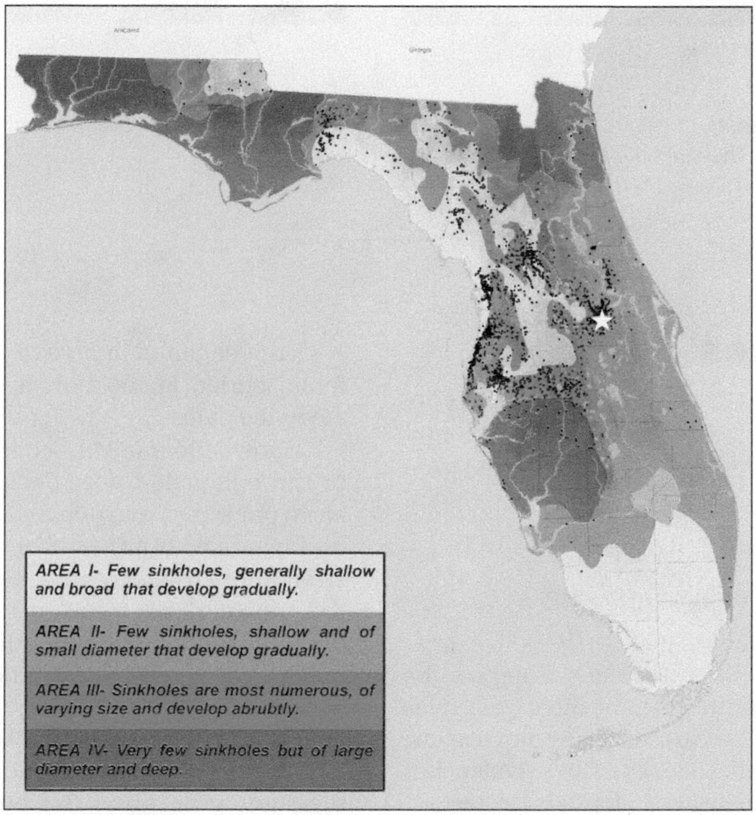

Figure 13.40

Areas of sinkhole occurrence, Florida. Cover-subsidence sinkholes develop in areas I, II and IV. Cover-collapse sinkholes develop in area II. The star indicates the location of the Winter Park sinkhole.

Source: Florida Center for Instructional Technology.

(a) (b)

Figure 13.41
The Winter Park sinkhole, then and now. (a) Aerial view, May 1981. Note the failed municipal swimming pool at bottom and the four-lane road on the left. (b) The sinkhole is now a tranquil circular pond.
Source: (a) © United States Geological Survey; (b) Claire Samson.

Snow Avalanches

Few things are more central to the Canadian way of life than snow. In fact, in the view of the French eighteenth-century writer Voltaire, Canada is simply reduced to "a few acres of snow. . ."

LO3

CAUSES OF SNOW AVALANCHES

Heavy snowfalls on steep slopes yield to the pull of gravity and fail, becoming snow avalanches. They can be understood using the same mass-movement principles for earth and rock. Just like earthen mass movements, snow avalanches creep, fall, slide, and flow. Avalanches begin in the starting zone where slopes are steepest (usually 30° to 45°) and then move downslope, commonly guided by topography along a narrow track, and finally come to a halt in the runout zone (slopes usually less than 20°) (compare Figure 13.27 and Figure 13.43). A victim engulfed in an avalanche is more likely to be found buried in the runout zone than anywhere else along the path.

Snow layers develop one by one, storm by storm, or through melt–freeze cycles. At any given time, the **snowpack** in a particular area is composed of several layers with different characteristics of thickness, strength, hardness, and density (Figure 13.44). Fresh, dry "powder" snow has a low density of 50 to 80 kg/m^3 and does not stick together in a ball. On the other hand, well-settled "old" snow can reach densities between 300 and 400 kg/m^3, and features strong bonds between the snow grains. Wet snow, which is typical of late-season snow, includes liquid water between the snow grains and can be of high density but low strength. Subtle differences in snow properties have been captured in the 31 words for "snow" used in Inuktitut. For example, *aqilluqqaaq* means "fresh and soggy snow," whereas *katakartanaq* is "crusty snow,

IN GREATER DEPTH

How to Create a Cave

Caves usually occur in limestone. The same equation that describes the formation of limestone also describes its dissolution into caves. The basic equilibrium equation is

$$Ca^{++} + 2HCO_3^{-} \rightleftharpoons CaCo_3 + H_2CO_3$$

where Ca^{++} is calcium ion, HCO_3^- is bicarbonate ion, $CaCO_3$ is limestone, and H_2CO_3 is **carbonic acid**. When the equation runs from left to right, limestone is precipitated. Droplet by droplet, this is the process that leads to the formation of exquisite stalagtites and stalagmites. When the equation runs from right to left, limestone is dissolved (Figure 13.42). The primary variable controlling whether limestone is precipitated or dissolved is the amount of carbonic acid present. The main variable controlling the concentration of carbonic acid is the amount of carbon dioxide (CO_2) in solution:

$$H_2O + CO_2 \rightleftharpoons H_2CO_3$$

If dissolved carbon dioxide content is high, the water is rich in carbonic acid and limestone is dissolved.

Figure 13.42
Dissolution has created a coarse honeycomb texture in the limestone of the Palisser formation at Canmore, Alberta. Rock climbers practise their skills on this rock face where voids are the perfect size (a few centimetres across) for anchoring hands and feet.
Source: Courtesy of Karin Michel.

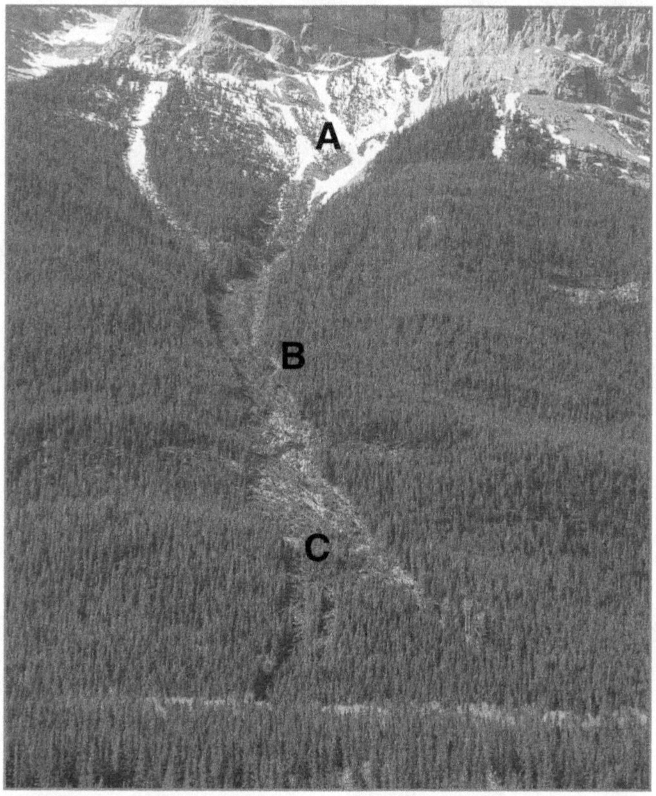

Figure 13.43
A recent avalanche has left its imprint on a mountain flank in Banff National Park. A: starting zone, B: track, C: runout zone.
Source: © Claire Samson.

broken by steps," and *pukak* refers to "dry snow crystals, like sugar powder."

The properties of the different snow layers change over time. A snowpack is commonly warmer than the surrounding air and colder than the ground, which causes the snow crystals within the snowpack to transform. New snow exhibits beautiful six-sided crystals (Figure 13.45a). As the crystals age, they metamorphose and become more rounded, more densely packed, and more cohesive (Figure 13.45b). This process causes the snowpack to settle and become stronger. In very cold weather, water vapour rising from the warmer ground and lower snow layers is deposited through deposition (see the diagram of the different states of water in Figure 8.9) onto the snow and ice grains, and forms depth hoar crystals at the base of the snowpack. In clear, cold, and calm weather conditions, water vapour from the atmosphere can be deposited on the snow surface, also forming hoar crystals. Hoar is characterized by relatively large crystals and low strength (Figure 13.46).

Most avalanches occur naturally during or soon after snow storms, with the 24 hours following a heavy snowstorm being the most critical. Avalanches commonly initiate on steep slopes when snowfall builds to 0.5 to 1.5 m thick. But snow thicknesses can reach

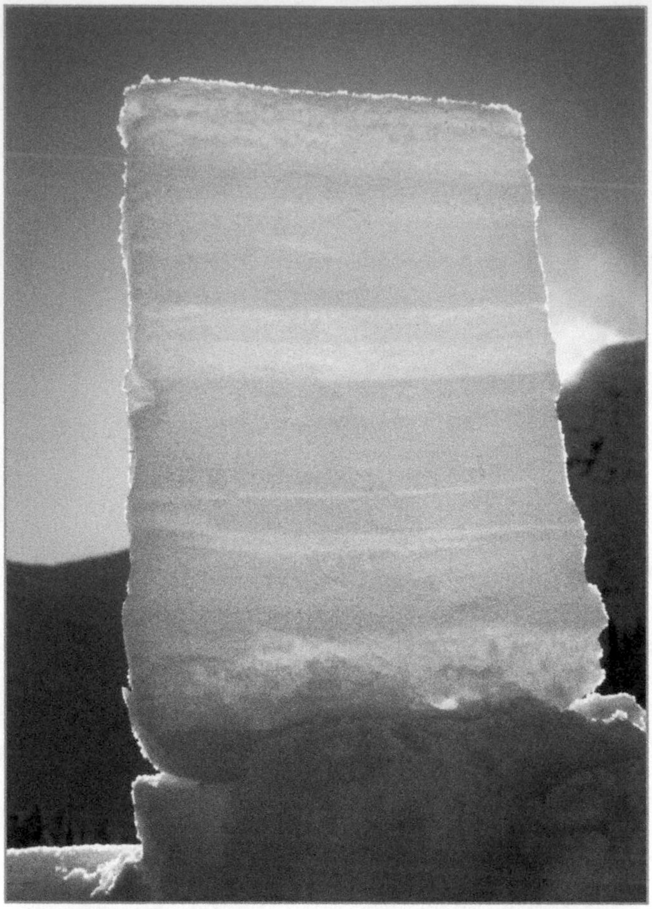

Figure 13.44
A heterogeneous snowpack. Weak layers are less dense and more transparent than adjacent layers.
Source: © Jim Bay.

(a)

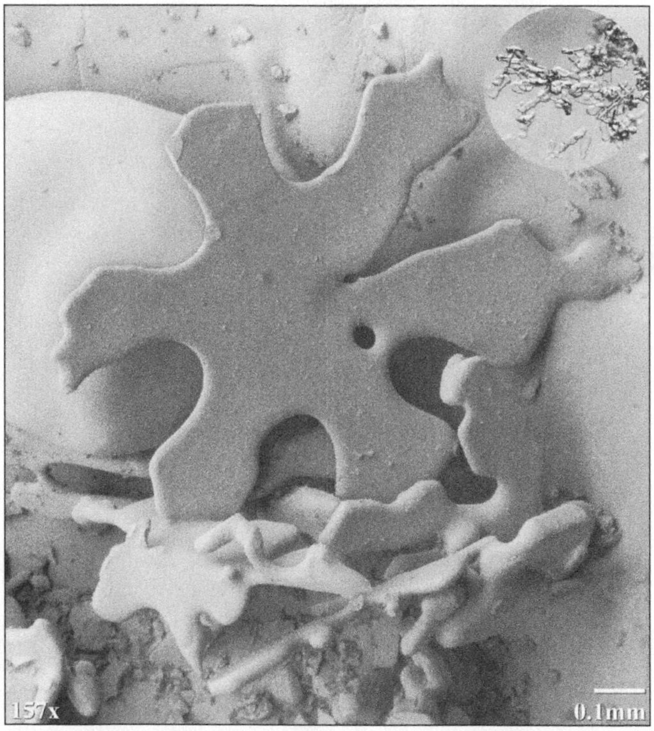

(b)

Figure 13.45
Electron microscope images of (a) fresh and (b) aging snow crystals.
Source: United States Department of Agriculture, Beltsville Agricultural Research Center.

Figure 13.46
Feather-shaped hoar crystals.
Source: Bruce Jamieson, Civil Engineering Department, University of Calgary.

2 to 5 m before failing in big avalanches that can be devastating. Why does snow sometimes build into thick masses on steep slopes? It depends on the internal structure of the snowpack. Conditions of decreasing stability include the presence of weak layers within the snowpack and the orientation of the slope with respect to the dominant wind direction or the sun. On downwind (lee) slopes, the wind decelerates and dumps snow, and can contribute to the formation of precariously suspended cornices.

1910 Snow Avalanche, Rogers Pass, British Columbia

Rogers Pass is surrounded by the rugged beauty of the Selkirk Mountains in Glacier National Park, British Columbia. The pass is a major transportation corridor through the Rockies, and includes the routes of the Canadian Pacific Railway and Trans-Canada Highway.

Since the opening of the pass by the Canadian Pacific Railway in 1884, the area had been plagued by numerous snow avalanches. Snow-removal technology at the time included a steam locomotive fitted with a huge rotary plough on the front, backed up by the efforts of a "shovel gang," a team of men equipped with shovels, saws, and picks. On the evening of 4 March 1910, under the light of lanterns, a group of night workers were busy removing the seven metres of hard-packed snow an avalanche from Cheops Mountain had dumped on the tracks a few hours before. A second avalanche, from the ominously named Avalanche Mountain located on the opposite side of the pass, caught them in action. Of the party of 63 men, only one survived. Historical photographs have captured the violence of the event and the frenzy of the rescue operation (Figures 13.47 and 13.48). By midday the following day, 600 people were digging in the snow and rubble, and 58 bodies had been recovered. The bodies of the four remaining victims were found in the spring when the snow melted.

This tragedy brought to 250 the number of people killed in avalanches in Rogers Pass since the construction of the railway. The avalanche of 4 March 1910 was to be the last major disaster in the area. It prompted the redesign of the railway route and the construction of the Connaught Tunnel, which opened in 1916.

Figure 13.47
The 1910 Rogers Pass avalanche overturned this 150 tonne locomotive.
Source: Image D-00188 courtesy of Royal BC Museum, BC Archives.

Figure 13.48
Rescue party digging in snow and rubble on 5 March 1910 in Rogers Pass.
Source: Image D-00186 courtesy of Royal British Columbia Museum, BC Archives.

LO4

TYPES OF SNOW AVALANCHES

Avalanches vary from the size-1 **sluff** to very large, size-5 events that can destroy a village or flatten a forest (Figure 13.49). They move at rates ranging from barely advancing to measured speeds of 225 km/h. Their travel distance varies from only a few metres

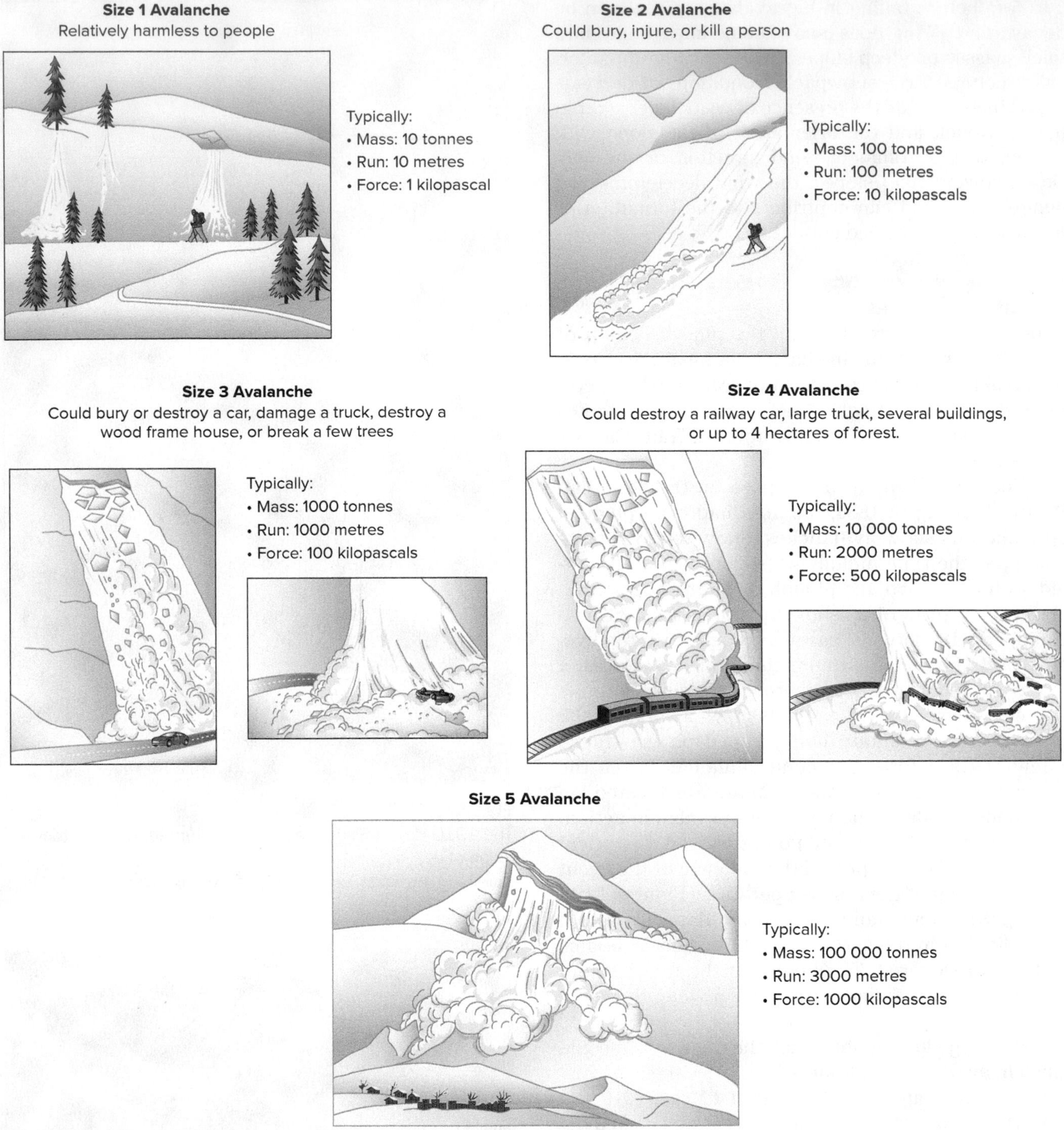

Figure 13.49

Avalanche sizes.

Source: Canadian Avalanche Association.

Figure 13.50
A classic inverted "V" shaped loose-powder avalanche.
Source: © Jim Bay.

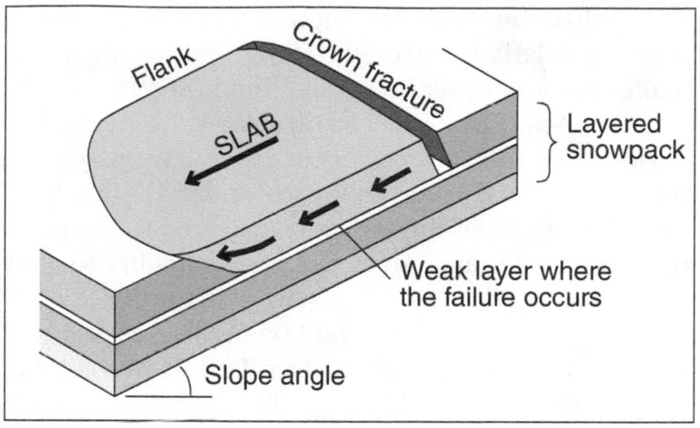

Figure 13.51
Development of a slab avalanche.
Source: Reproduced with the permission of Natural Resources Canada 2014, courtesy of the Geological Survey of Canada (Bulletin 548).

to several kilometres. For example, an avalanche of about 765 000 m^3 was unleashed down the slopes of Mount Sanford in Alaska on 12 April 1981; it dropped over 3 km and flowed for 13 km, including running up and over a 900 m high ridge.

The types of avalanches vary, depending on snow cohesion. Two main types are *loose-powder avalanches* (flows) and *slab avalanches* (slides).

Loose, powdery snow has a low amount of cohesion. A loose-powder avalanche typically fails at a single point and develops in an inverted "V" shape. It triggers more and more snow into moving during its downhill run and spreads out laterally (Figure 13.50). The speed of loose-powder avalanches is approximately 65–100 km/h.

Slab avalanches involve the breaking free of slabs of cohesive snow from their poorly anchored base (Figure 13.51). The failures are analogous to translational slides, where an upper mass breaks free and slides down and out on top of a layer beneath it. Slabs initially move in a gliding motion and then typically break up and turn into turbulent flows during their downslope movement (Figure 13.52). Slab avalanches

Figure 13.52
A slab avalanche is triggered by a downhill skier. Notice the vertical cracks at the head, the broad area of rupture, and the moving slabs.
Source: United States Forest Service/USGS.

occur when the stress/strength relationship between a slab of relatively stronger snow and an underlying weaker layer is upset by sudden load (heavy snowfall, skiers, snowmobiles, etc.) or by solar warming or local melting. The failure may occur in two ways. (1) The underlying weak layer collapses under the load, and when the weight of the slab is transferred to the perimeter, the cracks appear and the slab begins to move downhill. (2) The overlying slab is disturbed and the perimeter is breached at some point. The existing tension in the cohesive slab causes failure propagation, then the weak underlying layer fails, allowing the slab to move. Slab conditions can develop when a layer of firm wind-deposited snow is added on top of light, low-density snow, or a dense layer of snow sits on a smooth melt–freeze crust or surface hoar. Slab avalanches are the most dangerous avalanches. They move at speeds between 30 and 65 km/h, slower than loose-powder avalanches, but usually carry wet, heavy snow with enough momentum to hit hard.

AVALANCHE SAFETY

In the last decades, the trend in the number of fatalities per year related to snow avalanches has definitely been upward but so has the number of people enjoying the mountains, as we commented in Chapter 1 (Figure 13.53). A 21-year review, covering 1994 to 2005, by Jeff Boyd and co-workers showed that recreationists form the great majority of victims and that most of those who die die of asphyxiation (Figure 13.54). For shallow burials in 1.5 m of snow or less, the survival rate is 50% for a 30-minute burial and a mere 15% for a 2-hour burial. With all due respect to St. Bernard dogs, an icon of alpine mountain rescue, there have been no reports of avalanche victims found alive by specially trained dogs in Canada. The dogs simply cannot reach the scene quickly enough.

The challenge for Canadian society is to reduce risk while encouraging people to engage in mountain sports and promote local tourism. Established in 2004,

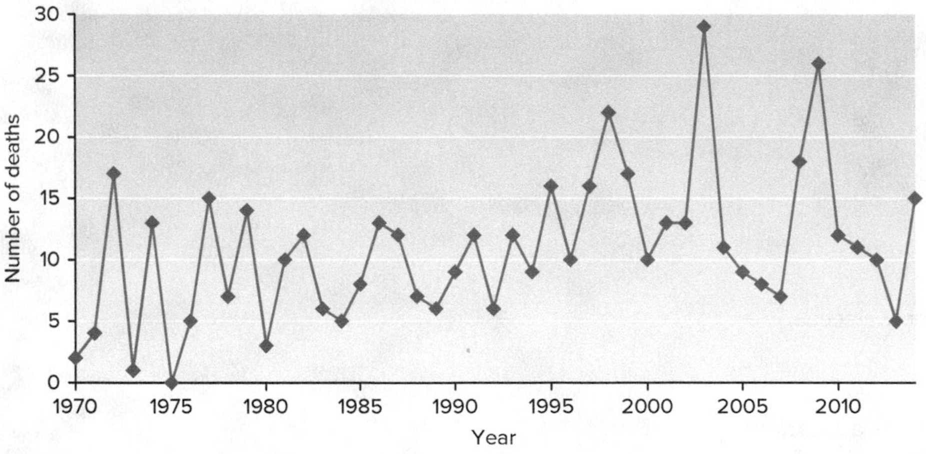

Figure 13.53
Deaths due to snow avalanches in Canada, 1970–2014.
Source: Data from Canadian Avalanche Association.

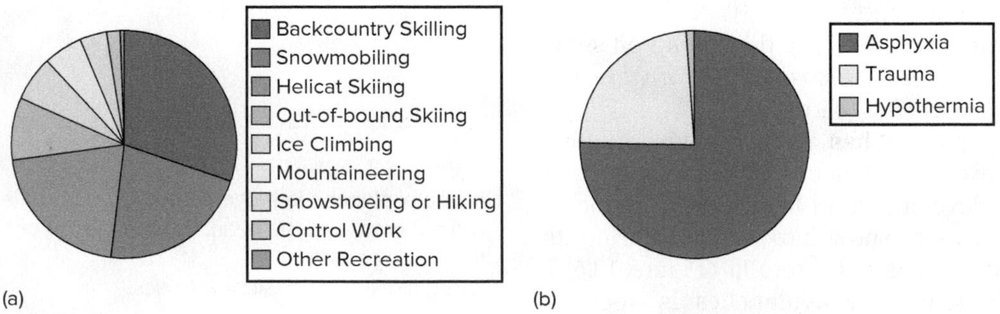

Figure 13.54
Characteristics of avalanche victims in Canada (1994–2005). (a) Activity groups. (b) Causes of death.
Source: Data from Boyd, J., Haegeli, P., Abu-Laban, R.B., Shuster, M., and Butt, J.C. 2009. Patterns of death among avalanche fatalities: A 21-year review. Canadian Medical Association Journal 180(5): 507-512.

the Canadian Avalanche Centre, headquartered in Revelstoke, British Columbia, is Canada's national public avalanche safety organization. The Centre and its partners issue avalanche forecast bulletins for 16 areas in the Rockies and the Haute-Gaspésie in Québec. Avalanche forecasting is based on observations of recent avalanches, assessments of snowpack stability, and weather conditions. Bulletins include colour-coded forecasts of avalanche danger, based on the international avalanche danger scale (Figure 13.55), and travel advisories. The best mitigation strategy in the back country remains avoidance. Closer to population centres, in the vicinity of winter sport resorts, for example, active measures might be necessary. Such measures include the use of explosive charges and artillery shells to artificially induce small avalanches and thus prevent the accumulation of threatening masses of snow in unstable areas.

Although isolated incidents can occur anywhere in Canada where there is a dangerous mix of steep topography and abundant snowfalls (see the case history of Kangiqsualujjuaq in Chapter 1), avalanche risk is highest in the Rockies. In recent years, prominent signage has been installed along the main thoroughfares in the area to keep motorists vigilant (Figure 13.56). No stops are allowed in known avalanche corridors. Similar signs inform skiers in risky areas (Figure 13.57).

Several new products are available on the market for personal protection. One interesting device is a flexible breathing tube and mouthpiece attached near the user's face and connected to a small hollow chamber strapped to the chest. The device, which resembles a snorkel, can allow a buried victim to breathe snow-free air and, via a system of valves, separates the exhaled from the inhaled air, reducing the risk of asphyxiation. Another recent development is the avalanche flotation bag system that includes a compressed air cylinder. The bag is incorporated into a backpack system, much like a parachute or an airbag in a car. It inflates by pulling a ripcord and provides buoyancy, assisting the person to remain on or near the snow surface (Figure 13.58). This is an important point since only 5 to 10% of victims survive being buried in more than 1.5 m of snow. These airbag/flotation-pack systems are very effective and have been widely adopted by snowmobilers. They are still somewhat cumbersome to wear for skiers but continue to improve, and their use is increasing. Organizations such as ski resorts and Parks Canada have procured systems based on a technology similar to that used in retailing against shop lifting. Reflective tags are attached to ski boots, jackets or tickets. These tags can reflect the signal emitted by a specialized "detector" unit, even through several metres of snow, and guide the searcher to the buried person.

Danger	Description	Travel Suggestions
LOW	Natural avalanches very unlikely. Human triggered avalanches unlikely. Generally stable snow; isolated areas of instability.	Travel is generally safe. Normal caution advised.
MODERATE	Natural avalanches unlikely. Human triggered avalanches possible. Unstable slabs possible on steep terrain.	Use caution in steeper terrain on certain aspects.
CONSIDERABLE	Natural avalanches possible. Human triggered avalanches probable. Unstable slabs probable on steep terrain.	Be more cautious in steeper terrain. Be aware of potentially dangerous areas of unstable snow.
HIGH	Natural and human triggered avalanches likely. Unstable slabs likely on a variety of aspects and slope angles.	Travel in avalanche terrain not recommended. Safest travel on windward ridges or lower angle slopes without steeper terrain above.
EXTREME	Widespread natural or human triggered avalanches certain. Extremely unstable slabs on most aspects and slope angles. Large destructive avalanches possible.	Travel in avalanche terrain should be avoided and travel confined to low angle terrain well away from avalanche path runouts.

Figure 13.55

International avalanche danger scale.

Source: American Avalanche Association.

(a) (b)

Figure 13.56
Avalanche warning signs.
Source: (a) courtesy of Karin Michel and (b) courtesy of Peter Fernberg.

Figure 13.57
Avalanche warning signs for cross-country skiers. Sadly, this sign is close to the location where a father and his son lost their lives while tobogganing during March break in 2014, near Lake Louise, Alberta.
Source: © Claire Samson.

Figure 13.58
Working principle of the avalanche flotation bag system.
Source: Beacon Reviews.

HUMAN FOCUS

Jim Bay, Avalanche Consultant

I grew up in Revelstoke, British Columbia. The mountains were my back yard and I have had an interest in snow for as long as I can remember (Figure 13.59).

I learned on the job. I worked in Roger's Pass for the protection of the Trans-Canada Highway, acquiring data on weather and snowpack conditions. I also worked as a ski guide in the back country. To me, both activities share the same goal: to stay safe and keep others safe in the mountains in the winter. Over the years, I have become expert at "reading" the snow. I am aware of subtle temperature changes—especially warming trends, which decrease stability—and how snow and wind interact to load a slope. Weather conditions are central to avalanche safety. In fact, I would go as far as saying that avalanche forecasts are only as good as weather forecasts.

In my current work, I provide snow safety advice to forest companies, mines, and utility companies that operate in avalanche-exposed terrain. As logging activities take place ever higher on mountain slopes, I help design avalanche safety plans for the protection of workers and the forest. Trees anchor snow on steep slopes. When they are cut down, the anchoring is removed and avalanches are possible unless proper harvesting techniques are used to reduce the likelihood of avalanche initiation (Figure 13.60). An avalanche safety plan therefore includes an initial risk assessment that identifies potential avalanche paths, a hazard assessment process, safe work procedures, a search and rescue plan in case of an incident, and advice on harvesting strategies. Workers are trained in avalanche awareness, safe work procedures, and search and rescue equipment and techniques.

I take part in active avalanche control, which is done by triggering avalanches artificially in a "controlled" manner, using explosives, artillery, and explosive gas technology. A very effective approach consists of dropping explosive charges in avalanche starting zones with precision from a low-flying helicopter. A new tool uses gas exploders permanently fixed high on the slopes above vulnerable segments of highways and on ski resorts. The exploders can be fired remotely at any time to prevent unsafe buildups of snow.

Over the years, I have participated in several search and rescue missions. I believe strongly in being proactive rather than reactive with regards to avalanche safety. I think highly of the strong leadership and effective programs of the Canadian Avalanche Association in promoting avalanche awareness and safety. After an encouraging few years (2009–2013) when the number of avalanche fatalities declined, the winter of 2013–2014 brought the statistics back to the pre 2000 levels of approximately 15 deaths per year. After normal early season snowfalls, the months of December 2013 and January 2014 saw cool, dry conditions. This extended dry spell created very weak base layers within the snowpack but with so little snow load, the situation was relatively safe. People ventured everywhere in the back country and developed a comfort with the snow conditions. When February and March brought heavy snowfalls, these new loads created a highly unstable snowpack. Overconfident recreationists may not have been fully aware of the significance of the changing conditions and increased risk. When analyzing statistics, however, we must not lose sight of the fact that many more people enjoy the mountains than 20 years ago. In particular, snowmobiling has become much more popular. In recent years, the Association has made a particular effort to educate snowmobilers. Social media is proving to be an effective tool, helping them reach out to as many people as possible.

Figure 13.59
Jim Bay in his work environment.
Source: © Jim Bay.

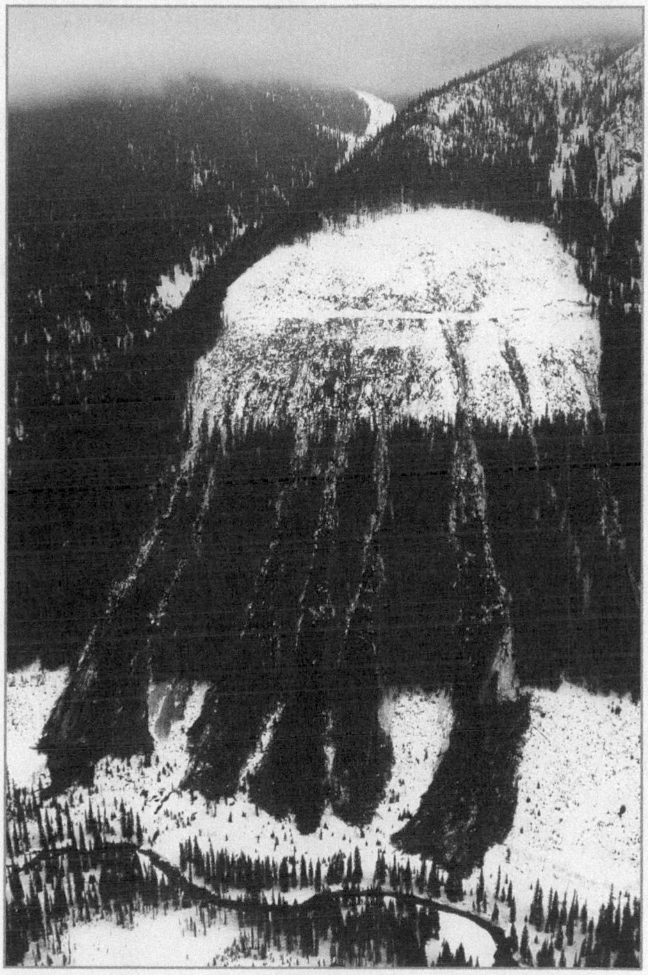

Figure 13.60
Logging "cut block" in British Columbia where a slab avalanche released over the entire width (300 m) and damaged a significant amount of forest below.
Source: © Jim Bay.

IN GREATER DEPTH

What to Do If You Are Caught in a Snow Avalanche

Before

Before venturing into the back country, consult avalanche forecast bulletins and travel advisories. Stay away from sensitive areas. Be alert to changing weather conditions.

Do not go out alone. Designate a group leader and have a plan in case an accident occurs. Everyone in your group should carry a first aid kit, a collapsible shovel, and a probe. As a minimum, people should wear transceivers, devices capable of both transmitting and receiving radio signals. Mountain enthusiasts are wise to invest in a ski jacket with a built-in beacon.

During

As soon as the snow starts to move, try to escape to the side. Attempts to outrun the avalanche will not work. If you are caught, rid yourself of skis, poles, backpack, etc. to make yourself lighter. Use a swimming motion to stay near the surface of the snow. If you are in over your head, try to maintain an air pocket in front of your face as many avalanche fatalities are caused by suffocation. If you are trapped, remain calm so that your body can better conserve energy.

After

In isolated areas, survival depends on the search organized by group members. Time is critical as survival rates drop rapidly with time. Initiate the search as soon as the area is safe from avalanche danger. Start from the "last seen position," and head to the avalanche toe in zigzagging patterns. Stop every 10 m to listen for a signal. Victims wearing transceivers are usually found within 5 to 15 minutes by their companions. Once the source of signal has been located, poke about the snowpack with your probe to locate the victim. Digging in the hard-packed snow will take several minutes. Extract the victim gently as the person might be injured.

IN GREATER DEPTH

The Sea-to-Sky Corridor

The Sea-to-Sky transportation corridor links Vancouver, Squamish, and Whistler, following the coast and a picturesque valley through British Columbia's Coast Mountains (Figure 13.61). The corridor includes a BC Rail line and Highway 99 running parallel to each other. Unfortunately, the winding highway has claimed several motorists' lives over the years, earning the sad nickname of "sea-to-die" highway. From 2004 to 2009, a major engineering project was undertaken to widen and straighten the road to ensure the safety of the spectators at the 2010 Winter Olympics travelling to Whistler.

Over the last hundred years, 154 reported landslide events occurred along the corridor, accounting for approximately 18% of Canada's landslide-related deaths (Figure 13.61). A single rock avalanche at Jane Camp in March 1915 took the lives of 56 mine workers, the second-worst Canadian landslide disaster in terms of casualties. The most frequent types of mass movement along the Sea-to-Sky corridor are rockfalls and debris flows, often triggered by weather events. On average, Highway 99 is closed once a year when heavy rain near the mountain summits runs off into torrents carrying a heavy load of detritus and sediment. The mix descends down the valleys at high speed, accumulating as debris fans at the foot of the slopes (Figure 13.62). The most recent incident occurred on 29 July 2008 near Porteau (a particularly sensitive area with more than five events reported in Figure 13.61), when 16 000 m^3 of rock detached from a cliff and moved downslope into the ocean, destroying 100 m of the highway and the adjacent rail line (Figure 13.63).

Although there was an increase in reported mass movements along the Sea-to-Sky transportation corridor in the 1980s and 1990s due to an increase in population and greater awareness, there has been no landslide-related casualty since the early 1990s. This fact can be attributed largely to a vigorous mitigation program. Travelling along Highway 99 is like getting a practical course in civil engineering!

In addition to classic mitigation measures such as rock scaling (Figure 13.64), culverts, and retaining walls (Figure 13.65), several innovative solutions have been put in place. In particular, several concrete flumes have been built to channel excess water, mud, and debris during major flooding events. Charles Creek, a particularly sensitive area that has experienced seven historical debris flows, is now protected by a large concrete catchment basin designed to collect debris upstream from Highway 99 before it reaches the road (Figure 13.66). The basin can be cleared out after a major debris flow.

Every steep slope along the highway has been secured. Some cliffs are draped with steel mesh (Figure 13.67) while others, exhibiting more crumbly rocks, have been covered with shotcrete, a type of liquid concrete sprayed through a hose at high velocity (Figure 13.68).

continued

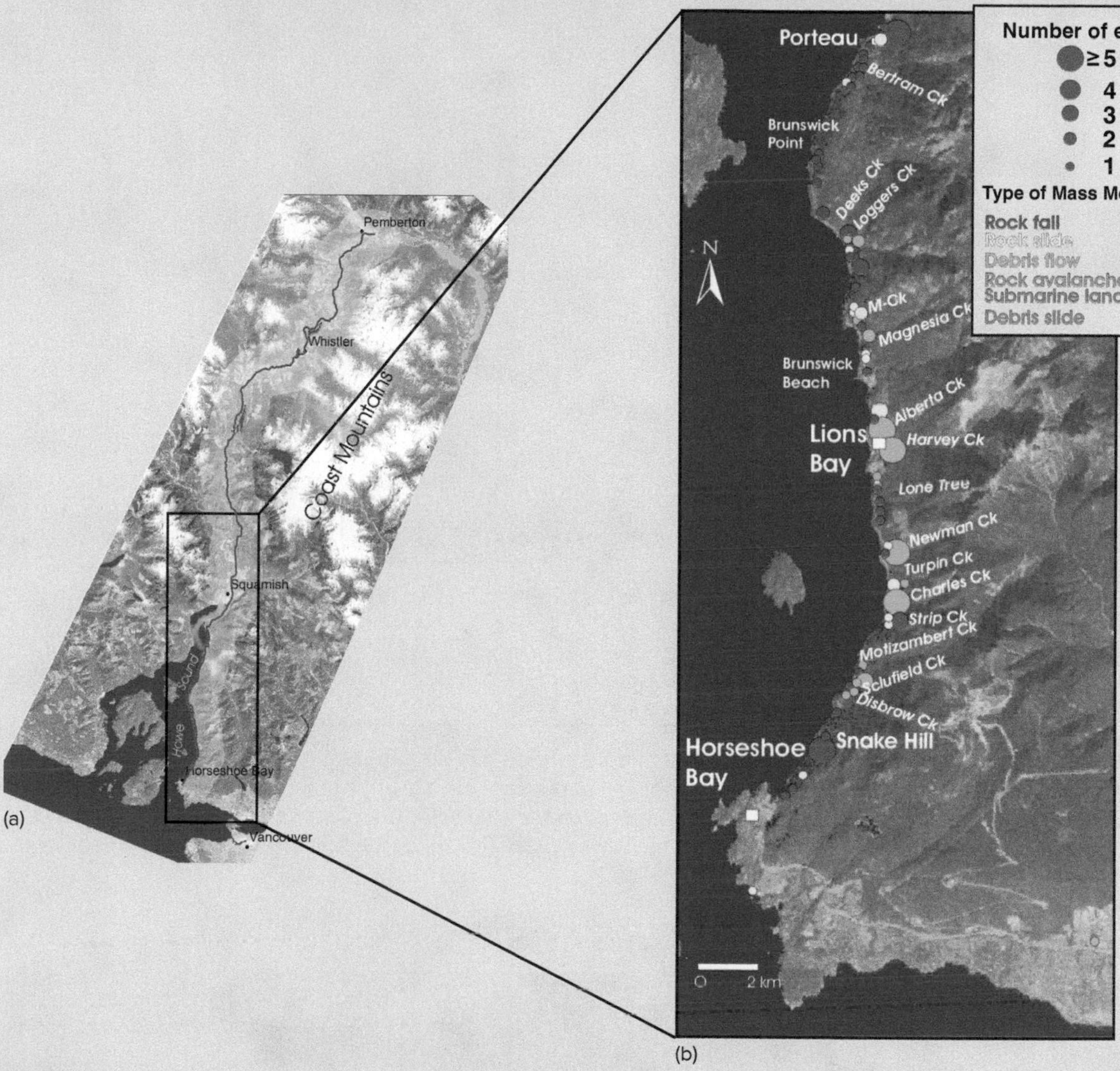

Figure 13.61

(a) An aerial landscape of the Sea-to-Sky corridor with Highway 99 drawn as a red line. The view has been created by fusing satellite images and computer-generated topography. (b) The southern section of the corridor is particularly active for mass movements.

Source: Blais-Stevens, A. and D. Septer, 2006, Landslides along the Sea to Sky corridor, Sea to Sky Geotechnique Conference, Canadian Geotechnical Association, Vancouver, Oct. 2006, 448–455. Department of Natural Resources Canada.

continued

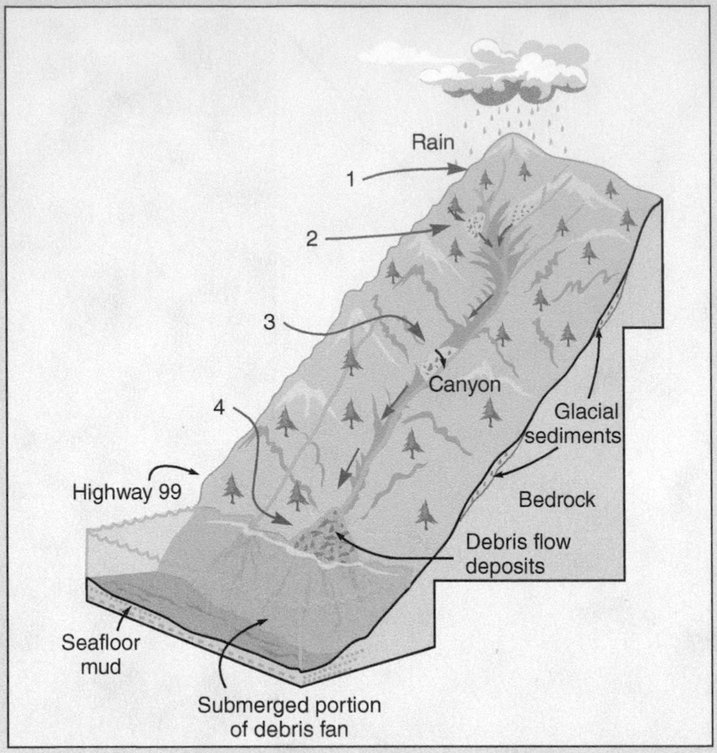

Figure 13.62

Typical debris flow in the Sea-to-Sky corridor. (1) Torrential rainfall swells streams along the mountain crest. (2) Sediment is collected into a raging stream, forming a debris flow that surges down the channel. (3) The debris flow swells in volume as it picks up additional sediment and trees from the channel and canyon walls. (4) The debris flow emerges from the canyon into a fan where it damages infrastructure.

Source: Natural Resources Canada.

Figure 13.63

Rock slide of 29 July 2008 near Porteau, British Columbia.

Source: JONATHAN HAYWARD/The Canadian Press.

continued

Figure 13.64
Rock scaling removes loose rock from unstable slopes.

Figure 13.65
Custom designed retaining wall. Gabion baskets—rectangular steel mesh containers filled with rock—hold the slope in place. A concrete buttress integrated in the centre of the wall provides extra strength around a protruding rock.
Source: © Claire Samson.

(a) (b)

Figure 13.66
The Charles Creek catchment basin collects and channels debris flow before it reaches the road, the railway track, and the homes built on the debris fan. (a) Aerial and (b) ground views.
Source: (a) © O. Hungr; (b) © Claire Samson.

continued

Figure 13.67
Steel mesh contains small rocks that might detach from this cliff.
Source: © Claire Samson.

Figure 13.68
Shotcrete and rock bolts hold crumbly rock in place.
Source: © Claire Samson.

LO5 Mitigation

Mass movements occur in so many places around the world that almost everyone can feel or see their effects. Various mitigation strategies are being deployed to control them.

Remove the hazard. You probably see this most often along road cuts. On the slopes above the road, the hazard is lessened by scaling loose rock (Figure 13.64); decreasing the slope angle; or benching, a technique in which the slope is remodelled as a series of steps (Figure 13.69).

Reinforce the hazard. Actions taken to control rotational and translational slides include unloading the head, reinforcing the body by inserting rock bolts, and supporting the toe with cylinder piles (Figure 13.70). Drainage systems are also often added to reduce the pore-water pressure on the potential failure surface or within the driving mass.

Figure 13.69
Two-step benched road cut in Gatineau, Quebec.
Source: © Claire Samson.

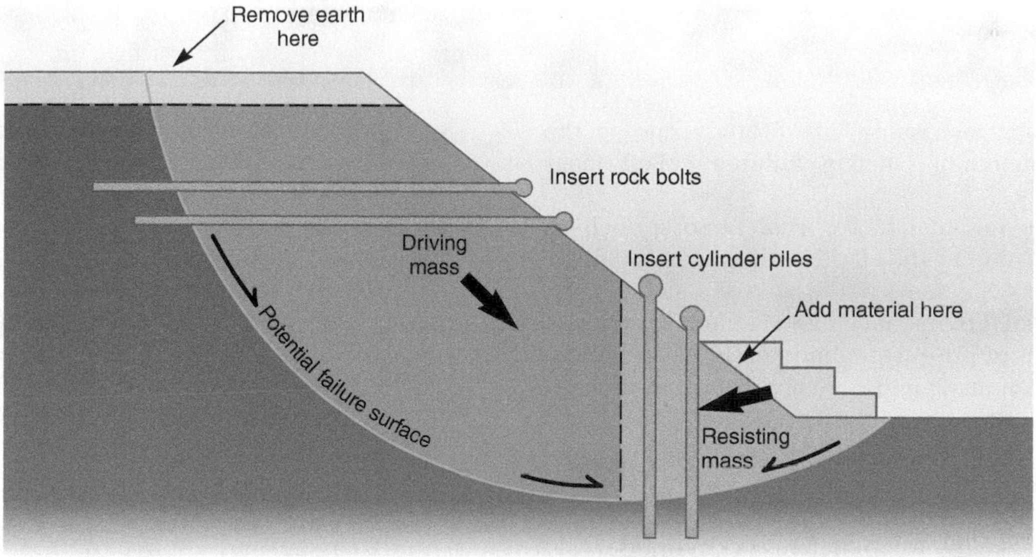

Figure 13.70
A hill slope of homogeneous materials may fail along a curved failure surface. The slope is in equilibrium when a driving-mass portion is kept from moving by a resisting-mass portion. Unloading the head, strengthening the body, or supporting the toe can prevent a rotational slide.

Contain the hazard. Unstable material can be held in place on the slope with shotcrete (Figure 13.68), nets of strong steel mesh (Figure 13.67), a fence, or a wall (Figure 13.16). Common actions to control flows involve steering the flow into the direction of least harm by building walls and digging channels.

Support the hazard. Special buttresses are sometimes designed to provide additional support to overhanging blocks, or weak and crumbly rock layers (Figure 13.19).

Protect against the hazard. In extreme circumstances, tunnels and snow sheds are built to provide direct-protection for roads and railway tracks against mass movements and snow avalanches (Figure 13.71).

Figure 13.71
A concrete shed (left) and tunnel (right) protect the railway track along a segment particularly vulnerable to earth flows and snow avalanches west of the Kicking Horse Pass near Field, British Columbia.
Source: © Claire Samson.

SUMMARY

- Gravity tugs incessantly at all landforms on the Earth, commonly causing failures called mass movements.
  - Slopes fail due to external factors, such as steepening of the slope, adding mass upslope, or removing mass at the base of a slope.
  - Internal factors that make a slope weak include weight of pore water, inherently weak materials such as clay; decreasing cohesion through dissolution or internal erosion; elevated pore-water pressure; melt–freeze cycles; and adverse geological structures, such as inclined rock layers and ancient failure surfaces.
- Movement usually is initiated by a triggering event, such as heavy rains, an earthquake, or human activities. In Canada, most mass movements occur in the spring and the fall in conjunction with meteorological events. They are prevalent in the Rockies because of the steep topography.
- Mass movements range from the barely perceptible surface creep of hill slopes and gelifluction of periglacial soils to events involving material moving in excess of 325 km/h.
- Major types of mass movement are downward, as in falling or subsiding, or downward and outward, as in sliding and flowing.
  - Falls are rock masses dislodged from elevated slopes.
  - Slides are mass movements on top of failure surfaces.
  - Flows are mass movements that behave like fluids, even when they are dry.
  - Complex events include characteristics of several types of mass movement in a single event.
  - Subsidence occurs when the surface drops down either slowly in response to removal of subsurface fluids, or catastrophically.
- In slides, the displaced material retains some coherence during movement.
  - Concave-upward, curved failure surfaces produce rotational slides. The slide head tilts backward, the toe bulges upward, and little distance is travelled. Rotational slides are a common destroyer of property, but their slow movements rarely kill anyone.
  - Slides on top of inclined, planar surfaces are called translational.
  - Block slides are a slow movement of large coherent rock masses that can destroy property.
  - Lateral spreads are extremely dangerous events during which a clay layer in the subsurface suddenly liquefies, carrying rafts of earth material rapidly downslope. Along the St. Lawrence and Ottawa River Valleys, and in neighbouring regions, areas underlain by post-glacial sensitive clay are particularly vulnerable to lateral spreads.
- In flows, the displaced material is thoroughly deformed during movement. Flows may be made of gravel, sand, mud, snow, ice, or mixtures of materials.
- Snow avalanches are similar to movements of earth materials. Loose-powder avalanches are flows and slab avalanches are slides.
- People are not defenceless against mass movements. Mitigation is achieved through a variety of engineering structures that remove, reinforce, contain, support, or protect against the hazard, such as buttresses, rock bolts and steel mesh, and protective sheds.

Terms to Remember

acoustic fluidization
bedrock
carbonic acid
chemical weathering
clay minerals
cohesion
congelifraction
creep
debris flow
falls
flows
friction
groundwater

Questions for Review

1. Which natural disasters can cause mass movements?
2. Which natural disasters can be triggered by mass movements?
3. Draw a cross-section through a slope and explain external actions that are likely to cause mass movements.
4. Draw a cross-section through a clay mineral. Explain the physical properties that promote swelling and shrinking.
5. Draw a water molecule and explain how it links up so readily with clay minerals.
6. How do pore waters become pressurized? What is their role in mass movements?
7. Why are mass movements more frequent in Canada in the spring and fall?
8. List some adverse geological structures inside hills that facilitate mass movements.
9. What triggering events set off rapid mass movements?

lateral spread
limestone
mass movements
permafrost
pore-water pressures
porosity
retrogressive sliding
rotational slides
sensitive clays
sinkholes
slate
slides
sluff
slumps
snowpack
soil
sturzstroms
subsides
talus slopes
topple
translational slides
water table

10. Why do large cave systems form in limestone? Why do they sometimes collapse and form sinkholes?
11. What types of economic activities are most adversely affected by mass movements?
12. Compare snow avalanches to mass movements of soil and rock.
13. What mitigation strategies can be used against both mass movements and snow avalanches?

Questions for Further Thought

1. Roadways are commonly cut into the base of slopes. When mass movements block the road, they are quickly removed. What is wrong with this whole process?
2. Does deforestation increase the risk of mass movements?
3. In your home area, how many engineering structures were built to stop or control mass movements? Look for them as you travel about.
4. Why are areas affected by regional subsidence more susceptible to flood and hurricane damage?
5. What circumstances warrant a preventive evacuation of people from their homes to protect them from a potential mass movement?
6. Should access to the back country be forbidden to recreationists when the avalanche danger is moderate, considerable, high, or extreme?
7. Can we speak of a truly "natural" disaster when snowmobilers in search of a thrill engage in risky behaviours and set off an avalanche?

Interesting Websites

- Landslides, Natural Resources Canada
  http://www.nrcan.gc.ca/hazards/landslides
- Landslides in BC, Ministry of Energy and Mines and Responsible for Core Review, Government of British Columbia
  http://www.empr.gov.bc.ca/Mining/Geoscience/SurficialGeology/Landslides/Pages/default.aspx
- Frank Slide Interpretive Centre
  www.frankslide.com
- Canadian Avalanche Centre
  www.avalanche.ca

CHAPTER FOURTEEN

14

Hazards from Space

The Chelyabinsk meteor lights up the Siberian morning sky on 15 February 2013, followed a few minutes later by a destructive shock wave.
Source: AP Photo/AP Video/The Canadian Press

"Something like the sun fell."

—Chelyabinskmeteor witness (as reported by BBC Europe News, 15 February 2013)

Outline

LO1 Identify where impactors come from and explain what they are.

LO2 List the consequences of impacts with space objects of different sizes.

LO3 Explain the sequence of events starting when a space object enters the atmosphere until the final crater has formed.

LO4 Describe several Canadian impact craters.

LO5 Explain the relationship between the solar wind and the Earth's magnetosphere, and its impact on technological systems.

LO6 Describe the Earth's magnetic field.

Illuminated by the Sun, planet Earth moves rapidly through space. As a result of its position in the universe, however, the third rock from the Sun is vulnerable to several hazards. On rare occasions, the Earth crosses paths with asteroids and comets with devastating consequences. Occasionally, the Sun showers the Earth's magnetosphere with charged particles that can trigger malfunctions in technological systems.

Impact Scars

On 15 February 2013, there was heavy traffic in space, close to our planet. In two unrelated events, the 2012 DA14 meteoroid made a record close encounter with Earth and the Chelyabinsk meteor exploded over Siberia (Figure 14.1). This cosmic coincidence highlights our vulnerability to impact hazards. Could a comet or asteroid impact destroy the human race? The statistics in Table 14.6 suggest that it is possible.

Impact scars are also called **astroblemes**, or, literally, star wounds (the Greek word *astro* means "celestial body" and *blema* means "wound" from a thrown object). A good place to see impact scars made by collisions with space debris is the surface of the Moon (Figure 14.2). In its first few hundred million years of existence, the Moon was a violent place as millions of objects slammed into it. The intense bombardment apparently occurred as a sweeping up of debris left over from the formation of the planets. The Moon's surface still displays tens of millions of ancient impact craters, some with diameters of hundreds of kilometres (Figure 14.2). Flood basalts poured forth on the Moon from about 3.8 to 3.2 billion years ago. They created the dark-coloured **maria** (*mare* is Latin for "sea") so prominent on the Moon's surface today. The maria have relatively few impact scars on them, thus providing evidence that the period of intense bombardment was over before 3.8 billion years ago.

For over three billion years, the Moon has been an orbiting museum showing only the scars of its ancient past. The Moon has no plate tectonics, no water or significant agents of erosion, and no life. About the only event that disturbs the cemetery calm of the Moon is the occasional impact of an asteroid or comet.

Why are impact craters so common on the Moon but so rare on the Earth? The Moon is geologically "dead", so impact scars remain. But the Earth is dynamic: it destroys most of the record of its past. Plate-tectonic movements consume impact scars during subduction and crumple them during continent collisions. The agents of erosion work to erase all impact craters on the Earth. Nevertheless, some impact scars, especially the younger ones, still remain as the slowly acting geological processes of destruction have not had enough time yet to obliterate them. Figure 14.3 shows

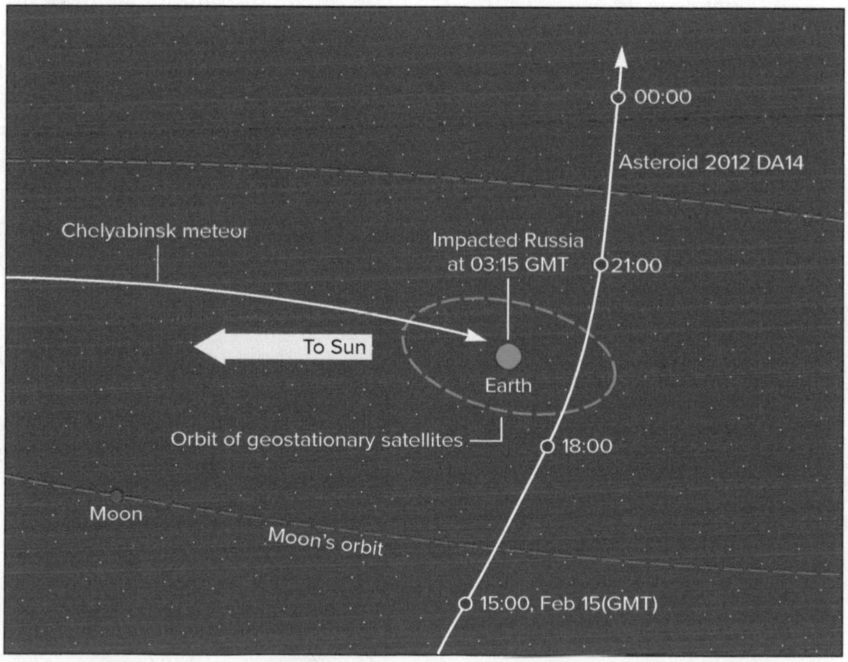

Figure 14.1

On the morning of 15 February 2013, the 20 m wide Chelyabinsk meteor exploded in midair. Only a few hours later, coming from another direction, the slightly larger 2012 DA14 meteoroid (30 m wide), flew so close to the Earth, it passed inside the orbit of geostationary satellites. This was the closest flyby by an object of its size ever documented.

Source: Modified from Green and Chodas.

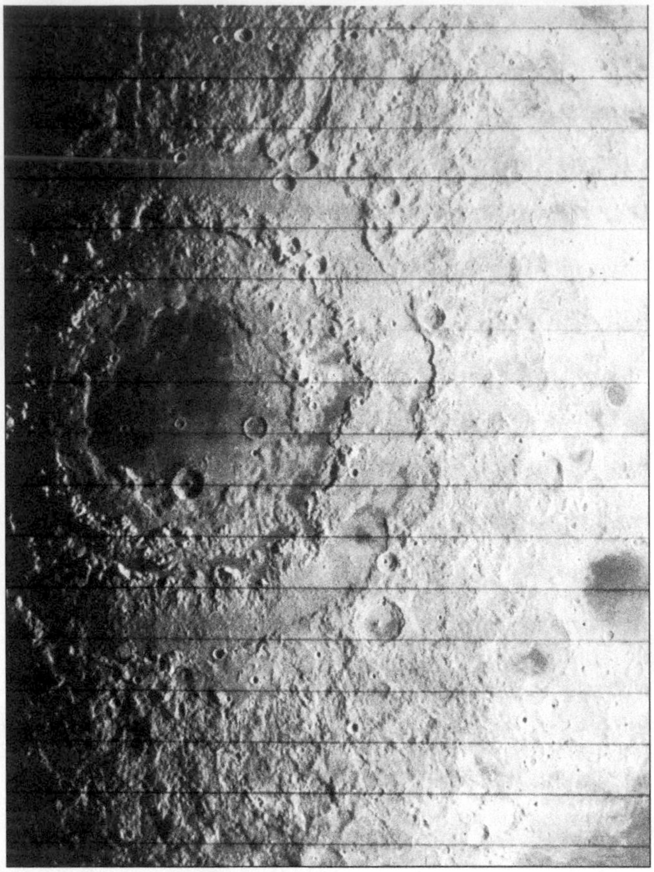

Figure 14.2
The Moon's surface is ancient and pockmarked by numerous impact craters. Notice the large Orientale multi-ring basin. Its outer ring is 1300 km across; on the Earth, it would stretch across the Prairies, from Winnipeg to the Rockies.
Source: © NASA.

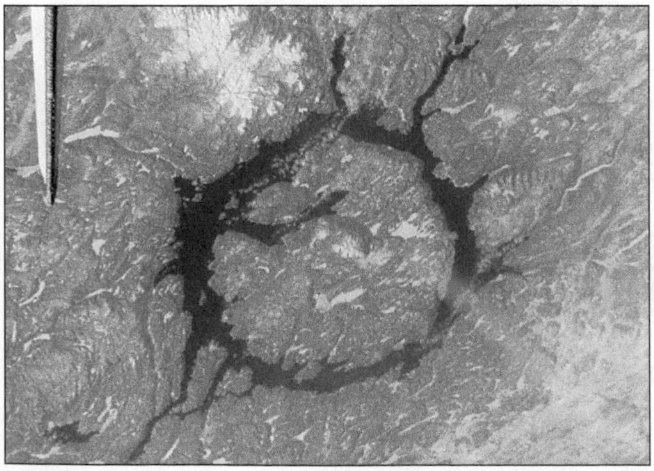

Figure 14.3
The Manicouagan impact crater formed about 214 million years ago, in northern Quebec. It is 75 km across but probably exceeded 100 km before glacial erosion stripped away its upper levels.
Source: © NASA.

the Manicouagan crater of northern Quebec. The site was confirmed as an impact crater in 1963 when **shock minerals** were discovered in its vicinity. The water reservoir of the Daniel-Johnson dam (Figure 4.40) has revealed its structure spectacularly.

LO1 Sources of Extraterrestrial Debris

Space debris that collides with the Earth comes primarily from fragmented asteroids and secondarily from comets. The pieces of asteroids and comets that orbit the Sun are called **meteoroids**. When meteoroids blaze through the Earth's atmosphere as a streak of light, they are referred to as **meteors**. The objects that actually hit Earth's surface are called meteorites. There are two main types of meteorites: stony and iron-rich (Figure 2.4). Although most space objects that reach the Earth's atmosphere are stony meteorites, these are not very abundant on the ground. Stony meteorites are less commonly collected because (1) they break up more readily while passing through the Earth's atmosphere, (2) those that reach the ground are weathered and destroyed more rapidly, and (3) they are not as easily recognized as iron-rich meteorites.

ASTEROIDS

The Solar System has eight planets in orbit around the Sun and a new and growing category of dwarf planets. The four inner planets are small, close together, near the Sun, and rocky. The four outer planets are larger, spaced far apart, lie at great distances from the Sun, and are composed mainly of hydrogen and helium gas surrounding rocky cores; they are orbited by icy moons and rings of icy debris with compositions of water (H_2O), ammonia (NH_3), carbon dioxide (CO_2), and methane (CH_4). Dwarf planets are objects smaller than planets yet larger than asteroids. They are massive enough to have their own gravity, but they have not cleared their orbit region of smaller objects and they are not moons of a planet. In 2006, Pluto was downgraded from planet to dwarf planet status whereas Ceres was raised from asteroid to dwarf planet status.

Asteroids are small bodies orbiting the Sun. The asteroids, a swarm of small (under 1000 km in diameter) rocky, metallic, and icy masses, lie mostly in a belt between the inner and outer planets (Figure 14.4). Many asteroids are composed of the same ingredients from which the planets were assembled via low-velocity collisions. However, the asteroids were apparently too strongly influenced by the gravitational pull of Jupiter and thus have been unable to combine to form a planet. The gravitational acceleration caused by the massive

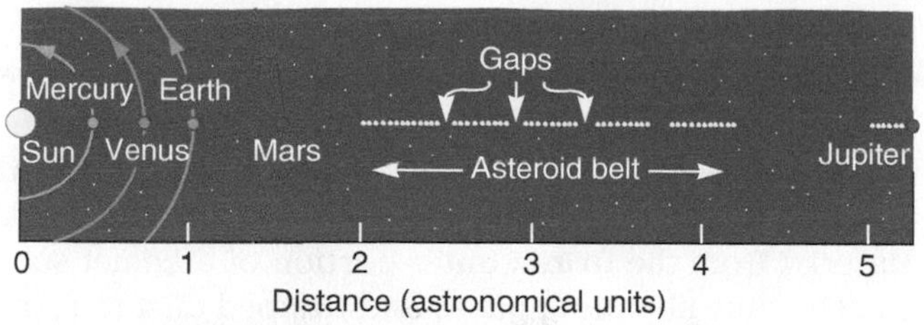

Figure 14.4
The Solar System from the Sun to Jupiter. The asteroid belt is composed of millions of rocky and metallic objects that did not combine to form a planet. One astronomical unit equals 150 000 000 km, the distance between the Sun and the Earth.

planet Jupiter creates asteroid velocities that are too fast and individual collisions that are too energetic to allow the asteroids to unite and stick together to form a planet.

Notice that there are gaps within the asteroid belt (Figure 14.4). The gaps occur at distances related to the orbit of Jupiter. The asteroids rarely collide, but when they do, their collisions can be spectacular impacts at 16 000 km/h. The force of these smash-ups may bump an asteroid into one of the gaps in the asteroid belt. An asteroid nudged into a gap experiences an extra gravitational acceleration from Jupiter that makes its orbital path more eccentric, and thus, it becomes more likely to collide with a planet.

The three largest bodies in the asteroid belt make up about half the combined total mass of all asteroids; they are Ceres (designated as a dwarf planet), Pallas, and Vesta, with respective diameters of 933, 523, and 501 km. More than 200 asteroids have diameters greater than 100 km, about 1000 have diameters greater than 30 km, and another million have diameters over 1 km. If all the asteroids were brought together they would make a planet about 1500 km in diameter; less than half the diameter of our Moon.

A recent photo of the asteroid Ida shows it has impact craters and its own moon, named Dactyl (Figure 14.5). When Ida and Dactyl collide with a planet, craters will form simultaneously in two different areas. This observation may explain some of the double-impact sites found on the Earth (Figure 14.6).

Recent radar data show that some asteroids are not solitary, solid masses but rather are made of two or more similar-size bodies bound together by gravitational attraction. Calculations indicate that the amount of energy needed to break up an asteroid is much less than the amount of energy required to scatter all its fragments. Thus, an asteroid may be broken into pieces during a collision, and then the pieces may be held together by gravity, creating a loose collection of rocky debris—a rubble pile.

The realization that collisions have made some asteroids into rubble piles raises interesting questions.

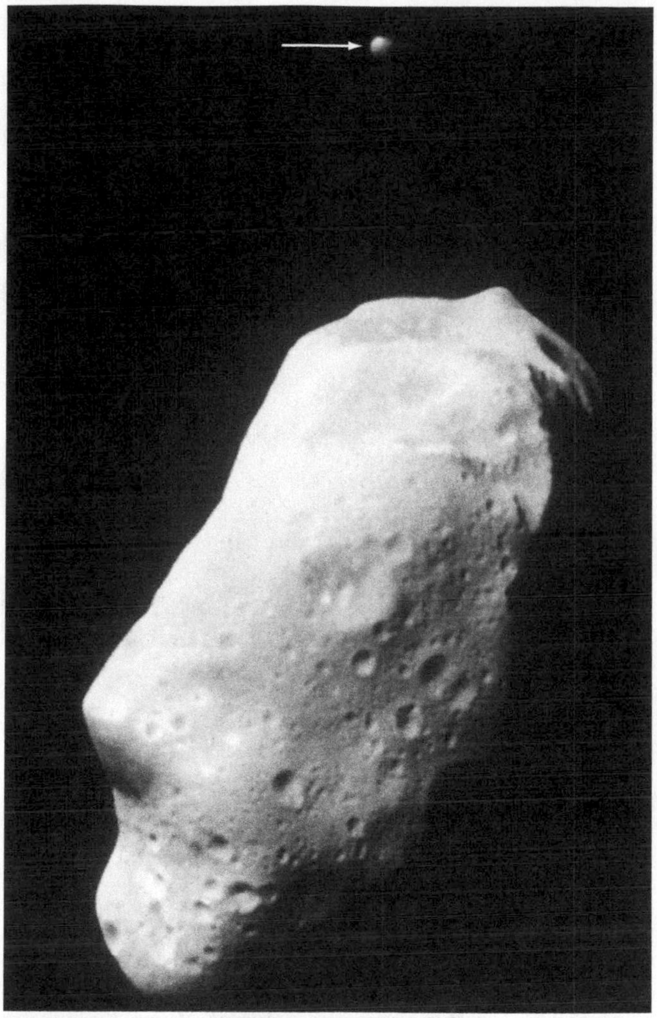

Figure 14.5
The asteroid Ida is 56 km long and pockmarked with impact craters. Travelling with Ida is its near-spherical moon Dactyl with a diameter of only 1.4 km.
Source: © NASA.

Did some of the impact craters on the Earth form within hours of each other when a multi-chunk asteroid hit the surface? Removing the effects of 214 million years of plate tectonics places three impact sites along a line 4462 km long and parallel to the ancient 22.8°N latitude. Saint Martin in Manitoba (40 km in diameter), lines up with Manicouagan in Quebec (100 km in diameter), and both line up with Rochechouart in France (25 km in diameter). If these three impacts occurred hours apart, then life on the Earth must have suffered a terrible blow.

Beside the objects orbiting the Sun in the asteroid belt, there are three groups of asteroids whose orbits intercept the orbits of the Earth or Mars (Figure 14.7). They include the Apollo, Aten, and Amor asteroid groups. There are more than 1000 mountain-size Apollo asteroids and a more modest number of Aten asteroids

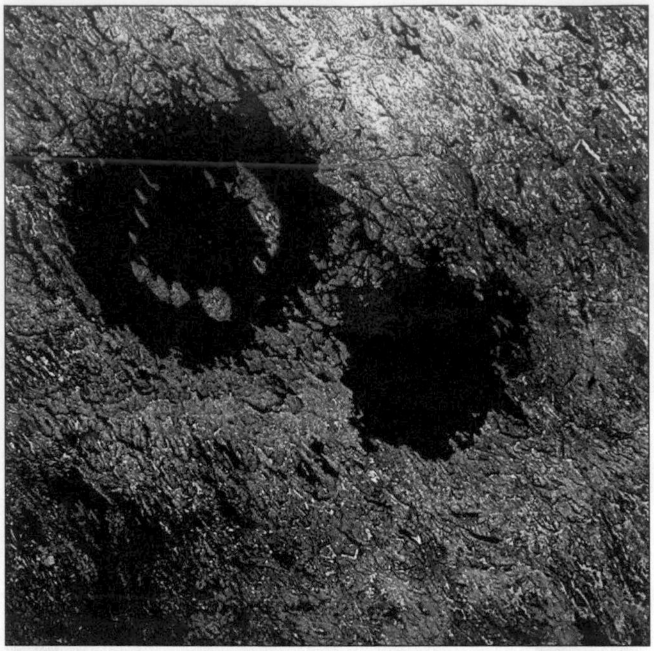

Figure 14.6
Space shuttle view of the Clearwater Lakes double impact site, northern Quebec. About 290 million years ago, a two-part asteroid hit the ground. The western crater is 32 km across and has a central uplift. The eastern crater is 22 km across; its central uplift is below water level.
Source: © NASA.

that could hit the Earth (Table 14.3). The Amors pass near the Earth but cross the orbit of Mars. An impact with the red planet could send debris toward the Earth. With so many asteroids whizzing about, we are lucky that space has such an immense volume and that the Earth is such a small target.

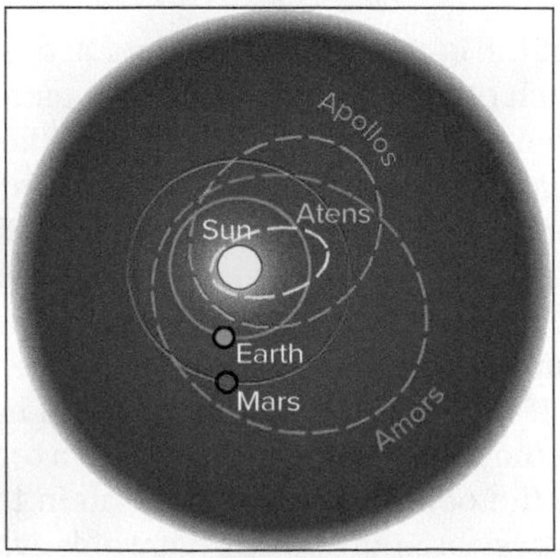

Figure 14.7
The Earth's orbit around the Sun is intersected by the Apollo and Aten asteroids. The Amor asteroids cross the orbit of Mars and pass near the Earth.

COMETS

Comets are called "dirty snowballs" to describe their composition of ice and rocky debris. When an incoming comet passes Saturn on its journey toward the Sun, it begins to be affected by sunlight and the solar wind. Material from the frozen outer portion of a comet sublimates, thus liberating gases and trapped dust to form the distinctive luminous "tail" of a comet (Figure 14.8). The term *comet* is derived from a Greek word for "long-haired." The nearer an icy comet approaches the Sun, the larger its tail becomes. As the comet curves around the Sun, its tail also rotates. Pushed away by the solar wind, the tail is always pointing away from the Sun. A comet that has lost most of its ice over time will have a dim and small tail. The remaining rocky body will be quite similar to an asteroid. Despite their visibility in the sky, comets are surprisingly small; most have heads less than 15 km in diameter.

Most of the comets we see have wildly eccentric orbits that bring them in near the Sun at one end of their orbit (**perihelion**), but allow them to swing out beyond the outermost planet at the other end of their journey (**aphelion**) (Figure 14.9). A comet may travel 100 000 astronomical units away from the Sun during its orbit. An astronomical unit (AU) is 150 million kilometres, i.e., the distance between the Earth and the Sun.

Comets are commonly divided into short- and long-period classes. A short-period comet makes a complete orbit in less than 200 years. There are at least 800 of these short-period comets. Some of them are found in the **Kuiper belt**, a flattened disk of comets with orbits ranging from near Neptune out to about 50 AU away.

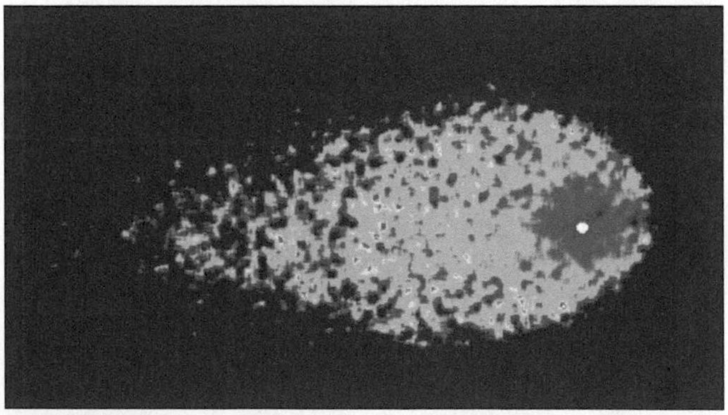

Figure 14.8
Enhanced image of the comet Nevski-Novichonok. The comet has a nucleus (white dot) of approximately five kilometres in diameter. It is surrounded by a cloud of gas, dust, and sublimated ice particles (in red). The comet, discovered in 2012, is a first time visitor to the inner solar system. Unfortunately, it disintegrated close to perihelion on 28 November 2013 without developing the spectacular tail much anticipated by astronomers.
Source: NASA/ESA J.-Y. Li of the Planetary Science Institute and the Hubble ISON Imaging Science Team.

IN GREATER DEPTH

Shoemaker-Levy 9 Comet Impacts on Jupiter

A once-in-a-lifetime event occurred during the week of 16–22 July, 1994, as a series of comet fragments plunged into Jupiter. The comet was named after its discoverers: geologists Eugene and Carolyn Shoemaker and comet hunter David Levy. In 1992, the comet had flown too close to Jupiter, and the planet's immense gravitational attraction pulled the comet closer and broke it into pieces. In 1994, the broken-up comet was stretched out like a string of beads as it again approached Jupiter. In succession, 21 large fragments plunged into Jupiter's dense atmosphere at speeds up to 200 000 km/h. Each impact caused (1) an initial flash as a fragment collided with the heavy atmosphere, (2) a superheated fireball of hot gas rising upward as a plume thousands of kilometres above Jupiter's clouds, and (3) radiation as the plume crashed back down at high velocity.

The largest fragment (G) was apparently only one kilometre across, yet it left an impact scar larger than the diameter of the Earth (Figure 14.10). Although the impacting fragments were small and penetrated only into Jupiter's upper atmosphere, the impact energy released by fragment G was equivalent to about 315 million World War II atomic bombs.

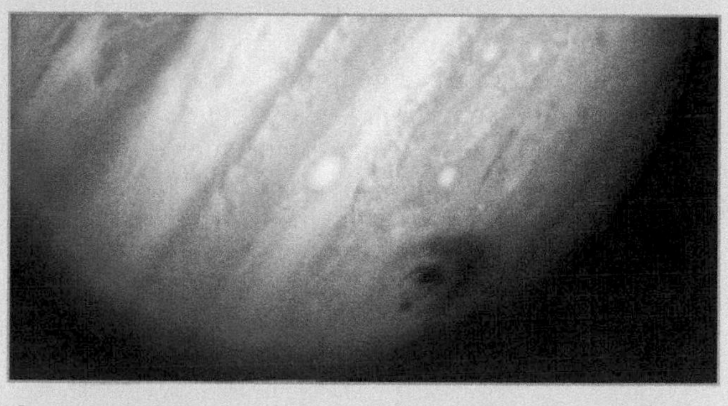

Figure 14.10
Impact scar of Shoemaker-Levy 9 comet fragment G on Jupiter (in lower right of photo), 17 July 1994. To lower left of G is the smaller impact scar of fragment D.
Source: © NASA.

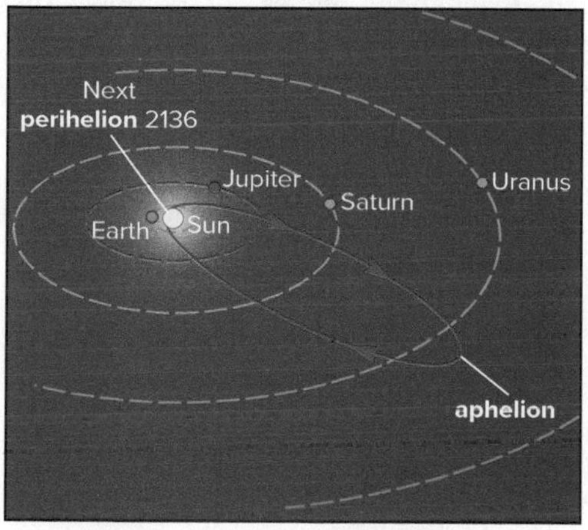

Figure 14.9
Elliptical orbit of the Swift-Tuttle comet during its 133-year round trip.

The Kuiper-belt comets are probably debris left over from the formation of the outer icy planets. They are the icy bodies that never collided and accreted onto a larger planet, analogous to the asteroid belt of rocky bodies that never accreted onto the inner rocky planets. There may be a billion Kuiper-belt comets greater than five kilometres in diameter.

Most of the short-period comets were captured by the gravitational pulls within the Solar System. These comets have had their orbits changed and it is only a matter of time until they meet their fate by (1) erosional destruction by sublimation and fragmentation or (2) colliding with a planet or the Sun.

The long-period comets have orbits lasting longer than 200 years. Our Solar System is surrounded by about a trillion (10^{12}) long-period comets, icy objects whose orbits take them *far* beyond the outermost planets of the Solar System. This vast and diffuse envelope of encircling comets is known as the **Oort cloud**. The Oort cloud has more than 200 comets with diameters greater than 500 km and common travel velocities of 240 000 km/h. They can enter the Solar System at any angle and potentially strike a planet, including the Earth.

The Swift-Tuttle comet (Figure 14.9) is one of the oldest known short-period comets with sightings spanning two millennia. Observed in 1737 and 1862, its return was predicted for 1982. The comet, however, did not show up until 10 years later; the reasons for the delay are unclear. Between 8 and 14 August each year, the Earth passes through the debris left behind by the comet on previous orbits, which gives rise to the Perseid meteor shower. Generations of Canadians have enjoyed the beautiful spectacle of the Perseids against the dark night sky in rural areas. Contrary to earlier announcements, which predicted a close call, the trajectory of the Swift-Tuttle comet on its next passage near the Earth in 2126 will avoid the planet by a comfortable 24 million kilometres. The Swift-Tuttle comet, however, is on an orbit that will almost certainly cause it to crash into the Earth or the Moon eventually.

The ices of comets contain carbon compounds, some of which are important building blocks of life on the Earth. For example, Halley's comet contains carbon (C), hydrogen (H), oxygen (O), and nitrogen (N) in ratios similar to ratios in the human body. Many scientists think that the compounds used to build life were brought to the Earth by comets. Are we the offspring of comets?

LO2 Impactor Size and Consequences of Impact

An estimated 100 billion or more meteoroids of different sizes enter the Earth's atmosphere every 24 hours (Table 14.1). All this incoming debris adds from 100 to 1000 tonnes of material to the Earth's surface each day. The Earth is gaining weight! The numbers of incoming objects seem to be directly related to their size; the smaller the meteoroids, the greater their abundance (Figure 14.11).

The Earth is largely protected from this bombardment by its atmosphere. Because of the great speeds at which they hit the atmosphere–from 40 000 km/h to over 100 000 km/h–the low-viscosity atmosphere behaves much like a solid to the incoming impactors. Remember how hard the water in a pool or lake feels when you hit it doing a belly flop? Meteoroids hitting the atmosphere at incredible velocities experience a similar effect. At about 115 km above the ground, the atmosphere is dense enough to cause many of them to begin to glow. A typical meteor is seen about 100 km above the ground and has vaporized or fragmented before reaching 60 km above the surface. Friction with the atmosphere also slows down incoming bodies; they typically hit the ground at "only" 320 to 640 km/h.

Incoming objects pass rapidly through the atmosphere upon entry, slowing down and compressing the air, producing shock waves that often take the form of a sonic boom (Figure 14.12). If an object is the size of a basketball or larger, its disintegration upon being crushed by the atmospheric resistance can cause booming sounds that might be heard from the ground. In rare extreme cases, such as the Chelyabinsk and Tunguska events, the blast shock waves can be powerful enough to cause damage on the ground (see section "Midair Explosions").

Table 14.1

Meteoroid sizes

Meteoroids	Diameter
Cosmic dust	A few molecules to 1 mm
Shooting stars	1 mm
Meteorites	1 mm–100 m
Asteroids	Larger than 100 m

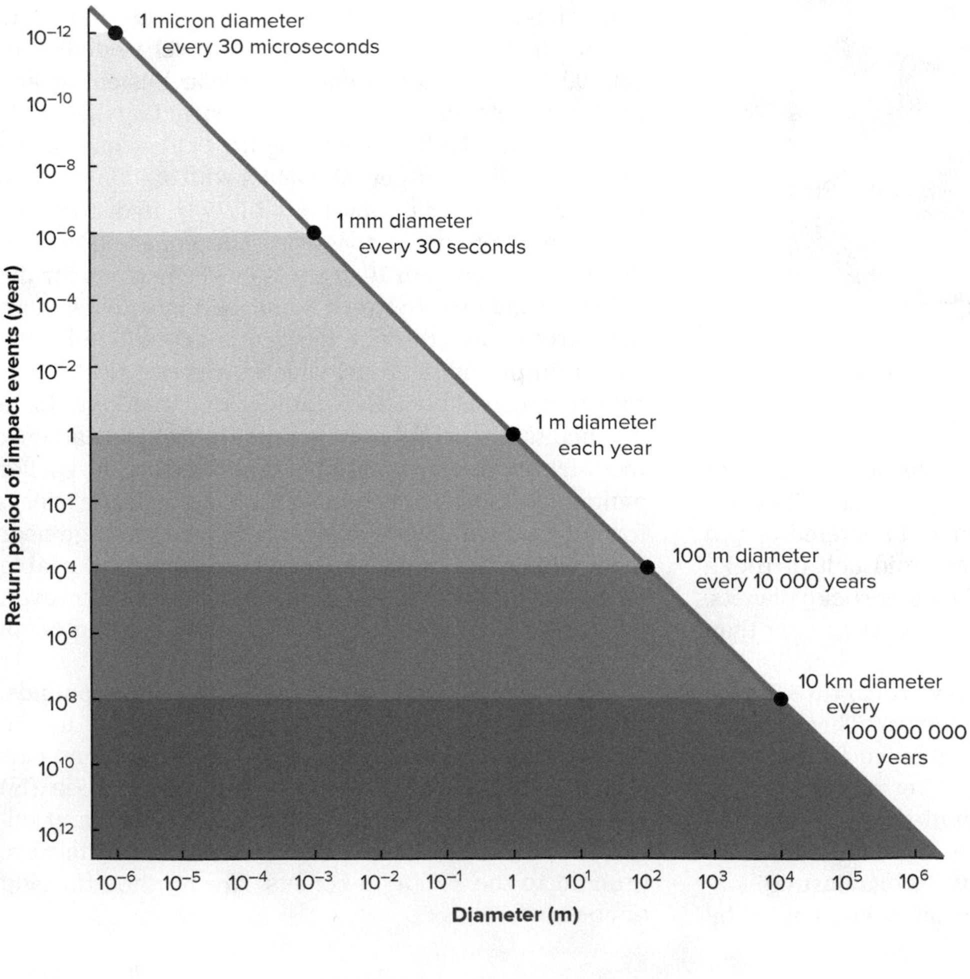

Figure 14.11
Return period of impact events versus size of impactors.

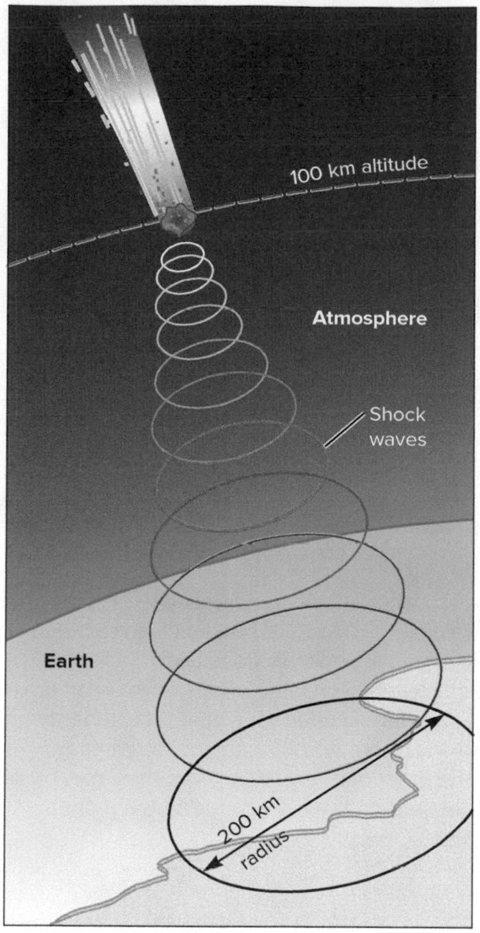

Figure 14.12
A meteor hitting the top of the atmosphere sends off shock waves that might be heard on the ground and cause destruction.

Both the smallest and the largest impactors pass through the atmosphere largely unaffected. However, impactors of intermediate sizes may suffer significant alterations.

COSMIC DUST

The smallest meteoroids are so small that they pass through the atmosphere effectively unchanged and settle onto the Earth's surface as a gentle rain. Particles with diameters around 0.001 mm have so much surface area compared to their volume that their frictional heat of passage is radiated as quickly as it develops, and they escape melting.

SHOOTING STARS

Incoming debris the size of sand grains, with diameters around 1 mm, typically flame out as **shooting stars**—flashes of friction-generated light about 100 km above the ground that blaze for about a second. It is the large incandescent cloud of hot air surrounding them that we witness from the ground.

METEORITES

Meteoroids weighing one gram or more will pass through the atmosphere and fall onto the surface of the Earth. Occasionally, some are recovered and identified as meteorites. Most meteorites come from the inner part of the Solar System and especially from the asteroid belt (Figure 14.4). During their entry, the frictional resistance of the atmosphere may raise their surface temperature to 3000°C (about one-half the temperature of the Sun's surface) and cause their exteriors to melt. Melted surface material is stripped off to feed the glowing tail of a fireball, lighting up the sky. The stripping process also removes heat and thus protects the interior of meteorites from melting. "Fresh" meteorites found on the ground shortly after a fall are cold. They can often be recognized by their glazed and blackened outer crusts (Figure 2.4a).

The number of humans directly killed by meteorites is zero! In 1954, however, Ann Hodges of Sylacauga, Alabama, experienced a close call. A four kilogram stony meteorite crashed through the roof of her home, bounced off several walls, and then hit her and severely bruised her hip. She survived the ordeal and the intruder is now on display at the University of Alabama's Museum of Natural History.

Around 6:30 p.m. on 27 September 2003, a large meteorite racing through the sky lit up like a giant greenish-blue floodlight over the coastal state of Orissa in eastern India. The meteorite broke apart with a thunderous cracking sound and then rained debris. A thatched-roof house in Mayurbhanj was set afire by meteorite debris, injuring three people. One 55-year-old man viewing the fireball collapsed from shock and died.

The best place on the Earth to find meteorites is Antarctica. Meteorites slam into its great ice sheet and are stored and preserved as if they were in a freezer. Meteorites encased in ice are protected from rainwater, carbonic acid, and plant chemicals that would decompose them elsewhere. The flow of ice concentrates meteorites at bends in glaciers, thus helping us discover and collect them. In the last 30 years, more than 16 000 meteorites have been collected, including the enigmatic and controversial ALH84001. This Martian meteorite features magnetite crystals interpreted by some scientists as being secreted by bacteria and by others as the product of inorganic chemical processes. The argument is still raging and ALH84001 has invigorated research efforts in the nascent field of astrobiology.

Unfortunately for Canadian meteorite hunters, the Arctic does not offer the same favourable conditions for meteorite finds as does Antarctica. A number

HUMAN FOCUS

Phil McCausland and the Grimsby Meteorite

I am a meteoriticist: I study meteorites to learn more about how the Solar System formed and how these rocks are delivered to the Earth. Meteorites provide a wide variety of samples to us "for free" from other bodies in the Solar System, complementing those few samples obtained by spacecraft sample-return missions such as the lunar samples collected during the American *Apollo* and Soviet robotic *Luna* missions. Meteorite-dropping fireballs also define the lower end of the flux of space objects that collide with the Earth; understanding these events can help us define the potential impact hazard from larger objects.

On the evening of Friday, 25 September 2009, many people in southern Ontario and the nearby United States witnessed a brilliant fireball accompanied by loud sonic booms. The event was captured by a network of automated cameras and sensors operated by Western University. Analysis of these records revealed that a 100 km object had entered the atmosphere at 75 000 km/h. Fragments with a total mass of several kilograms were determined to have survived and landed near Grimsby, Ontario.

With this information I was able to lead a ground investigation in the potential fall area. We spoke with landowners and other observers in the Grimsby area, attempting to find local evidence of a meteorite fall, such as reports of falling object sounds or damage to property. Finding some confirmation, we made a media announcement of the likelihood of meteorites having fallen in the Grimsby area.

Among the hundreds of public responses, Yvonne and Tony Garchinski reported the initial find: A 46 g individual meteorite that had broken the windshield of their parked vehicle. At the time, they did not know it was a meteorite, but kept the strange object anyway. In all, 13 individual Grimsby meteorite fragments have been found (Figure 14.13) by searchers and home owners in the area.

The Grimsby meteorite is an ordinary chondrite, the most common kind of meteorite to fall. What makes it special is that its arrival was so well recorded: The meteorite's orbit before its arrival could be calculated, placing it in its Solar System context, just as if we had done a sample return mission. Moreover, we could estimate that the original object was the size of a beach ball before it broke up in the Earth's atmosphere.

Although powerful enough to damage property and occasionally injure people, small meteorite falls are more of a scientific opportunity than a natural disaster. It is important, however, to populate the curve showing the relationship between the return period of impact events and the impactor diameter (Figure 14.11) with as much data as possible. We assume, but do not know, that the curve is a straight line. Critically, we can only estimate the return period of the fewer, but dangerous, big objects at lower left on the graph from the impact crater record of the Earth and the Moon, and from astronomical surveys of the near-Earth asteroid population.

Figure 14.13
Field location where the second Grimsby meteorite, fragment "HP-1", was found. This 21 g broken piece (the undisturbed grey triangular rock under McCausland's hands) was spotted by a search team walking line abreast across an open field. The inset (quarter included for scale) shows the meteorite fragment lying where it fell, on top of the ground. A dark fusion crust on the order of a few millimetres thick can be seen along its right side and on the surface facing the ground.
Source: Western University.

The 15 February 2013 Chelyabinsk midair explosion (a large fireball that released energy equal to that of a nuclear weapon) over Russia was a serious hazard, injuring more than 1500 people and causing widespread window damage over several thousand square kilometres, but fortunately killing no one (see section "Chelyabinsk, Siberia, 2013"). The middle range of possible impactors, such as Chelyabisnk, from 10^{-1} m to 10^{3} m in diameter (Figure 14.11), is not at all well known and the larger of these objects are a legitimate regional to global impact hazard! This is why death due to meteorite impact still ranks highly among possible causes of individual mortality—as a collectively shared risk—even though no one in recorded history has died from a meteorite impact.

Studying the arrival and original size of the smaller, more numerous meteorites such as the Grimsby chondrite, and the occasional larger events such as Chelyabinsk, helps us to calibrate the impactor curve to better understand the return period of the potentially devastating larger impacts.

of factors seem to contribute to the scarcity of Arctic meteorites on or around ice caps. Antarctic ice is 700 000 years old or more, and the ice is very dense. Most air bubbles have been squeezed out; that is what makes the ice blue. Anything falling on it does not sink into it very far, but gets rafted along, to accumulate where the flow is disrupted. The Antarctic ice cap is also huge and mostly located on land. There is less ice in the Arctic, especially covering land. Arctic ice is only 70 000 years old, and apparently there was a major melt about 7000 years ago. That would have dumped any glacier load and the material dumped would have been overriden when the glaciers re-advanced. This makes terminal and marginal moraines the best places to look for meteorites. Also Arctic ice is less dense than Antarctic ice. There is little blue ice and anything falling on the softer ice probably sinks deep into the glacier or ice cap, until it may ultimately turn up in moraines. Recognizing meteorites intermixed with other earth material in moraines is like looking for a needle in a haystack.

LO3 The Crater-Forming Process

The amount of energy released by an asteroid or comet impact depends on the body's speed and size. Asteroids may impact at 50 000 km/h and long-period comets at 250 000 km/h. Meteoroids with weights greater than 350 tonnes are not slowed down much by the atmosphere. The big ones hit the ground at speeds close to their original speed, explode, and excavate craters. Typically, craters have a diameter 20 times larger than that of the impactor.

The impact of smaller meteorites creates *simple craters* (less than five kilometres in diameter) with raised rims and concave bottoms lacking central uplifts, such as Meteor Crater in Arizona (Figure 14.14) and Pingualuit Crater in northern Quebec (Figure 14.31).

The impact of larger bodies (Figure 14.15a) forms *complex craters* (more than five kilometres in diameter) with central uplifts and collapsed outer rims. Complex craters do not normally contain meteorites because the impactor has vaporized entirely on contact (Figure 14.15b). In an instant, temperatures may reach thousands of degrees, and pressure may exceed 100 gigapascals. The shock wave pushes rock at the impact site downward and outward in a rapid acceleration of a few kilometres per second squared. The rock in the crater and the debris thrown out of the crater are irreversibly changed by the short-lived high temperature and pressure. Rock is broken, melted, and vaporized; new minerals, such as diamond, are created; and a common mineral such as quartz will have its atomic structure transformed by the high-pressure impact into its high-density form as the mineral stishovite.

Figure 14.14
View northwest of Meteor Crater, Arizona. Notice the upturned rock layers in the crater rim, the little hills of ejected debris surrounding the crater, and the individual blocks of resistant rock (e.g., limestone) strewn about the plateau.
Source: © John S. Shelton.

Still within the initial second, the crater floor rebounds, causing a deflection of material upward and outward, and the formation of a central uplift (Figure 14.15c). The crater that exists in this split second is transient and soon to be enlarged.

As the crater is emptied of vaporized and pulverized asteroid and rock, the fractured walls of the transient crater fail and slide in toward the centre of the crater (Figure 14.15d). This is the final crater with an upraised centre, surrounded by a circular trough and then by an outermost fractured rim. The outer circle of the final crater may have a diameter 100 times wider than the crater is deep.

The formation of a complex crater may be visualized in miniature using a falling drop of water hitting a still body of water (Figure 14.16). At the point of impact, water springs upward, ripples and troughs surround the impact, and a spray of fine water shoots upward and outward. Although the water quickly returns to its normal still condition and retains no evidence of impact, rock altered by impact remains in its broken, melted, and shocked states for the rest of its existence.

The Manicouagan complex impact crater shows an upraised central area surrounded by a circular trough (Figure 14.3). An outer circle of a final crater may have existed at higher elevations at Manicouagan but has been eroded away by post-impact continental glaciation. Similar features are seen on other planets as well. The Yuty crater on Mars (Figure 14.17) has a well-developed central uplift surrounded by a circular trough. Apparently, subsurface ice deposits were melted at Yuty, yielding muddy, liquefied ejecta that flowed over the adjacent area. Similar features would form on the Earth if impact occurred on the frozen ground of northern Canada, Siberia, or Alaska.

METEOR CRATER, ARIZONA

The world's classic simple crater lies on an arid portion of the Colorado Plateau in north-central Arizona. Meteor Crater, also known as Barringer Crater, is over 1 km wide, excavated nearly 185 m below the plateau, and surrounded by a rock rim rising 30 to 60 m above the countryside (Figure 14.14).

What evidence demonstrates that the crater formed by meteorite impact? (1) The crater is steep-sided and closed; (2) the rim of surrounding rock was created by uplifting the horizontal sedimentary rock layers of the region and tilting them away from the crater; (3) little hills of rock outside the crater rim are inverted piles of the rock sequence exposed in the crater walls; (4) huge

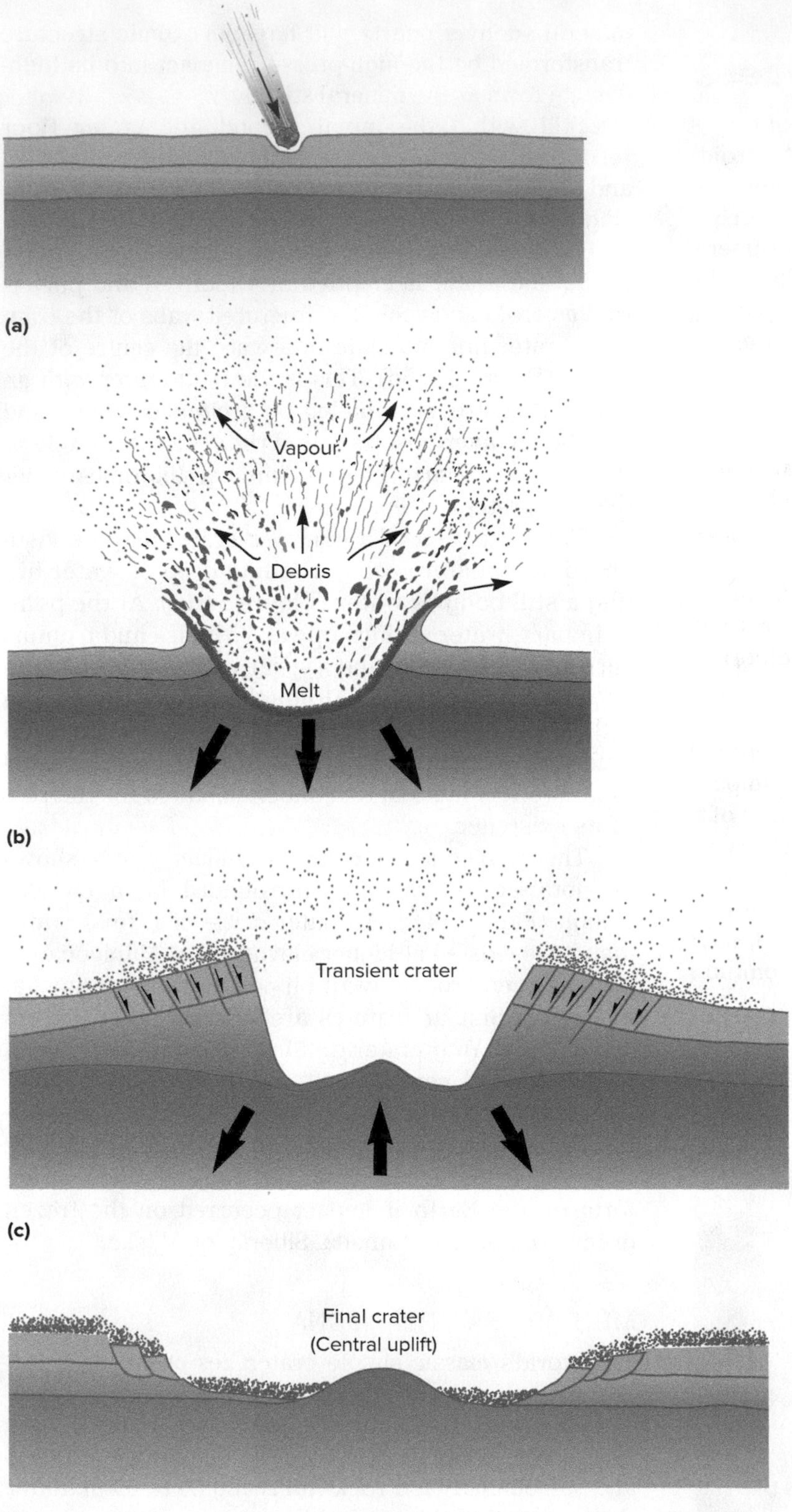

Figure 14.15

Formation of a complex crater. (a) An incoming meteoroid heavier than 350 tonnes is moving towards Earth at speeds greater than 50 000 km/h. (b) The shock wave excavates a large cavity. The impact causes such high temperatures and pressures that most of the meteoroid and crater rock are vaporized and melted. (c) The rock beneath the crater rebounds, causing the centre of the floor in the transient crater to rise. (d) The fractured walls fail and slide into the crater, creating a wider and shallower final crater.

blocks of limestone are strewn around outside the crater; (5) the crater floor holds a layer of shattered rock 265 m thick; (6) numerous pieces of iron-rich meteorite with a combined weight of nearly 30 tonnes have been collected in the area; and (7) several features indicate the occurrence of high temperature and pressure, such as unusual varieties of quartz (the minerals stishovite and coesite), cooled droplets of once-melted metal, fused masses of sand grains, and **shatter cones** (Figure 14.27).

There is also evidence that argues against other processes being responsible for the crater. (1) There is

Figure 14.16
Drop of water hits a body of water. Note the central uplift.
Source: © Stockbyte/PunchStock.

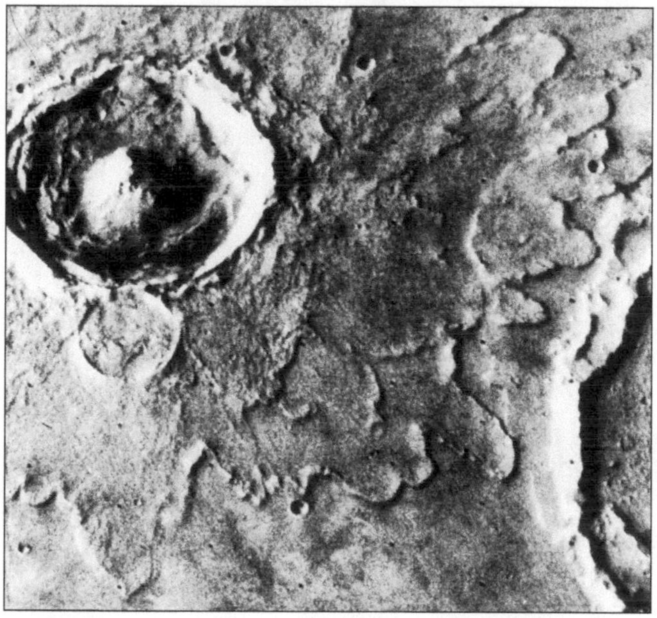

Figure 14.17
The Yuty crater on Mars has a well-developed central uplift and surrounding circular trough.
Source: © NASA.

no volcanic material within or nearby; thus, the crater is not the mouth of a volcano. (2) There are no features to argue for a solution-collapse process of subsidence similar to sinkholes.

When all the evidence is considered, the words of Sherlock Holmes in "The Adventure of the Bruce-Partington Plans" apply: "Each fact is suggestive in itself. Together they have a cumulative force." In sum, the evidence at Meteor Crater, Arizona, is overwhelming; the site has become the most photographed meteorite crater in the world.

Meteor Crater formed about 50 000 years ago when an iron-rich meteorite blazed through the atmosphere. The meteorite had a diameter of about 30 m, weighed around 110 000 tonnes, and hit the ground travelling about 40 000 km/h. The enormous energy of impact was largely converted into heat, which liquefied about 80% of the meteorite and the enveloping ground in less than a second. About 100 million tonnes of rock were pulverized in this event, generating about double the energy released by the Mount St. Helens volcanic eruption. The shock wave levelled all trees in the region, wildfires broke out, and dust darkened the sky.

LO4 The Great Canadian Impact Crater Tour

The record of crater-forming impacts on the Earth is sparse. Craters are erased by erosion, consumed by subduction, mangled by continent collisions, and buried beneath younger sediment. So far, there are 184 known impact craters including 59 in Canada and the United States (Figure 14.18 and Table 14.2). A large number of craters have been preserved in Canada because of the uneventful recent geological history of a large part of its territory, the Canadian Precambrian Shield.

We have already visited the Charlevoix (see Chapter 4), Manicouagan (Figure 14.3), and Clearwater Lakes (Figure 14.6) impact craters. Let's take a tour and explore a few more Canadian impact sites.

SUDBURY AND WANAPITEI, ONTARIO

Formed 1850 ± million years ago (Ma), Sudbury is the site of the largest and oldest impact crater in Canada and the fourth oldest in the world (Figure 14.19). Gravity data outline the Sudbury structure as an elliptical anomaly, approximately 50 km wide (Figure 14.20a). Using a simulation to remove the effects of almost two billion years of tectonic deformation, scientists of the Geological Survey of Canada have reconstructed the feature at the time of the impact (Figure 14.20b). Their results unmistakably unveil the circular shape of the original impact crater.

The people of Sudbury have enthusiastically embraced their "space-connection" and have featured the impactor and the crater on their city flag (Figure 14.21). The Sudbury area is also home to the world's largest nickel deposit. Could the wealth that miners are extracting from the ground be of extraterrestrial origin? Proponents of the hypothesis point out that iron-rich meteorites can contain up to 20% nickel. Was the Sudbury impactor an iron and nickel-rich meteorite that brought large quantities of the metal to the Earth? Actually, recent isotopic analysis of the Sudbury ore indicates that the nickel was there in the first place,

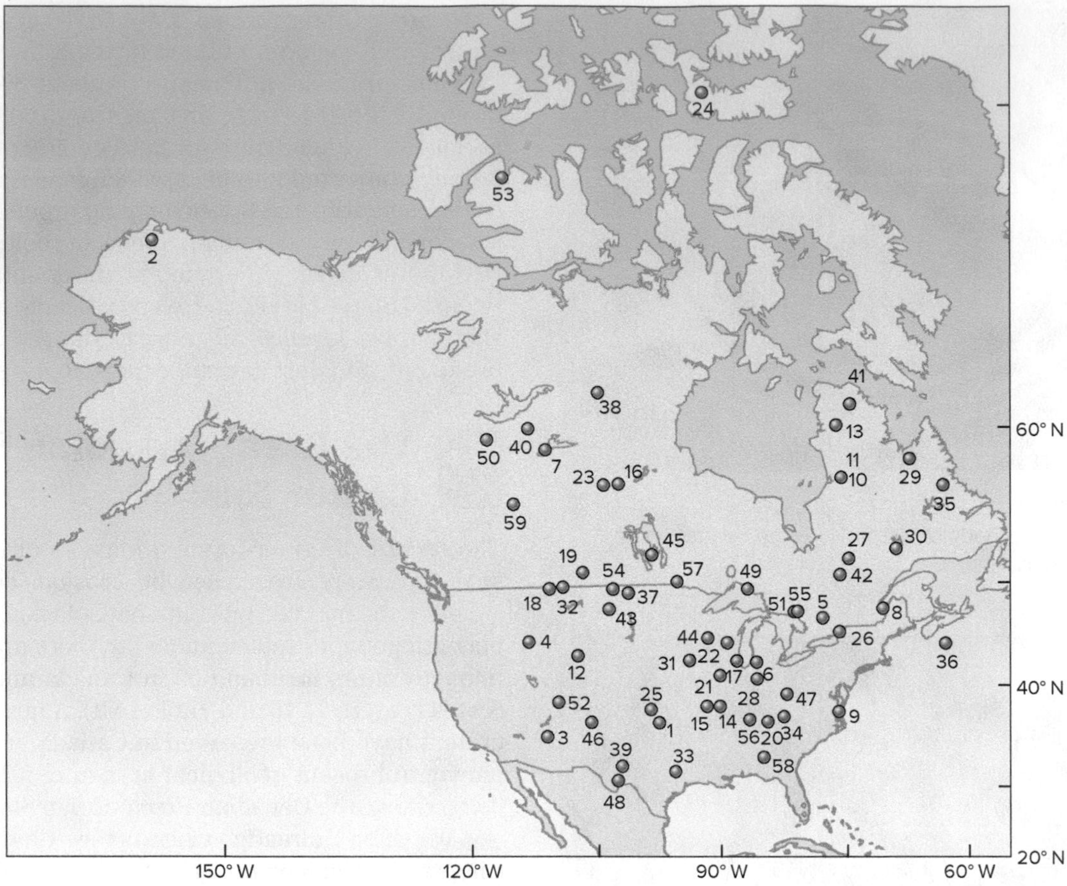

Figure 14.18
Impact crater locations, Canada and the United States. See Table 14.2 for names, sizes, and ages.
Source: © Planetary and Space Science Centre, University of New Brunswick.

Table 14.2

Names, Sizes, and Ages of Impact Craters in Canada and the United States

Crater Name	Location	Diameter (km)	Age (Millions of Years)
1 Ames	Oklahoma	16	470 ± 30
2 Avak	Alaska	12	95
3 Barringer	Arizona	1.18	0.049 ± 0.003
4 Beaverhead	Montana	60	~ 600
5 Brent	Ontario	3.8	396 ± 20
6 Calvin	Michigan	8.5	450 ± 10
7 Carswell	Saskatchewan	39	115 ± 10
8 Charlevoix	Quebec	54	342 ± 15
9 Chesapeake Bay	Virginia	90	35.5 ± 0.3
10 Clearwater East	Quebec	26	290 ± 20
11 Clearwater West	Quebec	36	290 ± 20
12 Cloud Creek	Wyoming	7	190 ± 30
13 Couture	Quebec	8	430 ± 25

continued

Table 14.2

Names, Sizes, and Ages of Impact Craters in Canada and the United States

Crater Name	Location	Diameter (km)	Age (Millions of Years)
14 Crooked Creak	Missouri	7	320 ± 80
15 Decaturville	Missouri	6	< 300
16 Deep Bay	Saskatchewan	13	99 ± 4
17 Des Plaines	Illinois	8	< 280
18 Eagle Butte	Alberta	10	< 65
19 Elbow	Saskatchewan	8	395 ± 25
20 Flynn Creek	Tennessee	3.8	360 ± 20
21 Glasford	Illinois	4	< 430
22 Glover Bluff	Wisconsin	8	< 500
23 Gow	Saskatchewan	5	< 250
24 Haughton	Nunavut	24	23 ± 1
25 Haviland	Kansas	0.01	< 0.001
26 Holleford	Ontario	2.35	550 ± 100
27 Ile Rouleau	Quebec	4	< 300
28 Kentland	Indiana	13	< 97
29 La Moinerie	Quebec	8	400 ± 50
30 Manicouagan	Quebec	100	214 ± 1
31 Manson	Iowa	35	73.8 ± 0.3
32 Maple Creek	Saskatchewan	6	< 75
33 Marquez	Texas	12.7	58 ± 2
34 Middlesboro	Kentucky	6	< 300
35 Mistastin	Newfoundland and Labrador	28	36.4 ± 4
36 Montagnais	Nova Scotia	45	50.50 ± 0.76
37 Newporte	North Dakota	3.2	< 500
38 Nicholson	Northwest Territories	12.5	< 400
39 Odessa	Texas	0.16	< 0.05
40 Pilot	Northwest Territories	6	445 ± 2
41 Pingualuit	Quebec	3.44	1.4 ± 0.1
42 Presqu'ile	Quebec	24	< 500
43 Red Wing	North Dakota	9	200 ± 25
44 Rock Elm	Wisconsin	6	< 505
45 Saint Martin	Manitoba	40	220 ± 32
46 Santa Fe	New Mexico	6-13	< 1200
47 Serpent Mound	Ohio	8	< 320
48 Sierra Madera	Texas	13	< 100
49 Slate Islands	Ontario	30	~ 450
50 Steen River	Alberta	25	95 ± 7
51 Sudbury	Ontario	250	1850 ± 3
52 Upheaval Dome	Utah	10	< 170
53 Tunnunik	Northwest Territories	25	> 130, <450
54 Viewfield	Saskatchewan	2.5	190 ± 20
55 Wanapitei	Ontario	7.5	37.2 ± 1.2
56 Wells Creek	Tennessee	12	200 ± 100
57 West Hawk	Manitoba	2.44	100 ± 1.5
58 Wetumpka	Alabama	6.5	81 ± 1.5
59 Whitecourt	Alberta	0.036	0.001

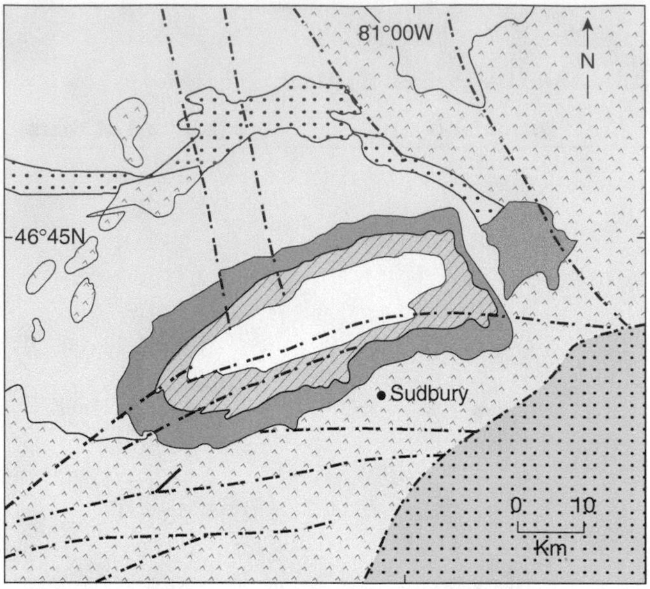

Figure 14.19
Simplified geological map of the Sudbury and Wanapitei impact sites. The elliptical Sudbury structure, including the Sudbury igneous complex (red), the Onaping formation (orange), and the Onwatin and Chelmsford formations (yellow), stands out against the rock of the Superior province of the Canadian Precambrian Shield (blue). The younger rock of the Grenville Province is shown in green, and Lake Wanapitei in grey. Regional faults are represented by dash-dot-dash lines. The original Sudbury impact site was larger and circular. It has eroded away and deformed over geological time.
Source: Modified from R.A.F. Grieve, *Impact Structures in Canada,* 2006.

disseminated in the rock of the Canadian Precambrian Shield. The melting that occurred as a result of the impact concentrated the metal. Approximately 25% of impact sites worldwide have associated economic mineral deposits.

The young Wanapitei crater (37.2 ± 1.2 Ma) lies entirely inside the limits of the original Sudbury complex crater. It is a crater within a crater. The crater is located under the waters of Lake Wanapitei and was first identified by a gravity survey (Figure 14.22). The local gravitational acceleration is less than in surrounding areas because rock fractured by impact is less dense than unaltered rock.

HOLLEFORD, ONTARIO

Impact scars in the landscape are often difficult to identify from the perspective of an observer on the ground; however, aerial and satellite photos are invaluable tools for identification. The Holleford impact crater (550 ± 100 Ma), located 27 km northwest of Kingston, Ontario, was discovered in 1955 during a systematic examination of aerial photographs for circular features of possible impact origin (Figure 14.23).

SLATE ISLANDS, ONTARIO

The Slate Islands are a small group of islands located in Lake Superior, offshore from Terrace Bay, Ontario (Figure 14.24). The Slate Islands lie in the centre of

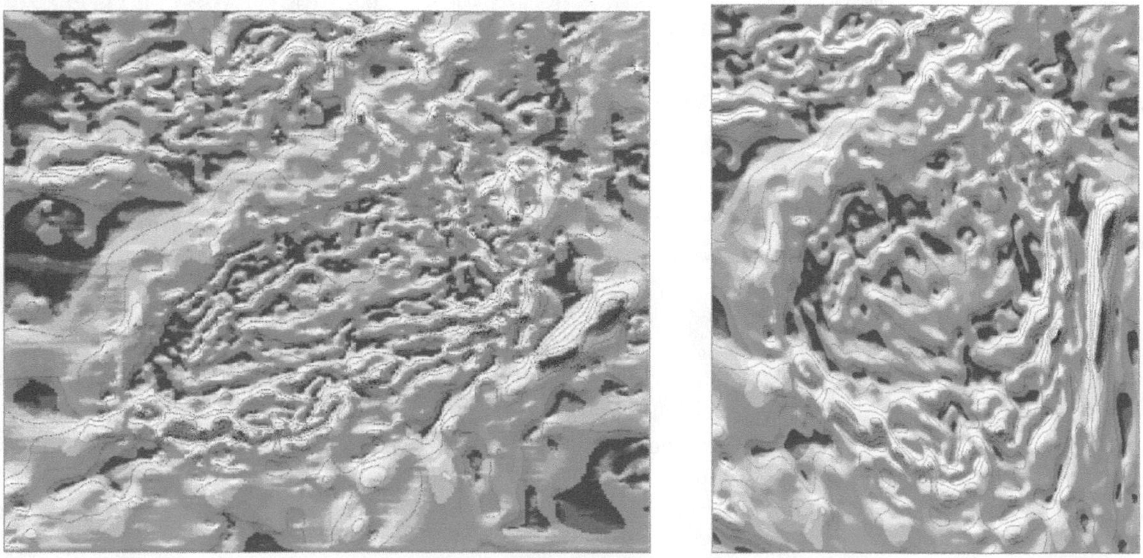

(a) (b)

Figure 14.20
Gravity data from Sudbury, Ontario (a) before and (b) after correcting for the tectonic deformation that took place since the impact some 1.85 billion years ago.
Source: Reproduced with the permission of Natural Resources Canada 2014, courtesy of the Geological Survey of Canada.

Figure 14.21
Flag of Greater Sudbury.
Source: Claire Samson.

Figure 14.23
Aerial photograph of the Holleford impact crater, Ontario. The crater depression stands out against the farmland grid.
Source: National Air Photo Library, Centre for Topographic Information, Natural Resources Canada, Image A17775.

Figure 14.22
Flying over Lake Wanapitei, Ontario. The smooth, semicircular northern shore of the lake is evidence of its impact origin.
Source: Claire Samson.

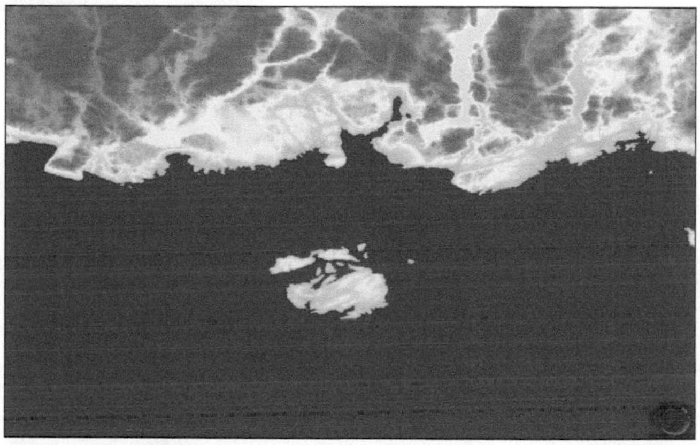

Figure 14.24
Digital elevation model of the Slate Islands, Lake Superior, Ontario. The complex shape of the islands suggests a violent, complicated geological history.
Source: Planetary and Space Science Centre, University of New Brunswick.

concentric underwater features: a trough where the water depth is in excess of 250 m and a larger ridge where the water depth is less than 100 m. The ridge is thought to correspond to the rim of the original crater, formed approximately 450 million years ago.

The first mention alluding to the Slate Islands as an impact site is a paper written in *Nature* by Professor Henry Halls of the University of Toronto in 1975. In summer 1973, Professor Halls, who has devoted his life to the study of the flood basalts of the Lake Superior region (Figure 5.27), was mapping lava flows when he discovered heavily fragmented rock and shatter cones at several sites on the islands. Subsequent laboratory analyses of revealed that these field samples carried a distinct magnetic direction that had been acquired by the rock almost instantaneously as a result of an impact.

BRENT, ONTARIO

The Brent impact crater (396 ± 20 Ma) is located in the boreal forest, near the northern boundary of Algonquin Provincial Park in Ontario. The remnants of the original 3.8 km wide crater is a 3.0 km wide and 60 m deep depression occupied by two kidney-shaped lakes (Figures 14.25 and 14.26). Twelve boreholes were drilled into the structure in the 1950s and 1960s (Figure 14.27). They revealed that the crater is filled with approximately 260 m of sedimentary rock deposited long after the impact. Beneath the sedimentary rock, a 600 m layer of shocked rock overlays a thin lens of impact melt rock, which is found immediately above the fractured Precambrian basement.

Figure 14.25
Aerial photograph of the Brent impact crater, Ontario. The red lines indicate the viewpoint from which the photo shown in Figure 14.26 was taken.

Source: National Air Photo Library, Centre for Topographic Information, Natural Resources Canada, Image A21463.

Figure 14.26
Lake Tecumseh lies within the Brent crater. The hills in the background mark the far rim of the crater. Impact craters are notoriously unspectacular as seen from the ground. This is why many of them go undetected until they are identified on aerial photographs, as in the case of the Holleford crater.

Source: © Claire Samson.

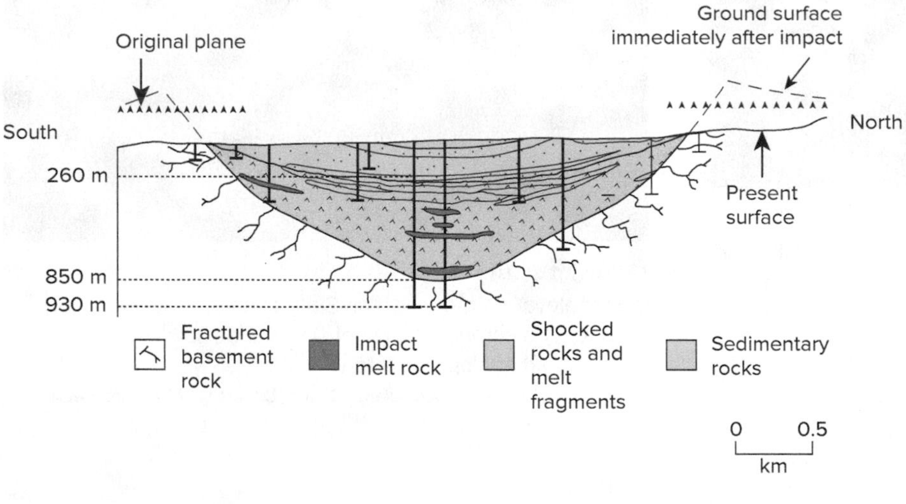

Figure 14.27
Geological cross-section through the Brent impact crater, Ontario.

Source: Modified from R.A.F. Grieve, *Impact Structures in Canada,* 2006.

Analyses suggest that the Brent impactor was a large stony meteorite, 150 m in diameter, that hit the Earth at approximately 70 000 km/h. The violence of the impact was such that more than a billion tonnes of rock were vaporized in less than a second. As vividly described by Dan Strickland in the Brent crater trail guide.

> If the Brent crater impact were to be repeated today, every tree in Algonquin Park to the south and every tree up to the Ottawa River, and well beyond into Quebec, would be flattened and covered with material ejected from the crater. Windows would be blown out in Ottawa, 225 km away, and the buildings would sway and crack as an earthquake (more powerful than any observed … in historic times), rolled under the city.

TUNNUNIK, NORTHWEST TERRITORIES

The most recent addition to the list of Canadian impact craters is the heavily eroded Tunnunik crater, located on Victoria Island in the Arctic. "Tunnunik" means "the other side" in Inuktitut, referring to its location on the northwestern part of the island far from the village of Ulukhaktok, home to the world's most northerly golf

Figure 14.28
Shatter cones from the Tunnunik impact crater, exhibiting a well-developed pattern of fractures radiating outward.
Source: Keith Dewing.

Figure 14.29
Panoramic aerial photograph of the Haughton impact crater, Devon Island, Nunavut.
Source: © Martin Lipman/Canadian Space Agency.

tournament. The age of the impact that created Tunnunik is poorly constrained. From its relationship with surrounding rocks, geologists estimate that the crater was formed between 450 Ma and 130 Ma.

The impact structure was discovered in the summer of 2010 by Dr. Keith Dewing of the Geological Survey of Canada and Dr. Brian Pratt of the University of Saskatchewan who were exploring this largely unknown area, mapped in detail for the first time. Their helicopter landed along a small creek where shatter cones seemed to be everywhere (Figure 14.28). The geologists also found heavily deformed rock, much different from the orderly subhorizontal sedimentary layers typical of this region. They had little doubt that they had come across an impact site. Upon reeximation of aerial photographs and topographic maps, the subtle circular feature filled with recent glacial sediments, which had been missed previously, emerged clearly.

The map of impact craters in Canada and the United States (Figure 14.18) shows a bias towards the more southern regions that have been extensively mapped by geologists. The story of Tunnunik indicates that the Canadian Arctic might hide a few more impact craters.

Figure 14.30
This eight-metre tall block of rock was tossed in the air during the Haughton impact.
Source: © Martin Lipman.

HAUGHTON, NUNAVUT

The Haughton impact crater (23 ± 1 Ma) lies on Devon Island, a large uninhabited island in the Canadian Arctic, where shatter cones were discovered in 1974 (Figure 14.29 and Figure 14.30). Cold, dry, windy, rocky, and dusty, the Haughton impact site has been described as "Mars on Earth." With its summers lasting just five weeks at an average temperature of only 2°C and its geographic remoteness, it is indeed an analogue of the conditions found on Mars. The Mars Institute and the SETI (Search for Extra-Terrestrial Intelligence) Institute are exploiting the opportunity and operate a research station at the Haughton crater, under the umbrella of the Haughton-Mars Project. The station is the focal point for multidisciplinary research on the effects of impacts on the Earth and on other planets, life in extreme environments, and technologies for future planetary exploration by robots and humans.

PINGUALUIT, QUEBEC

Pingualuit (1.4 ± 0.1 Ma) is a classic example of a simple crater (Figure 14.31). It was first recognized as a crater in 1943 when a pilot flew over it. *Pingualuit* means "large hill" in Inuktitut. The crater is a conspicuous landmark in the flat tundra and an important archeological site. The Pingualuit impactor is inferred to have been 100 to 150 m in diameter and to have struck the Earth at a velocity of 90 000 km/h. No meteorites have been recovered. The surrounding rock, however, is enriched in iridium and contains impactites, a type of glass produced by partial fusion of the rock as a result of the heat generated by the impact.

Pingualuit is "a lake fallen from the sky" in the words of Dr. Michel Bouchard, leader of several science expeditions to the site. The crater encloses a lake 3.4 km in diameter within a well-preserved rim rising some 160 m above the tundra surface. With a depth of 250 m, Pingualuit is one of the deepest freshwater lakes in the world. Only one **species** of fish, Arctic char, lives in the lake, and there are signs of fish cannibalism. How were fish introduced in the crater? Water levels in the crater changed through time. At one point, Pingualuit Lake overflowed and drained into a neighbouring lake. Fish probably swam upcurrent from that lake into Pingualuit Lake.

WHITECOURT, ALBERTA

The Whitecourt crater, located northwest of Edmonton, is the only crater in Canada where meteorites have been found. In early July 2007, local residents James "Sonny" Stevens and his brother Rod Stevens took a metal detector to investigate a circular depression south of the village of Whitecourt (Figure 14.32). The feature had been known for decades as an interesting spot in the woods, but Sonny and Rod had the intuition that perhaps this was the result of the collision of an extraterrestrial rock with the Earth's surface, by analogy with other similar craters elsewhere. Within a couple of hours, the brothers had found four angular, metallic pieces within 10 cm of the surface, on the rim of the depression. They contacted Dr. Christopher Herd, a meteorite researcher at the University of Alberta, and arranged to have one of the pieces analyzed. Analyses showed that the pieces were made of iron-nickel metal with tiny inclusions of iron nickel phosphide, a mineral unknown on Earth.

Figure 14.32
The small Whitecourt crater measures only 36 m across and is 6 m deep.
Source: Christopher Herd, Department of Earth and Atmosphere Sciences, University of Alberta.

Figure 14.31
The Pingualuit crater rises majestically above the flat tundra of northern Quebec.
Source: Photo by Michel Bouchard.

The brothers accompanied Dr. Herd and colleague Dr. Duane Froese to the site in late July 2007. It was immediately recognized that the circular depression was not a sinkhole or the result of glacial processes. An additional 17 meteorite specimens were found within a few hours. These specimens and the almost perfect bowl-shaped morphology confirmed the feature's origin as the result of impact (Figure 14.33).

Since the discovery, over 2500 meteorites with a cumulative mass over 100 kg have been recovered at the Whitecourt crater. Nearly all of them have a shrapnel-like shape and are distributed over an area about 600 m by 600 m on the east side of the crater (Figure 14.34). Preservation of the impact ejecta layer and the distribution of the meteorites, coupled with modelling of the collision events show that the crater formed by the impact of a meteoroid approximately 1 m in diameter traveling east-northeast at less than 36 000 km/h, and striking the surface at an angle between 40 and 55 degrees to the horizontal. The meteoroid fragmented upon impact, showering the area with thousands of meteorites.

(a)

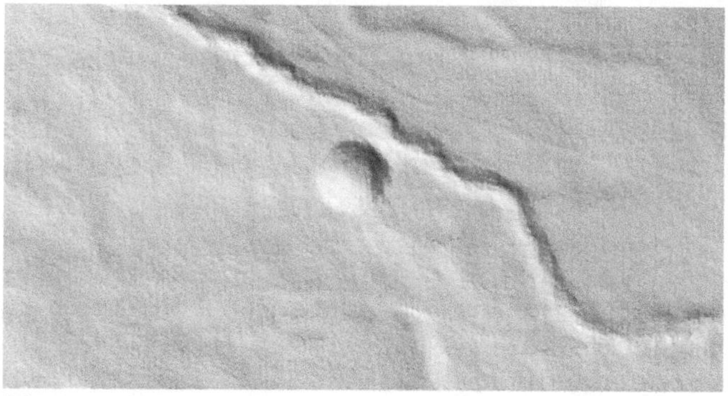

(b)

Figure 14.33

(a) Trees and bushes obscure the depression, so laser imaging (b) was used to virtually strip away the vegetation to reveal the Whitecourt crater.

Source: Christopher Herd, Department of Earth and Atmosphere Sciences, University of Alberta.

The Cretaceous/Paleogene Boundary Event

The human tragedies wrought by natural disasters involve individuals of the species, not the entire species. Several times in the last 543 million years however, many, or even most, of the species on the Earth became extinct in a geologically short time (Figure 14.35). These great dyings, or mass extinctions, are the largest natural disasters known to have occurred on the Earth.

What powerful events can drive large numbers of species into extinction all around the Earth? There are numerous possible causes of mass extinctions, including the long-lasting effects of plate tectonics, voluminous volcanic outpourings, climate changes, asteroid and comet impacts, and biological processes. When a number of processes interact in the same geologically short time, numbers of extinctions increase markedly.

In the last several million years of Cretaceous time, many groups of plants and animals, whether on land or in the seas, were losing species to extinction. It appears that slow-acting changes elevated the level of background extinction. Then this deteriorating situation was apparently finished off by a deadly one–two punch of asteroid impact and volcanism to end Cretaceous time.

Over 65% of species were lost. In the oceans, the reptiles and ammonoids went extinct, and major die-offs occurred in species of bony fishes, sponges, sea urchins, foraminifera, snails, and clams. On land, many species of mammals and reptiles and all the dinosaurs (except those that later evolved into birds) plunged

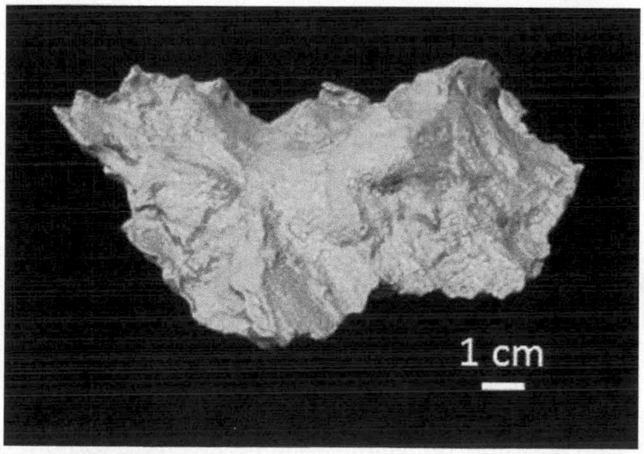

Figure 14.34

Model of a meteorite fragment recovered from the Whitecourt crater. The model has been generated using laser imaging, a non-contact technique that can capture the shape of samples in great detail in three dimensions.

Source: Christopher Fry, Carleton University.

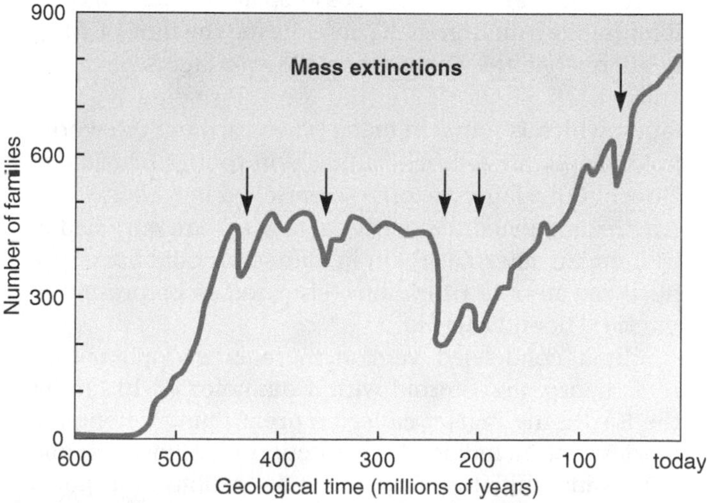

Figure 14.35

Number of families of marine animals with mineralized hard parts over geological time. The overall increase in families with time is interrupted by extinction events indicated by arrows. The Cretaceous/Paleogene extinction is the most recent (rightmost arrow).

into extinction. Land plant life took a heavy hit. The extinction of tiny floating organisms (plankton) in the oceans was overwhelming. With ten million years of the Cretaceous remaining, there were numerous genera of dinosaurs. With two million years to go, there were markedly fewer (most of the survivors were in North America). And then there were none.

To learn what happened at the close of Cretaceous time, one should follow the advice of Sherlock Holmes in "The Problem of Thor Bridge": "If you will find the facts, perhaps others may find the explanation." To find facts related to 66-million-year-old events means to examine rock of this age.

The modern search began near Gubbio, Italy, a locality where the Cretaceous/Paleogene boundary, sandwiched between two distinct types of rock, is particularly well exposed. The latest Cretaceous (K) rock is limestone loaded with fossils of unicellular organisms whose individuals had diameters up to one millimetre. The earliest Paleogene (Pg) limestone above it contains an impoverished and markedly changed fossil assemblage. Between the limestones lies a one-centimetre clay layer that marks the Cretaceous/Paleogene (K/Pg) boundary. Does the K/Pg boundary clay layer hold facts that might explain the events of its days? In the 1970s, the late Luis Alvarez, a Nobel Prize-winning physicist, and his geologist son Walter focused their research efforts on this topic. Their investigation discovered a high percentage of the element iridium in the clay layer, an enrichment about 300 times greater than the normal abundance. Here is a fact begging for an explanation.

Iridium is a siderophile, or iron-loving element. Most of the Earth's iridium lies deep in its iron-rich core; it migrated with iron to the core during the time of early heating when the Earth separated into layers of different density (Figure 2.10). But the K/Pg boundary clay layer, which is found in many places around the world, holds an estimated one-half million tonnes of iridium. How did this layer become so enriched in iridium? Luis Alvarez reasoned that since meteorites are enriched in iridium, an asteroid 10 km in diameter could have supplied the amount of iridium estimated to be present in the K/Pg boundary clay.

In a condensed version, here is a popular current theory: an asteroid with a diameter of 10 km hit the Earth; the impact caused a great dying among life worldwide, including the extinction of dinosaurs, and left its incriminating fingerprint as iridium in a global clay layer. The theory is intriguing, easy to grasp, and beguilingly simple to accept. But for a theory to gain widespread approval in the scientific community, it must explain all relevant facts and allow predictions to be made. If these predictions later become supported by facts, then the theory gains wider acceptance. Thus, before the K/Pg impact theory could gain wide acceptance in the scientific community, many more facts needed to be discovered to verify the predictions made as a result of this theory.

EVIDENCE OF THE K/PG IMPACT

Once the K/Pg theory was proposed, it excited scientists worldwide, and the search for facts shifted into high gear. Researchers around the world began examining the K/Pg boundary clay layer for other evidence of Earth-like versus meteorite-like components. (1) The clay layer was found on the continents, thus ruling out the possibility that the iridium enrichment was due simply to a change in ocean composition. (2) The minerals in the K/Pg boundary clay have a different composition from clays in the limestone layers above and below it; this anomalous composition might be explained by composition that included a mixture of 1 part asteroid to 10 parts Earth crust. (3) Quartz grains are present with shocked crystal structures, indicating a short and violent impact. Shocked quartz, with its planar deformation features, has been found only in association with impacts, so its discovery at the K/Pg boundary is strong evidence of impact. (4) Sand-size spherules of minerals are present, suggesting melting and resolidification. (5) Ratios of the radioactive element rhenium to its decay product osmium are similar to those in meteorites and are quite different from the ratios in the Earth's surface rock. (6) Abundant microscopic diamonds, found in some meteorites, occur in the K/Pg boundary clay layer. (7) Carbon-rich grains with "fluffy" structures indicative of fire are abundant in the K/Pg boundary clay layer.

SITE OF THE K/PG IMPACT

The facts from the K/Pg boundary clay layer compelled more scientists to agree that a massive impact had occurred, but even more evidence was sought. If an asteroid slammed into the Earth some 65 million years ago, then where was the impact site? Could it be found? Or had it been (1) subducted and destroyed? (2) buried beneath a continental glacier? (3) hidden under piles of sediment on land or the seafloor? (4) covered by flood basalt? (5) eroded and erased from the face of the Earth? (6) crunched into oblivion by a continent collision? Geologists searched for impact scars worldwide, but some were too small, while others were too old or too young.

Then related evidence began to focus the search. A 65.01 ± 0.8 Ma sedimentary rock layer was found in Haiti containing shocked quartz grains and glassy spherules one centimetre in diameter formed from melted rock. In Cuba, a thick, chaotic sedimentary deposit with huge angular blocks was discovered. In northeastern Mexico, similar particles were identified in a thick bed of sediment containing land debris, ripple marks, and other features interpreted as a tsunami deposit; this bed is 65.07 ± 0.1 Ma old. Similar but thinner deposits were found in the K/Pg boundary position in the banks of the Brazos River in Texas and in coastal deposits in New Jersey and the Carolinas. The sedimentary features suggested a Caribbean region impact, but where?

In a separate development, the Mexican national petroleum company (PEMEX) had drilled exploratory wells near Merida in the Yucatan Peninsula of Mexico. At depths of 2 km, the PEMEX well bores had encountered a 90 m thick zone of shattered rock containing shocked quartz grains and glassy blobs of once-melted rock. This information had not been relayed to the impact research circles. It was Alan Hildebrand, a Ph.D. candidate in planetary sciences at the University of Arizona at the time and now a professor at the University of Calgary, who put the pieces of the puzzle together in 1991 and proposed the Chicxulub structure as the K/Pg boundary impact crater.

The Chicxulub structure of Yucatan was created some 66 million years ago when a massive asteroid slammed into a shallow, tropical sea. Geophysical measurements show circular patterns of gravity and magnetic anomalies suggesting a circular disturbance at depth (Figure 14.36). A recent seismic survey has revealed a raised inner ring 80 km in diameter and an outer ring about 195 km in diameter.

CONSEQUENCES OF THE K/PG IMPACT

The Chicxulub impact was so great that its effects were not only regional but also would have been felt worldwide. (1) The impact of the K/Pg asteroid certainly created an earthquake of monumental magnitude along with numerous gigantic aftershocks. Seismologist Steven M. Day has assumed the magnitude of the K/Pg earthquake can be estimated by scaling up from the energy released in nuclear explosions. Extrapolating upward from an atomic bomb blast of moment magnitude 6.0 leads to a K/Pg impact earthquake of magnitude 11.3. (2) The oceanic splashdown of an asteroid 10 km in diameter would generate a tsunami up to 300 m tall. (3) Wildfires would rage regionally, or even globally. A recent study suggests that the K/Pg impact ejected so much hot debris into the atmosphere that it caused massive wildfires that consumed much of the vegetation in North America, the Indian subcontinent, and the equatorial region of the world. (4) Huge amounts of nitrogen oxides in the atmosphere would fall as acid rain and acidify surface waters. (5) Dust and soot in the atmosphere would block sunlight and turn day into night, thus making photosynthesis difficult and plunging much of the world into dark wintry conditions for weeks or months. (6) After the atmospheric dust settled, the water vapour and CO_2 remaining in the atmosphere would lead to global warming for years (Figure 14.37).

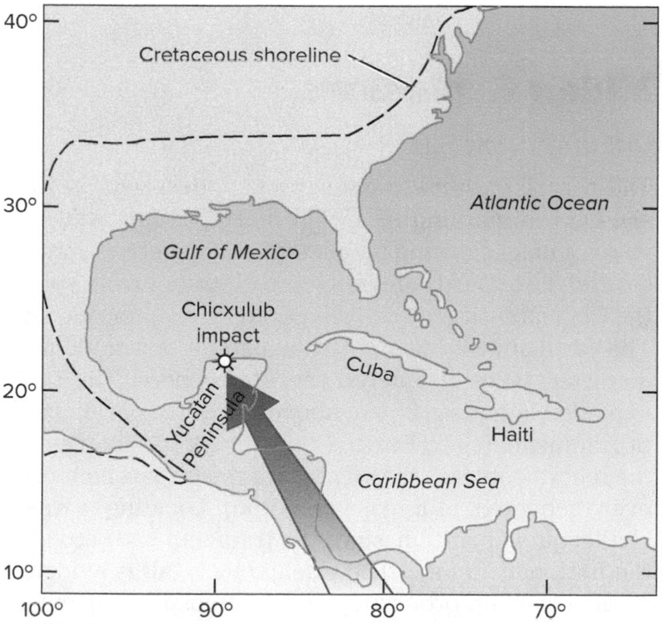

(a)

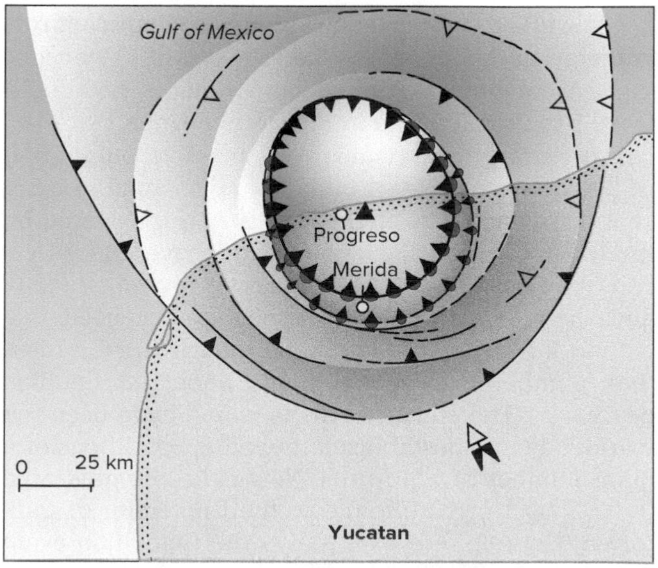

(b)

Figure 14.36
(a) The approximate path of the K/Pg asteroid. Its impact would have sent a superhot vapour cloud over North America. (b) The partially buried Chicxulub impact crater lies on the tip of the Yucatan Peninsula. Notice how the gravity data appear to open to the northwest, suggesting that the asteroid came from the southeast.

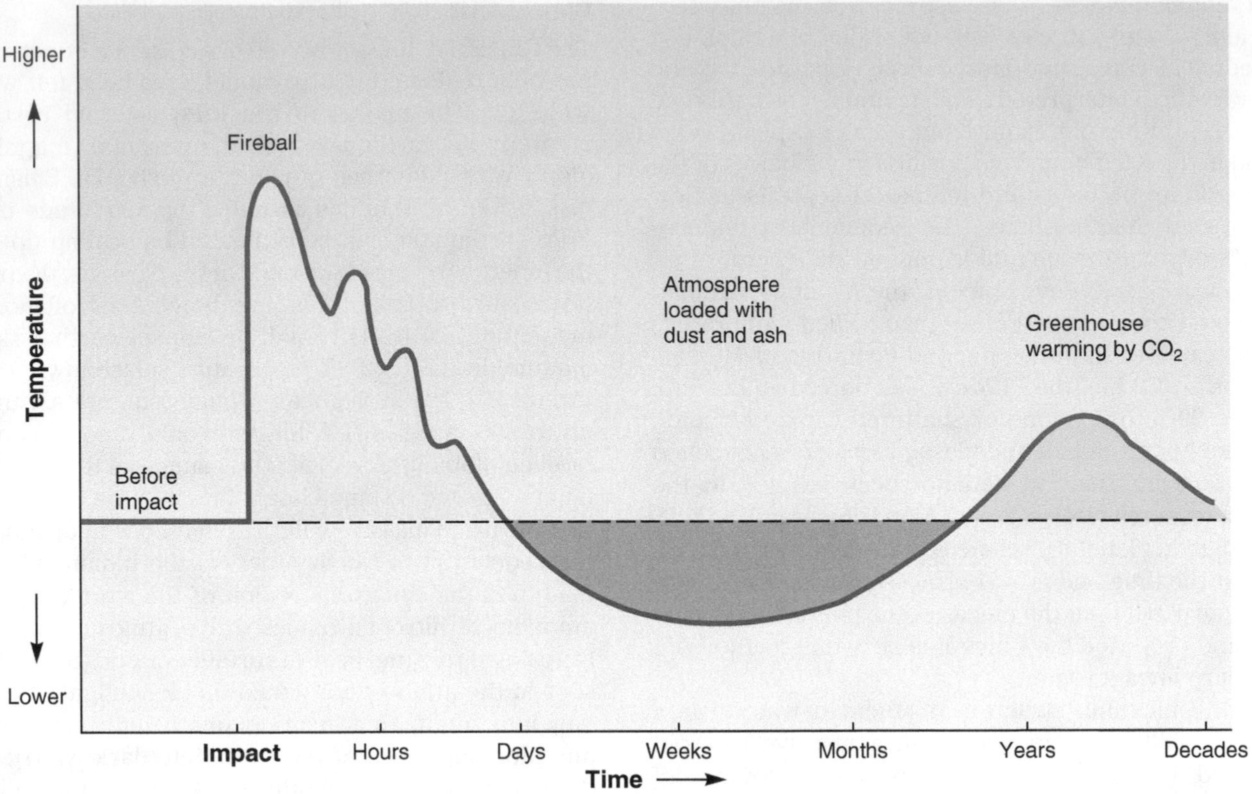

Figure 14.37
Impact of the K/Pg asteroid had marked effects on the Earth's surface temperatures. First, there was a fireball and hot gases that lasted for many hours. Second, temperatures dropped to wintry conditions as airborne dust and soot blocked much incoming sunlight for several months. Third, after the dust settled, CO_2 remained aloft, creating a greenhouse effect that lasted for years.
Source: © David A King.

The effects of the impact played a significant role in the great dying that marked the end of Cretaceous time. A compounding phenomenon might have been flood basalt volcanism in the Deccan traps. The Deccan traps are the remains of a massive outpouring of basaltic lava most prominently displayed in west-central India; much of the outpouring is covered by the Indian Ocean. The original area covered by Deccan flood basalt was probably about two million km^2, and the volume extruded probably exceeded two million km^3. The lavas probably poured forth in less than a million years, beginning about 65.5 million years ago. The climatic effects would have been felt worldwide and destabilized the living conditions of a great number of life forms. New evidence presented in 2013 by Dr. Paul Renne of the University of California, Berkely, however, dates the Chicxulub event at precisely 66 038 000 years ago, and shows that the impact and the extinction are coincident events, within experimental error. The impact dealt the dinosaurs their final blow.

Midair Explosions

CHELYABINSK, SIBERIA, 2013

The use of dashboard cameras is widespread in Russia. On the morning of 15 February 2013, however, it was not illegal driving manoeuvres that were caught on several dashboard cameras but an intruder from space, the Chelyabinsk meteor (see photo of chapter opener)! The Chelyabinsk impactor was a stony object, 20 m in diameter, when it entered the atmosphere. The body exploded in midair, 25 km above the ground. Hundreds of fragments fell to Earth. Chelyabinsk has its place in the record books as the location of the largest meteorite ever recovered, at a mass of 570 kg. Locating it was a challenging operation, since the fragment had settled at the bottom of a lake. The Chelyabinsk fall is evidence of the shielding properties of the atmosphere; from an initial mass of 11 000 000 kg only 0.005% was recovered, the rest of the material was pulverized. Dust was dispersed in the atmosphere and took four days to circle once around the Earth.

Previously undetected, the impactor arrived as a complete surprise and created panic in the Siberian city of Chelyabinsk, home to 1 million people. Almost 1500 people were injured in the event but not by direct impacts of falling solid objects. Injuries were mostly cuts from window glass shattered by the passage of the shock wave (Figure 14.12) approximately three minutes after the meteor.

The events at Chelyabinsk help us understand what happened at Tunguska, also in Siberia, more than a century earlier, without evoking aliens travelling in powerful spaceships and collisions with black holes.

TUNGUSKA, SIBERIA, 1908

The morning of June 30 1908 was sunny in central Siberia. Then, after 7:00 a.m., a massive fireball came streaking in from the east. It exploded about 8 km above ground in a monstrous blast heard 1000 km away. No humans lived immediately under the blast point, but many reindeer did, and they died. A man 60 km away was enveloped in such a mass of heat that he felt his shirt almost catch fire before an air blast threw him 2 m. People and horses 480 km from the explosion site were knocked off their feet. From 650 km away, visible in bright sunlight, a huge column of fire rose 20 km high. The ground shook enough to be registered on seismometers in Russia and Germany. Barometric anomalies were recorded as the air blast travelled twice around the world.

Scientists around the world speculated on what had happened, but it was years before an expedition went to the remote area to search for evidence of the event. Near the Tunguska River, the forest in an area greater than 1000 km^2 was found to have been knocked down and destroyed; many trunks were charred on one side. Over a broader area exceeding 5000 km^2, 80 million trees were down, and many others had tilted trunks, broken branches, and other signs of disturbance (Figure 14.38). But there was no impact crater or even broken ground. The relative lack of facts led unrestrained minds to invent all sorts of wild stories. It was not until 1958 that scientists returned to the site and collected little globules of once-melted metal and silicon-rich rock in the resin of surviving trees.

This evidence raised questions. There was an intense bluish white streak in the sky, a horrendous explosion, a searing blast of heat, blasts of air that encircled the globe, a brilliant sunset and bright night, yet no impact crater—only little globules of melted material. So what happened? A meteoroid racing through the atmosphere broke up and exploded about 8 km above the ground. It was either a fragment of an icy comet about 50 m in diameter, or a large, stony meteorite about 30 m in diameter. The object was travelling about 15 km/s when it disintegrated in a spectacular midair explosion. If it had been a metallic body, it would almost certainly have slammed into the ground. But comets and stony meteorites are weak bodies travelling at outrageous speeds, and the resistance of the Earth's atmosphere is so strong that they typically break apart upon entry. At the end of June 1908, the comet Encke was passing by the Earth; one of its fragments is the likely culprit for the Tunguska event.

Figure 14.38
Millions of trees were knocked down and burned by the Tunguska midair explosion. The photo is from the 1927 expedition led by Leonid Kulik.

Source: Fallen Trees Tunguska meteoroid impact http://commons.wikimedia.org/wiki/Image:Tunguska_event_fallen_trees.jpg.

"Near Misses" of the Twentieth and Twenty-First Centuries

In March 1998, the media widely and excitedly reported that an asteroid labelled 1997XF11 might hit the Earth in the year 2028. In the same year, two big-budget Hollywood movies were released, sensationalizing the effects of collision with a comet in *Deep Impact* and with an asteroid in *Armageddon*.

On 22 March 1989, the asteroid 1989FC, with a diameter of about 300 m, crossed the Earth's orbit at almost the wrong moment; the Earth was at the spot six hours earlier. The asteroid missed us by less than 700 000 km and was not discovered until it had passed the Earth! Had a collision occurred on land, the impact would have created a crater about 6 km across. Was this close call a freak occurrence? Apparently not: several close encounters between the Earth and asteroids and comets have been catalogued (Tables 14.3 and 14.4).

Table 14.3

Ten Closest Observed Asteroid Encounters (1900–2013)

Flyby Year	Asteroid Name	Type	Miss distance (thousands of km)	Diameter (m)
2011	2005 YU55	Apollo	325	400
2006	2004 XP14	Apollo	432	300–900
1996	1996 JA1	Apollo	453	220
2009	2009 DO111	Apollo	468	100
2002	2002 NY40	Apollo	528	800
2008	2007 TU24	Apollo	554	250
2011	2011 JA	Apollo	628	140–320
1989	1989 FC Asclepius	Apollo	684	300
1994	1994 WR12	Aten	709	130
1937	1937 UB Hermes	Apollo	735	300–450

Source: Data from Minor Planet Center.

Table 14.4

Ten Closest Observed Comet Encounters in History

Flyby Year	Comet Name	Type	Miss distance (thousands of km)
1770	D/1770 (Lexell)	Lost	2259
1336	55P/1366 U1 (Tempel-Tuttle)	Short-period	3426
1983	C/1983 H1 (IRAS-Araki-Alcock)	Long-period	4667
837	1P/837 F1 (Halley)	Short-period	4997
1805	3D/1805 V1 (Biela)	Destroyed	5475
1743	C/1743 C1	Long-period	5834
1927	7P/Pons-Winnecke	Short-period	5894
1702	C/1702 H1	Long-period	6537
2011	45P/Honda-Mrkos-Pajdusakova	Short-period	8991
1930	73P/1930 J1 (Schwassmann-Wachmann)	Short-period	9230

Source: Data from Minor Planet Center.

In order to communicate the threat of comet and asteroid impacts calmly, Richard Binzel developed the Torino scale (Table 14.5), which assesses the threat on a scale of 0 to 10.

The 330 m diameter asteroid 99942 Apophis, named after the Egyptian god of evil, caused some commotion upon its discovery in 2004. Preliminary estimates had predicted impact with the Earth for 13 April 2029 with a "rain date" of 13 April 2036 in case of a miss. The threat corresponded to level 4 on the Torino scale, the record for highest Torino rating. Refined calculations, however, have since then lowered the probability to a Torino rating of 0. The only object currently listed above 0 on the Torino scale is the 130 m diameter Apollo asteroid VK184 with a benign rating of 1 and a probability of 1 in 2700 of impacting the Earth on 3 June 2048.

For smaller objects, the number of near misses is surprisingly high. Detailed telescopic examination has shown that up to 50 house-size bodies pass between the Earth and the Moon every day. Should we worry about the consequences of impacts from speeding bodies 50 m in diameter? Apparently not, because the Earth has its own defence system against small bodies—its atmosphere. When comets and stony meteorites travelling at 50 000 km/h hit the atmosphere, the great strains break most of them into smaller pieces that burn up explosively. Most of the flameouts occur 10 to 40 km above the Earth's surface, which is too high for significant damage to occur on the ground. However, most iron meteorites are internally strong enough to stay intact as they pass through the atmosphere and they do hit the ground. Luckily, iron meteorites are relatively uncommon.

Table 14.5

The Torino Scale Assessing Comet and Asteroid Impact Hazards

Events with no likely consequences	
0	No collision hazard, or object is small.
Events meriting careful monitoring	
1	Collision is extremely unlikely.
Events of concern	
2	Collision is very unlikely.
3	Close encounter with > 1% chance of local destruction.
4	Close encounter with > 1% chance of regional devastation.
Threatening events	
5	Significant threat of regional devastation.
6	Significant threat of global catastrophe.
7	Extremely significant threat of global catastrophe.
Certain collisions	
8	Collision will cause localized destruction (one event every 50 to 1000 years).
9	Collision will cause regional devastation (one event every 1000 to 100 000 years).
10	Collision will cause global catastrophe (one event every 100 000 years).

A Defence Plan Against Large Impacts

How often do impacts of large bodies occur (Figure 14.39)? This question is hard to answer looking at our planet because of the continuous recycling of the Earth's surface materials by plate tectonics and their destruction by weathering and the agents of erosion. It is easier to answer this question by looking at the long-term record of impacts preserved on the dead surface of the Moon and then extrapolate the results back to the Earth. The dark volcanic maria on the Moon formed after the early period of intense asteroidal bombardment. The basalt-flooded maria cover 16% (6 million km^2) of the Moon's surface; they formed about 3200 million years ago. The maria are scarred by five craters with diameters greater than 50 km and another 24 craters with diameters between 25 and 50 km. This averages to one major impact somewhere on the maria every 110 million years.

Applying these impact rates to the Earth generates the following numbers: the Earth's surface area is more than 80 times the area of the lunar maria, so it would have had more than 80 times as many impacts, that is, about 2400 impacts leaving craters greater than 25 km in diameter. Land comprises about 30% of the Earth's

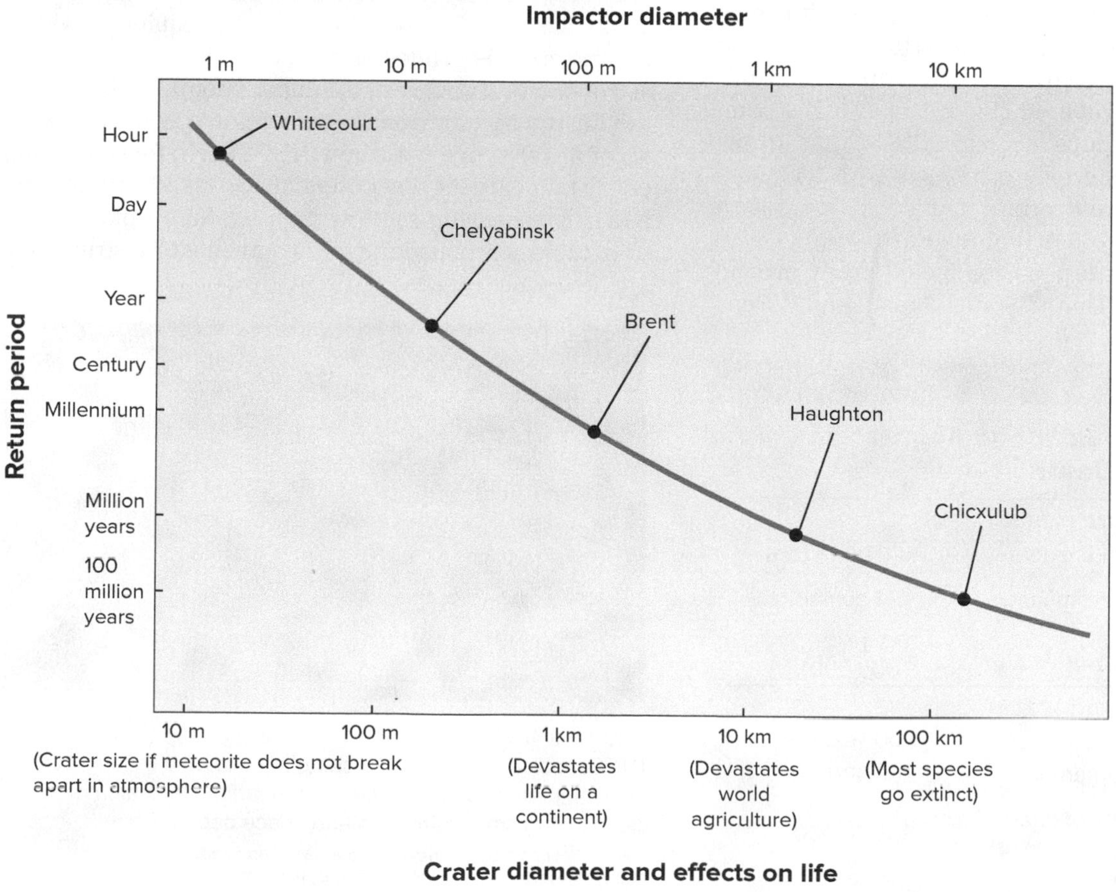

Figure 14.39 Relationship between impactor diameter, crater size, and effects on life, with a few examples.

surface, so about 720 of these craters should have formed on land. More than 160 craters have been discovered so far, but most of them are less than 25 km in diameter. Most of the missing craters have probably been destroyed or buried.

The odds are extremely small that a large asteroid will hit the Earth during your lifetime. However, so many people will be killed when a big space object does hit that it skews the probabilities. Statistically speaking, every individual has a greater chance of being killed by a comet or asteroid than of winning a big jackpot in a lottery! The probabilities of death by meteoroid impact were indirectly assessed in the words of paleontologist George Gaylord Simpson: "Given enough time, anything that is possible is probable."

RISKS OF IMPACT

U.S. astronomer David Morrison has described the Earth as a target in a cosmic shooting gallery of high-speed asteroids and comets. Impact risk has been assessed by the United States National Aeronautics and Space Administration (NASA) (Table 14.6).

There are over 2000 near-Earth objects (NEOs), and about 25 to 50% of them will eventually hit the Earth. The first step in a plan to protect ourselves is to locate them, determine their orbits, and identify which ones present immediate threats. Since 1998, NASA has been mandated to locate and track NEOs with diameters greater than 0.14 km, and this effort will be ongoing until 2020. As of October 2013, more than 10 000 NEOs have been discovered (Figure 14.40). The count of potentially hazardous objects (PHOs) has grown to 1439. PHOs are asteroids or comets with diameters greater than 150 m and orbits that could bring them within 7 500 000 km (0.05 AU) of the Earth.

While this inventory is conducted from ground-based stations in the United States, Japan, and Europe, Canada is providing a viewpoint from the sky. The Canadian NEOSSat satellite, launched on 25 February 2013 from the Satish Dhawan Space Centre in India, is the first dual-purpose space telescope designed to detect and track both asteroids (a natural hazard) and decommissioned satellites (a human-made hazard) (Figure 14.41). The microsatellite is the size of a suitcase, weighs only 75 kg, and is equipped with a modest-size 15 cm telescope, smaller than most amateur astronomers'. However, its vantage point 700 km above the Earth's surface and the exceptional pointing stability of its telescope will allow NEOSSat to focus steadily on distant targets. Its potential for discovery of new NEOs is especially high in the near-Sun region where brightness is problematic for ground-based instruments.

Table 14.6

Frequency of Impacts and Annual Probabilities of Death

For globally catastrophic events:	
Return period between impacts	500 000 years
Assumed fatalities from impact	$\frac{1}{4}$ of human race
Total annual probability of death	$\frac{1}{2\,000\,000}$
For Tunguska-sized events:	
Return period between impacts	300 years
Return period for urban areas	100 000 years
Total annual probability of death	$\frac{1}{30\,000\,000}$

Source: David Morrison (1992).

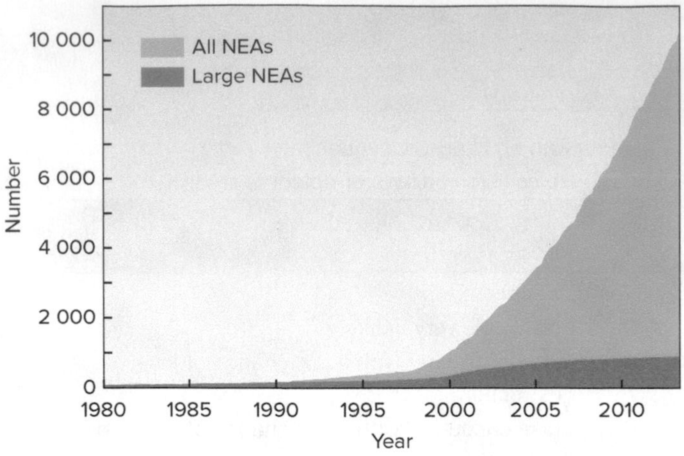

Figure 14.40
Cumulative number of near-Earth asteroids (NEAs) by year of discovery from 1980 until October 2013. Total NEAs are green; large NEAs (diameter over one kilometre) are red.
Source: Alan B. Chamberlin, JPL.

Figure 14.41
The Canadian NEOSSat microsatellite circles the Earth every 100 minutes, pointing at different locations in search of faint signals from small asteroids and space debris.
Source: Reprinted by permission of the Canadian Space Agency, http://www.asc-csa.gc.ca/eng/satellites/neossat/

PREVENTION OF IMPACT

One strategy for protective action is to launch a spacecraft, a heavy gravity tractor that would hover near an NEO, allowing the resultant gravitational attraction to pull the asteroid into an Earth-avoiding path. We have within reach the technological ability to deflect asteroids. The Japanese probe Hayabusa landed on Apollo asteroid Itokawa in November 2005. Itokawa is only 535 m long, yet this small target was intercepted 145 million kilometres away, almost the distance to the Sun. If the gravity tractor effect would be too small, the NEO could be rammed with a high-speed projectile that would transfer its momentum to alter the NEO's velocity or course. If an NEO is discovered too late for these actions to be implemented, the only option may be to hit it with a nuclear explosion that would blast some of its rocky and icy material away and alter its path.

Is a large impact too unlikely an event to take seriously? Arthur C. Clarke said:

> We tend to remember only the extraordinary events, such as the odd coincidences; but we forget that almost every event is an odd coincidence. The asteroid that misses the Earth is on a course every bit as improbable as the one that strikes it.

Figure 14.42
The coronal mass ejection of 27 February 2000 captured by the SOlar and Heliospheric Observatory (SOHO) satellite in orbit around the Sun. Direct light from the Sun is blocked in this picture with the Sun's relative position and size indicated by a white circle.

Source: Courtesy of SOHO/consortium. SOHO is a project of international cooperation between ESA and NASA.

LO5 Space Weather Hazards

SOLAR ACTIVITY

The Sun sends a stream of subatomic particles called the **solar wind** in all directions. Two mechanisms are responsible for strong gusts of solar wind: coronal holes and coronal mass ejections. In both cases, the hot, turbulent upper fringes of the Sun's atmosphere are released in space, gravity not being strong enough to hold them. Coronal holes are localized phenomena producing high-speed streams of **plasma**. Coronal mass ejections are star-scale events sending out gigantic clouds of plasma (Figure 14.42).

Sunspots are dark areas on the surface of the Sun. The number of sunspots follows an approximately 11-year cycle wherein solar radiation varies by about 0.15% (Figure 14.43), a higher number of sunspots indicating a more energetic Sun (Figure 14.44). The previous cycle (cycle 23) extended from May 1996 to January 2008, with a peak in 2000. The current cycle (cycle 24) has been much subdued with a delayed start until early 2010 and the weakest maximum in 100 years. Sunspots were nearly absent between 1645 and 1715 during the Maunder Minimum (Figure 8.16), causing the Earth's temperature to fall 0.2°C.

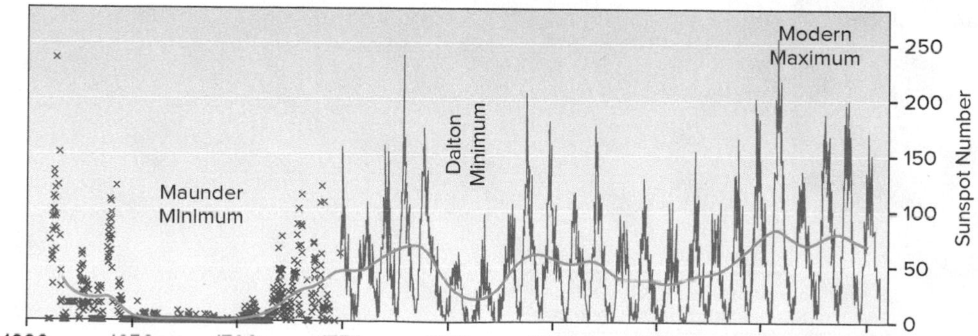

Figure 14.43
Number of sunspots since 1600. Notice the 11-year cycle.

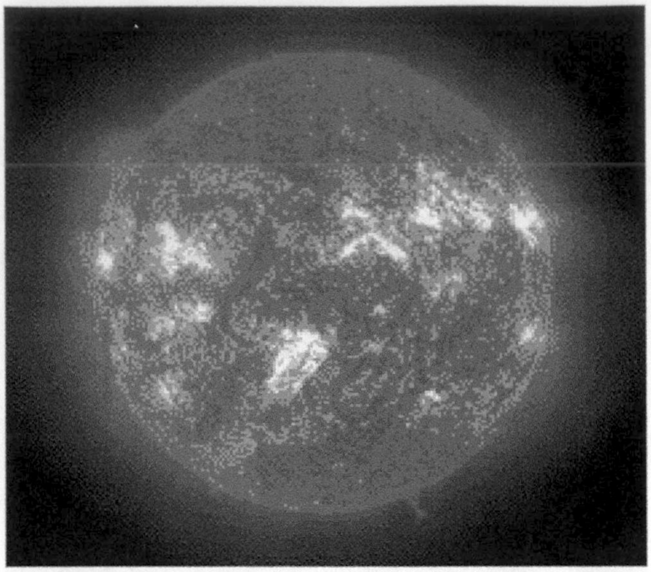

(a)

(b)

Figure 14.44
The Sun. (a) Ultraviolet light radiating from the Sun's atmosphere during the last peak of sunspot activity, 19 July 2000. Temperatures within these ultraviolet pulsations were about 1000 times hotter than the Sun itself. (b) During the sunspot minimum, ultraviolet activity was subdued, 18 March 2009.
Source: NASA.

By analogy with meteorological effects, the changing environmental conditions in space due to the varying solar activity are referred to as space weather. Several satellites and a network of ground stations monitor solar activity, and the information is used to compute space weather forecasts. In Canada, space weather forecasts are produced by the Canadian Space Weather Forecast Centre (CSWFC) operated by Natural Resources Canada in Ottawa. Integrating data from a dozen stations scattered across Canada, the CSWFC produces long-term and short-term forecasts of geomagnetic activity expected in the polar cap, auroral, and sub-auroral zones (Figure 14.45).

MAGNETIC STORMS

The physicists of the nineteenth century unravelled the relationship between **magnetism** and electricity. They found that magnetic field variations induce electrical currents in a medium. Induced currents then

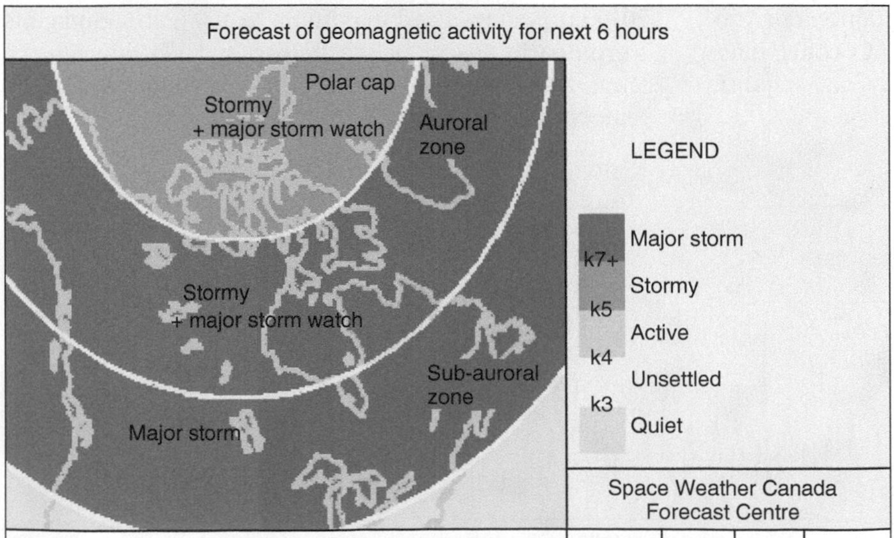

Figure 14.45
Forecast of geomagnetic activity for a "stormy" day.
Source: Reproduced with the permission of Natural Resources Canada 2014.

generate their own magnetic field. These laws describe the phenomenon of electromagnetic induction.

The laws of electromagnetism apply on a planetary scale. The solar wind takes two to five days to reach the Earth. As part of the Earth's response to solar wind disturbances, electric currents are produced in the ionosphere, some 100 km above the Earth's surface. These fluctuating ionospheric currents might cause rapid geomagnetic field variations. If they do, the Earth experiences a magnetic storm, which typically lasts 24 to 48 hours. During that time, electrical currents, referred to as **telluric currents**, are induced at the surface and in the subsurface of the Earth. They are also generated along conductive networks such as power transmission lines, telephone lines, and pipelines, which act like giant antennas.

Magnetic storms are most frequent near the peak of the solar cycle and during its declining phase. The very large storms that disrupt technological systems, however, are extreme "rogue" events that can happen anytime.

EFFECTS ON TECHNOLOGICAL SYSTEMS

The effects of space weather on technological systems can be grouped into three broad categories: (1) failures directly linked to bombardment by charged particles, (2) problems associated with disturbances in the ionosphere, and (3) electromagnetic induction effects (Figure 14.46).

The high-energy electrons and protons of the solar wind travel in interstellar space at a velocity of approximately 1800 km/h. The first targets they might hit as they get closer to the Earth are satellites in orbit. A direct impact could cause physical damage to onboard circuitry, or charges might accumulate until a sudden discharge bakes electronic components. Solar wind particles can inflict the same type of damage at lower altitude or on the ground, although this is much rarer, as Earth's atmosphere provides shielding. In August 1989, the Toronto Stock Exchange halted trading for three hours when particles disrupted the charge on a few microchips, causing the highly improbable failure of three disc drives in succession and the sophisticated financial computer system to crash.

Radio signals in the 3–30 megahertz frequency band can be transmitted around the curve of the Earth because of reflections from the ionosphere. During magnetic storms, the ionosphere becomes disturbed and can absorb signals instead of reflecting them, resulting in loss of communications. The Global Positioning System (GPS) uses much higher frequency radio signals from satellites that pass through the ionosphere. Nevertheless, during ionospheric disturbances, delays in signal propagation can cause errors in GPS positioning.

The telegraph was the first technological system involving long conductors to be deployed on the Earth's surface, so it is no surprise that the link between geomagnetic activity and technical problems was first noticed by telegraph operators. They observed that problems were often accompanied by fluctuations of compass needles and aurora sightings. Magnetic storms can also affect the telephone network, including submarine cables. Telluric currents induced by geomagnetic activity are the culprit as they interfere with the normal flow of electrical current in these systems. During the magnetic storm of 10 February 1958, transatlantic phone communication proceeded as loud squawks alternating with faint whispers as the telluric currents acted with or against the cable supply voltage.

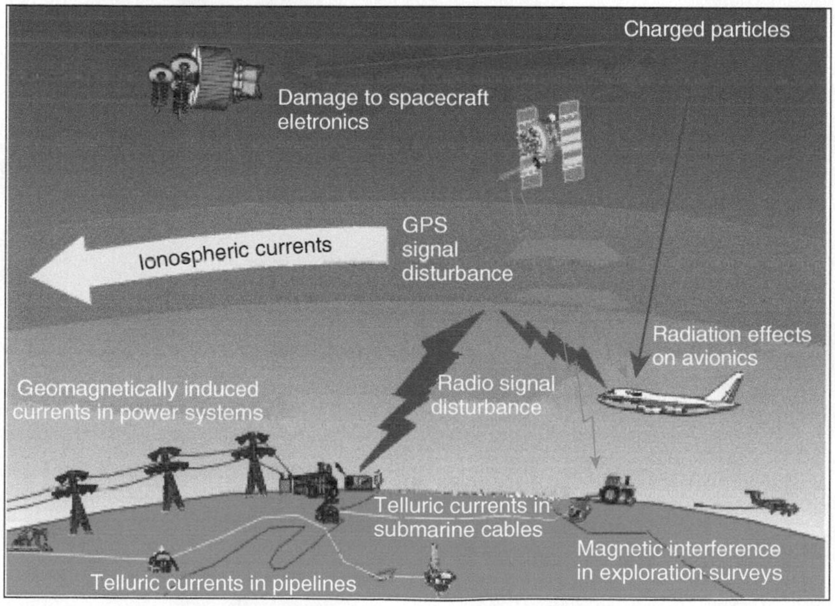

Figure 14.46
Effects of space weather on technological systems.
Source: Reproduced with the permission of Natural Resources Canada 2011. http://www.spaceweather.gc.ca/tech/se-eng.php.

IN GREATER DEPTH

LO6 Earth's Magnetic Field

Anyone who has ever held a compass and watched the free-turning needle point toward the north has experienced the magnetic field that surrounds the Earth. The Chinese were the first to use magnetic compasses, which appeared in Europe as early as 1190. In 1269, Peter Peregrinus of Maricourt described experiments on a sphere of lodestone (magnetite, a magnetic iron oxide mineral) and also gave instructions for building a compass. It was fourteenth-century European travellers to Asia, however, who are mostly responsible for bringing and disseminating the knowledge of the Chinese about the compass in Europe, where it was developed into the navigational tool that helped late-fifteenth-century explorers make their voyages of discovery.

The Earth is constantly bombarded by cosmic rays from outer space and by the subatomic debris emitted from the incinerator that is our Sun. The influx of high-energy radiation and tiny particles varies as the Sun's intensity changes or when a supernova (stellar) explosion occurs at astronomically close distances. The Earth's magnetic field defines a large region of space, the magnetosphere, where it offers partial protection from cosmic rays and the solar wind by deflecting particles (Figure 14.47). The magnetosphere is an asymmetric shield, with the magnetic field compressed on the day side and drawn out into a long tail on the night side. At closer distance, the magnetic field operates as if a gigantic bar magnet were located in the core of the Earth (Figure 14.48). The magnetic pole and geographic North Pole do not coincide, but the magnetic pole axis has apparently always been near the rotational pole axis. At the beginning of the twentieth century, there was a 20° difference between the north poles. Today, the south magnetic pole is 24° from the geographic pole. Notice in Figure 14.48 that the inclination of the magnetic lines of force with respect to the Earth's surface varies with latitude. At the magnetic equator, the magnetic lines of force are parallel to the Earth's surface (inclination of 0°). At high latitudes, the angle of inclination continuously increases until it is perpendicular to the surface at both the north and south magnetic poles (inclinations of 90°). Between 55° and 70° latitude, the magnetic lines of force guide some solar wind particles toward the upper atmosphere where they excite atoms that, in turn, release energy by emitting light. This phenomenon gives rise to aurorae.

In reality, the interior of the Earth is much too hot for a bar magnet to exist. Magnetism in rock is destroyed by temperatures above 550°C, and temperatures in the Earth's core are estimated to reach 5800°C. The origin of the Earth's magnetic field involves movements of the iron-rich fluid in the outer core, which generates electric currents that in turn create the magnetic field. The flow of fluid iron in the outer core has regions of turbulence as complex as whirlpools. Fluid iron is an excellent conductor of electricity. The molten iron flowing around the solid inner core is a self-perpetuating dynamo mainly deriving its energy from the convection of heat released by the crystallization of minerals at the boundary of the inner and outer cores.

A closer look at the Earth's magnetic field yields several problems awaiting resolution. The simplified magnetic field portrayed in Figure 14.8 does not show the complexities that occur over years and centuries as the magnetic field's strength waxes and wanes. More than 170 years of intensity measurements document variations in the strength and stability of the magnetic field. At present, the field strength is 10% weaker than in the year 1845, but it is still about twice as strong as the long-term average.

The magnetic north pole was first discovered in 1831 on the west coast of the Boothia Peninsula of what is now Nunavut and has moved 1600 kilometres across the Canadian Arctic since then (Figure 14.49). In recent decades, the magnetic pole has moved northwest at rates of 10 to 50 km per year and will reach Siberia in approximately 50 years, if it continues at the same speed and direction.

Every several thousand to tens of millions of years, a highly dramatic change occurs in the magnetic field: the magnetic polarity reverses. In a reversal, the orientation of the magnetic field flip-flops from a north (normal) polarity to a south (reverse) polarity or vice versa. It has been 780 000 years since the last long-term reversal. Models run on supercomputers indicate that reversals take a few thousand years to complete. During a reversal, the magnetic lines of force become twisted and tangled but the magnetic field does not entirely disappear (Figure 14.50). Its strength is reduced to about 10% of normal.

Figure 14.47
Artist's rendition of the Earth's magnetosphere deflecting the solar wind. The boxed area is shown in more detail in Figure 14.48.
Source: Heliophysics/NASA.

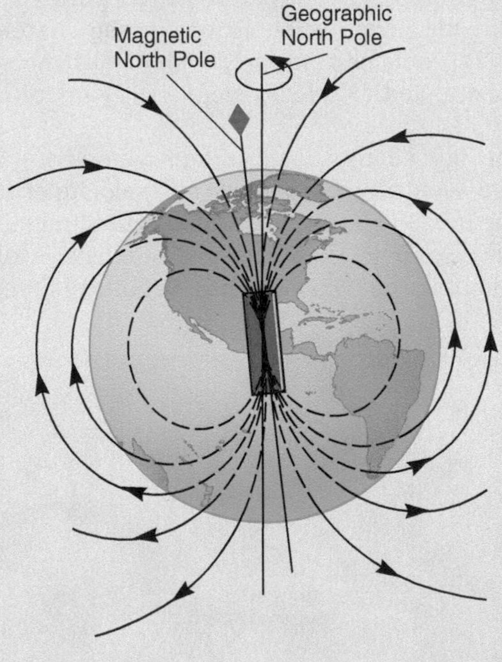

Figure 14.48
Schematic diagram of the Earth's magnetic field. The bar magnet pictured does not exist, but it would create the same magnetic field achieved by the electrical currents in the Earth's liquid, iron-rich outer core. Notice that (1) the magnetic pole and the rotational pole do not coincide, (2) the magnetic lines of force are parallel to the Earth's surface at the magnetic equator and perpendicular at the magnetic poles, and (3) the lines of force go into the Earth at the North Pole and out at the South Pole.
Source: © 1976 John Wiley & Sons.

continued

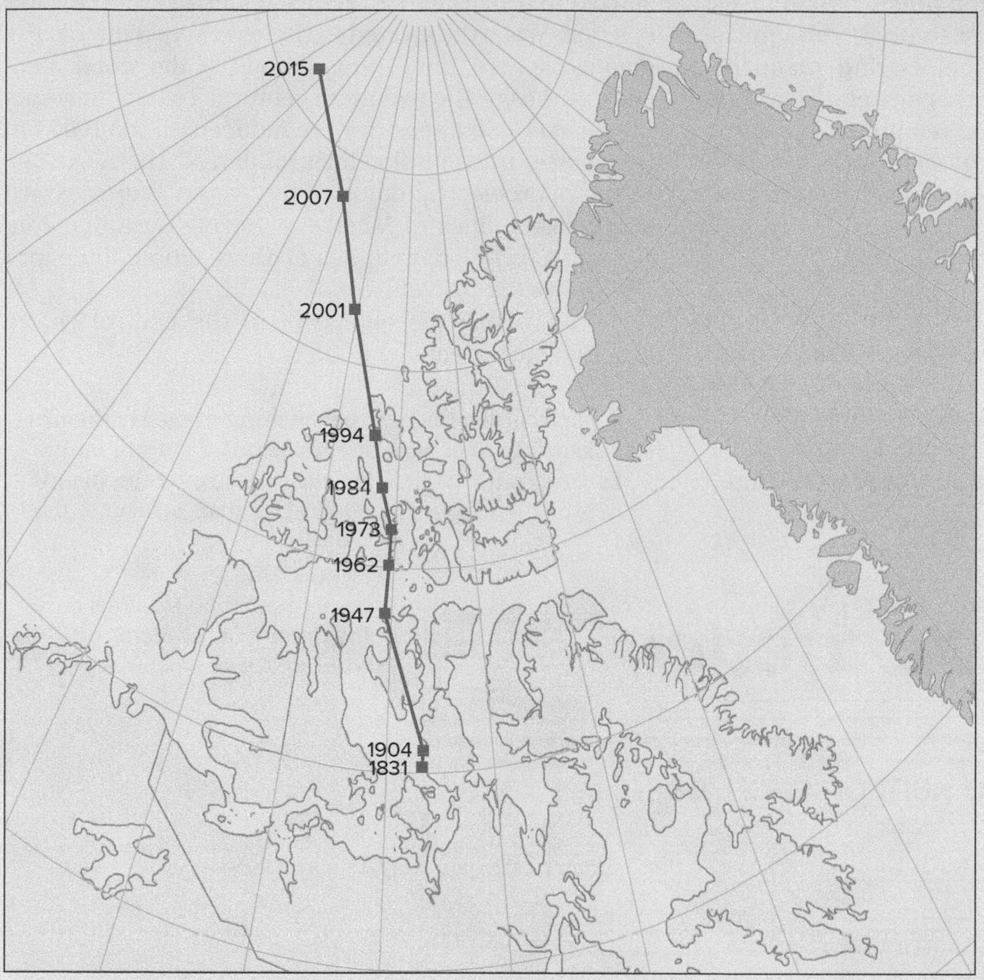

Figure 14.49
Path of the north magnetic pole since its discovery in 1831 to the last observed position in 2007 and its projected position for 2015.

Source: Reproduced with the permission of Natural Resources Canada 2014, courtesy of the Geological Survey of Canada.

The change in orientation of the magnetic field leaves its imprint in rock, where geologists (paleomagnetists) can read it. The paleomagnetic history contained in the rock has provided the most important evidence of seafloor spreading; it also has allowed charting of the paths of continents as they have moved through different latitudes. In addition, the record of magnetic reversals provides the data for a magnetic timescale, a third geological timescale. (The first timescale is based on the irreversible sequence of occurrence of fossils in sedimentary rock, and the second timescale is based on the decay of radioactive elements.)

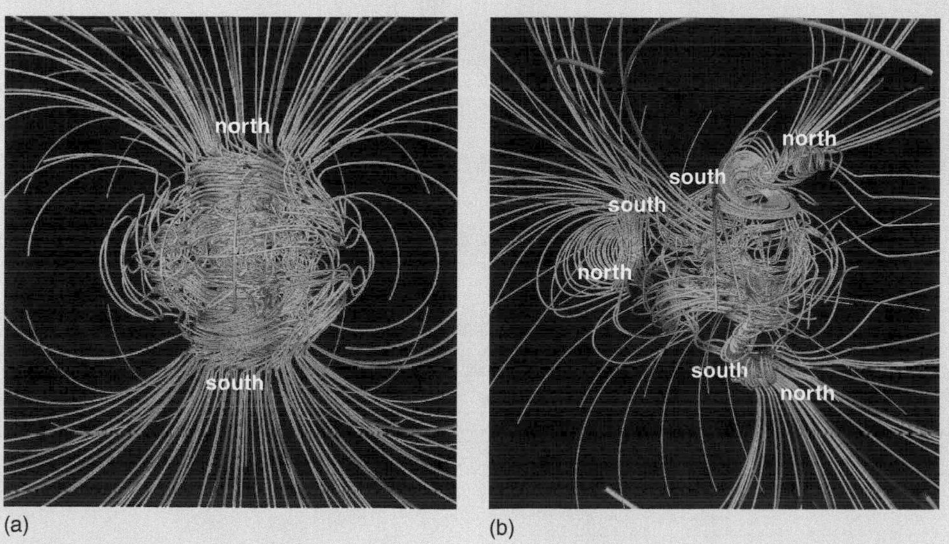

Figure 14.50
Supercomputer models of the Earth's magnetic field (a) between polarity reversals, and (b) during a reversal.

Source: © Gary A Glatzmaier, University of California Santa Cruz, and Paul H Roberts, University of California Los Angeles.

Steel pipelines are another example of a large conductive network. It is common practice to impress onto them a small, constant negative voltage as a mean of preventing corrosion. During magnetic storms, telluric currents cause this system to go out of range, leaving the pipeline temporarily unprotected. The cumulative effect of many storms over years might eventually compromise the integrity of the pipeline.

THE 1989 HYDRO-QUEBEC POWER BLACKOUT

The six million residents of Quebec spent most of the day on 13 March 1989 without electrical power and without much explanation as to the origin of the failure. The next morning, the headline of the Montreal daily *The Gazette* read, "Hydro blames Sun for power failure" (Figure 14.51).

The chain of events leading to the blackout had started four days earlier with a powerful coronal mass ejection. When the ejected particles reached the Earth's magnetosphere, they triggered one of the worst magnetic storms of the twentieth century. Telluric currents of considerable intensity were induced on the 1000 km long power transmission lines linking southern Quebec to the hydroelectric dams of the James Bay area. All transmission lines to Montreal became unstable, control systems failed, and, in a chain reaction, the entire Hydro-Quebec grid collapsed.

This is how the engineers at the control centre described the event:

> Telluric currents induced by the storm created harmonic voltages and currents of considerable intensity on the La Grande network. Voltage asymmetry on the 735 kV network reached 15%. Within less than a minute, the

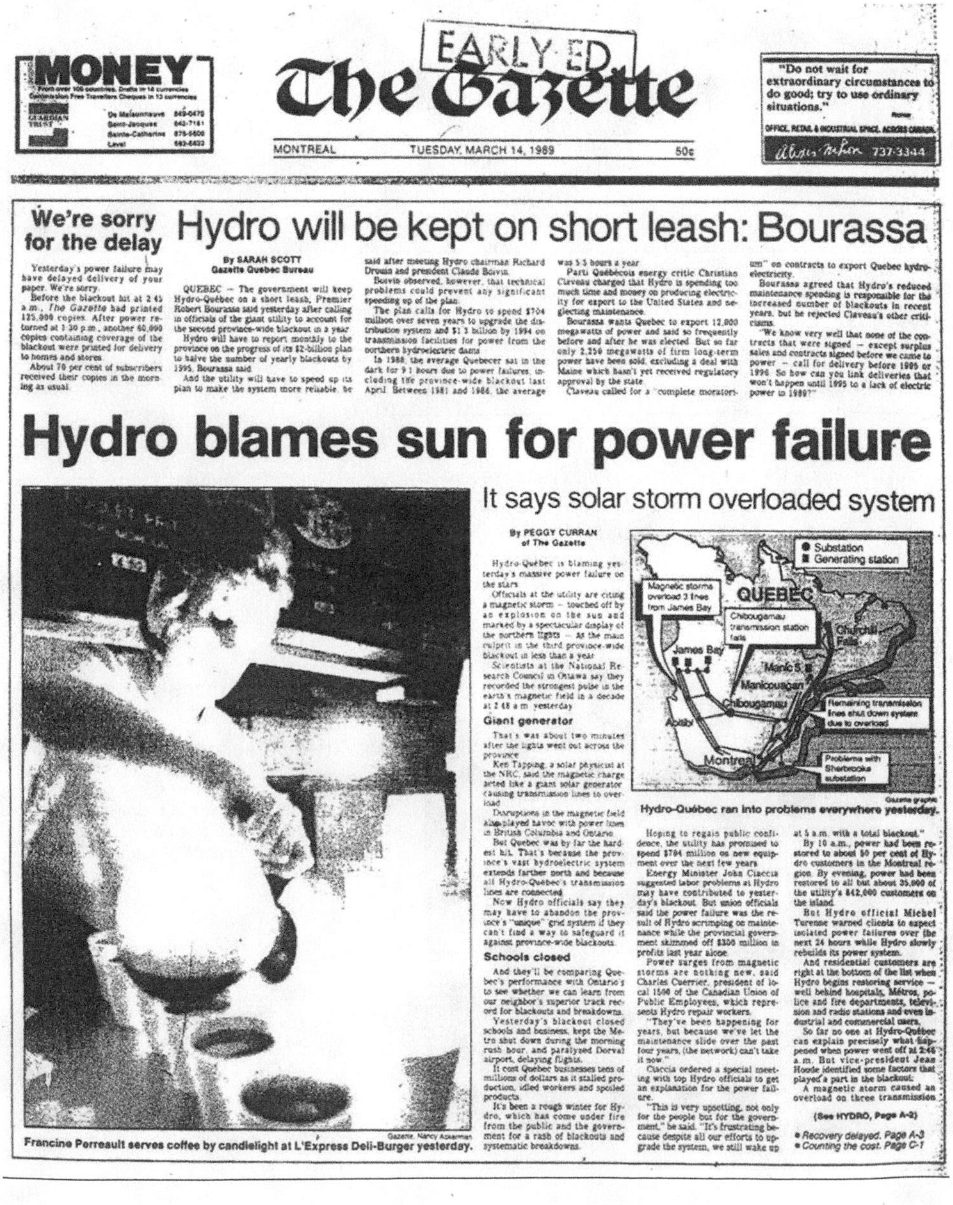

EARLY ED

The Gazette

MONTREAL TUESDAY, MARCH 14, 1989 50¢

"Do not wait for extraordinary circumstances to do good; try to use ordinary situations."

We're sorry for the delay

Yesterday's power failure may have delayed delivery of your paper. We're sorry.

Before the blackout hit at 2:45 a.m., *The Gazette* had printed 125,000 copies. After power returned at 1:30 p.m., another 60,000 copies containing coverage of the blackout were printed for delivery to homes and stores.

About 70 per cent of subscribers received their copies in the morning as usual.

Hydro will be kept on short leash: Bourassa

By SARAH SCOTT
Gazette Quebec Bureau

QUEBEC – The government will keep Hydro-Québec on a short leash, Premier Robert Bourassa said yesterday after calling in officials of the giant utility to account for the second province-wide blackout in a year.

Hydro will have to report monthly to the province on the progress of its $2-billion plan to halve the number of yearly blackouts by 1995, Bourassa said.

And the utility will have to speed up its plan to make the system more reliable, he said after meeting Hydro chairman Richard Drouin and president Claude Boivin.

Boivin observed, however, that technical problems could prevent any significant speeding up of the plan.

The plan calls for Hydro to spend $704 million over seven years to upgrade the distribution system and $1.3 billion by 1994 on transmission facilities for power from the northern hydroelectric dams.

In 1988, the average Quebecer sat in the dark for 9.1 hours due to power failures, including the province-wide blackout last April. Between 1981 and 1986, the average was 5.5 hours a year.

Parti Québécois energy critic Christian Claveau charged that Hydro is spending too much time and money on producing electricity for export to the United States and neglecting maintenance.

Bourassa wants Quebec to export 12,000 megawatts of power and said so frequently before and after he was elected. But so far only 2,250 megawatts of firm long-term power have been sold, excluding a deal with Maine which hasn't yet received regulatory approval by the state.

Claveau called for a "complete moratorium" on contracts to export Quebec hydro-electricity.

Bourassa agreed that Hydro's reduced maintenance spending is responsible for the increased number of blackouts in recent years, but he rejected Claveau's other criticisms.

"We know very well that none of the contracts that were signed – except surplus sales and contracts signed before we came to power – call for delivery before 1995 or 1996. So how can you link deliveries that won't happen until 1995 to a lack of electric power in 1989?"

Hydro blames sun for power failure

It says solar storm overloaded system

By PEGGY CURRAN
of The Gazette

Hydro-Québec is blaming yesterday's massive power failure on the stars.

Officials at the utility are citing a magnetic storm – touched off by an explosion on the sun and marked by a spectacular display of the northern lights – as the main culprit in the third province-wide blackout in less than a year.

Scientists at the National Research Council in Ottawa say they recorded the strongest pulse in the earth's magnetic field in a decade at 2:48 a.m. yesterday.

Giant generator

That's was about two minutes after the lights went out across the province.

Ken Tapping, a solar physicist at the NRC, said the magnetic charge acted like a giant solar generator causing transmission lines to overload.

Disruptions in the magnetic field also played havoc with power lines in British Columbia and Ontario.

But Quebec was by far the hardest hit. That's because the province's vast hydroelectric system extends farther north and because all Hydro-Québec's transmission lines are connected.

Now Hydro officials say they may have to abandon the province's "unique" grid system if they can't find a way to safeguard it against province-wide blackouts.

Schools closed

And they'll be comparing Quebec's performance with Ontario's to see whether we can learn from our neighbor's superior track record for blackouts and breakdowns.

Yesterday's blackout closed schools and business, kept the Metro shut down during the morning rush hour, and paralyzed Dorval airport, delaying flights.

It cost Quebec businesses tens of millions of dollars as it stalled production, idled workers and spoiled products.

It's been a rough winter for Hydro, which has come under fire from the public and the government for a rash of blackouts and systematic breakdowns.

Hydro-Québec ran into problems everywhere yesterday.

Hoping to regain public confidence, the utility has promised to spend $704 million on new equipment over the next few years.

Energy Minister John Ciaccia suggested labor problems at Hydro may have contributed to yesterday's blackout. But union officials said the power failure was the result of Hydro scrimping on maintenance while the provincial government skimmed off $300 million in profits last year alone.

Power surges from magnetic storms are nothing new, said Charles Cuerrier, president of local 1500 of the Canadian Union of Public Employees, which represents Hydro repair workers.

"They've been happening for years, but because we've let the maintenance slide over the past four years, (the network) can't take it now."

Ciaccia ordered a special meeting with top Hydro officials to get an explanation for the power failure.

"This is very upsetting, not only for the people but for the government," he said. "It's frustrating because despite all our efforts to upgrade the system, we still wake up at 5 a.m. with a total blackout."

By 10 a.m., power had been restored to about 50 per cent of Hydro customers in the Montreal region. By evening, power had been restored to all but about 35,000 of the utility's 842,000 customers on the island.

But Hydro official Michel Turenne warned clients to expect isolated power failures over the next 24 hours while Hydro slowly rebuilds its power system.

And residential customers are right at the bottom of the list when Hydro begins restoring service – well behind hospitals, Métros, police and fire departments, television and radio stations and even industrial and commercial users.

So far no one at Hydro-Québec can explain precisely what happened when power went off at 2:45 a.m. But vice-president Jean Houde identified some factors that played a part in the blackout:

A magnetic storm caused an overload on three transmission

(See HYDRO, Page A-2)

- *Recovery delayed. Page A-3*
- *Counting the cost. Page C-1*

Gazette, Nancy Ackerman

Francine Perreault serves coffee by candlelight at L'Express Deli-Burger yesterday.

Figure 14.51
Cover page of the Montreal daily *The Gazette* on 14 March 1989.
Source: *The Gazette* (Montreal).

> seven La Grande network static var [Volt-Amperes Reactive] compensators on line tripped one after the other ... With the loss of the last static var compensator, voltage dropped so drastically on the La Grande network ... that all five lines to Montréal tripped through loss of synchronism ..., and the entire network separated. The loss of 9450 MW of generation provoked a very rapid drop in frequency at load-centre substations. Automatic underfrequency load-shedding controls functioned properly, but they are not designed for recovery from a generation loss equivalent to about half system load. The rest of the grid collapsed piece by piece in 25 seconds.

Through the technical jargon, we can feel their anxiety as they were helplessly losing control of a very complex system. The vulnerability of power systems to telluric currents exacerbated due to the fact that problems occur simultaneously on many subsystems, as opposed to lighting strikes or equipment failures, which are more localized. Modern systems are designed to provide safeguards against localized failures but do not cope as effectively with the domino effect of several issues in parallel.

Significant economic loss resulted from the nine-hour blackout that nevertheless served to increase the utility companies' awareness of geomagnetic hazards. It is now common practice to reduce the power on transmission lines when a magnetic storm warning is in effect.

SUMMARY

- The Earth revolving around the Sun in the vastness of space can become a target for impact. Space debris colliding with the Earth is primarily comprised of stony or metallic asteroids, and ices and solid debris from comets.
- The consequences of impact are related to the size of the impactor.
  - Cosmic dust (diameter ≤ 1mm) passes through the atmosphere relatively unchanged.
  - Some impactors with diameters between 1 mm and 100 m reach the surface of the Earth and are recovered as meteorites.
  - Meteoroids larger than 100 m in diameter are slowed little by the atmosphere and may hit the ground at high speeds, explode, and excavate craters.
- The impact of a large asteroid generates tremendous heat and pressure. Rock in the crater and debris thrown out of the crater is broken, melted, and vaporized; minerals develop new atomic structures. As the transient crater is emptied, the crater bottom rebounds upward, and the fractured walls slide inward toward the crater centre, forming a final, enlarged crater.
- It is difficult to recognize impact sites on the Earth because plate tectonics and erosion destroy the evidence. Nevertheless, 59 sites have been identified in Canada on the basis of aerial photographs and geological evidence, including the presence of shatter cones and shock minerals.
- Life on the Earth is subjected to great stress by a large impact.
- The Sun sends solar wind particles in all directions. When strong gusts of solar wind reach the Earth, we experience a magnetic storm.
- Strong magnetic storms, which can occur at any time during the solar cycle, affect several technological systems.
  - The direct hit of charged particles on electronic components can damage circuitry.
  - Radio and GPS signals are lost or become unreliable because of ionospheric disturbances.
  - Spurious induced currents interfere with the normal operations of power transmission lines, telephone lines, and corrosion protection systems.

Terms to Remember

aphelion
astroblemes
Kuiper belt
magnetism
maria
meteors
meteoroids
Oort cloud
perihelion

Questions for Review

1. Why does the Moon display impact scars so well?
2. Why are impact scars relatively rare on the Earth?
3. Distinguish between a meteor, a meteoroid, a meteorite, an asteroid, and a comet.
4. Why are metallic meteorites so commonly collected?
5. Why did the asteroids of the asteroid belt not assemble into a planet?
6. Why does a comet's tail glow brighter as it nears the Sun? Why does a comet's tail point away from the Sun?
7. How much space debris is added to the Earth each day? How big must a meteoroid be to pass through the atmosphere with little slowing?

plasma
shatter cones
shock minerals
shooting stars
solar wind
species
telluric currents

8. Draw a series of cross-sections showing what happens when an asteroid 10 km in diameter hits the Earth at 32 000 km/h.
9. List evidence you could collect to demonstrate that a specific area was the site of an ancient asteroid impact.
10. Describe the sequence of life-threatening events that occur when an asteroid 10 km in diameter slams into the Earth.
11. Explain the Torino scale of impact hazards.
12. What causes aurorae?
13. What are telluric currents? How are they generated? How do they interfere with technological networks?

Questions for Further Thought

1. Extrapolating impact rates from the Moon, about 720 craters with diameters greater than 24 km should have formed on land on Earth; only about 160 have been found so far. Might some of the missing impact sites have been large and caused mass extinctions? How could you proceed scientifically to investigate this possibility?
2. Should the international community spend the money and effort to develop engineering devices that could land on large asteroids and comets and change their courses away from hitting Earth?
3. It is proposed that we send rockets or explosives to divert incoming large asteroids or comets. Might this action just shatter the incoming object into many devastating impactors? Might it cause the object to hit Earth on a more direct path?
4. What effects have Hollywood movies had on public policy regarding natural disasters?
5. Would it be profitable for an insurance company to offer coverage against accidental death by meteorite impact?
6. Who should check space weather forecasts regularly?

Interesting Websites

- Earth Impact Database, Planetary and Space Science Centre, University of New Brunswick
  www.passc.net/EarthImpactDatabase/index.html
- Impact Earth! Purdue University and Imperial College, London
  http://www.purdue.edu/impactearth
- Meteoritical Bulletin Database, The Meteoritical Society
  www.lpi.usra.edu/meteor/metbull.php
- Near-Earth Space Surveillance, NEOSSat
  http://neossat.ca/
- Sentry Risk Table, Near Earth Object Program, NASA
  http://neo.jpl.nasa.gov/risk
- Geomagnetism, Geological Survey of Canada, Natural Resources Canada
  http://www.geomag.nrcan.gc.ca/index-eng.php
- Space Weather Canada
  www.spaceweather.gc.ca

Glossary

A

aa A lava flow with a rough, blocky surface.

acceleration The rate of change of motion.

accelerographs Instruments that record the acceleration of the ground during an earthquake.

acoustic fluidization A theorized process where sound waves trapped inside a dry, fallen mass lessen internal friction to enable fluid-like flow.

active volcano A volcano currently erupting or that has erupted in historical times; for example, Kilauea, Hawaii; Krakatau, Indonesia.

adaptation Making adjustments in decisions and activities because of changes in climate, with the goals of moderating harm.

adiabatic processes The changes in temperature of masses without adding or subtracting heat. Examples are cooling with expansion and warming upon compression.

aftershocks Smaller earthquakes following a mainshock on the same section of a fault. Aftershocks can continue for years following a large mainshock.

air masses Large bodies of air that have little horizontal variation in moisture content or temperature.

albedo The reflectivity of a body; for the Earth, how much solar radiation is reflected back to space.

amplitude The maximum displacement above or below the undisturbed position; for example, the height of a wave crest or depth of a trough.

andesite A volcanic rock named for the Andes Mountains in South America. It is intermediate in composition between basalt and rhyolite, and commonly results from melting of continental rock in basaltic magma.

anticyclone A region of high atmospheric pressure and outflowing surface air that rotates clockwise in the northern hemisphere.

aphelion The point in the orbit of a body that is farthest from the Sun.

arrival time The time at which a seismic wave is detected by a seismograph.

asteroids Small, rocky bodies that orbit the Sun.

asthenosphere The layer of the Earth below the lithosphere in which isostatic adjustments take place. The rocks here deform readily and flow slowly.

astroblemes Impact sites on Earth usually recognized by circular outlines and highly disturbed, shocked rocks; also called impact craters.

Atlantic Multidecadal Oscillation (AMO) A shifting of atmospheric pressures over the North Atlantic Ocean occurring on a multi-year timescale.

atmosphere The gaseous envelope around the Earth, composed chiefly of nitrogen and oxygen. The average atmospheric pressure at sea level is 101.3 kilopascals (kPa).

avulsion An abrupt change in the course of a stream and adoption of a new channel.

B

backfires Fires deliberately set to consume fuel in front of an advancing wildfire in order to stop it.

basalt A dark, finely crystalline volcanic rock typical of low-viscosity oceanic lavas.

base isolation A system protecting buildings from earthquakes by isolating the base of the structure from the shaking ground via rollers, shock absorbers, etc.

bathymetry The mapping of depths of water in oceans, rivers, and lakes; the underwater equivalent of topography.

BCE Before the common era. Equivalent to BC.

bedrock Solid rock lying beneath loose soil or unconsolidated sediment.

blizzard Strong cold winds filled with snow.

body waves Seismic waves that travels through the Earth. Primary (P) and secondary (S) waves are body waves.

braided stream An overloaded stream carrying so much sediment that water flow is forced to divide and recombine in a braided pattern.

brittle Property of material in which stress causes abrupt fracture.

C

caldera A large (over two kilometres in diameter), basin-shaped volcanic depression, roughly circular in map view, that forms by a piston-like collapse of rock into a partially evacuated magma chamber.

carbonic acid A common but weak acid (H_2CO_3) formed by carbon dioxide (CO_2) dissolving in water (H_2O).

carrying capacity The maximum population size that can be supported under a given set of environmental conditions.

CE Common era. Equivalent to AD.

chaparral A dense, impenetrable thicket of stiff shrubs especially adapted to a dry season about six months long; abundant in the State of California and Baja California, Mexico. Fire is part of the life cycle of these plants.

chemical weathering The decomposition of rocks under attack of base- or acid-laden waters.

chondrules Small, glassy spheres crystallized in space from semi-molten or molten droplets of rock.

clay minerals Very small (under 0.0039 mm in diameter) minerals with sheet- or book-like internal crystalline structure. Many varieties absorb water or ions into their structure, causing swelling.

climate The average weather conditions at a place over several decades.

cohesion A property of sediments where particles stick together.

combustion The action of burning.

comets Icy bodies moving through outer space.

compression A state of stress that causes a pushing together or contraction.

conduction A process of heat transfer through collisions between particles. Hot, rapidly vibrating particles transfer kinetic energy to neighbouring colder, slow-moving particles.

congelifraction The mechanical disintegration of a rock due to the pressure exerted by the freezing of water contained in pores, fractures, and/or bedding planes.

continents Lower-density masses of rock, exposed as about 40% of the Earth's surface: 29% as land and 11% as the floor of shallow seas.

convection A process of heat transfer through movement of a fluid; for example, air or water.

convergent zones Linear areas where plates collide and move closer together. These are zones of earthquakes, volcanoes, mountain ranges, and deep-ocean trenches.

core The central zone of the Earth about 2900 km below the surface. The core is made mostly of iron and nickel, and exists as a solid inner zone surrounded by a liquid outer shell. The Earth's magnetic field originates within the core.

Coriolis effect The tendency of moving objects on the surface of the Earth to be deflected due to the Earth's rotation.

crater An abrupt basin commonly rimmed by ejected material. In volcanoes, craters form by outward explosion, are commonly less than two kilometres in diameter, and occur at the summit of a volcanic cone. Similar rimmed basins form by impacts with space bodies.

creep The slow, gradual, more or less continuous movement of ice and soil under gravity.

creeping zone A section of a fault where seismic energy is released frequently in small to moderate earthquakes.

crust The outermost layer of the lithosphere, composed of relatively low-density materials. The continental crust has lower density than the oceanic crust.

crystallization The growth of minerals in a fluid such as magma.

Curie point The temperature above which a mineral will not be magnetic.

cyclone A region of low atmospheric pressure and converging surface air that rotates counterclockwise in the northern hemisphere.

D

debris flow Loose sediment plus water that is pulled downslope directly by gravity.

decompression melting The most common process of creating magma. Melting occurs by reducing pressure on hot rock.

derecho Winds that blow straight ahead.

dielectric constant A measure of a material's ability to store electrical charge.

dikes Long artificial mounds of earth constructed to hold back water. Dikes differ from levees as they are not necessarily built along river banks.

discharge The volume of water flowing in a stream per unit of time.

divergent zones Linear zones formed where plates pull apart; for example, spreading centres.

dormant volcanoes Volcanoes that have erupted during the last several thousand years but have been quiet in historical times; for example, Mount Meager, British Columbia.

downbursts Localized, severe downdrafts of air that include outbursts of strong winds on the ground.

drainage basin The land area that contributes water to a river system.

droughts Prolonged intervals of dryness causing damage to plants and animals.

ductile Behaviour of material where stress causes permanent flow or strain.

duff A mat of organic debris where fire can smoulder for days.

E

earthquakes The shaking of the Earth by seismic waves radiating away from disturbances, most commonly fault movements.

El Niño A climate pattern that occurs every two to seven years when the trade winds relax and warm ocean water in the equatorial Pacific Ocean flows to the west coast of North America.

elastic Behaviour of material where stress causes deformation that is recoverable; when stress stops, the material returns to its original state.

elements Distinct varieties of matter; atoms are the smallest particles of elements.

energy Capacity for performing work.

epicentre The point on the surface of the Earth directly above the fault that moved to generate an earthquake (i.e., the point directly above the hypocentre).

equilibrium A state of balance in a system; a condition in which opposing processes are so balanced that changes cause compensating actions.

erosion The processes that loosen, dissolve, and wear away earth materials. Active agents include gravity, streams, glaciers, winds, and ocean waves.

extinct volcano A volcano that has not erupted during the last several thousand years and is not expected to erupt again; for example, Kilimanjaro, Tanzania.

F

failed rifts Spreading centres that did not open wide enough to create ocean basins.

falls Mass movements where the bodies move downward nearly vertically under the influence of gravity.

faults Fractures in rocks where the two sides move relative to each other.

felt area An area of perceptible earthquake ground motion.

fire The rapid combination of oxygen with organic material to produce flame, heat, and light.

firebrands Burning debris such as branches and embers that are lifted above the fire by wind and carried away to possibly start new fires.

fire-danger rating A system of computer-generated indices used as indicators of fire hazard.

firestorms Fires of large enough size to disturb the atmosphere with excess heat, thus creating their own winds.

fissures Narrow cracks in rock.

flank collapse A catastrophic event where the side of a volcano falls into the sea.

flood basalts Tremendous outpourings of basaltic lava that formed thick, extensive plateaus in the geological past.

flood plains The nearly flat lowlands that border streams and act as stream beds during floods.

floods Overflowing of bodies of water onto normally dry land when discharge exceeds the capacity to contain the flow or when there are obstructions to flow.

flood stage The level of water beyond which conditions become hazardous along the banks of a flooding river.

flows Mass movements where the moving bodies of material behave like a fluid.

force Mass times acceleration.

foreshocks Smaller earthquakes that precedes a mainshock on the same section of a fault.

fracture A general term for any breaks in rock.

fracture zones Major lines of weakness in oceanic crust; former transform faults.

freezing rain Supercooled rain that turns to ice when it touches objects such as trees and powerlines.

frequency The number of events in a given time interval. For waves, it is the number of cycles that pass in a second; frequency = 1/period.

friction The resistance to motion of two bodies in contact.

fronts Boundaries separating air masses of different temperatures or moisture contents.

fuel Any substance that produces heat by combustion.

fuel-driven fires Fires burning on calm-weather days that advance slowly through the fuel, giving firefighters opportunities to stop them.

fuel models Computer algorithms predicting the rate of spread of fires based on vegetation characteristics.

G

glaciers Large masses of ice that flow downslope or outward.

global warming potential (GWP) The ability of a greenhouse gas to trap heat in the atmosphere as compared to CO_2.

Gondwanaland A southern supercontinent that included South America, Africa, Antarctica, Australia, New Zealand, and India from about 180 to 75 million years ago.

gradient The slope of a stream bed; change in elevation divided by distance.

gravity The attraction between bodies of matter.

great natural disaster A natural disaster so overwhelming that outside assistance is needed to handle the response and recovery for the region.

greenhouse effect The buildup of heat beneath substances such as glass, water vapour, and carbon dioxide that allow incoming, short-wavelength solar radiation to pass through but block long-wavelength reradiation.

groundwater The volume of water that has soaked the subsurface filling fractures and other pores.

H

haboob Strong dust storms powered by thunderstorm downbursts in arid regions of the world.

Hadley cells Thermally driven atmospheric circulation patterns where hot air rises at the equator, divides and flows toward both poles, and then descends to the surface at about 30°N and 30°S latitudes.

hail Precipitation of hard, semispherical pellets of ice.

haze Suspended aerosols and particles that reduce visibility.

heat The capacity to raise the temperature of a mass, expressed in joules.

heat capacity The amount of energy required to raise the temperature of a body by one degree.

hertz A unit of frequency. One hertz (Hz) equals one cycle per second.

hot spots Places on Earth where plumes of magma have risen upward from deep in the mantle and through plates to reach the surface.

humidity A measure of the amount of water vapour in an air mass.

hurricane A large, tropical cyclonic storm of the Atlantic Ocean and eastern Pacific Ocean with wind speeds of 119 km/h or more; called a typhoon in the western Pacific Ocean and a cyclone in the Indian Ocean.

hydrograph A plot of discharge with respect to time.

hydrologic cycle The solar-powered cycle where water is evaporated from the oceans, dropped on the land as rain and snow, and pulled by gravity back to the oceans as glaciers, streams, and groundwater.

hypocentre The initial portion of a fault that moved to generate an earthquake. Hypocentres are below the ground surface; epicentres are projected above them on the surface.

I

igneous rocks Rocks formed by the solidification of magma.

ignition temperature The minimum temperature to which a material must be heated for combustion to start.

inertia The property by which matter will remain at rest unless acted on by an external force.

infiltration The slow passage of rainwater through soil.

Intertropical Convergence Zone (ITCZ) The zone where the trade winds of the northern and southern hemispheres collide.

intraplate earthquakes Earthquakes occurring within a tectonic plate, far away from plate boundaries.

intrusion (1) The process by which magma forces into fissures of preexisting rocks and crystallizes below the surface of the Earth. (2) Bodies formed by the process of intrusion.

ions Electrically charged atoms.

island arc A curved linear belt of volcanoes above an oceanic-oceanic subduction zone; for example, Japan.

isoseismal maps Maps that uses contour lines to represent areas of equal Mercalli intensity.

isostasy The condition of equilibrium wherein the Earth's crust floats upward or downward as loads are removed or added.

isotopes Any of two or more forms of the same element. The number of protons is fixed for any element, but the number of neutrons in the nucleus can vary, thus producing isotopes.

J

jet streams Fast-moving belts of air in the upper troposphere that flow toward the east.

jokulhlaup A glacial outburst flood.

K

Kuiper belt A flattened disk of comets with orbital periods less than 200 years travelling in an orbital plane similar to the planets of the Solar System but extending out 50 astronomical units (AU).

L

La Niña A climate pattern that occurs when cooler than normal seawater exists in the tropical eastern Pacific Ocean.

ladder fuels Vegetation of varying heights in an area that allows fire to move easily from the ground to the treetops.

lahars Mudflows composed of unconsolidated volcanic debris and water.

latent heat The energy absorbed or released during a change of state.

lateral spread A translational slide in which a subsurface layer behaves like a fluid, causing the overlying material to move down gentle slopes.

Laurasia A northern supercontinent that included most of North America, Greenland, Europe, and Asia (excluding India) from about 180 to 75 million years ago.

lava Magma that flows on the Earth's surface.

lava dome A mountain or hill made from highly viscous lava, which has plugged the central conduit of a volcano.

levees Natural or human-built embankments along the sides of stream channels.

lifting condensation level The altitude in the atmosphere where rising air cools to saturation (100% humidity) and condensation begins.

lightning A flashing of light as atmospheric electricity flows between clouds or between cloud and ground.

limestone A sedimentary rock composed mostly of calcium carbonate ($CaCO_3$), usually precipitated from warm saline water. Limestone on continents may later be dissolved by acidic groundwater to form caves.

liquefaction The temporary transformation of water-saturated, loose sediment into a fluid, typically caused by strong earthquake shaking.

lithosphere The outer rigid shell of the Earth that lies above the asthenosphere and below the atmosphere and hydrosphere.

Little Ice Age A colder interval between about 1400 to 1900 CE with renewed glaciation in the northern hemisphere.

load The amount of material moved and carried by a stream.

locked zone A section of a fault that has not released seismic energy for a long time.

M

magma Molten rock material. It solidifies on the Earth's surface as volcanic rock and at depth as plutonic rock.

magnetic field A region where magnetic forces affect any magnetized bodies or electric currents. Earth is surrounded by a magnetic field.

magnetic pole Either of two regions—the north and south poles—where the lines of force of the magnetic field are perpendicular to the Earth's surface. Magnetic poles do not coincide with geographic poles but are in their vicinity.

magnetism A group of physical phenomena associated with moving electricity.

magnitude An assessment of the amount of energy released during an event. Magnitude scales exist for earthquakes, volcanic eruptions, hurricanes, and tornadoes. In seismology, different magnitudes are calculated for the same earthquake when different types of seismic waves are used.

mainshock The largest earthquake in a sequence.

mantle The largest zone of the Earth comprising 83% by volume and 67% by mass.

maria Dark, low-lying areas of the Moon filled with dark volcanic rocks.

mass movements The large-scale transfers of materials downslope under the pull of gravity.

Maunder Minimum A cooler interval between 1645 to 1715 CE that coincided with a minimum in the number of sunspots.

meander The curves, bends, loops, and turns in the course of an underloaded stream that shifts bank erosion from side to side in its channel.

Medieval Maximum A relatively warm interval in the northern hemisphere between about 1000 to 1300 CE.

megathrust earthquakes Very large earthquakes that occur when stress accumulates at the contact between a subducting plate and an overriding plate.

mesosphere The mantle from the base of the asthenosphere to the top of the core.

meteors Space objects entering the Earth's atmosphere and becoming incandescent because of friction.

meteorites Stony or iron-rich space objects that passed through the atmosphere and landed on the surface of the Earth.

meteoroids A general term for space objects made of metal, rock, dust, or ice.

methane A gaseous hydrocarbon (CH_4).

methane hydrates Ice-like deposits in deep-sea sediments of methane combined with near-freezing water.

Milankovitch theory A theory that states that glacial advances and retreats on Earth are controlled by variations in the amount of solar radiation received at high latitudes during summer due to changes in Earth's orbit around the Sun and in the tilt angle and direction of Earth's axis of rotation.

mineral A naturally formed, solid inorganic material with characteristic chemical composition and physical properties that reflect an internally ordered atomic structure.

mitigation Actions taken to minimize the risk associated with a natural hazard.

monsoon Winds that reverse direction seasonally. In summer, warm air rises above hot land, drawing in rain-bearing winds from over the ocean. In winter, the flow reverses.

N

natural disaster An extreme event triggered by destructive forces occurring in nature that causes significant disruption to society.

natural frequency The frequency at which a mechanical system (e.g., a soil, a building) vibrates when disturbed.

natural hazard A source of danger to life, property, and the environment, from atmospheric and geological phenomena.

nor'easters Severe winter storms of the east coast of Canada and the United States accompanied by winds from the northeast.

nuclear fission Splitting the nucleus of an atom with resultant release of energy.

nuclear fusion Combining of smaller atoms to make larger atoms with a resultant release of energy.

nuée ardente A turbulent "glowing cloud" of hot, fast-moving volcanic ash, dust, and gas; also called a pyroclastic flow.

O

obsidian Dark volcanic glass.

Oort cloud A vast and diffuse envelope of comets surrounding the Solar System.

outburst floods Sudden releases of large quantities of water.

ozone A gaseous molecule composed of three atoms of oxygen.

P

pahoehoe A lava flow with a smooth, ropy surface.

Pangaea A supercontinent that existed during Late Paleozoic time when all the continents were unified into a single landmass.

perihelion The point in the orbit of a body that is closest to the Sun.

period The length of time for a complete cycle of waves to pass; period = 1/frequency.

permafrost Soil or rock that remains frozen throughout the year.

photosynthesis The process where plants produce organic compounds from water and carbon dioxide using the energy of the Sun.

plasma A state of matter, distinct from solids, liquids, and gases, in which charged particles wander freely among the nuclei of atoms.

plastic The behaviour of a material that flows as a fluid (liquid) over time, but is strong (solid) at a moment in time.

plates Pieces of lithosphere that move atop the asthenosphere. There are a dozen large plates and many smaller ones.

plate tectonics The description of the movements of plates and the effects caused by plate formation, collision, subduction, and slide past.

Plinian eruption A type of volcanic eruption where an immense column of pyroclastic debris and gases is blown vertically to great heights.

plumes Upwellings of magma rising from deep in the mantle.

plutonic rocks Rocks formed by the solidification of magma deep below the surface.

pore-water pressures Pressure buildups in groundwater that offset part of the weight of overlying rock masses.

porosity The percentage of void space in a rock or sediment.

post-tropical transition A gradual transformation of a hurricane into a post-tropical storm, occurring typically between 30°N and 40°N latitudes.

preparedness Actions taken in advance to ensure people are ready when disaster strikes.

primary (P) wave The first seismic wave to reach a seismometer. Movement is by alternating push–pull pulses that travel through solids, liquids, and gas.

pumice Volcanic glass so full of holes that it commonly floats on water.

pyroclastic Pertaining to magma and volcanic rock blasted up into the air.

pyroclastic flows High-temperature, fast-moving clouds of fine volcanic debris, steam, and other gases; also called a *nuée ardente.*

pyrolysis Chemical decomposition by the action of heat.

R

radiation A process of heat transfer where energy is emitted as electromagnetic waves.

radioactive elements Unstable elements containing excess subatomic particles that are emitted to achieve smaller, more stable atoms.

recovery Actions taken in the long term to restore the pre-disaster conditions of a community.

resonance A vibrating body moves with maximum amplitude when the frequency of an imposed external forcing function is the same as its natural frequency.

response Actions taken in the short term to provide assistance after an emergency has occurred.

resurgent caldera A large topographic depression formed by a piston-like collapse of rock into a magma chamber with a later central uplift of the caldera floor.

resurgent domes The uplifted floors and masses of magma in the centres of large volcanic calderas.

retrofitting Reinforcing or strengthening an existing building or other structure.

retrogressive sliding Sliding in which the rupture extends in the direction opposite to the movement of the displaced material.

return period The amount of time between similar events.

rhyolite A volcanic rock formed from high-viscosity magma and typical of the continents.

ridges Long and narrow volcanic mountain ranges.

rift The valley created at a pull-apart zone.

risk The possibility of being harmed or damaged, often expressed as the product of vulnerability and hazard.

rotational slides Downward-and-outward movements of masses on top of concave-upward failure surfaces; also called slumps.

runoff The portion of precipitation that travels across land and ultimately reaches streams.

run-up The height above a reference level (often chosen as the mean sea level) that tsunami waves reach onshore.

S

scoria cones Small cone or horseshoe-shaped hills made of pyroclastic debris from Hawaiian- or Strombolian-type eruptions. They commonly occur in groups.

seafloor spreading The movement of two oceanic plates away from each other, resulting in magma welling up and solidifying to create new ocean floor.

secondary (S) wave The second seismic wave to reach a seismometer. Movement occurs by shearing particles at right angles to the direction of propagation. S waves move through solids only.

sediments Fragments of material of either inorganic or organic origin. Sizes are gravel (over 2 mm in diameter), sand (2 to 0.0625 mm in diameter), silt (0.0625 to 0.0039 mm in diameter), and clay (less than 0.0039 mm in diameter). A mixture of silt and clay forms mud.

seiches Oscillating waves on a lake or landlocked sea that vary in period from a few minutes to several hours.

seism An earthquake.

seismic-gap method A theory that states that earthquakes are expected next along those fault segments that have not moved for the longest time.

seismicity The frequency and spatial distribution of earthquakes.

seismic waves A general term for all vibrations generated by earthquakes.

seismic zonation A geographical delineation of areas having similar damage potential from future earthquakes.

seismograms The records made by a seismograph.

seismology The study of earthquakes and the Earth's interior, based on the analysis of seismic data.

seismometers Instruments that detect Earth motions.

sensitive clays Clays that can suddenly lose strength and liquefy when disturbed.

shakemaps Maps of Mercalli intensity derived automatically from data recorded by a network of seismographs and computed in near real-time.

shatter cones Conical fragments of rock fractured by the shock wave generated by a strong impact.

shear stress A state of stress that causes internal planes within a body to move parallel to each other.

shield volcanoes Very wide volcanoes built of low-viscosity lava.

shoaling A process whereby waves coming into shallow waters are slowed by seafloor friction and become closer together and higher in amplitude.

shock minerals Rare minerals formed in rock subjected to the passage of a powerful impact shock wave.

shooting stars The light phenomena that occur when meteoroids enter Earth's atmosphere and vaporize; also called meteors.

sinkholes Circular depressions on the surface created where acidic water has dissolved limestone.

sinuosity The length of a stream channel divided by the straight-line distance between its ends.

slash Debris such as logs, branches, and needles left on the ground by logging or high winds.

slate Mud changed to hard rock by the high temperatures and pressures of metamorphism.

sleet Precipitation consisting in small pellets of ice.

slides Mass movements where the bodies of material move on top of failure surfaces.

sluff A small avalanche usually made up of loose snow.

slumps Downward-and-outward movements of masses on top of concave-upward failure surfaces; also called rotational slides.

snowpack A column of snow and ice on the ground, including both the new snow and the previous snow and ice that has not melted.

soil The surface layers of sediment, organic matter, and mineral particles.

solar radiation The energy emitted from the Sun mostly in the infrared, visible light, and ultraviolet wavelengths.

solar wind The outflow of charged particles from the Sun.

species Organisms similar enough in life functions to breed freely together.

spreading centres Sites where plates pull apart and magma flows upward to fill the gaps and then solidifies as new ocean floors.

storms Violent weather events featuring strong winds and heavy precipitation (rain, snow, or hail).

strain A change in form or size of a body due to external forces.

stratosphere The stable atmospheric layer above the troposphere.

stratovolcanoes Volcanoes constructed of alternating layers of pyroclastic debris and lava flows; also called composite volcanoes.

stress Force per area; forces include shear, tension, and compression.

sturzstroms Long-runout flows of huge masses of earth materials at great speeds.

subduction The process of one lithospheric plate descending beneath another one.

subsides Mass movements where the materials sink slowly or catastrophically.

supercell thunderstorms Complex thunderstorms formed from huge updrafts. They commonly are tilted, allowing rain, hail, and tornadoes to exist side-by-side.

surface tension The attractive force between molecules at the surface of a liquid.

surface waves Seismic waves that travel along the Earth's surface only. Love and Rayleigh waves are surface waves.

surges Large mounds of seawater that build up due to suction from the eye of a hurricane and strong winds and then spill onto the land.

T

talus slopes Large piles of boulders that accumulate at the foot of cliffs.

tectonic cycle Describes how new lithosphere forms at oceanic volcanic ridges, how lithospheric plates spread apart to open ocean basins, and how the oceanic plates are ultimately reabsorbed into the mantle at subduction zones.

telluric currents Electrical currents propagating in the Earth or through the sea.

tension A state of stress that tends to pull the body apart.

thunder The sound given off by rapidly expanding gases along the path of a lightning discharge.

thunderstorms Tall, buoyant clouds of moist air that generate lightning and thunder, accompanied by rain, gusty winds, and sometimes hail.

topography The mapping of the shape of the surface of the Earth; the land equivalent of bathymetry.

topple A mass movement where the body pivots forward from its base as if it were top-heavy.

tornado A spinning funnel of wind whose rotating wind speed can exceed 500 km/h.

transform faults Strike-slip faults that connect the ends of two offset spreading centres.

translational slides Downward movements of masses on top of inclined planar surfaces.

trenches The elongate and narrow troughs where ocean water can be more than twice as deep as usual. Trenches mark the downgoing edges of subducting plates.

triple junction A place where three plate edges meet.

tropical cyclones Any weather systems formed over tropical waters that rotate counterclockwise in the northern hemisphere.

tropical depression A tropical cyclone with wind speeds between 37 and 63 km/h.

tropical disturbance A low-pressure system in the tropics with thunderstorms and weak surface wind circulation. Winds do not exceed 36 km/h.

tropical storm A tropical cyclone with wind speeds between 64 and 118 km/h.

tropopause The top of the troposphere.

troposphere The lowest layer of the atmosphere, 18 km thick at the equator to 8 km thick at the poles.

tsunamis Long-period sea waves caused by oceanic disturbances, such as fault movements, volcanic eruptions, meteorite impacts, and landslides.

tuya A volcano that erupts initially beneath a glacier, melts through the ice, and develops a flat lava cap.

typhoons Large, tropical cyclonic storms of the western Pacific Ocean with wind speeds of 119 km/h or more; called hurricanes in the Atlantic and eastern Pacific, and cyclones in the Indian Ocean.

U

ultra-Plinian A type of volcanic eruption characterized by exceptionally large outpourings of pyroclastic material in high eruption columns and voluminous ash-flow sheets that cover wide areas.

V

viscous Resistant to flowing. The more viscous a substance, the less readily it flows

volatiles Substances that readily become gases when pressure is decreased, or temperature increased.

volcanic belt A group of volcanoes located in a specific area.

volcanic rocks Rocks formed by solidification of magma at the Earth's surface.

volcanoes Openings of the Earth's surface where magma has poured or blown forth, typically creating hills or mountains.

vulnerability Exposure to being harmed or damaged.

W

wall cloud A markedly lower cloud that may form in the area of strongest updraft in a supercell thunderstorm. Many tornadoes form within wall clouds.

water table The upper surface of the groundwater body. It is nearer the surface during rainy intervals and deeper below the surface during droughts.

wavelength The distance between two successive wave crests, or troughs.

weather The state of the air at a place with respect to hot or cold, wet or dry, calm or stormy.

wildfires Unplanned fires occurring in a forested area or thick brush.

wind-driven fires Fire fronts that move quickly, pushed by winds. The wind carries firebrands forward, starting spot fires up to 0.6 km ahead.

Index

C

D

E

F

G

H

I

P

Q

R

S